s-TRIAZINES
and
DERIVATIVES

Edwin M. Smolin   *and*   Lorence Rapoport

*Central Research Division, American Cyanamid Company,
Stamford, Connecticut*

1959

INTERSCIENCE PUBLISHERS INC., NEW YORK
INTERSCIENCE PUBLISHERS LTD., LONDON

Library of Congress Catalog Card Number 59-8840

INTERSCIENCE PUBLISHERS, INC., 250 Fifth Avenue, New York 1, N.Y.

For Great Britain and Northern Ireland:

Interscience Publishers Ltd., 88/90 Chancery Lane, London, W.C. 2

PRINTED IN THE NETHERLANDS

The Chemistry of Heterocyclic Compounds

The chemistry of heterocyclic compounds is one of the most complex branches of organic chemistry. It is equally interesting for its theoretical implications, for the diversity of its synthetic procedures, and for the physiological and industrial significance of heterocyclic compounds.

A field of such importance and intrinsic difficulty should be made as readily accessible as possible, and the lack of a modern detailed and comprehensive presentation of heterocyclic chemistry is therefore keenly felt. It is the intention of the present series to fill this gap by expert presentations of the various branches of heterocyclic chemistry. The subdivisions have been designed to cover the field in its entirety by monographs which reflect the importance and the interrelations of the various compounds, and accommodate the specific interests of the authors.

Research Laboratories
Eastman Kodak Company
Rochester, New York

ARNOLD WEISSBERGER

v

Preface

The subject matter contained in this book was originally intended to be part of a single volume covering the entire field of Triazines and Tetrazines. It became apparent from a preliminary consideration of the literature that this area encompassed too large an amount of published work to be covered in a single volume of reasonable size. Accordingly, the 1,2,4-, and 1,2,3-triazines and the tetrazines have been covered by Drs. Erickson, Wiley, and Wystrach leaving the 1,3,5- or s-triazines and the borazoles for the present volume.

We have made an effort to consider the s-triazines from the point of view of an organic chemist who, entering the field to do research, wants information about the literature. An attempt has been made to give physical properties, especially melting or boiling point and solubility, but without taking the space to do more than mention other readily accessible seldom used data. Modern electronic concepts of organic chemistry have been called upon where possible although mechanistic and kinetic data are largely lacking in this field. Frequently the classical "balloon" equations were retained to indicate a possible course for certain complex reactions. They are, of course, in no way intended to represent actual reaction steps. Emphasis is laid on monomeric finite compounds and on their preparation and reactions rather than on their applications. The voluminous fields of melamine, guanamine, and ammeline resins have been by-passed with only a few introductory paragraphs.

The chemistry of the borazoles is taken up because of their admittedly superficial structural relationship to the s-triazines, because of the recent interest in this branch of boron chemistry, and because the borazoles are not covered in any of the other volumes of this series. Hexamethylenetetramine chemistry is treated only in so far as it is of interest for s-triazines. The field has been covered in the readily available literature and duplicating appeared unwarranted.

s-Triazine, the fundamental member of the series of compounds treated in this volume, was unknown at the time of completion of the manuscript, and has been characterized only recently. Its discussion has been included as part of the Introduction rather than as an Appendix because the authors feel that it ought to be discussed in the most easily accessable location possible.

An effort has been made to cover the literature from 1860 through 1953 comprehensively except for historical purposes. From January 1, 1954 to April 1, 1955, all literature references that were for any reason considered important were incorporated into the text. This was especially necessary for the example of s-triazine discussed in the preceding paragraph.

We wish to express our deep gratitude to the following without whose help this work would have been immeasurably more difficult if not impossible: Dr. D. W. Kaiser and Dr. F. C. Schaeffer for making available to us their authoritative opinions and wide experience in the entire field of s-triazine chemistry: Dr. R. S. Long for his suggested revisions in the section on s-triazine dye chemistry; Dr. J. H. Fletcher for his suggestions on nomenclature; Dr. R. C. Hirt for ultraviolet spectra interpretation; Dr. V. P. Wystrach who, with Dr. J. G. Erickson, first interested us in participating in this project; and the American Cyanamid Company for contributing the use of library and secretarial facilities, kindly authorized by Dr. J. H. Paden and generously continued by Mr. D. W. Jayne.

We also thank Dr. A. L. Peiker and Dr. E. R. Northey for reviewing Chapter I and suggesting appropriate changes.

E. M. SMOLIN
L. RAPOPORT

February, 1959

Contents

    * Where Ring Index No. is omitted, none could be found. This indicates doubtful structure if before 1938—if after, the number was not listed because there has been no supplement to the Ring Index.

Introduction

I. General

As cyanuric acid, melamine, and certain related s-triazines were first prepared in the early days of organic chemistry, rather nonsystematic nomenclature has been carried in the literature through to the present day. The s-triazine ring system allows little ambiguity in its numbering, as, following the usual convention, the numbering begins at a hetero atom. Thus the recently identified parent compound s-triazine (I) is a six-membered ring consisting of alternating N and C atoms joined by alternating single and double bonds.

$$\underset{(I)}{\overset{\displaystyle 1}{\underset{5}{N}} \quad \underset{3}{N}}$$

Common names which have been used for many years and are retained in the current literature, have been accepted if they appear in Chemical Abstracts. In certain cases where complex structures make retention of common names cumbersome, the systematic s-triazine nomenclature has been adapted. Aside from the s-triazine or 1,3,5-triazine systems of general nomenclature, the only other system which has received any attention in the literature is that of Diels and Lichte[1] who named s-triazine (I) "cyanurin." The name "cyanurin" has the same origin as the name cyanuric acid, which is the parent compound of a considerable number of s-triazine derivatives. Cyanuric acid was so named because it was found by analysis[2] to contain the cyano or –CN aggregate and because it was originally prepared by pyrolysis of uric acid.

Cyanuric acid (II), 2,4,6-trihydroxy-s-triazine, is among the compounds the common name of which has been retained. Other such

1

compounds which are associated with the chemistry of (II) are: cyanuric halides (III), trialkyl (and triaryl) cyanurates (IV), cyanuric triazide (V), thiocyanuric acid (VI) and trialkyl (and triaryl) thiocyanurates (VII).

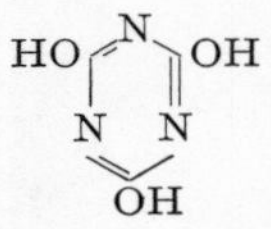

(II)	(III)	(IV)
HO—⟨triazine⟩—OH, OH	X—⟨triazine⟩—X, X	RO—⟨triazine⟩—OR, OR
Cyanuric acid 2,4,6-Trihydroxy-*s*-triazine	Cyanuric halide 2,4,6-Trihalo-*s*-triazine	Trialkyl cyanurate 2,4,6-Trialkoxy-*s*-triazine

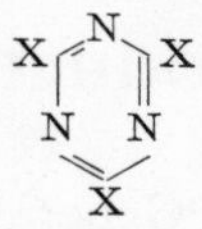

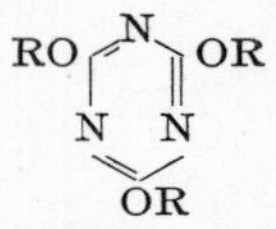

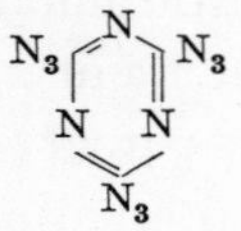

(V)	(VI)	(VII)
N$_3$—⟨triazine⟩—N$_3$, N$_3$	HS—⟨triazine⟩—SH, SH	RS—⟨triazine⟩—SR, SR
Cyanuric triazide 2,4,6-Triazido-*s*-triazine	Trithiocyanuric acid 2,4,6-Trimercapto-*s*-triazine	Trialkyl thiocyanurate 2,4,6-Trialkylthio-*s*-triazine

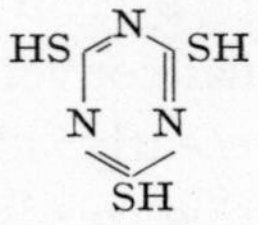

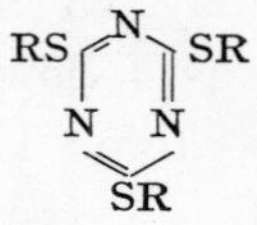

In certain instances in which common names become cumbersome and impractical, they are not used either in this volume or in Chemical Abstracts. Usually this is true when more than one of the above class substituents are on the same *s*-triazine ring. For example, compound (VIII) is named 2,4-dichloro-6-butoxy-*s*-triazine rather than as a derivative of either cyanuric chloride or butyl cyanurate.

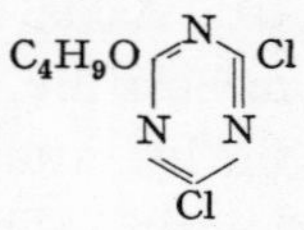

C_4H_9O—⟨triazine⟩—Cl, Cl

(VIII)

2,4-Dichloro-6-
butoxy-*s*-triazine

Isocyanurates are compounds isomeric with the cyanurates. They retain their common name in the same way as the latter substances and may be represented by (IX). The isocyanurates possess the hexahydro-*s*-triazine ring structure and are the only compounds having partially or totally hydrogenated noncondensed *s*-triazine rings for which common names are assigned.

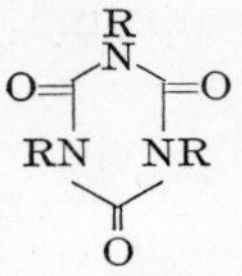

$$\underset{\text{O}}{\underset{\text{RN}\quad\text{NR}}{\overset{\text{R}}{\overset{\text{N}}{\underset{}{\bigg|}}}}}$$

(IX)

Trialkyl isocyanurate
1,3,5-Trialkyl-2,4,6-trioxohexahydro-*s*-triazine

In naming the perhydro-*s*-triazines, a departure from Chemical Abstracts has been made; the basic system derived from hexahydro-*s*-triazine is used rather than the system derived from triazacyclohexane. For example compound (IXa) is named 1-Nitro-3,5-dicyclohexylhexahydro-*s*-triazine and *not* 1-nitro-3,5-dicyclohexyl-1,3,5-triazacyclohexane.

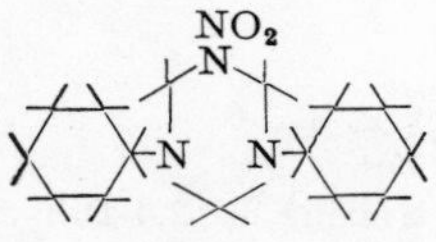

(IXa)

The various classes of amino-*s*-triazines are of considerable commercial importance, and the respective common names have attained widespread acceptance for the parent compounds and also for certain of the less complicated derivatives. Thus 2,4,6-triamino-*s*-triazine (X)

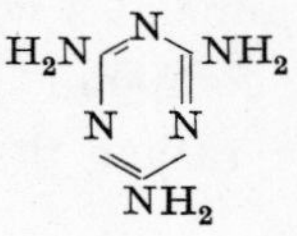

$$\text{H}_2\text{N}\underset{\text{N}\quad\text{N}}{\overset{\text{N}}{\bigg|}}\text{NH}_2$$
$$\text{NH}_2$$

(X)

was given the name "melamine" by Liebig[3] who adopted the name because of the basic properties of this derivative of "melam." The name melamine has been retained by most of the later workers in the field. Substituted melamines have been named by designating the point of attachment of substituent groups with superscripts. Thus 2,4,6-tri-(methylamino)-*s*-triazine (XI) is commonly designated as $N^2N^4N^6$-trimethylmelamine. This later nomenclature has been used in this volume.

Isomelamines bear the same relationship to the melamines that the isocyanurates bear to the cyanurates and in general the same nomenclature system is used; thus, compound (XII) is 1-phenyl-isomelamine.

$$CH_3NH \underset{N \quad N}{\overset{N}{\bigwedge}} NHCH_3$$

(XI)   NHCH₃

$$HN= \overset{C_6H_5}{\underset{HN \quad NH}{\overset{N}{\bigwedge}}} =NH$$

(XII)   NH

The hydroxyamino-s-triazines are usually given the names ammelines and ammelides. Thus 2-hydroxy-4,6-diamino-s-triazine (XIII) is called ammeline and 2,4-dihydroxy-6-amino-s-triazine (XIV) is usually referred to as ammelide. The thio derivatives are named thio-

$$H_2N \underset{N \quad N}{\overset{N}{\bigwedge}} OH$$

(XIII)   NH₂

Ammeline
2-Hydroxy-4,6-diamino-s-triazine

$$H_2N \underset{N \quad N}{\overset{N}{\bigwedge}} OH$$

(XIV)   OH

Ammelide
2,4-Dihydroxy-6-amino-s-triazine

ammeline and thioammelide. The ammeline and ammelide nomenclature is used for the parent compounds only. In the case of the substituted ammelines and ammelides, the systematic s-triazine nomenclature is used in the interest of clarity. In this we have departed from the Chemical Abstracts system of designating the hydroxyl groups of substituted ammelines and ammelides with the suffix "-ol" following the word triazine. For example compound (XV) will be called 2-hydroxy-4,6-di(methylamino)-s-triazine rather than 4,6-di(methylamino)-s-triazine-2-ol.

$$CH_3NH \underset{N \quad N}{\overset{N}{\bigwedge}} OH$$

(XV)   NHCH₃

Another important group of amino-s-triazines are the 2-substituted-4,6-diamino-s-triazines in which the 2-substituent may be H, alkyl or aryl, but none other. The generic name *guanamines* has been widely used for this class of compounds. Chemical Abstracts does not recognize the guanamine nomenclature, and this is a good step in the direction of removing from usage a particularly inappropriate trivial name. The name *guanamine* was derived from the earliest method of synthesis—from a guanidine salt. Accordingly we have used the s-triazine names for compounds in this group and also for the related guanides (2-substituted-4-hydroxy-6-amino-s-triazines) and guanamides (2-substituted-4,6-dihydroxy-s-triazines). Here again the 2-substituent may be only hydrogen, or an alkyl or aryl group. Examples from this category of compounds are illustrated in formulas (XVI), (XVII) and

(XVI)	(XVII)	(XVIII)
Propioguanamine	Benzoguanide	Acetoguanamide
2-Ethyl-4,6-diamino-s-triazine	2-Phenyl-4-hydroxy-6-amino-s-triazine	2-Methyl-4,6-dihydroxy-s-triazine

(XVIII). When the amino or hydroxy groups are substituted, the *guanamine* nomenclature becomes very awkward and is not used in the literature. Here the s-triazine system gives an unambiguous name and is always used.

Hexamethylenetetramine and its derivatives which do not involve a change in the fundamental ring structure retain the common and Chemical Abstracts name, hexamethylenetetramine. Many of the derivatives of hexamethylenetetramine comprise an eight-membered ring of alternating amino and methylene groups containing an endo-methylene bridge. These compounds are discussed with other condensed ring systems rather than under hexamethylenetetramine. They are named as derivatives of 1,5-endomethylenecyclooctane in this volume and in Chemical Abstracts. In the older literature—and there are only a few compounds of this type reported prior to 1940—the system of naming the compounds by the number of amino groups and methylene groups present has been used. Current literature has perhaps made overzealous use of the abbreviations in the form of initials which may stand for an old name, a method of preparation, or a description of the physical properties of the compound. These conventional abbreviations have been retained with adequate accompanying explanation in the

interest of brevity and in deference to their ubiquity in current literature. Compound (XIX) offers an example of each nomenclature system.

$$\begin{array}{c} -\!\!\!-\!\!\!-\text{N}-\!\!\!-\!\!\!- \\ | \\ \text{O}_2\text{NN} \quad \text{CH}_2 \quad \text{NNO}_2 \\ | \\ -\!\!\!-\!\!\!-\text{N}-\!\!\!-\!\!\!- \end{array}$$

(XIX)

Systematic name: 3,7-Dinitro-1,5-endomethylene-1,3,5,7-tetraza-
cyclooctane.

Older literature: Dinitropentamethylenetetramine from whence
comes *Recent literature:* DPT.

Other condensed ring systems are named according to the Ring
Index. In cases of compounds not listed in the Ring Index, the most
logical name based on conventional Chemical Abstracts nomenclature
was adopted. Systematic names are presented for each compound,
however trivial names predominate in the discussion of certain condensed ring compounds. Frequency of usage in the literature and
brevity were the criteria used to determine the propriety of any given
trivial or common name. Where a common name has met with acceptance in the important pertinent literature it has been retained.
Inappropriate and incorrect trivial names have been discarded after
brief mention and the systematic name is applied.

In the case of condensed ring systems, reference regarding nomenclature should be made to the individual compound or group of compounds. Further generalization on compounds of this category appears
unwarranted in this section (see Chapter VIII).

II. *s*-Triazine[a]

1. General

In 1895, Nef[4] treated hydrogen cyanide with ethanol in an ether
solution saturated with hydrogen chloride. The resulting salt was
treated with alkali and distilled giving a compound formulated as
iminoformyl carbylamine, $C=N\!-\!CH=NH$. The basis for this struc-

---

[a] An extensive historical review of work through 1954 leading to the
ultimate correct formulation for *s*-triazine has been compiled by von Ruske.[33]

ture was a molecular weight determined ebullioscopically in benzene. The high (64 versus the calculated 54) value obtained was ascribed to unsatisfactory benzene and the result has only recently[5, 6] been clarified. As early as 1883, Pinner[7] also isolated the compound

$$HC\underset{}{\overset{\nearrow NH}{\underset{}{\diagdown}}}OC_2H_5 \cdot HCl$$

from the reaction of hydrogen cyanide, hydrogen chloride and ethanol in ether, but with alkali he reported small yields of $HC(=NH)OC_2H_5$ and none of Nef's compound. Pinner later, in a refutation of Nef's work, postulated[8] that since benzimino ether trimerized to triphenyl-s-triazine, why should not the formimino ether condense to give a polymer of hydrogen cyanide such as formyl carbylamine? Had this postulation been pursued, s-triazine might have been recognized a long time ago.

When hydrogen cyanide is treated with hydrogen chloride,[9] the first product is the "sesquihydrochloride" of hydrogen cyanide, $2 HCN \cdot 3 HCl$, formulated[10] as $CHCl_2NHCHClNH_2$. This compound readily loses two equivalents of hydrogen chloride to give chloro-methyleneformamidine, formulated as $CHCl=NCH=NH$, which when treated with a base loses a third equivalent of hydrogen chloride, the ultimate product being the so-called dimer of hydrogen cyanide[10, 11]. On the basis of Nef's two incorrect molecular weight determinations, the compound was regarded as a dimer until, in 1954, Grundmann and Kreutzberger[5, 6] proved that it actually was the trimer of hydrogen cyanide, s-triazine (I). Perhaps one factor which served to perpetuate the error was the finding by Hinkel that s-triazine and hydrogen chloride regenerated "chloromethyleneformamidine," $2 HCN \cdot HCl$. This shows that "s-triazine hydrochloride" is not the simple compound that might be anticipated, $3 HCN \cdot HCl$.

s-Triazine is an extremely volatile crystalline solid which melts[4, 5] at 86° and boils at 114° at one atmosphere pressure. It is easily soluble[4] in ether and in ethanol at —5°. The density of the highly refracting rhombohedral crystals has been determined[12] to be approximately 1.38 g/cm³. The heat of combustion for s-triazine has been calculated to be 424.4, the heat of fusion 40.2, the heat of vaporization 12.15, and the resonance energy 41.2, all in Kcal. per mole.[5A] Ultraviolet and infrared spectra for *s*-triazine are presented in Figures 1 and 2, respectively, and are discussed below.

s-Triazine can be purified without appreciable loss[6] by repeated distillation over metallic sodium. Crystals of the pure substance poured on the surface of water exhibit the Leidenfrost phenomenon known as the "camphor dance," which is characteristic of many solid substances with a high vapor pressure and surface tension.

Grundmann and Kreutzberger's recent finding[5] that the substance, previously called "hydrogen cyanide dimer," was actually *s*-triazine

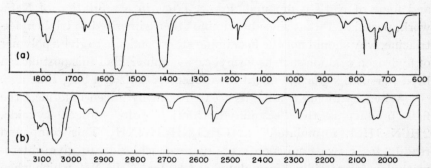

Fig. 1. Infrared spectrum of *s*-triazine (gas) at 25° C., taken with (a) 10-cm. and (b) 1-meter cells, using a Perkin-Elmer model 21 spectrometer

initiated a considerable amount of work to elucidate the structure of the compound. Siegel and Williams,[12] who have examined crystalline *s*-triazine by X-ray methods, concluded that the structure (I) proposed by Grundmann and Kreutzberger was correct. The rhombohedral cell contains two molecules. An empirical estimate of the ultraviolet absorption spectrum of *s*-triazine was made several years ago[13,14] and, with the availability of the compound, an examination of the actual spectrum[31] proved that it agreed in general with the predicted data. It resembles that of 2,4,6-trimethyl-*s*-triazine; this finding was expected since the two molecules have essentially the same symmetry, and methyl groups have little effect on the spectrum. The infrared spectrum of *s*-triazine which has been studied in the vapor, liquid, and solid states by Lancaster and Colthup,[16] is presented in Figure 1. It is interesting to consult the reviews of Ruske[33,35,36] some of which were written before *s*-triazine was identified as such and others afterwards.

2. Synthesis

Several methods of synthesis are available for s-triazine.

(1) The most satisfactory method is via the so-called sesquihydro-chloride of hydrocyanic acid.[5] This compound, the structure of which is discussed below, is prepared from hydrogen cyanide and hydrogen chloride. It really loses two-thirds of its hydrogen chloride and splits off its last one-third as a result of treatment with a basic acceptor (1). Overall yields of s-triazine are 55–60%.

$$6\,HCN + 9\,HCl \longrightarrow [C_3H_6N_3Cl_3]_2 \cdot 3\,HCl \xrightarrow{-6\,HCl} [C_3H_3N_3]_2 \cdot 3\,HCl \longrightarrow$$

$$\xrightarrow[\text{base}]{-3\,HCl} 2 \quad\underset{(I)}{\left[\begin{array}{c} N \\ \\ N \quad N \end{array}\right]} \tag{1}$$

(2) Nef[4] prepared s-triazine by treating hydrogen cyanide with ethanol in ether saturated with hydrogen chloride. The resulting salt, iminoethyl formate hydrochloride, was neutralized with sodium hydroxide and then distilled giving s-triazine in less than 10% yields (2).

$$3\,HC\overset{NH}{-}OC_2H_5 \xrightarrow{-C_2H_5OH} 3\,HC\equiv N \longrightarrow (I) \tag{2}$$

(3) s-Triazine was obtained[17] in less than 20% yield from difficultly preparable thioformamide (3).

$$3\,HC\overset{NH}{-}SH \xrightarrow{-H_2S} 3\,HCN \longrightarrow (I) \tag{3}$$

(4) Most recently, Grundmann described[6] the preparation of s-triazine by either thermal or base-catalyzed decomposition of formamidine hydrochloride (4).

$$3\,HC\overset{NH}{-}NH_2 \xrightarrow{-NH_3} 3\,HCN \longrightarrow (I) \tag{4}$$

Excellent yields are obtainable by this method.

Grundmann has observed that for each one of the last three methods, splitting off the group added to the —CH=NH residue, gives an intermediate in which we can assume the existence of an activated or polar transition state of hydrocyanic acid of the structure $HC \overset{+}{=} \overset{-}{N}$ which spontaneously trimerizes.

(5) It is probable[33] that the Rakshit[34] report of the preparation of s-triazine by heating diformamide sodium in ether with formamidine hydrochloride is true, but the s-triazine is shown[37] to come only from the formamidine hydrochloride.

Attempts to prepare s-triazine by removing substituents on the s-triazine ring have all met with failure to date. Diels and Lieber-mann,[18,19] among others, tried to remove the chlorine atoms of cyanuric chloride by various reduction methods. In reduction with lithium aluminum hydride, it was shown[20] that s-triazine was actually produced but was also detrimerized as a result of the action of aluminum chloride, one of the products of the reaction. The low stability of s-triazine contrasted with the rigorous conditions often required to effect transformation of some of its derivatives, furnishes a partial explanation of the difficulties experienced in attempting to prepare it by these routes. Hantzsch and Bauer,[21] who tried to saponify 2,4,6-tricarbethoxy-s-triazine with the object of decarboxylating the free acid to get s-triazine, obtained only decomposition products. Weddige[22] was not able to obtain s-triazine by decarboxylation of the acid. s-Triazine-2,4,6-tricarboxylic acid was prepared by Lander,[23] but he did not report any attempt to decarboxylate it. An interesting route to s-triazine (1) was suggested by Bamberger and Dieckmann[24] utilizing formamidine and formic acid (5). The method was unsuccessful, however. Another method[33] was the catalytic hydrogenation of RDX followed by thermal elimination of ammonia.

$$
\begin{array}{ccc}
\overset{\displaystyle NH}{\underset{\|}{}} & \overset{\displaystyle NH}{\underset{\|}{}} & \overset{\displaystyle NH}{\underset{\|}{}} \\
2\,HC{-}NH_2 & \longrightarrow & HC{-}NH{-}CH\ +
\end{array}
$$

$$
+\ H_3N \xrightarrow{\ HCOOH\ } \overset{\displaystyle NH}{\underset{\|}{}}\ HCNHCH{=}NCHO \xrightarrow{\ -H_2O\ } \text{(I)} \qquad (5)
$$

Grundmann, Ulrich and Kreutzberger[25] tried catalytic reduction of cyanuric chloride, but obtained no s-triazine. They also experimented with hydrogenolysis of trimethyl thiocyanurate using Raney nickel and with thermal decomposition of 1,3,5-tribenzoylhexahydro-s-triazine. Wieland[26] obtained no (I) on reduction of 2,4,6-trihydroxy-s-triazine.

3. Reactions

As is mentioned later, s-triazine displays little of the characteristics of an aromatic nucleus because of the strong electronegatively of the nitrogen atoms in the ring.

A. Salt formation

Several salts of s-triazine are known: usually they are obtained by indirect means. Nef assigned[4] the formula $AgC_2NH_2 \cdot H_2O$ to a silver salt which gave an incorrect analysis. Hinkel[27] recognized that water was an unsuitable solvent and, using alcohol instead, obtained $2\,AgNO_3 \cdot 5\,HCN$. Grundmann and Kreutzberger[6] found that the composition of the salt was somewhat dependent upon the mode of preparation and that the addition product tends to lose the elements of s-triazine by volatilization. Thus despite the excellent appearance of the crystals, the compound is not a good means of identification. By working in acetonitrile, which is normally inert to s-triazine, they established the formula as $AgNO_3 \cdot 2\,C_3H_3N_3$. The pure compound melts with decomposition at 203°. With silver nitrite in acetonitrile, the addition compound $AgNO_2 \cdot C_3H_3N_3$ was obtained.[6] Hinkel[27] established the correct structure of the salt formed from s-triazine and mercuric chloride in ether or benzene as $HgCl_2 \cdot (HCN)_3$ or $HgCl_2 \cdot C_3H_3N_3$. The mercuric chloride salt is somewhat soluble in organic solvents and water. Upon treatment with hydrogen chloride, the salt ($HgCl_2 \cdot C_3H_3N_3 \cdot 1\frac{1}{2}HCl$) was isolated. s-Triazine and its hydrochlorides participate in salt formation with aluminum chloride;[27] this is discussed under section H below.

A sodium salt is believed to be formed in liquid ammonia. The trivalent tricyano groups in Prussian Blue and Turnbull's Blue have been assigned[28] the s-triazine structure which would be tantamount to proposing that they are iron salts of s-triazine.

B. Hydrolysis

While s-triazine has been shown to be stable to near red heat[29], it is sensitive to hydrolysis[6] in water and to a lesser degree in alcohols and other hydroxyl containing compounds. No s-triazine could be detected[6] after a 10% solution in distilled water had stood for 10 minutes at 25°. The decomposition is probably autocatalytic, base-catalyzed by the formamidine initially liberated by hydrolysis. A buffered solution at pH 7 would undoubtedly be more stable. Hydro-lysis occurs almost instantaneously in the presence of even dilute aqueous mineral acids giving[5,6] rise to formic acid and ammonia (6).

$$C_3H_3N_3 + 6H_2O \xrightarrow{H^+} 3HCOOH + 3NH_3 \tag{6}$$

Cleavage of the ring is the chief characteristic of reaction (6) and the greater share of other s-triazine reactions, for (I) demonstrates a nuclear instability almost unique in the s-triazine series. Hydrolysis with alkali also readily ruptures the ring.

C. Reaction with Hydrogen Chloride

Hinkel and Dunn found[30] that s-triazine reacts with hydrogen chloride to regenerate chloromethyleneformamidine which it will be recalled is isolated in the preparation of s-triazine from "hydrogen cyanide sesquihydrochloride." They could not substantiate Nef's claim[4] to have converted s-triazine back to hydrogen cyanide sesqui-hydrochloride upon treatment of (I) with hydrogen chloride in ether. Grundmann and Kreutzberger[6] have recently confirmed Hinkel's findings, and have logically postulated that the addition compound of s-triazine and hydrogen chloride which has the empirical formula $2(HCN) \cdot HCl$, and from which s-triazine is easily recoverable by re-moving the hydrogen chloride with a base such as quinoline, is actually the sesquihydrochloride of s-triazine, $(C_3H_3N_3)_2 \cdot 3HCl$ (II). The in-solubility of (II) in all nonpolar solvents and its tendency to sublime in vacuo without decomposition agree much better with structure (II) than with the formulation chloromethyleneformamidine. To go one step further, the ease of formation of (II) from the "sesquihydrochloride of hydrogen cyanide," suggested that the latter already contains the s-triazine ring and is actually the sesquihydrochloride of 2,4,6-tri-chlorohexahydro-s-triazine (III). This structure explains the facile formation of (II) from (III) as analogous to the formation of trichloro-benzene from hexachlorocyclohexane by dehydrochlorination-aromati-zation. No direct proof could be presented for structures (II) and (III) since no solvent has as yet been found in which they are soluble without change.

On the basis of the above considerations, the formation of s-triazine from hydrocyanic acid may be explained more logically[6] as proceding through the intermediate formylimidochloride (IV). The latter trimerizes spontaneously to (III) which is stabilized in the form of the sesquihydrochloride. The course of the reaction is represented by equation (7).

$$6 \text{ HCN} + 6 \text{ HCl} \longrightarrow 6 \text{ HClC} = \text{NH} \xrightarrow{3 \text{ HCl}} \left[\begin{array}{c} \text{H} \\ \text{N} \\ \text{ClH} \diagup \diagdown \text{HCl} \\ \text{HN} \quad \text{NH} \\ \diagdown \diagup \\ \text{HCl} \end{array} \right]_2 \cdot 3 \text{ HCl} \longrightarrow$$

$$\text{(IV)} \qquad\qquad\qquad\qquad \text{(III)}$$

$$\xrightarrow{-6 \text{ HCl}} \left[\begin{array}{c} \text{N} \\ \diagup \diagdown \\ \text{N} \quad \text{N} \\ \diagdown \diagup \end{array} \right]_2 \cdot 3 \text{ HCl} \; \underset{+3 \text{ HCl}}{\overset{-3 \text{ HCl}}{\rightleftarrows}} \; 2 \begin{array}{c} \text{N} \\ \diagup \diagdown \\ \text{N} \quad \text{N} \\ \diagdown \diagup \end{array} \qquad (7)$$

$$\text{(II)} \qquad\qquad\qquad \text{(I)}$$

D. Reaction with Amines

Primary and secondary amines undergo a general reaction with s-triazine to give substituted formamidines as a result of ring cleavage and 1,2-addition across the carbon to nitrogen double bond. No mechanism has been proposed for the reaction (8).

$$\begin{array}{c} \text{N} \\ \diagup \diagdown \\ \text{N} \quad \text{N} \\ \diagdown \diagup \end{array} + 3 \text{ R}_1\text{R}_2\text{NH} \longrightarrow 3 \text{ HC} \overset{\text{NH}}{\underset{\text{NR}_1\text{R}_2}{\Big\backslash}} \qquad (8)$$

$$\text{(I)}$$

E. Reaction with Halogens[32]

s-Triazine (I) is not easily chlorinated. With chlorine in carbon tetrachloride and at room temperature, an insoluble hygroscopic precipitate which may be a perchloride forms. When the temperature is raised to 105° only s-triazine sesquihydrochloride resulted, while at 140–200° in a sealed tube, chlorine in carbon tetrachloride gave 25% cyanuric chloride and 4% 2,4-dichloro-s-triazine.

With bromine in carbon tetrachloride, (I) gives an orange crystalline precipitate of a tribromide at 0°. The product, $C_3H_3N_3Br_3$, has a melting point of 70° (dec.) and is soluble in water and ethanol. It was obtained in 85% yield. The compound is unstable above 20°, evolving bromine and forming a resin, but is stable when dry, at 0°. It may be purified by sublimation at 40°. All the bromide in the tribromide is free bromine and can be titrated as such. Heating the tribromide to 150–160° for four hours in a tube gives 2,4-dibromo-s-triazine hydrobromide. The latter can also be prepared directly in 95% yield from (I) with bromine in carbon tetrachloride in a sealed tube at 120–125° for 5 hours. It is a yellow powder which decomposes at 290–300° and is insoluble in nonpolar organic solvents. Reaction with aniline gives 2,4-di(phenylamino)-s-triazine; this shows that two of the bromine atoms are attached to the nucleus of the s-triazine ring.

F. Reaction with Sodamide

s-Triazine differs from pyridine and pyrimidine in that it cannot be ammonated to amino-s-triazines. Instead, decomposition occurs giving sodium cyanamide according to equations (9 and 10).

$$(I) + 3\,NaNH_2 \longrightarrow 3\,NaCN + 3\,NH_3 \qquad (9)$$
$$3\,NaCN + 3\,NaNH_2 \longrightarrow 3\,Na_2NCN + 3\,H_2 \qquad (10)$$

G. Hydrogenation[32]

s-Triazine (I) could not be hydrogenated catalytically. Instead, it acts as a poison. Even trace amounts poison platinum oxide catalyst for the hydrogenation of cyclohexene.

H. Friedel-Crafts reaction of s-triazine and its hydrochloride derivatives[32]

Grundmann and Kreutzberger reviewed the work of Hinkel on the salt formation of s-triazine and its hydrochlorides with aluminium chloride and reinterpreted the results in terms of their work elucidating the identity of s-triazine.[5,6] Starting with the first reaction product from hydrogen cyanide and hydrogen chloride, the sesquihydrochloride of 2,4,6-trichlorohexahydro-s-triazine (III), all the derivatives form salts with aluminum chloride. Compound (III) forms a salt (V) with three equivalents of aluminum chloride which melts at 62°. Two moles of the sesquihydrochloride of s-triazine form a salt (VI) with three moles of aluminum chloride melting at 60°. This salt can also be prepared from the s-triazine-aluminum chloride salt, $(C_3N_3H_3)_2 \cdot 3\,AlCl_3$, which melts at 120°. These relationships are summarized below.

$$[(I) \cdot 3\,HCl]_2 \cdot 3\,HCl \rightarrow [(I) \cdot 3\,HCl]_2 \cdot 3\,AlCl_3 \quad \text{m.p. } 62°$$
$$(V)$$

$$2\,(I) \cdot 3\,HCl \;\rightleftharpoons\; 2\,(I) \cdot 3\,HCl \cdot 3\,AlCl_3 \quad \text{m.p. } 60°$$
$$(VI)$$
$$(I)$$

$$2\,(I) \cdot 3\,AlCl_3 \quad \text{m.p. } 120°$$

Aluminum chloride weakens the carbon-nitrogen bonds so that s-triazine and its derivatives are easily depolymerized. As a result of this action, hydrogen cyanide can be isolated when $2\,(I) \cdot 3\,AlCl_3$ is heated or even dissolved in ether. Compounds (V) and (VI) give hydrogen cyanide plus formimidochloride, $NH{=}CHCl$, and hydrogen cyanide plus formamidodichloride, NH_2CHCl_2, respectively. Under Friedel-Crafts conditions, they react with aromatic compounds giving an aromatic aldehyde. In addition (V) generates a two carbon unit (VII)

$$\cdot 3\,HCl \cdot 3\,AlCl_3 \;\longrightarrow\; 2\,NH{=}CHNHCHCl_2 + 2\,NH{=}CHCl \quad (11)$$
$$(VII)$$
$$+\; 3\,HCl + 3\,AlCl_3$$

according to equation (11). It is (VII) which must be responsible for the formation of benzhydrylformamidine hydrochloride from benzene and (V) observed by Gattermann and Schnitzspahn[9] and also similar derivatives observed by Hinkel and Summers.[10]

I. Grignard Reaction

The action of phenylmagnesium iodide on s-triazine, followed by hydrolysis, yields benzaldehyde, formic acid and ammonia. This is probably best explained[33] by 1,2 addition of the Grignard reagent followed by decomposition of the resulting dihydro-*s*-triazine.

$$(I) + C_6H_5MgI \longrightarrow$$

References

1. O. Diels and R. Lichte, *Ber.*, **59**, 2778 (1926).
2. J. Liebig and F. Wohler, *Ann. Phys. Chem.*, **20**, 369 (1835).
3. J. Liebig, *Ann.*, **10**, 11 (1834).
4. J. Nef, *Ann.*, **287**, 333 (1895).
5. C. Grundmann and A. Kreutzberger, *J. Am. Chem. Soc.*, **76**, 632 (1954).
5A. American Cyanamid Co. Unpublished Data.
6. C. Grundmann and A. Kreutzberger, *J. Am. Chem. Soc.*, **76**, 5646 (1954).
7. A. Pinner, *Ber.*, **16**, 250 (1883).
8. A. Pinner, *Ber.*, **28**, 2457 (1895).
9. L. Gattermann and K. Schnitzspahn, *Ber.*, **31**, 1770 (1898).
10. L. Hinkel and G. Summers, *J. Chem. Soc.*, **1952**, 2813.
11. L. Hinkel et al., *J. Chem. Soc.*, **1930**, 1834; **1932**, 2793; **1935**, 674; **1936**, 184; **1940**, 407; **1949**, 1953.
12. L. Siegel and E. Williams, *J. Chem. Phys.*, **22**, 1147 (1954).
13. F. Halverson and R. Hirt, *J. Chem. Phys.*, **19**, 711 (1951).
14. R. Hirt and D. Salley, *J. Chem. Phys.*, **21**, 1181 (1953).
15. R. Hirt, F. Halverson and R. Schmitt, *J. Chem. Phys.*, **22**, 1148 (1954).
16. J. Lancaster and N. Colthup, *J. Chem. Phys.*, **22**, 1149 (1954).
17. R. Willstatter and T. Wirth, *Ber.*, **42**, 1918 (1909).
18. O. Diels and M. Liebermann, *Ber.*, **36**, 3191 (1903).
19. O. Diels, *Ber.*, **32**, 691 (1899).
20. C. Grundmann and E. Beyer, *J. Am. Chem. Soc.*, **76**, 1948 (1954).
21. A. Hantzsch and H. Bauer, *Ber.*, **38**, 1010 (1905).
22. A. Weddige, *J. prakt. Chem.*, (2), **10**, 212 (1874).
23. G. Lander, *J. Chem. Soc.*, **83**, 411 (1903).
24. E. Bamberger and W. Dieckmann, *Ber.*, **25**, 534 (1892).
25. C. Grundmann, H. Ulrich and A. Kreutzberger, *Ber.*, **86**, 181 (1953).
26. H. Wieland, *Ber.*, **42**, 803 (1909).
27. L. Hinkel, E. Ayling and J. Beynon, *J. Chem. Soc.*, **1935**, 676.
28. E. Justin-Mueller, *Melliland Textilber.*, **29**, 170 (1948) through *Chem. Abstracts*, **44**, 9200 (1949).
29. L. Hinkel and T. Watkins, *J. Chem. Soc.*, **1940**, 407.
30. L. Hinkel and R. Dunn, *J. Chem. Soc.*, **1930**, 1834.
31. J. Goubeau, E. Jahn, A. Kreutzberger and C. Grundmann, *J. Phys. Chem.*, **58**, (1954)
32. C. Grundmann and A. Kreutzberger, *J. Am. Chem. Soc.*, **77**, 44 (1955).
33. W. von Ruske, *Chem. Tech. Berlin*, **6**, 489 (1954).
34. J. Rakshit, *J. Chem. Soc.*, **103**, 1557 (1913).
35. W. Ruske, *Chem. Tech. Berlin*, **5**, 308 (1953).
36. W. Ruske, *Chem. Tech. Berlin*, **5**, 368 (1953).
37. C. Grundman, H. Schroeder and W. Ruske, *Chem. Ber.*, **87**, 1865 (1954).

CHAPTER I

Cyanuric Acid and Derivatives

I. Introduction

The 1,3,5-triazines or s-triazines, as represented by cyanuric acid, are among the oldest recognized organic compounds. Cyanuric acid was known to Scheele[1] as early as 1776, as "pyro-uric" acid, the name being descriptive of his preparation of the compound by uric acid pyrolysis.

The fundamental compound in the series, s-triazine (I) has only recently been identified[1a] as such in the literature. The simplest monofunctional s-triazine is 2-amino-s-triazine (II). There may be some doubt that (II) is completely unsaturated since tautomerization could produce a dihydrotriazine. After compounds (I) and (II), cyanuric acid

(I) 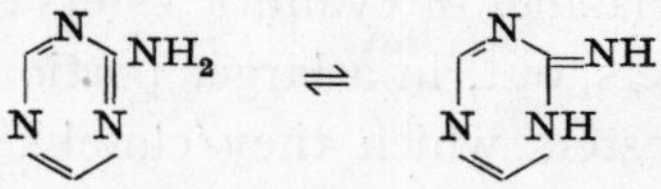 (II)

(III) may be regarded as the most fundamental compound although not the simplest in regard to ring substituents. It is encountered often in triazine chemistry as a by-product in synthetic work and an end-product of mild degradative experiments. Closely related to s-triazine are the 2,4,6-trialkyl derivatives in which no tautomerism can exist.

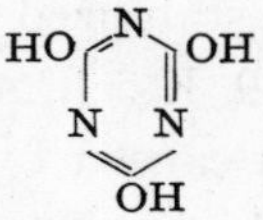

(III) 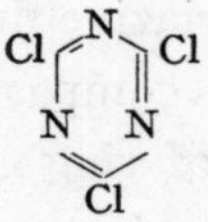 (IV)

Cyanuric chloride (IV) is not quite so closely related to s-triazine as the 2,4,6-trialkyl-s-triazines, but it is closely related to cyanuric

acid and is far more important than the latter as a fundamental compound for the synthesis of a great many members of the s-triazine
series. Because of the close historical and chemical interrelation of these
two fundamental compounds, they are to some extent discussed
simultaneously as well as successively in this chapter. Moreover, they
precede other members of the series which might have been presented
first in deference to classical chemical considerations and series
organization.

   The s-triazine ring is numbered in the same manner as a benzene
ring starting with a nitrogen atom as number one. The "s-triazine"
system has been adopted for simplicity in favor of the term "1,3,5-
triazine." The latter is employed only where it adds clarity and avoids
ambiguity, particularly in cases of compounds which are highly substituted or which have partially hydrogenated rings. Thus, cyanuric
chloride is 2,4,6-trichloro-s-triazine, and cyanuric acid may be represented as 2,4,6-trihydroxy-s-triazine (III). Other nomenclature used
in this chapter also follows accepted Chemical Abstracts rules and
involves nothing unusual. When one or more of the hydrogen atoms in
cyanuric acid is replaced by an alkyl or by an aryl group, the alkoxy-
and aryloxy-s-triazines or cyanuric esters result. These compounds are
structurally ethers, but, in a larger portion of the literature, they are
referred to as esters which they closely resemble in many of their
chemical properties and reactions. The ester designation has been
retained in this volume.

   It will become apparent that much of the chemistry of the
s-triazines is simply chemistry of substituent groups on a ring which is
not often involved in the reactions save for its effect on charge distribution. The chemistry of the triazine derivatives cannot be compared
with that of the corresponding benzene derivatives. Pauling[2] has
calculated that the triazine nucleus is stabilized by a resonance energy
of 82.5 K.cal./mole, compared to 39 K.cal./mole for benzene. The
increase in number of ring electrons caused by replacing carbon by
nitrogen is perhaps a reason for the high resonance energy. Thus, for
each nitrogen atom introduced, two additional electrons are also
introduced. In the s-triazine ring, six nonbonding electrons are present
in addition to the pi-electrons, and these can enter into the resonating

system. Since this is so, there should be (1) an increase in the resonance energy over benzene and (2) a greater electron density about the nitrogen atoms which would act to stabilize, to a degree greater than with benzene, the ring double bonds. That the resonance energy is increased is seen above. Later it will be seen that some double bond stabilization is actually observed.

In addition to resonance energies, the triazine and benzene systems differ chemically. For example, primary aminotriazine groups such as those of melamine do not form diazonium salts, in contrast to the behavior characteristic of a primary aromatic amino group. It is only with the greatest difficulty that nuclear hydroxyl groups can be acylated. Thus, the hydroxyl groups of cyanuric acid, unlike those of phenols and naphthols, are very difficult to acylate. A study of the magnetic suceptibilities of some s-triazines[4] shows that these substances have many aromatic properties. They are strongly anisotropic although less so than benzene or its derivatives If the six ring electrons occupy molecular orbits of approximately the same area as that of the triazine nucleus itself, the anisotropy should be almost twice that found experimentally. On the other hand, if the electrons are definitely paired, forming double bonds, very little anisotropy should exist. The experimental data show that the pi-electrons do occupy molecular orbits,

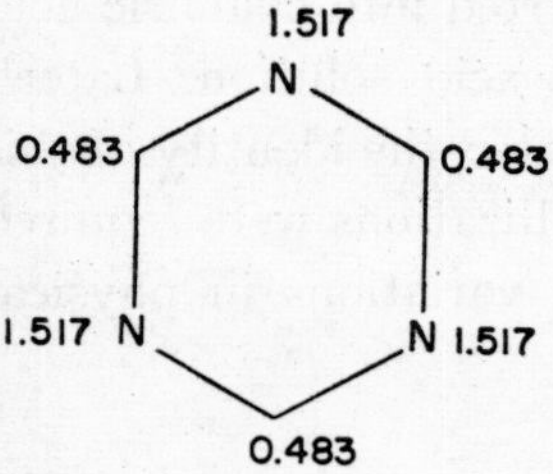

(IVa) 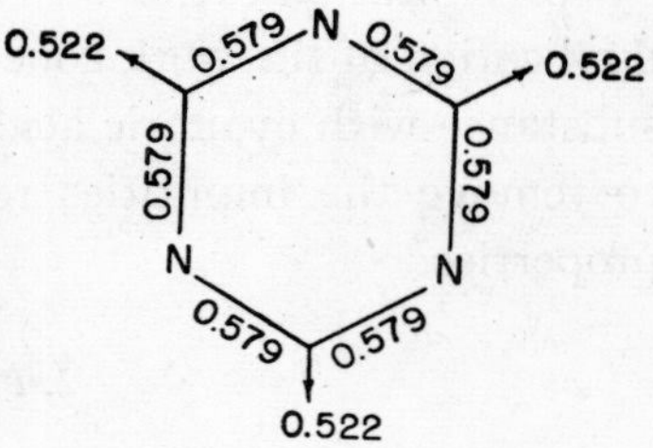   (IVb)

but with a strong tendency toward fixation of double bonds in the nucleus. That is, there is an alternation of electron density around the nucleus, but not as great as would be expected for alternate double and single bonds between carbon and nitrogen atoms. Pullman[5] has written charge (IVa) and index (IVb) diagrams for the s-triazine ring.

II. Cyanuric Acid

1. Historical

Scheele's pyrolysis of uric acid to yield cyanuric acid, accomplished in the last quarter of the eighteenth century, was repeated[6] in 1820 and the properties of cyanuric acid were well described. In 1820, Serullas[7] obtained cyanuric acid from cyanogen in water, but it was not until 1830[8] that this "cyanic" acid isomer and pyrouric acid were found to be identical. Liebig and Wohler[9] collaborated in that same year to achieve the first correct analysis of cyanuric acid and its dihydrate. The name cyanuric acid was coined since the compound was considered to be composed of $C \equiv N$ groups and had been made from uric acid by destructive distillation. Other synonyms used at various times are tricyanic acid, trioxytriazine and trioxycyanidine. The excellent work of Liebig and Wohler[9] correlated and clarified many previous discrepancies. Liebig[10] determined that the ratio of the elements in cyanuric acid was 1, but his formula $C_6H_6N_6O_6$ was double the correct one which was not deduced until 1875 by Drechsel.[11] Liebig,[12] in 1834, had reported a new acidic compound, different from cyanuric acid in its physical properties but identical in composition. He named it cyanilic acid and found that it could be converted into cyanuric acid by precipitation with water from a sulfuric acid solution. Later[13] duplication of the work conclusively demonstrated the identity of this substance with cyanuric acid. Repeated crystallizations were required to remove the impurities responsible for the variations in physical properties.

2. Physical Properties

A. General

Cyanuric acid, 2,4,6-trihydroxy-s-triazine (III), crystallizes with two molecules of water in colorless monoclinic prisms[14]; occasionally in terraced aggregates. In dry air the crystals effloresce. The anhydrous acid forms octahedric crystals decomposing without melting above 360°.

The product of the thermal decomposition or depolymerization of cyanuric acid is cyanic acid and the procedure constitutes a simple method of preparing this reactive compound.

$$\text{HO} \diagup \overset{\text{N}}{\diagdown} \text{OH} \quad \xrightarrow{\Delta} \quad 3 \text{ HCNO}$$

(III) OH

Cyanuric acid is only slightly soluble in water, 0.125%, or about 1 part in 800 parts of water[2] at room temperature and 4% in boiling water. It is even less soluble in alcohol. The acid is odorless but of a somewhat bitter taste. It is not poisonous in trace amounts.

It turns blue litmus slightly red and may be titrated as a monobasic acid with 0.1 N sodium hydroxide and phenolphthalein indicator. In the presence of a large excess of strong inorganic base, cyanuric acid forms salts at two of the hydroxyl groups. The third group is unreactive at temperatures below 100°.

B. Density

t, °C	d	Ref.
—5	1.753	16
0	1.768	16
19	2.500	17
24	2.228	17
48	1.725	17

According to the data cited, cyanuric acid has a maximum density at 19°. The data are open to some question, since a density change of 31% over a range of only 24° seems unique. Some of the sources are almost ninety years old.[17,18] The "overall average" density of cyanuric acid in the solid state has been measured[18] as 1.729, a value which again appears odd, this time because it corresponds to the lowest density in the table compiled from the literature.

C. Thermal Properties[19,20,21]

Solid State

	Heat of Combustion	Heat of Formation	Heat of Vaporization	R.E.[a]
Anhydrous	219.5 Kcals.	—165.1	38.3	88.7
Dihydrate	219.5 Kcals.	307.9	—	—

[a] Resonance Energy.

D. Heat of Neutralization[4]

	NaOH	KOH	NH₃
1st hydrogen	6.74 Kcals.	6.84	4.88
2nd hydrogen	4.12	4.2	1.65
3rd hydrogen	1.74	2.1	1.0
Total	12.6	13.3	7.53

E. Dissociation Constant

At 25°, the dissociation constant is 1.8×10^{-5} (pKa = 4.745), varying slightly depending on the source of the acid.[22] The percentage dissociated at 35° determined by conductivity measurements is as follows:

F. Percentage Dissociated at 35°[23]

Dilution	% Dissociation
128	0.360
512	0.686
1020	0.869
2048	1.15

G. Conductivity

The molecular conductivity of cyanuric acid at 25° is as follows[23]:

Volume (Dilution)	Molecular Conductivity
128	1.46
512	2.78
1024	3.52
2048	4.67

The conductivity of cyanuric acid in a supersaturated aqueous solution was measured[24] and K was found to average 32.4×10^6 mhos.

H. Viscosity and Density of Solutions

Solution[25]	Temperature	Viscosity	Density
3.20% aqueous	25° C	0.01038 poises	0.9874 g/cc.
20 mole % in pyridine	25° C	0.0120 poises	—

I. Specific Heat[26]

The specific heats and average atomic heats of cyanuric acid and two of its salts are as follows:

Substances	Specific Heat	Average Atomic Heat
Cyanuric acid	0.327	3.5
Trisodium cyanurate	0.165	2.7
Trisilver cyanurate	0.098	3.4

J. Magnetic Susceptibility

The magnetic susceptibility of cyanuric acid has been measured[27, 28] as -61.5×10^{-6} and -50.5×10^{-6}.

K. Raman, Infrared and Ultraviolet Spectra

Cyanuric acid exhibits[29] absorption at wave numbers of 700, 1000, and 1739 cm.$^{-1}$. The last point is characteristic of carboxyl absorption, a fact which, together with the failure to find absorption characteristic of the benzene or pyridine aromatic system, is good evidence that neutral cyanuric acid exists in the keto form. Infrared spectra for cyanuric acid in both anhydrous and hydrated forms have been published.[30] The characteristics of the ultraviolet spectrum of cyanuric acid are discussed below. (Sect. II, 4).

L. Polarographic Behavior

In 0.1 N KOH cyanuric acid yields a distinct polarographic wave,[53a] the height of which is a linear function of the concentration of (III).

M. Crystallography and Miscellaneous Properties

A great deal of early work on the optical properties and crystallography[31,32,33] of cyanuric acid has been done; Groth[34] lists the experimental work on the crystalline structure of all of the known cyanuric acid salts and derivatives through 1910. These properties do not need to be restated here. Other properties of cyanuric acid which are too specialized to warrant a detailed discussion are listed below.

Property	Ref.
Molecular weight in H_2SO_4	35
Acidity in pyridine solution	36
Electrocapillarity	37
Affinity constant	38
Molecular volume	39

3. Synthesis and Occurrence

A. Natural Occurence

Cyanuric acid is known to exist in nature. It has been isolated from acid humus soil[40] usually by dilute alkali extraction.[41] Its presence in a wide variety of soils is not considered to be general[42] and its isolation from other natural sources is limited.

B. From Cyanuric Halides

Cyanuric acid can be readily obtained from cyanuric halides. (For methods of preparation of the cyanuric halides see Sect. III 1.C). Cyanuric chloride is stable in water at 0° for at least twelve hours, but as the temperature is raised, hydrolysis proceeds quite readily[43] until at 36°, 65% hydrolysis (of one chlorine atom) occurs after one hour. Commercially available cyanuric chloride offers a convenient source of cyanuric acid in the laboratory. When cyanuric chloride is refluxed with a large excess of glacial acetic acid[44] for about an hour, the acid is obtained in 95% yields and can be readily isolated in contrast to some of the older procedures.

(IV)   (III)

Cyanuric bromide can likewise serve as a source of the acid by hydrolysis. Heating cyanuric bromide at 100° in water gives pure cyanuric acid[45]; a better method is to conduct the hydrolysis[46] in a closed container with water at 120°.

C. Polymerization of Cyanic Acid

Cyanic acid, HO—C≡N, is a liquid boiling at 23.5°. It is very unstable and rapidly polymerizes giving two principal products, cyanuric acid and cyamelide.[47] At 0°, the polymerization occurs spontaneously, but not violently, and requires about an hour to be complete. At room temperatures, the reaction may sometimes reach explosive proportions. It is complete within a few minutes and is accompanied by the evolution of considerable quantities of heat. The nature and superficial area of the walls of the reaction vessel influence the polymerization which occurs three times as rapidly[48] in a vessel coated on the inside with cyamelide as in an ordinary glass reactor.

The proportion of cyanuric acid and cyamelide formed from cyanic acid is a function of temperature. The higher the temperature, the more cyanuric acid is formed. From a consideration of the structures of cyanuric acid and cyamelide, the formation of these compounds from cyanic acid and urea can be readily explained. Urea, when heated, can dissociate[49] into cyanic acid. At higher temperatures, the existence of the latter as H—N=C=O, isocyanic acid, has been shown[50-53]; while at lower temperatures the normal structure, HO—CN, is favored. Cyanic acid trimerizes to give cyanuric acid (III), while isocyanic acid trimerizes to give cyamelide (V).

and

Cyamelide can be isomerized to cyanuric acid by heating it with sulfuric acid[54]. The cyclic structure written above for cyamelide may not be as correct as the linear structure postulated by Sidgwick.[55] He suggested that its non-volatility and complete insolubility are more characteristic of a high molecular weight linear polymer analogous to that of formaldehyde. The suggested formula is

$$\cdots -O-\overset{\overset{\displaystyle NH}{\|}}{C}-O-\overset{\overset{\displaystyle NH}{\|}}{C}-O-\overset{\overset{\displaystyle NH}{\|}}{C}-\cdots$$

Treating potassium cyanate with concentrated hydrochloric acid causes liberation of cyanic acid which at once trimerizes to cyanuric acid. With acetic or other weak acids, monopotassium cyanurate precipitates from the reaction mixture.

D. From Urea and Urea Derivatives

Early work had shown[56, 57] that heat or chemical treatment converted urea to cyanuric acid; later the reaction was improved and elucidated.

When urea is heated[56] at 120°, ammonia and carbon dioxide are evolved and cyanuric acid is obtained. Treatment with phosphoric anhydride leads to a similar result.[58] The reaction proceeds first through the formation of biuret from two molecules of urea.

$$\begin{matrix} \overset{\overset{\displaystyle O}{\|}}{H_2NC}-NH_2 \\ \overset{\overset{\displaystyle O}{\|}}{H_2NC}-NH_2 \end{matrix} \longrightarrow NH_3 + H_2N-\overset{\overset{\displaystyle O}{\|}}{C}-NH-\overset{\overset{\displaystyle O}{\|}}{C}-NH_2$$

Biuret may then react[59] with another molecule of urea forming triuret and/or cyanuric acid by rapid, consecutive or simultaneous deammonations or, as some evidence shows,[60] it may react with dicyanic acid.

$$\begin{matrix} H_2N\,CONHCO\,NH_2 \\ \overset{\displaystyle H}{H\,N}-CO-\overset{\displaystyle H}{N\,H} \end{matrix} \longrightarrow 2\,NH_3 + \text{(III)} \rightleftharpoons$$

(III)

The latter comes from cyanic acid. The product of such a reaction is hypothetically triuret,

$$NH_2-\overset{\overset{\displaystyle O}{\|}}{C}-NH-\overset{\overset{\displaystyle O}{\|}}{C}-NH-\overset{\overset{\displaystyle O}{\|}}{C}-NH_2$$

which might simultaneously decompose in two ways. One would produce cyanuric acid with ammonia and the other would produce ammelide and water, both of which are observed. It appears surprising in view of the apparent theoretical ease of formation of cyanuric acid from triuret that only small amounts of cyanuric acid are obtained[62] when it is heated to 232°, and none when it is boiled[63] in water for several hours. The temperature of the urea to cyanuric acid conversion is important. When powdered urea was added to a hot inert oil such as paraffin or mineral oils in which neither urea nor cyanuric acid is soluble, yields[61] increased from 47% at 220° and 68% at 235° to 79% at 245°.

Treatment of molten urea with chlorine, a method which Wurtz[64-66] used, but did not originate, is the basis for a reliable, if complicated, preparation[67] of cyanuric acid. Purification of the product is accomplished by means of the copper ammonium salt. Hydrogen chloride[68] may be used in place of chlorine, although the yield[69] is only 25% and much biuret is produced. A more valuable modification of these methods is one in which anhydrous zinc chloride and molten urea are heated at 220°. Yields[70] of cyanuric acid of 62% can be realized. This is a method which has served as a basis for a cyanuric acid pilot plant designed[71] to produce about 70 lbs./week and operating at a yield at about 10% less than the laboratory yield (62%).

Yields of 85% are obtained if ammonium chloride and urea are fused[72] at 250° for fifteen minutes. The cyanuric acid is leached from the reactions mixture with hot water.

$$NH_2CONH_2 + NH_4Cl \xrightarrow[\text{15 min.}]{\text{fuse 250°}} \quad (III)$$

Other reagents will cause the self-condensation of urea. Sulfuryl chloride and chlorosulfonic acid are two such reagents.[63] Under mild conditions urea forms biuret; under more vigorous conditions triuret; and finally, under still more severe conditions, good yields of cyanuric acid can be obtained. Thiourea, as will be seen later, does not react with sulfuryl chloride or chlorosulfonic acid.

Although treatment[73] of urea with acetic anhydride gives principally acetylurea, some cyanuric acid is produced. A patent[74] has been issued for the production of cyanuric acid as a by-product when an amino group is substituted for a halogen atom by the action of urea on compounds containing a halogen in a position not meta to a nitro group.

(VI)   (VII)   (III)

When nitrates (of urea or ammonia) are heated[75-77], little or no cyanuric acid is obtained. The reason is probably the formation of nitric acid which causes the decomposition[78] of whatever cyanuric acid intermediates may have formed to NH_3, CO_2, and $(NH_4)_2CO_3$. Biuret, however, gives cyanuric acid when it is heated with concentrated nitric acid[79] and urea nitrate is the chief by-product. It may be that heat alone converts biuret to cyanuric acid and that once the biuret stage is reached, the destructive action of nitric acid is lessened so that some cyanuric acid results.

Both biuret and urethan, heated at 160–170°, give cyanuric acid,[80] although biuret appears to act as the more effective source. Triuret (carbonyl diurea), as might be expected, splits out ammonia completing the formation of the triazine ring when heated[81] with any of the

(VIII)   (III)

following reagents: NaOH, Na_2CO_3, HCl (gas), $COCl_2$ or HNO_3. Heat alone, in the absence of a catalyst, does not produce substantial amounts of deammoniation.

A 75% yield of cyanuric acid results when p-tolylsulfonylurea (IX)

(IX)   (X)

is heated for thirty minutes at 210–220°.[82] The reaction undoubtedly proceeds via cyanic acid which trimerizes at once giving cyanuric acid. The formation of cyanuric acid accounts for the resolidification after fusion of arylsulfonylureas and for the resumed decomposition at higher temperatures.

E. From Uric Acid

The oxidation of uric acid (XI) with alkaline permanganate[83] or very strongly alkaline hydrogen peroxide leads directly[84,85] to the formation of cyanuric acid in 50% yields. If only very mildly alkaline or neutral peroxide is used on uric acid, triuret is a probable intermediate, for both triuret and allantoin (XII) can be found. Both of these compounds are converted to cyanuric acid on further treatment with alkaline peroxide. Furthermore, when the oxidizing agent is

$$
\begin{array}{ccc}
\text{NH—CO} & & \\
| \quad | & & \\
\text{CO} \quad \text{C—NH} & & \\
| \quad \| \quad \text{CO} & \xrightarrow[\text{Neutral}]{H_2O_2} & (NH_2CONH)_2CO \\
\text{NH—C—NH} & & \\
\text{(XI)} & &
\end{array}
$$

$$
\begin{array}{ccc}
\text{NH—CH—NH} & \\
| \quad | & \\
+ \quad \text{CO} \quad \text{CO} \\
| \quad | \\
\text{NH}_2 \quad \text{CO—NH} \\
\text{(XII)}
\end{array}
$$

(XI) → (via H_2O_2, NaOH) and (alkaline KMnO$_4$ or H_2O_2 + strong NaOH) → (III)

(XII) → (via H_2O_2 Alkaline) → (III)

$$
\begin{array}{ccc}
& \text{H} & \\
\text{NH—C——NH} & \\
| \quad | \quad | & \xrightarrow[\text{H}^+]{H_2O_2} \\
\text{CO} \quad \text{COOH} \quad \text{CO} \\
| \quad \quad | \\
\text{NH}_2 \quad \quad \text{NH}_2 \\
\text{(XIII)}
\end{array}
$$

$$
\begin{array}{c}
\text{N} \\
\text{HO} \diagup \quad \diagdown \text{OH} \\
\text{N} \quad \text{N} \\
\diagdown \quad \diagup \\
\text{OH} \\
\text{(III)}
\end{array}
$$

moderately alkaline hydrogen peroxide, the intermediate allantoic acid (XIII) is isolated[86]; it can also be converted to (III) with acidic hydrogen peroxide or bromine water. The mechanism of the oxidation of uric acid to cyanuric acid has been carefully studied[3, 92a] with isotopes. It has been shown that 2,4-dihydroxy-s-triazine-6-carboxylic acid (oxonic acid) is an intermediate in the oxidation. It decarboxylated to give 2,4-dihydroxy-s-triazine (allantoxidine) which is readily oxidized to cyanuric acid. The s-triazine ring contains uric acid carbons 2,4 and 8 and uric acid nitrogens 3 and 9.

F. From Allophanates and Carbamyl Chlorides

Cyanuric acid of a high degree of purity and in good yield is obtained by heating at 250–300° the chlorides which result when carbamic acid chlorides are dehydrohalogenated and condensed. Examples are: allophanic chloride, $NH_2CONHCOCl$, and biuret carboxylic chloride, $NH_2CONHCONHCOCl$. Cyanuric acid is then formed in nearly quantitative yields[87] by the splitting out of hydrogen chloride. Carbamyl chloride may be directly converted to cyanuric acid by allowing the two stages of heating to follow one another. For example, carbamyl chloride is heated first either with or without a solvent under a reflux condenser and the resulting product is then heated further at 250–500° after removal of the diluent.

$$HNCO \overset{\fbox{H}}{Cl} \longrightarrow HNCO \longrightarrow C_3N_3(OH)_3 \quad (III)$$

Lower temperatures may be used by employing[88] a diluent such as chlorobenzene or trichlorobenzene. The vapor phase synthesis of carbamyl chloride from phosgene and ammonia at 500° offers[89] a practical direct method of obtaining 98% pure cyanuric acid in 85% yield. In this method the carbamyl chloride is converted to the triazine by heating at 180° in a hydrocarbon solvent. A small amount of isomeric cyammelide (V) is obtained but this is removable by virtue of its insolubility in alkali.

$$3\,NH_3 + 3\,COCl_2 \xrightarrow{500°} 3\,HCl + 3\,NH_2COCl$$

$$\Big\downarrow 180°$$

HO–N–N–OH   + 3 HCl

(III)

Ammonia and carbon dioxide have been shown to give small amounts of cyanuric acid when passed[90] over alumina or thoria catalysts at 400°. The chief product, however, is ammonium cyanate. Good yields of cyanuric acid have been obtained[91] by heating above 190° the crude product from the reaction of ammonia and phosgene suspended in an inert liquid such as carbon tetrachloride or paraffin.

This product is undoubtedly akin to carbamyl chloride or to an allophanate and the reaction is probably not different from the ammonia-carbamyl chloride reaction above.

Treating ethyl allophanate with thionyl chloride in an inert solvent at 140–150° gives cyanuric acid,[92] and if the temperature is raised to 200°, a yield of 94% is obtained after only 45 minutes.[93]

$$NH_2CONHCOOC_2H_5 + SOCl_2 \xrightarrow[\text{Xylene}]{\substack{140-150° \\ 3-4 \text{ hrs.}}}$$ [cyanuric acid structure] $+ HCl + H_2SO_3 + C_2H_5Cl$

(III)

Cyanuric acid (III) is obtained in small amounts[94] when ethyl or butyl carbamates are treated with thionyl chloride to give the corresponding esters of allophanic acid:

$$\underset{\text{ROC—NH}_2}{\overset{O}{\parallel}} + SOCl_2 \longrightarrow \underset{\text{ROOC—NH—C—NH}_2}{\overset{O}{\parallel}} + (III)$$

G. From Carbonyl Diurethane and Carbethoxybiuret

When carbonyl diurethane[95] (XIV) is treated with ammonia in a closed container, cyanuric acid is obtained together with carbethoxybiuret (XV) and traces of biuret. Carbethoxybiuret is probably an intermediate which upon elimination of the elements of ethanol can give rise to cyanuric acid.

$$\underset{\text{NHCOOC}_2\text{H}_5}{\overset{\text{NHCOOC}_2\text{H}_5}{OC{<}}} \xrightarrow[\Delta]{NH_3} [\text{cyanuric acid structure}] + H_2NCONHCONH + H_2NCONHCONH_2$$

$$\downarrow (XV)$$

[cyanuric acid structure] $+ C_2H_5OH$

H. From Formamide Electrolytically

Electrolysis of formamide below 45° using a platinum anode and a lead cathode gives[96] a 20% yield of cyanuric acid. The products become more complex at higher temperatures or if the current density is increased. Formation of HOCN, which is no doubt the primary product of decomposition, may occur because of a discharge of form-amide ions (–CONH⁻), when the formamide contains a little water; or from anodic oxidation of formamide, when more water is present.

Several miscellaneous preparations of cyanuric acid, which are listed below, give fair yields, but are seldom encountered.

I. From Acetoxamide

Heating moist monoaceto-oxamide at 100–110° with acetic an-hydride gives cyanuric acid in 60% yield:

$$NH_2COCONHCOCH_3 \xrightarrow{100-110°} \quad (III)$$

J. From Carbaminothioglycolic Acid Anilide

Carbaminothioglycolic acid anilide heated above its melting point gives very pure cyanuric acid.[98]

$$H_2NCOSCH_2CONHC_6H_5 \xrightarrow{\Delta} \quad (III)$$

K. Miscellaneous Preparations

The following are brief descriptions of a few reactions which might be considered as minor or merely incidental preparations of cyanuric acid. Cyanuric acid is a stable chemical entity. It is frequently obtained as the terminal reaction product of drastic oxidations, in pyrolytic decompositions, or in synthetic work where there is opportunity for formation of the s-triazine nucleus or for hydrolysis of already existing substituted triazines.

When various amino derivatives of cyanuric acid such as melamine, melon, ammeline, etc., are heated with hydrolytic agents, cyanuric acid can be obtained[99-106]. Guanidine,[104] which forms melamine, is oxidized by nitric acid to cyanuric acid. Pyroguanazole can be oxidized to cyanuric acid with alkaline permanganate. Thiocyanic acid upon treat-ment with hydrochloric acid leaves a residue from which, after strong heating[107,108] with an alkaline carbonate, cyanuric acid can be isolated. Ammonium thiocyanate[109] also yields cyanuric acid, in this case by means of heat treatment. Isothiourethan,

$$\overset{S}{\underset{\|}{NH_2-C-OC_2H_5}}$$

decomposes[110] at 150° giving among the products of decomposition, cyanuric acid and ethyl isothiocyanate.

Destructive distillation of such compounds as xanthogenic acid amide,[111] oxaluramide,[112] or a mixture of butrylphenylhydrazine and carbamyl chloride,[113] has been reported to give cyanuric acid as the chief identifiable product. Herzig[114] reported an isomeric cyanuric acid obtained by treating hexabromoacetone with urea, and compared its properties with those of cyanuric acid. The structure of this product has not been elucidated. Any cyanuric acid possibly obtained could be formed only as a result of the action of heat or of an acidic catalyst (HBr) formed in situ on urea.

A small quantity of cyanuric acid is obtained[115] in the thermal decomposition of benzalurethane, $C_6H_5CH(NHCOOC_2H_5)_2$. A considerable number of other products is also formed. In this case cyanuric acid is undoubtedly formed by trimerization of cyanic acid, one of these products.

An 8% yield of cyanuric acid was obtained[114a] by heating ethyl carbamate with benzyl alcohol. By the addition of a small amount of sulfuric acid, the yield of cyanuric acid was raised to 32%.

4. Structure

Cyanuric acid may exists in two limiting tautomeric forms[116] as well as two intermediate keto-enol forms. These correspond to enol-keto tautomerism in carbonyl compounds. In the case of cyanuric acid the triketo form is known as isocyanuric acid (XVI) and its N-alkyl or N-aryl derivatives as isocyanurates.

(III)   (XVI   (V)

Compound (V), cyamelide, is not a triazine but it is frequently encountered in s-triazine chemistry. The cyclic structure (V) is written here for cyamelide but the linear structure postulated by Sidgwick may be the more correct one.[55] Cyamelide (V) and cyanuric acid (III) are interrelated in this manner: heating cyanic acid above 150° gives[117] cyanuric acid, but below that temperature cyamelide is the chief product. This transformation has been shown[118] to be reversible with heat; cyamelide can also be used as a more direct source[119] of cyanuric acid by heating it to its decomposition point in concentrated H_2SO_4 and quenching rapidly with water. Molecular susceptibility studies[116] show that cyanuric acid has the same type of nucleus as benzene. However, the magnetic properties of both isocyanuric compounds and cyamelide show the existence of identical bond types which in both cases correspond to a degree of ring saturation less than that of cyanuric acid.

Ultraviolet absorption studies[120, 121] showed that the cyclic structure was likely for cyanuric acid, but arguments on isomerism[122] have persisted. Cyanuric acid exists[123] almost exclusively in the keto form in acid solution and has a low ultraviolet absorption, however, in neutral solution, conclusions based on ultraviolet absorption show that it is enolized,[124, 125] to the extent of 5.6%. In very strongly basic solution, it is probably almost[134a] completely enolized.[125] Its relatively high absorbtivity in neutral or weakly basic solutions is indicative of resonance among such forms as:

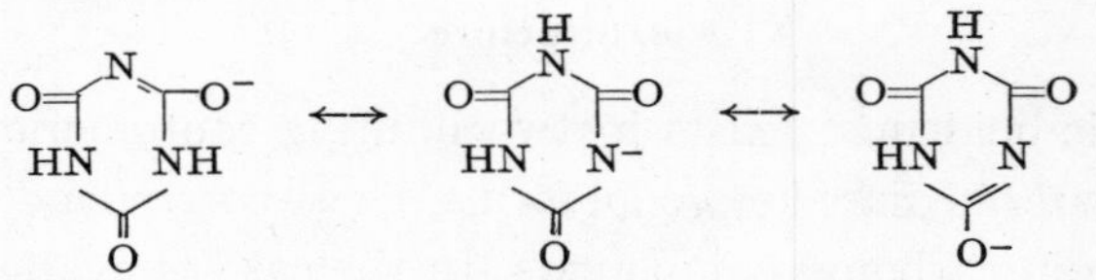

Recent ultraviolet absorption spectra studies[126, 127] have shown the isocyanuric or tri-keto structure to exist in acidic solutions, below pH 6. The di-keto structure predominates in the range from pH 7 to 10.5, and the mono-keto structure above pH 11. No spectra of the fully ionized form were obtained even in 4 N sodium hydroxide solution. These ionizations may be represented by:

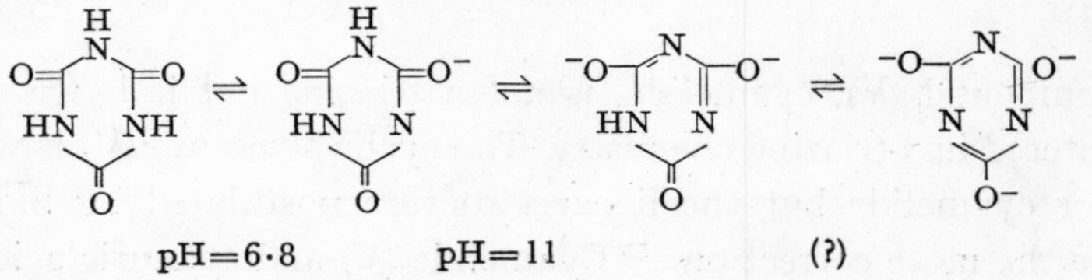

pH=6·8   pH=11   (?)

Hughes has shown[128] lucidly that the crystalline structure of cyanuric acid supports the iso or keto form. There are two hydrogen bridges between oxygen and nitrogen atoms which bind the crystal together in the (101) plane. These form angles of about 120° with both the nitrogen to carbon and the oxygen to carbon bonds. The hydrogens might be on either oxygen or nitrogen without violation of sterochemical considerations. However, the third bridge, linking molecules along the (010) plane, makes an angle of 120° with the carbon nitrogen bond but an angle of 180° with the carbon-oxygen bond. Were this hydrogen on the oxygen atom, it would point away from the nitrogen to which it is supposed to be attracted by at least 50° and probably more. If it were on the nitrogen atom, on the other hand, it would point exactly at the oxygen atom to which it is bridged. Only one of the hydrogens is thus definitely fixed on the ring, but it is unlikely that the others differ. They do not differ in the case of melamine (see Chapter VI).

Wiebenga[129] has conducted an intensive X-ray study of crystalline cyanuric acid and his data indicate that the keto form is the one which exists—not a resonating intermediate. The carbon to oxygen bond was found to be 1.21 Å $\pm$ 0.02 Å. This is significantly smaller than the

1.29 Å expected from mesomerism between the usually accepted resonating structures with standard lengths of 1.47, 1.265, 1.43, and 1.215 Å for the pure C—N, C—N, C—O, and C—O bonds, respectively. The values of bond distances ($\pm$ 0.02 Å) and bond angles ($\pm$ 1.5°) for crystalline cyanuric acid are indicated.

This work is in substantial agreement with that of Newman and Badger[141a] who found that the carbon to oxygen bonds were all nearly equal and not greater than 1.24 Å, and that much stronger bonds were formed when the C=O and N—O bond directions make an angle of about 124° with each other. Newman and Badger also found that the NH—O distance was not less than 2.87 Å. Some of their work[141a] was carried out with partially deuterated cyanuric acid which was prepared by allowing ordinary cyanuric acid to stand for twenty-four to forty-eight hours in excess deuterium oxide.

Maruha,[28] who has measured the magnetic susceptibility of cyanuric acid, favors the tri-enol structure but suggests that the ionic form (XVII) also contributes to the normal state.

(III)   (XVII)

Hantzsch[131] has cited as a reason why solid cyanuric acid must exist in the trilactam (triketo) not the lactam-lactim or keto-enol equilibrium mixture, the fact that dry ammonia gas gives no salt, but aqueous ammonia gives ammonium salts. Only in solutions in which enolization can occur does the salt form.

The six bonds in the triazine ring are electronically equivalent and[132] the ring is stabilized by resonance[2] to the extent of 88.7 Kcal./mole. The remarkable anisotropy[27, 130] of cyanuric acid in particular, and cyanuric compounds in general, has been explained.[4] The assumption is made that, whereas their normal valency electrons behave as if they were spherically symmetrical, the pi electrons occupy planar orbits which are free to precess only in their own plane. The anisotropy of cyanuric compounds is about one half of the value expected for complete conjugation.

5. Salts of Cyanuric Acid

The salts of cyanuric acid are numerous. They have been extensively investigated although agreement in some cases has left much to be desired, particularly in the case of the copper salts. The formation of several of the salts furnishes qualitative tests for cyanuric acid itself. The characteristic insolubility of the trisodium salt has been suggested by Hofmann as a means for identifying cyanuric acid. Indeed the copper-ammonium salt has been used since the early work on cyanuric acid as a means of identification. The latter test[83] is carried out by adding dropwise to about 1 g. of material in 5 ml. of hot water containing 6 drops of concentrated ammonia solution, a solution of copper sulfate; the mixture is boiled after each drop until a permanent blue color is attained. A glistening amethyst precipitate of cupric cyanurate·$2NH_3$ is obtained when the solution is cooled.

Recent work, however, has shown that mono- and dimethyl iso-cyanurates also give color reactions which are indistinguishable from that of copper ammonium cyanurate. It is probable that other triazines with free hydroxy groups also give the test which is therefore of only limited specificity and value. Reports in the older literature of cyanuric acid identified only by means of the copper ammonia test should be treated with reserve.

A point concerning the structure of alkali salts of cyanuric acid may be mentioned here. The O-esters and the O-mercury salts on warming go over to the respective N-derivative. The N-derivative is the more stable one. The fact that treatment of an alkali cyanurate gives exclusively an O-mercury salt indicates the non-existence of N-alkali salts. Thus, in isomeric compounds in which the equilibrium

$$\overset{O}{\overset{\|}{C}}-NH- \quad \rightleftharpoons \quad -\overset{OH}{\overset{|}{C}}-N-$$

may take place, an O-compound gives rise to an O-derivative which may persist or, depending on its inherent stability, change to a N-derivative either at room temperature or under the influence of increased temperature.

Cyanuric acid is a weak monobasic acid and can be titrated as such with phenolphthalein. The disodium salt is obtained with excess caustic soda. Boiling with caustic soda produces the slightly soluble trisodium salt which can be decomposed to the mono-sodium salt with carbon dioxide. Table I-1 contains the principal salts of cyanuric acid and references to their preparation.

TABLE I–1. Salts of Cyanuric Acid^b A. Salts of Metals

Formula	Hydrate or Adduct	Temperature at which loss of H$_2$O occurs, °C	Solubility in water	Remarks	References
Ammonium					
NH$_4$C$_3$N$_3$O$_3$H$_2$	H$_2$O	130	S. sol.	Efflorescent prisms dec. 130° to cyanuric acid + NH$_3$	1, 4
(NH$_4$)$_2$	?			Doubtful existence	4
Barium					
Ba(C$_3$N$_3$O$_3$H$_2$)$_2$	2 H$_2$O		Insol.	Shining prisms	4
Ba$_2$(C$_3$N$_3$O$_3$H)$_2$	4 H$_2$O		Insol.		13
BaC$_3$N$_3$O$_3$H	3 H$_2$O	Retains H$_2$O at 200°			1, 4, 7
BaC$_3$N$_3$O$_3$H	H$_2$O	Retains H$_2$O at 200°			1
Ba(C$_3$N$_3$O$_3$H)$_2$					1
Cadmium					
Cd(C$_3$N$_3$O$_3$H$_2$)$_2$					8
Calcium					
Ca(C$_3$N$_3$O$_3$H$_2$)$_2$	8 H$_2$O	165°	S. sol.	Needles	1, 5
CaC$_3$N$_3$O$_3$H	3 H$_2$O	—2 H$_2$O/100° —3 H$_2$O/165°			1
Ca$_3$(C$_3$N$_3$O$_3$)$_2$?					1
Ca(C$_3$N$_3$O$_3$H$_2$)$_2$	6 H$_2$O		S. sol.	Melts at low temperature	16
Cobalt					
Co(C$_3$N$_3$O$_3$H$_2$)$_2$	6 H$_2$O	—6 H$_2$O at 100°		Red plates; dark blue when anhydrous	8

Formula	Hydrate or Adduct	Temperature at which loss of H_2O occurs, °C	Solubility in water	Remarks	References
Copper					
$Cu(C_3N_3O_3H_2)_2$	2 NH_3		Insol. cold H_2O S. sol. in NH_3	Violet crystals	8, 9, 10, 11
$Cu(C_3N_3O_3H_2)_2$	3 NH_3				8, 9
$Cu(C_3N_3O_3H_2)_2$	4 NH_3	—NH_3 on standing			8, 9
$Cu(C_3N_3O_3H_2)_2$	2 H_2O			a	8
$Cu(C_3N_3O_3H)$				By add'n. of Mg cyanurate to a sol'n. of Cu salt	16
$Cu(C_3N_3O_3H)$	3 H_2O			a	8
Copper-Sodium					
$CuNa_2(C_3N_3O_3)_2$	6 H_2O			Lilac $<$ 150° and turquoise $>$ 150°	11, 13
Lead					
$Pb(C_3N_3O_3)_2$	3 H_2O			From basic Pb acetate	8
$Pb_3(C_3N_3O_3)_2$	2 H_2O				7, 13
Magnesium					
$Mg(C_3N_3O_3H_2)_2$	14 H_2O	Dec. before dehydration			1
$Mg(C_3N_3H_3O_2)_2$	3 H_2O				8
Manganese					
$Mn(C_3N_3O_3H_2)_2$				Colorless, poorly formed	8
Mercury					
$Hg_2(C_3N_3O_3H)$	?				1
$HgCl_2(C_3N_3O_3H_3)_2$	4 H_2O			From $HgCl_2$ + Na cyanurate, plates	1
$Hg_3C_3N_3O_3$	2 H_2O	—H_2O at 100°			1

(Table continued)

TABLE I-1A (*continued*)

Formula	Hydrate or Adduct	Temperature at which loss of H$_2$O occurs, °C	Solubility in water	Remarks	References
Nickel					
Ni(C$_3$N$_3$O$_3$H)	4 NH$_3$	To free salt below 100		Green	8
Ni(C$_3$N$_3$O$_3$H$_2$)$_2$	2 HN$_3$			Red	8
NiC$_3$N$_3$O$_3$H	8 H$_2$O	—8 H$_2$O at 100°			8
Potassium					
KC$_3$N$_3$O$_3$H$_2$	H$_2$O	130	S. sol.	Small needles	4, 5, 13
K$_2$C$_3$N$_3$O$_3$H	H$_2$O		Sol.	Prisms or white needles. With H$_2$O, KOH + mono K salt	4, 13
Radium					
?				Similar in appearance to barium salt	16
Silver					
AgC$_3$N$_3$O$_3$H$_2$	?				4, 7
Ag$_2$C$_3$N$_3$O$_3$H	H$_2$O	100			1, 4, 7
Ag$_3$C$_3$N$_3$O$_3$			Insol. Sol. NH$_3$	Small needles from warm acetic acid	1, 4, 7
AgC$_3$N$_3$O$_3$H$_2$	× NH$_3$	—NH$_3$ at 60° —all NH$_3$ 200–300°		Formula not conclusive	7
Silver-Lead					
Ag$_4$Pb(C$_3$N$_3$O$_3$)$_2$	2 H$_2$O			By boiling Pb salt with AgNO$_3$	16
Silver-Potassium					
Ag$_2$KC$_3$N$_3$O$_3$				By boiling Ag$_3$ salt with KOH	16

Formula	Hydrate or Adduct	Temperature at which loss of H$_2$O occurs, °C	Solubility in water	Remarks	References
Sodium					
NaC$_3$N$_3$O$_3$H$_2$	H$_2$O	120–130	0.7 % at 20° C	Hygroscopic needles	4, 13
Na$_2$C$_3$N$_3$O$_3$H	H$_2$O	130			1, 4, 13
Na$_3$C$_3$N$_3$O$_3$	H$_2$O	120	Insol.		1, 2, 3, 4, 13
Trimethylammonium					
C$_3$N$_3$O$_3$H$_2$—N(CH$_3$)$_4$	H$_2$O				8
Zinc					
Zn(C$_3$N$_3$O$_3$H)	2 NH$_3$				8

B. Alkaloid Salts

Formula	Hydrate	Melting Point	Solubility in water	Remarks	References
Caffeine					
C$_3$N$_3$O$_3$H$_3$·C$_8$H$_{10}$N$_4$O$_2$	4 H$_2$O	Dec. with heat	S. sol.	S. sol. ethanol	8
(C$_3$N$_3$O$_3$H$_2$·C$_8$H$_{10}$H$_4$O$_2$)	8 H$_2$O	Dec. with heat	S. sol.	S. sol. ethanol	8
Cinchonine					
C$_3$N$_3$O$_3$H$_3$·C$_{19}$H$_{22}$N$_2$O	4 H$_2$O	M.p. 254° (dec.)	Insol.	S. sol. hot ethanol	8
(C$_3$N$_3$O$_3$H$_3$)$_2$·C$_{19}$H$_{22}$N$_2$O	10 H$_2$O	M.p. 286° (dec.)	Insol.	S. sol. hot ethanol	8
Guanidine					
C$_3$N$_3$O$_3$H$_3$·CN$_3$H$_5$				Long needles	14

(Table continued)

TABLE I-1B (*continued*)

Formula	Hydrate	Melting Point	Solubility in water	Remarks	References
Quinine					
$C_3N_3O_3H_3 \cdot C_{20}H_{24}O_2$	9 H_2O	M.p. 237° (dec.)		Sol. ethanol; insol. hot H_2O	8
$(C_3N_3O_3H_2) \cdot C_{20}H_{24}N_2O_2$	7 H_2O	M.p. 243° (dec.)		Sol. hot ethanol; insol. hot H_2O	1
Quinoline					
$C_3N_3O_3H_3 \cdot (C_9H_7N)_3$				Colorless	8
Strychnine					
$C_3N_3O_3H_3 \cdot (C_{21}H_{22}N_2O_2)_2$	H_2O	M.p. 287° (dec.)	Sol.	S. sol. ethanol	8
$C_3N_3O_3H_3 \cdot C_{21}H_{22}N_2O_2$	H_2O	M.p. 295° (dec.)	S. sol. hot H_2O	White needles, Sol. ethanol	8

C. Metal Salts of Esters

Formula	Hydrate or Adduct	Temperature at which loss of H_2O occurs, °C.	Solubility in water	Remarks	References
Diethyl cyanurate					
$C_3N_3O_3(C_2H_5)_2Ag$				Gelatinous	13, 15
$(C_3N_3O_3(C_2H_5)_2)Ba$	H_2O and 12 H_2O ?NH_3	—H_2O at 120–130			13
$(C_3N_3O_3(C_2H_5)_2)Cu$				Pink	15
$(C_3N_3O_3(C_2H_5)_2)_2Pb$					13
Dimethyl cyanurate					
$C_3N_3O_3(CH_3)_2Na$			S. sol.	S. sol. methanol	15

Formula	Hydrate or Adduct	Temperature at which loss of H_2O occurs, °C.	Solubility in water	Remarks	References
Trialkyl cyanurates					
$(C_3N_3O_3)(CH_3)_3 \cdot HgCl_2$					13
$(C_3N_3O_3)(C_2H_5)_3 \cdot HgCl_2$					13
Miscellaneous					
Solid add'n. compd. of cyanuric con'tg.	30 % KOH			From cyanuric on standing over KOH. May be a hydrated salt	18
D. Addition Compds. of Triethylcyanurate and Cyanogen Halides					
$C_3N_3O_3Et_3 \cdot CNBr$					16, 17
$C_3N_3O_3Et_3 \cdot 2\ CNBr$					16, 17

[a] Table I-1A: The existence of these salts is incompletely substantiated.

[b] Heats of combustion and formation of the solid and dissolved salts of cyanuric acid have been listed by Lemoult.[21]

1. A. Hantzsch, *Ber.*, **39**, 145 (1906).
2. A. Hofmann, *Ber.*, **3**, 770 (1870).
3. E. Spencer and G. Wright, *Can. J. Research*, **24B**, 204 (1946).
4. P. Lemoult, *Ann. phys. chim.*, (7), **16**, 368 (1899).
5. E. Bamberger, *Ber.*, **23**, 1861 (1890).
6. R. Haworth and F. Mann, *J. Chem. Soc.*, **1943**, 603.
7. F. Wöhler, *Ann.*, **62**, 241 (1847).
8. A. Claus and O. Putensen, *J. prakt. Chem.*, (2) **38**, 208 (1888).
9. A. Benrath, *Z. anorg. Chem.*, **151**, 31 (1926).
10. C. Venable and F. Moore, *J. Am. Chem. Soc.*, **39**, 1750 (1917).
11. H. Ley and F. Werner, *Ber.*, **46**, 4040 (1913).
12. A. Ostrogovitch and G. Ostrogovitch, *Atti V. congr. nazl. chim. pura applicata Pt.*, **1**, 431 (1936).
13. J. Pomomarew, *Ber.*, **18**, 3261 (1885).
14. E. Bamberger, *Ber.*, **20**, 71 (1887).
15. A. Hofmann, *Ber.*, **19**, 2063 (1886).
16. H. Williams, *Cyanogen Compounds*, 2nd Ed., Arnold & Co., London, 1948, p. 79.
17. W. Dehn and R. Merling, *J. Am. Chem. Soc.*, **39**, 2646 (1917).
18. Senior, *Inaug. Dissert.*, Berlin, **1887**, 30.

Hantzsch found that at ordinary temperatures trisodium cyanurate and silver nitrate give the disilver salt, but in boiling water the trisilver salt alone is obtained. This clearly shows that cyanuric acid may also function as a dibasic acid at room temperatures, while it is tribasic at higher temperatures. The existence of a trimercury salt at ordinary temperatures is explained by the fact that mercury salts of weak oxygen acids are dissociated to only a slight extent at room temperature and hence are very slightly hydrolyzed in aqueous solution. The trimercury (analysis corresponds to mercurous, but chemistry to mercuric) salt is formed from cyanuric acid, sodium hydroxide and mercuric acetate free of nitric acid, but does not result from the action of mercuric chloride on sodium cyanurate. In the latter case, the double salt $(C_3N_3O_3H_3)_2 \cdot HgCl_2 \cdot 4\,H_2O$ is produced.

As has been previously mentioned, cyanuric acid detrimerizes to isocyanic acid when heated. Some of its salts react in a corresponding fashion; thus barium cyanurate yields barium cyanate when heated strongly.[134] Calcium cyanurate behaves differently; strong heating produces calcium cyanamide,[135]

$$C_3N_3O_3HCa \xrightarrow{\ \Delta\ } CaNCN.$$

Reactions of the metallic salts are important particularly for the preparation of various esters. These are discussed in the following section.

6. Reactions of Cyanuric Acid

A. Hydrolysis

Hot mineral acids decompose cyanuric acid to carbon dioxide and ammonia but it is stable to hot caustic, forming salts.

$$+ 3\,H_2O \xrightarrow[\Delta]{H^+} 3\,NH_3 + 3\,CO_2$$

B. Reaction with active halogen compounds

Phosphorous pentachloride converts cyanuric acid to cyanuric chloride in good yields at temperatures of 150–200°.[136] However, none of the following effects this reaction:[137] thionyl chloride, sulfuryl chloride for one hour at 90°, chlorsulfonic acid for two hours at 160–170°,

$$
\text{(III)} \quad + 3\,PCl_5 \xrightarrow[\text{tube}]{150-200°} \text{(IV)} \quad + 3\,POCl_3 + 3\,HCl
$$

(III)   (IV)

calcium chloride-ammonia for eight hours at 240°, or zinc chloride-ammonia for five hours at 300°.

C. Thermal action

Cyanuric acid may be heated to over 500° in a sealed tube without undergoing decomposition. With moderate heating, above 200°, in the open, it decomposes without melting to cyanic acid.

$$
\text{(III)} \xrightarrow[360°]{\Delta} 3\,N\equiv C-OH
$$

D. Reaction with ammonia

Under conditions of high temperature (350°) and pressure, cyanuric acid can be converted to melamine[138] (XVIII). For a further discussion of this reaction, see Chapter VI.

$$
\text{(III)} \quad + 3\,NH_3 \xrightarrow[\alpha]{\Delta} \text{(XVIII)} \quad + 3\,H_2O
$$

(III)   (XVIII)

E. Esterification

Attempts to esterify cyanuric acid directly or by means of its alkali salts have been unsuccessful. Instead of cyanurates, esters of isocyanuric acid are isolated, and then only when such active alkylating agents as benzyl and alkyl chlorides are used. While isocyanuric acid (XVI) cannot be isolated as a separate entity, isocyanuric acid esters (XX) which are formed when either silver cyanurate (XIX) or sodium cyanurate and alkyl halides react, are finite substances. The isocyanuric compounds are treated in Chapter VII.

(XIX) (Na)   (XX)

F. Acetylation

The resemblance of cyanuric acid to phenols is only superficial. Cyanuric acid is an acid without a carbonyl group. As such it does not undergo acetylation with the same ease that phenols do. It can be acetylated, however, in the form of its silver salt. Either benzoyl chloride[140] or acetyl chloride[140, 141] can be used to produce the respective esters (XXI). The reaction resembles formation of an acid anhydride from an acid chloride and the sodium salt of the acid.

$$RCOCl + RCOONa \longrightarrow (RCO)_2O + NaCl$$

(XIX)   (XXI)

G. Reaction with Fatty Acids

If cyanuric acid or urea, which is converted to cyanuric acid under reaction conditions, is heated with a high molecular weight fatty acid such as lauric, oleic, stearic, palmitic, etc., at 250° for a little under three hours, a quantitative yield of the corresponding pure alphatic nitrile occurs.[142] Acids of 8–12 carbons boiling below 250° may also be used although the yields are lower and the products less pure.

$$C_{17}H_{35}COOH + (III) \xrightarrow{250°} C_{17}H_{35}CN$$

Information on the course of the reaction is lacking at present.

H. Reaction with α-Haloacids

Cyanuric acid when refluxed in alkaline solution with chloracetic acid forms carboxymethyl isocyanuric acid or (2,4,6-trioxohexahydro-s-triazinyl) acetic acid (XXII). Carboxymethyl isocyanuric acid may be regarded in a strict sense as a carboxy substituted monoester of isocyanuric acid.

HO⌐N⌐OH + ClCH$_2$COOH + NaOH ⟶ O=⌐N(CH$_2$COOH)⌐=O + NaCl + H$_2$O

(III)   (XXII)

I. Rearrangement

Cyanuric acid has been reported to undergo exothermic change to cyamelide under the influence of excess potassium hydroxide.[145]

7. Applications of Cyanuric Acid

A. Physiological and Technical Significance

Although cyanuric acid may be handled safely, when taken internally it is a neurological, as well as a muscular poison.[144] It has twelve times the potency of urea or acetamide in equivalent nitrogen concentrations. The latter two are muscular poisons at 0.7% N concentration. Cyanuric acid however is not sufficiently toxic to be used as a rat poison, a potential use for which it has been evaluated.[146]

Cyanuric acid has not found wide industrial application, but several of its uses are of interest.

B. Melamine Formation

Already mentioned is the use of cyanuric acid for the preparation of melamine which in turn is of tremendous commercial importance. (See Chapter VI).

C. Rubber Manufacture

A finely ground mixture of urea and biuret or biuret alone,[165a] which generates cyanuric acid and ammonia, has been used[147] to prepare sponge rubber in the temperature range of 307–330° F. Formation of ammonia generates the tiny bubbles needed in sponge rubber.

D. Resins

Resinous condensation products are prepared by heating cyanuric acid with formaldehyde with[148] or without[149] a diluent; a clear resin forms. Acid condensation agents such as hydrogen chloride may be used to promote the reaction. Products suitable for molding are formed by condensing cyanuric acid, melamine, ligninsulfonic acid, and furfural or formaldehyde.[150]

III. Cyanuric Halides

1. Cyanuric Chloride

A. History

Cyanuric chloride has been known[7] since 1827 when it was considered to be the trichloride of cyanogen. Its composition was determined by Liebig[152] who prepared it by passing chlorine over dry potassium thiocyanate.

Serullas[7] converted impure cyanogen chloride to cyanuric chloride with sunlight; however, the latter was considered to be an isomer rather than the trimer of cyanogen chloride for some years. As late as

(I)

1867, the trimer to monomer relationship of cyanuric chloride and cyanogen chloride was misunderstood.[151] The infrared and ultraviolet spectra[123] support the triazine structure and indicate that the chlorine atoms are on the carbon atoms as in (I).

B. *Physical Properties*

Cyanuric chloride is a colorless solid which crystallizes from carbon tetrachloride in large monoclinic prisms. It melts[44] at 145.75°, boils[44] at 198°, and has a specific gravity of 1.32[44]. The cryoscopic constant for purity is 1.7 mole % impurity/degree of melting point lowering.[137a]

Heat of formation[155] (ΔE_p)		
At constant volume	107	Kcal./mole
At constant pressure	108	Kcal./mole
Heat of combustion[30] (ΔH_c)		
At constant volume	294	Kcal./mole
At constant pressure	293	Kcal./mole
Heat of vaporization[44] (ΔH_v)	11.2	Kcal./mole
Heat of sublimation[44] (ΔH_s)	17.3	Kcal./mole
Heat of fusion[44] (ΔH_f)	5.4	Kcal./mole

The infrared spectrum[44, 155] of solid cyanuric chloride in Nujol and in perfluorokerosene shows strong absorption bands at 1505, 1260, and 850 cm.$^{-1}$ regions. The ultraviolet absorption spectrum has been reported for ethyl alcohol solutions[123] and for cyclohexane solutions,[156] and these data used in a valence-bond discussion of the then unknown s-triazine[157] (see Introduction, part II).

Cyanuric chloride is soluble in acetonitrile,[158] ether,[44] and heptane.[44] It is also soluble in acetic acid and absolute ethanol, but in time undergoes reaction with these solvents. It is insoluble in cold water[43] and undergoes hydrolysis in water[43] above 10°. The solubility of cyanuric chloride in other solvents at 25° is as follows[44]:

Solvent	Solubility in g./100 g. solvent
Acetone	25
Acrylonitrile	19
Benzene	19
Carbon tetrachloride	7.5
Chloroform	20
Dioxane	55
Nitrobenzene	18

The crystallographic properties have been published in summary form.[44]

Cyanuric chloride is readily hydrolyzed by water vapor to cyanuric acid and hydrochloride acid.

C. Synthetic Methods

(1) From Cyanogen Chloride. Cyanuric chloride is easily and directly prepared by the trimerization of cyanogen chloride. The reaction may be carried out in several ways:

(a) At 0° in chloroform-dioxane in the presence of hydrogen chloride.[159] Chloroform readily dissolves cyanuric chloride, but not the hydrogen chloride catalyst. Dioxane on the other hand dissolves hydrogen chloride but not cyanuric chloride. The use of both solvents together dissolves a quantity of catalyst adequate to effect trimerization, but also reduces the solubility of the product so that it can be more easily isolated as precipitation occurs.

(b) In an inert diluent in the presence of hydrogen chloride.[160]

(c) Just above the boiling point (12°) of cyanogen chloride in chloroform-dioxane and preventing loss of cyanogen chloride by formation of the boron trichloride complex.[161] In this procedure, such oxygen containing compounds as dibutyl ether, dipropyl ether, or diethyl Cellosolve may be used to replace dioxane while carbon tetrachloride, chlorobenzene or 1,2-dichloroethane may be used instead of chloroform.

Commercially the reaction is carried out in the vapor phase with charcoal alone or charcoal impregnated with an alkaline earth chloride[162] at temperatures from 250–480°.

Actually activated carbon alone is probably the most efficient catalyst.[164] It operates specifically in the case of cyanogen chloride, not exclusively because of its high surface area. This has been confirmed[164] by extensive research with other familiar high-surface agents, such as silica gels from various sources and activated alumina. In the case of the silica gels, no reaction occurs, while with aluminium oxide, there is vigorous absorption of cyanogen chloride with the evolution of large amounts of heat even at room temperature. Aluminum chloride is formed and a cyanogen polymer that has not been studied develops.[164] In plants for the production of cyanuric chloride, cyanogen chloride is continuously synthesized by means of the vapor phase reaction of chlorine and hydrogen cyanide and is passed through a fluidized bed of activated carbon. The life of the carbon catalyst is dependant on the purity of the cyanogen chloride used in the process, but even with very pure cyanogen chloride, gradual inactivation occurs. This is explained at least in part by the decomposition of cyanogen chloride into chlorine and cyanogen as evidenced by traces of the former in the off-gases from the converter. Furthermore, in an industrial installation, it is virtually impossible in practice to free the cyanogen chloride and the activated carbon completely of water which is also responsible for decomposition products and which therefore causes catalyst inactivation. Non-volatiles such as cyanuric acid are formed and these inactivate the catalyst. As the catalyst increases in age, the degree of purity of the product decreases and a bright yellow crystalline side product forms, among others, as the conversion decreases. For these reasons, the carbon catalyst is continuously replaced while the unit is in operation. Following this procedure conversion of the cyanogen chloride is 90–100% and the yield[164] based on cyanogen chloride is 95%. The trimerization is also effected in the vapor phase[163] by $AlCl_3$ over a temperature range of 180–200°. Air is blown through the crude reaction product and cyanuric chloride sublimes out. In practice, an aluminum chloride-cyanogen chloride complex forms. This makes the separation of cyanuric chloride difficult.

Another procedure[165] utilizes one part of aluminum chloride in nitromethane per eleven parts of cyanogen chloride at 40–60°. Yields of 60% of cyanuric chloride are obtained by filtration.

(2) From Hydrocyanic Acid.[159] Diels[153] developed a practical laboratory synthesis of cyanuric chloride from a method originated by Klason[166] and in turn improved by Fries[167] and Lemoult.[155] The procedure consists first of adding chlorine, then chlorine and hydrogen chloride to a solution of hydrogen cyanide in cold chloroform which contains a trace of alcohol. The trace of alcohol is necessary. Its probable beneficial effect is to permit the formation of chloral. Chloral serves as an intermediate[43] and forms an addition compound with HCN. This cyanohydrin then decomposes in the presence of chlorine to form nascent cyanogen chloride or cyanuric chloride directly.

$$CCl_3CHO + HCN \longrightarrow CCl_3CH{\overset{\displaystyle OH}{\underset{\displaystyle CN}{}}}$$

$$CCl_3CH{\overset{\displaystyle CN}{\underset{\displaystyle OH}{}}} + Cl_2 \longrightarrow CCl_3CHO + (ClCN)_3 + HCl$$

(3) From Cyanuric Acid. The preparation of cyanuric chloride (I), from cyanuric acid (II) by the action[136] of phosphorous pentachloride has been noted.

$$(II) + 3 \ PCl_5 \quad \xrightarrow[150-200°]{\text{tube}} \quad (I) + 3 \ POCl_3 + 3 \ HCl$$

(4) Miscellaneous Methods. Cyanuric chloride has also been prepared by the reaction of chlorine with potassium thiocyanate,[102] methyl thiocyanate,[168-170] or hexacyanogen,[171] none of which is as yet of more than academic interest.

D. Structure

Cyanuric chloride exists exclusively in the chlorine to carbon structure (I) C—Cl.

The chlorine atoms of cyanuric chloride show none of the reactions typical of a N—Cl bond[172] such as liberating iodine from potassium iodide, liberating sulfur from hydrogen sulfide or oxidizing sodium sulfite.

Chattaway and Wadmore,[172] in order to conclusively prove the carbon to chlorine structure, prepared hexahydro-1,3,5-trichloro-2,4,6-trioxo-s-triazine (1,3,5-trichloro isocyanuric acid) (III) in 90% yield

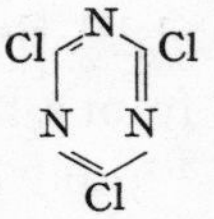

(I) 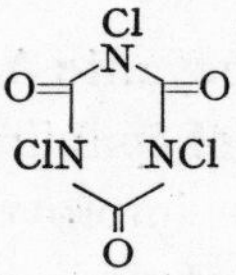   (III)

from potassium cyanurate in water at 0° by means of a stream of chlorine. This compound undergoes all of the above reactions. When it is added to aqueous ammonia, a violent reaction occurs accompanied by evolution of nitrogen and formation of cyanuric acid. Boiling with water, acid, or base gives cyanuric acid and hypochlorite decomposition products.

Cyanuric chloride is the acid chloride of cyanuric acid. The chlorine atoms are much more active than those of an alkyl chloride but somewhat less active than those in acyl chlorides.[173] This of course depends on the acyl halide. Undoubtedly the first chlorine atom is less active than that of acetyl chloride, probably similar to that of benzoyl chloride, and more active than that of stearoyl chloride.

Despite the superficial similarity in structure to 1,3,5-trichlorobenzene, there is no similarity between cyanuric chloride and the inert aromatic halogens.

E. Reactions

(1) **Hydrolysis and Alcoholysis.** Fierz-David has reported that cyanuric chloride is stable in water at 0° for at least twelve hours, but is hydrolyzed readily at slightly elevated temperatures.[43] It was reported to remain unaffected by warm aqueous potassium hydroxide, but on prolonged treatment, potassium cyanurate was obtained. Hydrolysis with 10% sodium hydroxide at 100° was said to proceed only as far as 2-chloro-4,6-dihydroxy-s-triazine (IV); at 125° the third chlorine atom was replaced. According to Fierz-David,[43] the slow

$$(I) \xrightarrow[100°]{10\% \text{ NOaH}} \text{(IV)} \xrightarrow[125°]{10\% \text{ NaOH}}$$

hydrolysis of cyanuric chloride in water or in the presence of water vapor gives intermediate hydroxychlorotriazines and hydrochloric acid. Data presented do not appear to support this conclusion; it seems probable that the hydrolysis does not stop at the hydroxychloro-s-triazine stage, but that the second and third chlorine atoms are hydrolyzed at least as readily as the first one. Thus hydrolysis does not stop in a given molecule until cyanuric acid is produced. Data presented[43] in the literature tend to support this view rather than the concept of a definite temperature requirement for each successive hydrolyzable halogen.

Although cyanuric chloride is hydrolyzed[174] by nitric or sulfuric acids at room temperatures after some time, it remains unchanged when heated with concentrated sulfuric acid[43] at 100° for five minutes. However, at 150° the ring is destroyed.

$$(I) + 6 H_2O \xrightarrow[150°]{H_2SO_4} 3 HCl + 3 CO_2 + NH_4HSO_4$$

Treating cyanuric halides with hot alcohols produces cyanuric acid[174] and the corresponding alkyl halide with almost no etherification. If the alcohol is not anhydrous, the heat of reaction has been known[175] to raise the temperature to a point where it assumes violent proportions.

(2) Reaction with Hydroxy Compounds. Cyanuric chloride and other cyanuric halides react with alkaline earth alkoxides[176, 177] or with alcohols in the presence of a basic acceptor[177] to form mono-, di- and trialkyl esters of cyanuric acid. This important class of compounds is discussed in more detail in Section IV, 1. Only two chlorine atoms are replaced when zinc dust is the acceptor[176] (1). However, to carry out a stepwise replacement it is preferable to use sodium carbonate or sodium hydroxide.[178]

$$(I) + ROH \xrightarrow{\text{Zn dust}} \begin{array}{c} RO \overset{N}{\diagup} Cl \\ N \quad N \\ \diagdown \diagup \\ OR \end{array} \tag{1}$$

(I)

Cyanuric chloride reacts with monocyclicphenols at 170–210° in the absence of solvents to give high yields of triaryl cyanurates.[179] Cyanuric chloride can be made to react with either one, two or three moles of sodium phenoxide in acetone by limiting the amount of sodium aryloxide and operating at slightly lower temperatures[179] when less than complete chlorine replacement is required (2).

$$(I) + 3\, C_6H_5ONa \xrightarrow{\text{acetone}} \begin{array}{c} C_6H_5O \overset{N}{\diagup} OC_6H_5 \\ N \quad N \\ \diagdown \diagup \\ OC_6H_5 \end{array} + 3\, NaCl \tag{2}$$
$$(1 \text{ or } 2) \qquad\qquad\qquad\qquad\qquad (1 \text{ or } 2)$$

Triaryl esters of cyanuric acid are also formed when cyanuric chloride is treated with three equivalents of the sodium salt of a phenol[180] in aqueous solution.

$$(I) + 3\, NaOAr \longrightarrow \begin{array}{c} ArO \overset{N}{\diagup} OAr \\ N \quad N \\ \diagdown \diagup \\ OAr \end{array}$$

If cellulose, pretreated with alkali, is heated gently with cyanuric chloride,[181] the resulting compound is a dichloro ester (V). Substance

(V) may then react with aromatic amines, and the product can be diazotized. A diazonium salt coupled with β-naphthol gives a dye bound directly to the cellulose fiber.

$$(I) + RONa \longrightarrow \text{[structure]} \quad R=\text{cellulose residue}$$

(V)

(3) Reactions with Amino Compounds. Cyanuric chloride reacts with primary and secondary amines, hydrazines, and related compounds in three steps. The oversimplified rule of thumb expressed frequently[43, 167, 182–189] in the literature that the first chlorine atom is replaced at 0°, the second at 30–50°, and the third at 90–100° cannot be used generally. First it applies only to water solutions and not to other solvents. Some amines will react with three chlorine atoms at 0°; others not at all or only with one chlorine even at 100°. Thus reaction (3) is at best an inaccurate summary.

$$(I) \xrightarrow[0°]{R_2NH} \quad \xrightarrow[30–100°]{R_2NH} \quad \xrightarrow[90–100°]{R_2NH} \quad (3)$$

The reactions of cyanuric halides and cyanogen halides to form amino compounds are discussed in some detail in Chapters V and VI. The principal reactions involving cyanuric halides are mentioned below.

Cyanuric halides react with primary or secondary alphatic or aromatic amines to produce substituted melamines or with anhydrous or aqueous ammonia to produce melamine (4). Under proper conditions,

$$(I) + \begin{matrix} 3\,R_2NH \\ or \\ 3\,RNH_2 \\ or \\ 3\,NH_3 \end{matrix} \longrightarrow \text{[structure]} \quad (4)$$

the replacement may proceed stepwise and the two intermediate halogen derivatives obtained. For example, a cold solution of cyanuric chloride in ether yields[153] 2-amino-4,6-dichloro-s-triazine, while with aqueous

ammonia a second chlorine is replaced at just above room temperature[190] to give 2,4-diamino-6-chloro-s-triazine. Melamine results when
ammonia and cyanuric chloride are heated at 100° under pressure.[191]
For cyanuric acid to be converted to melamine a temperature of at
least 350° is required.[192]

It has been shown[193] that if the basic character of the amino group
in aromatic amines is too greatly weakened by negative substituents,
replacement of the third halogen atom may not occur. In the case of
2,4-dinitroaniline, reaction with cyanuric bromide, which is more active
than cyanuric chloride, is completely prevented under ordinary conditions.[193]

The straightforward reaction of all three chlorine atoms of cyanuric
chloride with amino groups in the following types of compounds has
been shown: aminophenols,[194] $C_6H_4(OH)(NH_2)$; aminoesters,[195] H_2N-
CH_2COOR; aminoarylsulfonamides,[196] $H_2NC_6H_5SO_2NHR$; semicar-
bazides[197] and thiosemicarbazides,[198] $RNHNH(CO)NHR$; hydrazine,
NH_2-NH_2; and metal salts of ureas, substituted ureas, thioureas, or
substituted thioureas.[198] The reaction with compounds of the final

$$\text{(I)} + 3\,NaNHCONH_2 \longrightarrow + 3\,NaCl \quad (4a)$$

category may be written as in equation (4a). Reaction with the potassium
salts of monosubstituted cyanamides results ultimately in the formation of tricyanomelamines (5).[199]

$$\text{(I)} + 3\,KNCN \longrightarrow + 2\,KCl \quad (5)$$

Ethylenimine reacts with cyanuric chloride extremely rapidly and
completely at 0° in water, or in benzene at a slightly higher temperature.
The presence of an acceptor, especially when benzene is used, is essential
to prevent formation of hydrogen chloride which would attack the
ethylenimine ring. Triethylamine is a satisfactory acceptor and must be
used in excess of the amount that will be tied up in forming a hydro-

chloride salt. Even with triethylamine some byproducts of rearrangement are nevertheless encountered. The product is triethylene melamine (VI), commercially called[200] "Persistol Ho 11193" by the Germans.

$$(I) + 3 \; CH_2—CH_2 \longrightarrow$$

When it is polymerized in neutral solution at 70°, the product is used to reduce the swelling and water absorption or regenerated cellulose (an animalization). Triethylenemelamine has recently attained importance in the field of cancer therapy.

Probably the reactions of aliphatic amines with cyanuric chloride in particular and other cyanuric halides in general are predominantly influenced by steric factors—"F" strain in the transition state. All aliphatic amines thus far tested and also many non-aliphatic amines react instantaneously at 25° with one chlorine atom. Unhindered amines, such as ethylenimine, morpholine, or piperidine, react with all three chlorine atoms quantitatively at 25° in a few minutes at rates which depend on their relative steric effects. Slightly hindered amines, for instance, diethylamine, or iminodipropionitrile, give the mono- and diaminotriazines at 25° but no triamino-s-triazines. The reactivities of the hindered amines depend on their basicities. Strong bases can be made to give substituted triaminotriazines at 50 or 60°; however, weak bases do not go beyond the diamino stage even at 80°. The reactions take place only slightly more readily in polar solvents, water if the solubility of the amines permits its use. Acetonitrile is preferable to benzene.

Cyanuric chloride reacts in water solution with pyridine[201] and, depending on the conditions, the products are 4,6-dihydroxy-2-α (or γ)-pyridyl-s-triazine or 4-hydroxy-2-α (or γ)-pyridyl-s-triazinyl-6-pyridinium chloride. These compounds are said to result from the hitherto unknown chlorohydroxy-s-triazines formed during the base catalyzed hydrolysis of cyanuric chloride. It is more likely that they are formed directly from cyanuric chloride and then hydrolysis of the chloro groups occurs.

(4) Reaction with Sulfhydryl Compounds. The chlorine atoms of cyanuric chloride are sufficiently active so that reaction occurs with certain mercaptans or their alkali metal salts. Trithiocyanuric acid[202] results with sodium acid sulfide, the sodium salt of the very weak acid hydrogen sulfide (6). Thiocyanuric acid is a stronger acid than hydrogen

$$(I) + 4\,NaSH \longrightarrow \underset{\substack{N \quad N \\ SH}}{HS\,\diagup^{N}\diagdown SNa} + 3\,NaCl + H_2S \qquad (6)$$

sulfide; therefore the monosodium salt of trithiocyanuric acid forms. The corresponding derivatives of this acid result when ω-cyano-mercaptans[203] or mercaptoamides[204] of fatty acids react with cyanuric chloride. For example, 3-mercaptopropionamide or -thioamide produce 2,4,6(tri-β-carboxamidoethyl) thiocyanurate or the corresponding thio-amide derivative (7).

$$(I) + 3\,\overset{(S)}{HSCH_2CH_2CONH_2} \longrightarrow \overset{(S)}{H_2NOCCH_2CH_2S}\diagup^{N}\diagdown\overset{(S)}{SCH_2CH_2CONH_2} \qquad (7)$$
$$\underset{SCH_2CH_2CONH_2}{\overset{(S)}{\underset{N\ \ N}{}}}$$

(5) Reaction with Salts of Hydrazoic Acid. The powerful explosive, cyanuric triazide (VII), is produced[205] by a metathesis between sodium azide and cyanuric chloride.

$$(I) + 3\,NaN_3 \longrightarrow \underset{\substack{N \quad N \\ N_3}}{N_3\,\diagup^{N}\diagdown N_3} + 3\,NaCl$$

(VII)

(6) Reaction with Silver Nitrite. Cyanuric chloride in acetonitrile solution has been reported[206] to react vigorously with silver nitrite to form a trinitro-s-triazine which is not well characterized.

(7) Grignard Reaction. One of the chlorine atoms of cyanuric acid reacts with alkyl Grignard reagents[207, 208]; in the case of some aryl Grignard reagents, two chlorine atoms[208, 209] undergo replacement. The products are 2-alkyl-4,6-dichloro-s-triazines and 2,4-diaryl-6-chloro-s-triazines, respectively. The reaction is illustrated (8) for the second instance. These reactions are discussed more fully in Chapter III.

$$(I) + 2\,ArMgX \longrightarrow \underset{Ar}{\overset{Cl\overset{N}{\diagdown}Ar}{\underset{N\;\;\;N}{}}} + 2\,MgXCl \qquad (8)$$

(8) Wurtz-Fittig Reaction. Cyanuric chloride reacts[210] with iodo- or bromobenzene[176, 211] or with bromophenetole and sodium to give a mixture of di- and triaryl-s-triazines (9).

$$(I) \xrightarrow{AgX + Na} \underset{Ar}{\overset{Ar\overset{N}{\diagdown}Ar}{\underset{N\;\;\;N}{}}} + (VIII) \qquad (10)$$

(9) Friedel-Crafts Reaction. Cyanuric chloride reacts with phenols in the presence of aluminum chloride to give tris(hydroxyaryl)-substituted triazines.[43] In the case of α-naphthol, the orientation is in the 4-position (11).

$$(I) + \text{(naphthol structure)} \longrightarrow \text{(triazine structure)} + 3\,HCl \qquad (11)$$

With benzene, the use of at least a theoretical amount of aluminum chloride is required[212, 213] to produce good yields of 2,4,6-triphenyl-s-triazine which is commonly called cyaphenine. Hydrolysis of this compound with 75% H_2SO_4 yields benzoic acid.

(10) Reaction with Carboxylic Acids and Salts. Cyanuric chloride reacts with sodium salts of organic acids[140] to form sodium cyanurate and the corresponding acyl halide; the reaction will also proceed with the free carboxylic acid in the same manner.

$$(I) + 3\,RCOOH \longrightarrow (II) + 3\,RCOCl$$

(11) Reaction with Malonic Ester.   One chlorine atom in cyanuric chloride reacts[214] with the active hydrogen of diethyl malonate to form the α-(4,6-dichloro-s-triazinyl) diethyl malonate (IX). The primary reaction is base-catalyzed. Hydrolysis of the product in moist

$$(I) + CH_2(COOC_2H_5)_2 \xrightarrow{OH^-} \underset{\underset{\overset{|}{Cl}}{N \diagdown\diagup N}}{\overset{Cl \diagdown \diagup N}{}} CH(COOC_2H_5)_2 \quad (IX) \quad + NaCl + H_2O$$

$$\downarrow H_2O$$

$$\underset{\underset{\overset{|}{OH}}{N \diagdown\diagup N}}{\overset{HO \diagdown \diagup N}{}} CH(COOC_2H_5)_2 \quad (X) \quad + 2 HCl$$

air proceeds readily and the dihydroxy compound, α-(4,6-dihydroxy-s-triazinyl) diethyl malonate (X) is usually isolated. Using at least three equivalents of sodium malonic ester and vigorous conditions, it is possible[214] to cause all three of the chlorines of cyanuric chloride to react (12).

$$(I) + 3 NaCH(COOC_2H_5)_2 \longrightarrow \underset{\underset{\overset{|}{CH(COOC_2H_5)_2}}{N \diagdown\diagup N}}{\overset{(H_5C_2OOC)_2CH \diagdown \diagup N}{}} CH(COOC_2H_5)_2 \quad + 3 NaCl \quad (12)$$

(12) Reaction with Hydriodic Acid.   Klason has reported[174] that as a result of the action of 57% hydriodic acid on cyanuric chloride in the cold a mixture of cyanuric iodide and 2-chloro-4,6-diiodo-s-triazine is produced. This again is essentially a simple exchange reaction wherein iodine replaces chlorine on the triazine nucleus.

$$(I) + 57\% HI \xrightarrow{\Delta} \underset{\underset{\overset{|}{I}}{N \diagdown\diagup N}}{\overset{I \diagdown \diagup N \diagdown I}{}} + \underset{\underset{\overset{|}{I}}{N \diagdown\diagup N}}{\overset{I \diagdown \diagup N \diagdown Cl}{}}$$

(13) Reduction.   Cyanuric chloride is resistant to the action of most strong reducing agents. With lithium aluminium hydride in ether, Grundmann and Beyer[181a] found only the inorganic products LiCl, $AlCl_3$ and $LiAl(CN)_4$, while hydrogen was evolved during the reaction.

In view of his recent discovery of s-triazine, Grundmann interpreted the action of lithium aluminum hydride on cyanuric chloride as occurring first with formation of s-triazine.

$$3 \text{ LiAlH}_4 + 4 \text{ C}_3\text{N}_3\text{Cl}_3 \longrightarrow 3 \text{ LiCl} + 3 \text{ AlCl}_3 + 4 \text{ C}_3\text{H}_3\text{N}_3$$

The s-triazine is catalytically depolymerized by the aluminum chloride to hydrogen cyanide which reacts further with lithium aluminum hydride.

$$4 \text{ C}_3\text{H}_3\text{N}_3 \longrightarrow 12 \text{ HCN}$$

$$3 \text{ LiAlH}_4 + 12 \text{ HCN} \longrightarrow 3 \text{ LiAl(CN)}_4 + 12 \text{ H}_2$$

If the reaction was conducted with excess cyanuric chloride present at —10° in ether and the product fractionally sublimed, 2,4-dichloro-s-triazine[181a] and 2,4-dichloro-6-dimethylamino-s-triazine[181a, 216] could be isolated. The former is apparently the first product of reduction, while the latter probably was formed by hydrogenolysis of the s-triazine ring with formation of dimethylamine, which could react with some of the remaining cyanuric chloride.[216]

When one or two of the chlorine atoms of cyanuric chloride is first replaced by an amino group, reduction with hydrogen iodide and phosphonium iodide can be accomplished.[153] The products are 2-amino- or 2,4-diamino-s-triazine (13, 14).

$$(\text{I}) \xrightarrow[\text{red P}]{\text{HI}} \text{No reduction}$$

(13)

(14)

(14) Reaction with Benzamide. Cyanuric chloride is converted to cyanuric acid upon heating with benzamide.[140] Water for the hydrolysis arises in situ by the dehydration of benzamide to benzonitrile.

$$(\text{I}) + 3 \text{ C}_6\text{H}_5\text{CONH}_2 \longrightarrow (\text{II}) + 3 \text{ C}_6\text{H}_5\text{CN} + 3 \text{ HCl}$$

From this discussion of the reactions of cyanuric chloride, one of
the most reactive, fundamental and important members of the
s-triazine derivatives, the compound may be classified as an acyl
halide[217]; it will be seen later that aminotriazines react as amides and
that the cyanurates, structurally ethers, behave similarly to esters of
the aliphatic and aromatic series.

The technological applications of cyanuric chloride are discussed
at the end of this chapter following a discussion of the chemistry of the
other compounds related directly to cyanuric acid.

F. Physiological Properties

Cyanuric chloride is a poisonous pungent lacrymator[218] attacking
the eyes and nose. Contact with the skin causes rashes but without
vesication.

2. Cyanuric Bromide

The first recognition of cyanuric bromide as a separate entity is
obscure. It was probably obtained[219] in 1827 along with cyanogen
bromide, but the first practical method of preparation and recognition[220] of the compound as a trimer did not come until 1869.

Cyanuric bromide deposits crystals from benzene which melt at
264–265° when pure, but which otherwise may not melt until above
300°. The compound is insoluble[220] in anhydrous ether and absolute
alcohol. At room temperature it is soluble in benzene[193] to the extent of
0.278%.

A. Synthesis

(1) Polymerization of Cyanogen Bromide.   Cyanuric bromide.
(XI) can be prepared by the polymerization of cyanogen bromide. This
is a method similar in principle to that employed for the preparation

$$3 \text{ BrCN} \longrightarrow \text{(XI)} \tag{15}$$

(XI)

of cyanuric chloride from cyanogen chloride (15). The trimerization may be effected satisfactorily in several ways:

(a) allowing an ethereal solution of cyanogen bromide[221] to stand,
(b) heating such a solution,[220]
(c) addition of a trace of hydrogen bromide[139] to the ethereal solution at room temperature,
(d) action of nascent hydrogen bromide on a benzene solution[173] of the monomer, or
(e) yields of 60% of cyanuric bromide can be obtained[165] by treating cyanogen bromide with 10 mole per cent of aluminum bromide in nitromethane at 40–60°.

$$3 \text{ BrCN} \xrightarrow[\text{CH}_3\text{NO}_2]{\text{AlBr}_3} \quad \text{(XI)}$$

(2) From Bromine and Potassium Ferrocyanide. Yields of up to 55% cyanuric bromide are obtained[222, 223] by heating bromine with potassium ferrocyanide at 200° for about seven hours.

Whatever existing method of preparation is chosen for cyanuric bromide, purification of the crude material is necessary to obtain a satisfactory product for even simple evaluation. Purification may be accomplished by first removing all of the volatiles at 100°. Following this, repeated vacuum sublimation[224] at 250–300° is carried out through a long tube, so that several sublimations can be accomplished in the same piece of apparatus by the alternate heating and cooling as a given charge of crude material.

B. Reactions and Structure

Cyanuric bromide possesses the same s-triazine ring structure as cyanuric chloride.

(1) Hydrolysis. It is readily decomposed to cyanuric acid and hydrogen bromide in the presence of moist air or warm water.[220] The hydrolysis proceeds rapidly although no data have been published permitting a comparison with the hydrolytic rates of cyanuric chloride or other acid halides.

(2) Reaction with Amines. Cyanuric bromide reacts with primary and secondary amines and ammonia even more rapidly than does cyanuric chloride. The reaction products are melamine in the case of ammonia, and substituted melamines in the case of amines. It combines with hydrazine to form cyanuric trihydrazide, with o-chloroaniline in boiling benzene to form trichlorophenylmelamine, with α-nitroaniline to form trinitrophenylmelamine, with α-naphthylamine to form tri-α-naphthylmelamine, and with methylaniline to form triphenyltrimethyl-melamine. These products and other substituted melamines are discussed more fully in Chapter VI. It will undoubtedly enter into all of the reactions that cyanuric chloride undergoes, but because of the differences in availability, cyanuric bromide reactions have not been reported extensively.

(3) With Acetic Acid. Cyanuric acid and acetyl bromide are produced when cyanuric bromide is heated[139] with acetic acid at 140–150°.

$$(LI) + 3\ CH_3COOH \xrightarrow{\ 140-150° \ } (III) + 3\ CH_3COBr$$

(4) Reaction with Urea. Cyanuric bromide reacts with urea at 130–140°. The product was formerly thought to be tricarbamylmelamine (XIII),[173] but more recently has been identified as ammelide

(XII). The reaction product may form from decomposition of urea as well as from cyanuric bromide. Further work is necessary to elucidate the course of the reaction.

Other reactions of cyanuric bromide, as well as those mentioned above, are similar to the ones listed for cyanuric chloride (Section III 1,C). In many of these reactions, the bromide is more reactive than the chloride. An example is the Friedel-Crafts reaction with aromatic hydrocarbons where, with hindered and weakly basic amines, the last halogen atom is replaced more easily in the case of cyanuric bromide then cyanuric chloride.

Cyanuric bromide because of its lower vapor pressure is some what less pungent and lacrymatory[139] than cyanuric chloride but is, nevertheless, an irritating and poisonous substance.

3. Cyanuric Iodide

Cyanuric iodide was first prepared by Klason[174]. It has not been prepared in a highly purified state and is usually obtained as a dark brown powder insoluble in ordinary solvents.

It may be prepared in three ways:

(a) The action of 57% hydriodic acid on cyanuric chloride produced[174] cyanuric iodide (16).

$$\qquad\qquad\qquad (16)$$

(b) Cyanuric iodide is the ultimate product obtained[225] when iodo-cyanate, I–OCN is polymerized (17).

$$3 \text{ I-OCN} \longrightarrow (\text{IOCN})_3 \qquad\qquad (17)$$

(c) It may be prepared in 83% yield by the exchange reaction between cyanuric chloride and sodium iodide in methylisobutyl ketone solution.[226]

$$(\text{I}) + 3 \text{ NaI} \xrightarrow[\text{CH}_3\text{COCH}_2\text{CH(CH}_3)_2]{} (\text{IOCN})_3 + 3 \text{ NaCl}$$

Because of its infrequent preparation the properties and reactions of cyanuric iodide are neglected in the literature. Presumably it does not differ greatly from the bromide and chloride in this respect, although some differences are to be expected because of (1) the greater reactivity of an iodo compound and (2) the insolubility of cyanuric iodide, a property which would tend to decrease certain reaction velocities

At temperatures above 200°, it is decomposed to iodine and para-cyanogen.[166]

$$2 \, (IOCH)_3 \xrightarrow{200°} (CN)_x + 3 \, I_2$$

Heated with water to 125°, it undergoes hydrolysis[166] to cyanuric acid (II).

$$(IOCN)_3 \xrightarrow[H_2O]{125°} (II) + 3 \, HI$$

4. Cyanuric Fluoride*

Several scanty references to cyanuric fluoride exist. Huckel[233a] reported having obtained cyanuric fluoride in "good" yield by the reaction of mercuric fluoride and cyanogen iodide at 160°. The vapor density of a compound "boiling around 150°" indicated a trimer of cyanogen fluoride. A trace of cyanuric fluoride was indicated by the absorption peak observed for the reaction product of cyanogen iodide with silver fluoride.[228a] If cyanogen fluoride does exist, and there is only one indication[227] that it does, it is not unreasonable to anticipate that the corresponding s-triazine could be prepared.

5. 2-Bromo-4,6-dichloro-s-triazine

This halotriazine has not been isolated, but is obtained by[228] the action of bromine on cyanogen chloride as the molecular compound (XIV) which comprises two molecules of cyanuric chloride and one of 2,4-dichloro-6-bromo-s-triazine.

$$6 \, ClCN + Br_2 \longrightarrow 2 \left[\begin{array}{c} Cl \diagup N \diagdown Cl \\ N \quad N \\ \diagdown C l \diagup \end{array} \right]_2 \cdot \left[\begin{array}{c} Cl \diagup N \diagdown Br \\ N \quad N \\ \diagdown C l \diagup \end{array} \right] + Cl_2$$

(XIV)

The double compound is obtained as shining plates from chloroform. It melts at 160–161° and sublimes above 100°. It is soluble in ether, carbon disulfide, carbon tetrachloride, petroleum ether, acetone and benzene. Dissociation takes place in the last solvent. Alcohol causes decomposition to cyanuric acid. In keeping with the properties of cyanuric chloride and bromide, the double compound has a strongly pungent odor and is lacrymatory.

* Cyanuric fluoride and the intermediate fluorochloro compounds have been prepared and described by Bigelow and co-workers. See *J. Am. Chem. Soc.*, **80**, 548 (1958).

6. 2-Chloro-4,6-diiodo-s-triazine

2-Chloro-4,6-diiodo-s-triazine (XV) has been described[166] as a by-product of the preparation of cyanuric iodide from cyanuric chloride. It was obtained as a white sublimate when impure cyanuric iodide contaminated with cyanuric chloride was heated to 360°.

IV. Cyanuric Acid Esters

This section will be confined, so far as practical, to the normal esters of cyanuric acid

$$\begin{array}{c} N \\ \| \\ C\text{—OR}; \\ | \end{array}$$

the esters (actually substituted cyclic amides) of isocyanuric acid,

$$\begin{array}{c} \text{—N—R} \\ | \\ C\text{=}O \\ | \end{array}$$

are treated in Chapter VII.

1. Alkyl Esters

The most widely known and completely investigated of the alkyl esters are the trimethyl and triethyl derivatives. Accordingly these two compounds are discussed in detail. Other methyl and ethyl esters are mentioned briefly, while discussion of the higher homologs is confined to a listing of any unusual methods of preparation and physical properties in Table I-2. The alkyl esters are discussed in reverse of the most logical order followed elsewhere in this volume. The triesters are discussed first. There as three reasons for doing this. First, continuity of the chemistry discussed in connection with cyanuric chloride is thereby best maintained. Second, the triesters are the most important cyanuric esters. Third, discussing the di- and monoesters after the triesters permits a smoother transition of the discussion to the chemistry of the haloalkoxy-s-triazines.

A. Methyl Esters

(1) Trimethyl Ester. Trimethylcyanurate was synthesized[229] in 1870 by the polymerization of methyl isocyanate, generated in situ from cyanogen chloride and sodium methoxide.

(a) *Physical Properties.* Trimethyl cyanurate melts at 135° after repeated crystallizations from water.[177] It boils at 265°. Crystallized from ether,[177] it forms rhombic or long prismatic, colorless crystals.

It is soluble in cold, concentrated hydrochloric acid solution, from which it is precipitated unchanged by the rapid addition of ammonia; it is slightly soluble in water and ether.

Thermal Properties

Heat of combustion[21]
at constant volume	704 cal./g.
at constant pressure	704 cal./g.

Heat of formation
at constant volume	704 cal./g.
at constant pressure	172.5 cal./g.

The optical properties of crystalline trimethyl cyanurate have been examined by Hofmann.[133]

(b) *Synthetic Methods.* The trimethyl ester of cyanuric acid, or 2,4,6-trimethoxy-s-triazine (XVI), may be prepared by an excellent general method[178] which is also useful for the preparation of other trialkoxy-s-triazines. It consists in the addition of cyanuric chloride to powdered sodium hydroxide suspended in methanol (or other alcohols).

$$\text{(I)} \quad + \text{CH}_3\text{OH} + 3\,\text{NaOH} \longrightarrow \text{(XVI)} \quad + 3\,\text{NaCl} + 3\,\text{H}_2\text{O}$$

The reaction is conducted at room temperature over a period of about three hours. Sodium carbonate can sometimes be used to greater advantage than sodium hydroxide although the "external" conditions required are usually more rigorous. There is less hydrolysis and other side reactions when sodium carbonate is used. As it is insoluble in the reaction medium in contrast to caustic soda, it cannot compete for the cyanuric chlorine atoms to the extent that the caustic soda does, and therefore the reaction requires more external heat. Thus the "internal" reaction conditions are milder with sodium carbonate as the acceptor, but "external" conditions are milder with sodium hydroxide.

Cyanuric chloride can also be converted to trimethyl cyanurate in good yields by the use[177, 230] of sodium methoxide. Cyanuric bromide can be substituted in both methods mentioned above,[31,139] although the use of cyanuric chloride is preferable since it is now commercially available.

Another older and now obsolescent method of preparing trimethyl cyanurate is to treat[229] cyanogen chloride with a solution of sodium methoxide in methanol. The mechanism of the reaction may include initial formation of methyl cyanate which readily trimerizes giving the normal ester. This method is accompanied by diverse side reactions which lower the yields and contaminate the product.

$$ClCN + NaOCH_3 \longrightarrow CH_3OCN$$

$$CH_3OCN + HOCH_3 \longrightarrow \begin{matrix} CH_3O \\ \diagdown \\ CH_3O \end{matrix} C=NH$$

$$CH_3OCN + H_2O \longrightarrow CH_3OC\overset{\displaystyle O}{\diagup}NH_2$$

$$3\ CH_3OCN \longrightarrow (XVI)$$

The iminocarbonates are generally the main products. They can also produce a cyanurate by loss of the elements of methanol.

$$3 \begin{matrix} CH_3O \\ \diagdown \\ CH_3O \end{matrix} C=N\ H \longrightarrow 3\ CH_3OH + (XVI)$$

The latter reaction is one which occurs on storage of iminocarbonates.

If water is present carbonates are formed. Trimethyl cyanurate is never formed in good yields.

(c) *Structure.* The existence of the carbon to oxygen bond of the normal trimethyl ester of cyanuric acid is demonstrated by its hydrolysis to cyanuric acid and methanol, products which can only come from trimethyl cyanurate.

$$(XVI) \xrightarrow[\text{HCl or KOH + H}_2\text{O}]{\Delta} (II) + 3 \text{ CH}_3\text{OH}$$

On the other hand, isocyanurates, Chapter VII, compounds in which the alkyl group in on the nitrogen atom, give the alkyl amine and carbon dioxide with alkaline hydrolysis.

Trimethyl cyanurate exists in the vapor state as a trimer of methyl cyanate as determined[232] in the Victor-Meyer apparatus in boiling benzophenone. At the boiling point of sulfur, it suffers partial detrimerization, but the vapor volume indicates that this reverse reaction is slight.

(d) *Reactions.* (1) *Hydrolysis.* Either acid or base-catalyzed hydrolysis converts the trimethyl ester to cyanuric acid and methanol. Heating with sodium and methanol in a closed tube at 100° for 90 minutes results in a loss of one of the methyl groups and produces dimethyl cyanurate [177] Partial hydrolysis can also be accomplished by the use of boiling methanolic sodium hydroxide.[233] The yields are 85% (18).

$$(XVI) \xrightarrow[\text{in CH}_3\text{OH}]{\text{NaOH or CH}_3\text{ONa}} \begin{array}{c} \text{CH}_3\text{O} \diagup^{N}\diagdown \text{ONa} \\ \text{N} \quad \text{N} \\ \text{OCH}_3 \end{array} + \text{CH}_3\text{OH} \qquad (18)$$

(2) *Isomerization* Trimethyl cyanurate boils at 265° and distills with only slight decomposition [177] If, however, it is heated under reflux for a short time, quantitative conversion to trimethyl isocyanurate occurs and the boiling point rises to 274°.

$$\begin{array}{ccc} \text{CH}_3\text{O} \diagup^{N}\diagdown \text{OCH}_3 & & \text{CH}_3 \\ \text{N} \quad \text{N} & \xrightarrow{\text{reflux}} & \text{O}=\diagup^{N}\diagdown=\text{O} \\ \text{OCH}_3 & & \text{H}_3\text{CN} \quad \text{NCH}_3 \\ & & \text{O} \\ (\text{XVI}) & & (\text{XVII}) \end{array}$$

Trimethyl isocyanurate or 1,3,5-trimethyl-2,4,6-trioxohexahydro-s-triazine (XVII) resembles the oxygen or normal compound in physical properties except that hydrolysis converts it to methylamine and carbon dioxide. The properties of the iso series are discussed in Chapter VII.

(3) *Transesterification.* Trimethyl cyanurate behaves as a typical ester with respect to its ability to undergo ester interchange. Heating the methyl compound for 15 minutes with one equivalent of sodium ethoxide in absolute ethanol[177] at reflux effects complete replacement of the methyl groups by ethyl groups. For the best results in such a transesterification, removal of the methanol is desirable to complete the reaction and to avoid the necessity for a large excess of ethanol.

(4) *Compound Formation.* An addition compound is formed between mercuric chloride and trimethyl cyanurate. A similar addition compound is also formed from the iso-ester. The addition compound with the iso-ester is three times as soluble in water as that derived from the normal compound. This furnishes a rough means of distinguishing and separating the two.

(2) Dimethyl Ester. Dimethyl cyanurate is obtained as long flat needles, the melting point of which has been reported[177, 234, 235] as 186° and 220.5°. It is soluble in hot water, hot alcohol and hot acetic acid, but insoluble in ether.

The dimethyl ester is prepared in 85% yields by partial hydrolysis of trimethyl cyanurate using either sodium hydroxide or sodium methoxide in methanol. A second preparative method[1] consists[234] of heating methylurea and benzaldehyde at 220°. The yield is reported to be 94%. Benzaldehyde appears to serve no function other than to raise the reaction temperature and allow the substituted urea to undergo thermal self-condensation.

Dimethyl cyanurate or 2,4-dimethoxy-6-hydroxy-s-triazine is probably as strong an acid as cyanuric acid in spite of the fact that it has only one free hydroxyl group.

(3) Halomethoxy-s-triazines. (a) *2,4-Dichloro-6-methoxy-s-triazine* (*XVIII*). This recently prepared[178] compound is a colorless, crystalline solid which melts at 88–90° when crystallized from heptane in which it is slightly soluble.

Preparation of 2,4-dichloro-6-methoxy-s-triazine is accomplished conveniently by the controlled replacement of one of the chlorine atoms of cyanuric chloride by a methoxyl group. Cyanuric chloride, treated with sodium bicarbonate in methanol at 30° for 30 minutes, gives a 58% yield of the triazine which is recrystallized from heptane. It has been reported[236] that 2-methoxy-4,6-dichloro-s-triazine is formed when one equivalent of sodium methoxide in methanol is slowly added to a cold solution of one mole of cyanuric chloride in benzene.

This derivative of both cyanuric chloride and trimethyl cyanurate can undergo the reactions of both substances. The chlorine atoms are about equal in activity to those of cyanuric chloride, possibly because of the equivalence in electron activity of the chloro and methoxy groups. For the same reasons 2-methoxy-4,6-dichloro-s-triazine is much more active than, for example, an aminodichloro-s-triazine. Hydrolysis produces cyanuric acid. Primary and secondary amines react[178] with the two chlorine atoms producing 2-methoxy-4,6-diamino-s-triazines

$$
\underset{\text{(XVIII)}}{\text{Cl}\!\!\begin{array}{c}N\\ \\N\quad N\\ OCH_3\end{array}\!\!OCH_3} \quad + \text{ 2 RNH}_2 \longrightarrow \quad \underset{\text{NHR}}{\overset{H}{RN}\!\!\begin{array}{c}N\\ \\N\quad N\end{array}\!\!OCH_3} \quad + \text{ 2 HCl} \tag{19}
$$

(19). The ease with which amines react with 2-methoxy-4,6-dichloro-s-triazine depends on (1) steric hindrance of the amine (2) its basicity and (3) reaction temperature, in that order.

(b) *2,4-Dimethoxy-6-chloro-s-triazine.* This mixed alkoxychloro-triazine was first prepared in 1903.[176] It is a colorless crystalline compound melting at 75–76°. It is soluble in ether, benzene, glacial acetic acid and slightly soluble in ethanol and heptane. It is best recrystallized[178] from a mixture of benzene and petroleum ether.

The original[176] method for the preparation of 2-chloro-4,6-di-methoxy-s-triazine was treatment of cyanuric chloride with excess wet

$$
\underset{\text{(I)}}{\text{Cl}\!\!\begin{array}{c}N\\ \\N\quad N\\ Cl\end{array}\!\!Cl} \quad \xrightarrow[\text{Zn dust}]{\text{CH}_3\text{OH}} \quad \underset{OCH_3}{\text{Cl}\!\!\begin{array}{c}N\\ \\N\quad N\end{array}\!\!Cl} \tag{20}
$$

methanol and zinc dust (20). A method described[178] for the preparation of 2-methoxy-4,6-dichloro-s-triazine can be readily extended[178] to the dimethoxy compound. A methanolic solution of cyanuric chloride (in this case) is refluxed with sodium bicarbonate. After thirty minutes no more carbon dioxide is evolved. The product is obtained in 74% yield. If a solution of two moles of sodium methoxide in methanol is slowly added to a cold benzene solution of cyanuric chloride, it is reported[231] that 2,4-dimethoxy-6-chloro-s-triazine results.

The reactions of this triazine resemble closely those described for 2-methoxy-4,6-dichloro-s-triazine. The only reaction in which it has found some application has been the synthesis of substituted ammelines. The chlorine atom displays essentially the same degree of reactivity toward ammonia, and primary or secondary amines as does the third chlorine atom of cyanuric chloride. The products of this reaction (21) are ethers or esters of ammelide and substituted ammelides. Ammelide is 2,4-dihydroxy-6-amino-s-triazine.

$$CH_3O\underset{N\ \ N}{\overset{N}{\diagup}}Cl \quad +\ RNH_2\ \longrightarrow\quad CH_3O\underset{N\ \ N}{\overset{N}{\diagup}}NHR \tag{21}$$
$$\underset{OCH_3}{} \qquad\qquad\qquad \underset{OCH_3}{}$$

(4) Mixed Methyl Esters. Attempts to prepare mixed methyl esters, that is, esters in which methyl groups are on both oxygen and nitrogen atoms in the same triazine molecule, have been reported by Hantzsch and Bauer.[31,238] They claim to have prepared the N,N,O trimethyl and N,O,O-esters by methods which are discussed briefly. Sidgwick[238] however, entertains reservations as to whether mixed esters have actually been prepared.

$$AgCNO + CH_3I \xrightarrow[\text{dry ether}]{8\ days} CH_3O\underset{N\ \ N}{\overset{N}{\diagup}}OCH_3 \quad + \quad O=\underset{N\ \ N}{\overset{\overset{CH_3}{N}}{\diagup}}OCH_3$$
$$\underset{OCH_3}{} \qquad\qquad \underset{OCH_3}{}$$

$$\downarrow \Delta\ |HCl$$

$$O=\underset{HN\quad NH}{\overset{\overset{CH_3}{N}}{\diagup}}=O \tag{22}$$
$$\underset{O}{}$$

Silver cyanate added to methyl iodide in dry ether gave two parts of the normal trimethyl ester and one part of 1-methyl-2,4-dimethoxy-6-oxo-1,6-dihydro-s-triazine, the N,O,O-ester (22). Proof of structure was offered for the latter. It was converted by hydrolysis to the N-methyl isocyanuric acid, and the melting point reported for the latter checks with recently obtained values.

Trisilver cyanurate and methyl iodide similarly gave 1,3-dimethyl-6-methoxy-2,4-dioxo-1,2,3,6-tetrahydro-1,3,5-triazine (23).

Some additional, indirect evidence was obtained which predicted[239] the existence of mixed normal and iso esters. Subsequent work, however, has failed to confirm the work of Hantzsch and Bauer. The usual[240] reaction products of silver cyanurate and methyl iodide are the iso esters, and since the reaction occurs at temperatures lower than those necessary to isomerize trimethyl cyanurate to trimethyl isocyanurate, it is doubtful that any alkoxytriazine forms even at low temperatures. The iso compounds probably form directly. Moreover, Hantzsch and Bauer's finding that the low temperature reaction of silver cyanurate and alkyl iodide gives normal cyanurates and also mixed oxygen and nitrogen derivatives has never been duplicated.

Hantzsch and Bauer reported correct melting points for the methyl and dimethyl isocyanuric acids they obtained. This point alone lends some credence to their claim of mixed esters. Hence it cannot be completely overlooked.

Attempts to prepare cyanuric acid partly methylated on nitrogen and partly methylated on oxygen by methods different from the above have resulted in failure and the formation of what is known[233] as the "Principle of Symmetry." As is often the case in organic chemistry, this principle expresses the tendency for cyanuric acid to form symmetrical alkyl esters. For example, treatment of cyanuric acid with diazomethane is known to give exclusively the N-triester. However, methylation of the dimethyl-O-ester with this reagent gives the trimethyl-O-ester exclusively and no O,O,N ester. Treatment of 2-methoxy-4,6-dichloro-s-triazine with diazomethane gives the tri-methoxy compound and no O,N,N-ester. By the same token, treating dimethyl isocyanurate with phosphorous pentachloride and then sodium methylate, a method which produces normal esters, does not effect any reaction; no N,N,O-ester is obtained.

It must, therefore, be concluded that mixed normal and iso ester have not been prepared as yet.

B. Ethyl Esters

(1) Triethyl Ester. Triethyl cyanurate was first prepared[242] in 1848 by the action of potassium ethyl sulfate on potassium cyanurate. It melts at 29–30° and boils at 270° at one atmosphere, 235° at 35–40 mm., and 135° at 5 mm. A considerable amount of confusion exists, particularly in the older literature, with respect to the physical properties of triethyl cyanurate. The same is true of trimethyl cyanurate. The tendency for isomerization of these compounds to the iso-esters on heating or upon distillation often results in a product containing appreciable quantities of the iso compounds. Unless isomerization is avoided, incorrect values for physical constants result.

Triethyl cyanurate is steam volatile. It is soluble in ethanol, chloroform, carbon disulfide and ether.

(a) *Thermal Properties*

Heat of formation[21]	
at constant volume	1168 cal./g.
at constant pressure	1168 cal./g.
Heat of combustion[21]	
at constant volume	1168 cal./g.
at constant pressure	198 cal./g.

(b) *Synthetic Methods.* (1) The simplest and most reliable preparation of triethyl cyanurate is the addition[178] of one equivalent of cyanuric chloride, over a one hour period, to excess ethanol in which three equivalents of powdered sodium hydroxide have been dissolved. The reaction temperature is held at 25–30°. Sodium carbonate may replace sodium hydroxide in which case temperatures of 30–40° for five hours followed by a short heating at 60–80° must be used.

(2) Sodium ethoxide reacts with cyanuric chloride[177] or cyanuric bromide[139, 243, 244] to give excellent yields of triethyl cyanurate (XIX).

(3) Cyanogen bromide may be used directly for the preparation of triethyl cyanurate; it is added to an alcohol-ether solution containing dissolved sodium[245-248] or powdered sodium ethoxide is added to an ethereal solution of cyanogen bromide.[249]

(4) Potassium cyanurate and potassium ethyl sulfate or ethyl iodide have been reported[24, 250, 251] to give (XIX) but these methods are obselete. It is probable that isocyanurates would be obtained almost exclusively by this procedure. Such is the case when alkyl and methallyl chlorides react with alkali metal cyanurates.

(5) If trimethyl cyanurate is refluxed with sodium ethoxide in ethanol for a short time, ester interchange occurs and the triethyl ester is obtained[177] quantitatively.

(6) Doubtful methods of preparation reported:

(a) (XIX) is also reported[13] to be produced as a result of the polymerization of oxamic acid.

(b) Very slow formation of triethyl cyanurate has been reported[252, 253] to occur when solutions, from which the hypothetical compound ethyl cyanate was said to have been isolated, were heated.

(c) The action of sodium ethoxide on cyanogen is reported[249] to produce triethylcyanurate. Evidence concerning the course of the reaction is meager.

$$(CN)_2 + NaOC_2H_5 \longrightarrow (XIX)$$

(c) *Structure.* There is little doubt that 2,4,6-triethoxy-s-triazine has the "aromatic" triazine structure. The fact that it has a much greater absorption power in the ultraviolet than does triethyl isocyanurate demonstrates that, like benzene, it is conjugated.[254]

(d) *Reactions.* The reactions of 2,4,6-triethoxy-*s*-triazine are not greatly different from those of the trimethoxy triazine. A good deal more work has been done on the ethoxy compound, however. Consequently the variety of reactions reported in the literature is greater.

(1) *Isomerization.* Although it is somewhat less sensitive to heat than 2,4,6-trimethoxy-*s*-triazine, refluxing[177,244,245] for two hours converts 2,4,6-triethoxy-*s*-triazine (XIX), melting point 29°, to the corresponding isocyanurate, 1,3,5-triethyl-2,4,6-trioxohexahydro-*s*-triazine, which melts at 95°. The isomerization accounts for much of the confusion in the early literature concerning the physical constants of these esters.[24,250]

(2) *Hydrolysis.* Strong acids or alkalis will ultimately produce cyanuric acid and ethyl alcohol. Aqueous sodium hydroxide at room temperature causes two reactions (24). Isomerization to the isocyanurate takes place and is accompanied by hydrolysis at one of the ether

linkages of a portion of the triethyl compound. The second reaction produces[247,251,255] diethyl cyanurate and also some of its isomerization product,[255] diethyl isocyanurate.

It has been reported[251] that barium hydroxide hydrolyzes the normal triethyl compound to diethyl urea.

(3) *Ammonation and Ammonolysis.* Aqueous ammonia at 170°–180° produces a mixture of melamine and ammeline from triethoxy-*s*-triazine.[139]

(4) *With Amines.* Alkoxy-*s*-triazines, including triethyl cyanurate, do not react cleanly[217] with amines. The reaction (25) which might be expected giving substituted melamines is accompanied by the com-

petitive reaction (26) which very often predominates. In practice, the second reaction may proceed at one, two, or three ether groups. The result is a complex mixture.

$$RO \underset{\underset{OR}{N}}{\overset{N}{\nearrow}} OR \;+\; 3\,R'R''NH \;\longrightarrow\; R'R''N \underset{\underset{NR'R''}{N}}{\overset{N}{\nearrow}} NR'R'' \;+\; 3\,ROH \qquad (25)$$

$$RO \underset{\underset{OR}{N}}{\overset{N}{\nearrow}} OR \;+\; 3\,R''R'NH \;\longrightarrow\; (I) + 3\,RR'R''N \qquad (26)$$

(5) *Pyrolysis.* When the ester is vaporized in a high vacuum and the vapor passed over a red hot platium spiral, decomposition to cyanic acid and ethylene occurs.[256] Under similar conditions, the trimethoxy triazine which, in the vapor state exists as a trimer of the hypothetical methyl cyanate, is converted to methyl isocyanate (27).

$$(XIX) \xrightarrow[\text{heat}]{\text{Pt at red}} 3\,HCNO + CH_2{=}CH_2 \qquad (27)$$

(6) *Compound Formation.* Inorganic complexes of esters of cyanuric acid are listed with the salts of cyanuric acid in Table I-1.

Triethyl cyanurate may be distinguished from the triethyl iso-cyanurate by the formation of an addition compound with mercuric chloride on the part of the normal compound only. In the case of the methyl esters, both form salts with $HgCl_2$, but the iso-ester salt is three times more soluble in water.

(e) *Physiological Action of Triethyl Cyanurate.* The subcutaneous administration[257] of 0.23 g./kg. body weight of triethyl cyanurate to guinea pigs produced no symptoms of poisoning except accelerated breathing. An oral dose of 0.08 g./kg. in the rabbit caused temporary symptoms of poisoning such as accelerated respiration, secretion of sputum and swelling of blood vessels. An oral dose of 0.4 g./kg. in the rabbit produced the symptoms of lame muscles, accelerated respiration, cramps; death ocurred after one and one half hours. In normal laboratory handling, no hazard is presented by triethyl cyanurate.

(2) Diethyl Ester.   The diethyl ester of cyanuric acid was prepared in 1859[251] from triethyl cyanurate. It is a crystalline compound[177, 251] melting at 152° and is about as weakly acidic as cyanuric acid. It is soluble in water, from which it forms prisms, slightly soluble in ethanol, and insoluble in ether.

The compound is most easily prepared by partial hydrolysis[251] of the triethyl ester with aqueous sodium hydroxide at room temperature.

(3) Monoethyl Ester.   The monoethyl ester melts at 171–173°. It is weakly acidic and has a water solubility close to that of cyanuric acid.

Monoethyl cyanurate (XX) has been prepared quite differently from other members of the series: ring closure rather than replacement of ring substituent was the principle used. The starting materials[258] are ethyl chloroformate and ammonium thiocyanate. Thionoimido-

dicarboxylic acid diethyl ester is the primary reaction product which reacts further with two moles of urea. That the second step proceeds in the indicated manner is demonstrated by the fact that no thio-cyanuric acid derivative is obtained when urea is used. When urea is replaced by thiourea, the s-triazine obtained contains sulfhydryl groups in the 4- and 6-positions, but still only an ethoxy group in the 1-position.

(4) Haloethoxy-s-Triazines.   Like the corresponding methoxy compounds, 2-ethoxy-4,6-dichloro-s-triazine[236] and 2,4-diethoxy-6-chloro-s-triazine[231] are reported formed when a solution containing one or two equivalents, respectively, of sodium ethoxide in ethanol is slowly added to one equivalent of cyanuric chloride in benzene. No data are available for 2,4-dichloro-6-ethoxy-s-triazine.

2-Chloro-4,6-diethoxy-s-triazine melts at 43–44° and boils[176] at 144–145° at 12–14 mm. It is soluble in benzene, ether, and ethanol and deposits in the form of needles from acetic acid.

Again in a manner analagous to the methyl compound, 2-chloro-4,6-diethoxy-s-triazine (XXI) may be prepared[176] by the action of zinc dust and absolute ethanol on cyanuric chloride. It is probable that the

$$\text{(I)} \xrightarrow[\text{C}_2\text{HOH}_8]{\text{Zn dust}} \text{(XXI)} + \text{Zn Cl}_2$$

use of sodium bicarbonate in aqueous ethanol with cyanuric chloride, described[178] for the preparation of the halomethoxy-s-triazines,[3] could be adapted for preparation of the haloethoxy compounds.

A general method of preparing haloalkoxy-s-triazines has been patented.[261] It consists of refluxing a mixture of cyanuric chloride and the respective alcohol in an inert diluent, such as toluene, for a number of hours while a stream of nitrogen gas in passed through the system to remove hydrogen chloride. The diluent should be one in which hydrogen chloride is insoluble. Either one or two equivalents of alcohol can be used to prepare the chloroalkoxy-s-triazine, and three equivalents of alcohol to obtain the cyanurate. Nearly quantitative yields have been claimed for 2,4-dichloro-6-n-butoxy-s-triazine and tri-n-butyl cyanurate which are the only compounds reported to have been made by this modification of standard methods previously described.

C. Triallyl Cyanurate

(1) Physical Properties.[259]   Triallyl cyanurate (XXII) is a color-less liquid or a solid freezing at 27.5° and melting[260] at 31°. The cryoscopic constant for freezing point depression is 2.2 mole per cent impurity per degree lowering.[161a] It can be recrystallized from aqueous methanol.[260]

Density[260] = 1.1133 g./cm. at 30° C
Refractive index $n_D 25° = 1.5049$
Viscosity at 30° = 12.55 cp.

Vapor pressure:
at 100°   1 mm.
at 120°   5 mm.

Boiling point = 137–140°/0.4–0.5 mm.
Flash point (Tagliabue open cup) = 80°.

It is completely miscible with acetone, benzene, chloroform, dioxane, ethyl acetate, ethanol, and xylene. It is soluble in water to the extent of 0.6 g/100 g. and in heptane to the extent of 80 g/100 g.

Both ultraviolet and infrared spectra are known.[259]

(2) Synthesis. Cyanuric chloride and allyl alcohol in the presence of caustic react very readily giving 85 % yields[178, 260] of the ester (XXII). The reaction is carried out[260] by dissolving powdered sodium hydr-

$$(I) \ + 3 \ CH_2{=}CHCH_2OH \ \xrightarrow[\text{NaOH, powdered}]{20-30°}$$

CH$_2$=CHCH$_2$O ⫫ OCH$_2$CH=CH$_2$

ỌCH$_2$CH=CH$_2$ + 3 NaCl
(XXII)

oxide in excess allyl alcohol and adding cyanuric chloride to the solution. It is vigorous and rapid and requires cooling. After completion, the sodium chloride is removed by filtration. Excess unreacted allyl alcohol is distilled off azeotropically after water is added. Sodium carbonate or other basic acceptors may replace[260] the powdered caustic.

Triallyl cyanurate also can be made by transesterification with other trialkyl cyanurates. Yields of 71 % may be obtained[260] by heating trimethyl cyanurate with allyl alcohol and sodium methoxide. Methanol is removed by means of a partial condenser.

(3) Reactions. (*a*) *Hydrolysis.* Triallyl cyanurate is readily hydrolyzed (28) by dilute or concentrated mineral acids[259] to give cyanuric acid and three equivalents of allyl alcohol. This behavior is typical of trialkyl cyanurates. Furthermore, it displays the

$$(XXII) + 3 \ H_2O \ \xrightarrow{H^+} \ (I) + 3 \ CH_2{=}CHCH_2OH \tag{28}$$

stability[259] of trialkyl cyanurates toward alkalis. No hydrolysis occurs with strong sodium hydroxide at 40° for over an hour. More drastic conditions cause rapid hydrolysis to the alkali metal salt of cyanuric acid and allyl alcohol.

(*b*) *Transesterification.* Triallyl cyanurate will undergo exchange[178, 260, 262] with alcohols. The reaction is catalyzed by sodium or sodium methylate and the products are the corresponding cyanuric esters and allyl alcohol. Usually esters containing mixed groups are obtained. For instance[178, 259, 262] ethylene glycol forms a mixture of hydroxyethoxyallyloxy-s-triazines which on further heating, polymerize.

$$
\text{(XXII)} \quad \text{HOCH}_2\text{CH}_2\text{OH} \quad \xrightarrow[\text{80–120°}]{\text{NaOCH}_3} \quad
\underset{\underset{\text{OCH}_2\text{CH}=\text{CH}_2}{|}}{\overset{\text{HOCH}_2\text{CH}_2\text{O}\,\diagdown\overset{N}{\diagup}\,\text{OCH}_2\text{CH}=\text{CH}_2}{\text{(triazine ring)}}} \quad +
$$

$$
\underset{\underset{\text{OCH}_2\text{CH}_2\text{OH}}{|}}{\text{HOCH}_2\text{CH}_2\text{O}\,\text{OCH}_2\text{CH}=\text{CH}_2} \quad + \quad \underset{\underset{\text{OCH}_2\text{CH}_2\text{OH}}{|}}{\text{HOCH}_2\text{CH}_2\text{O}\,\text{OCH}_2\text{CH}_2\text{OH}} \tag{29}
$$

(c) *Polymerization.* Triallyl cyanurate polymerizes alone or copolymerizes with a number of other vinyl monomers. Polymerization is catalyzed by peroxides and leads to the formation of hard clear polymers.[259, 264] Polytriallyl cyanurate itself is a glass-like material having a Barcol hardness in the neighborhood of 66. Triallylcyanurate copolymerizes[264] with styrene, methyl methacrylate, and alkyd resins such as the diethyleneglycol-fumaric-acid-sebacic acid type. Triallyl cyanurate is stable at 125° under nitrogen for periods up to twenty-four hours.[259] In the presence of air at this temperature, polymerization[259] starts within two hours. When heated in the range of 160–170° in the presence of air, it has been known to polymerize violently. However, it has been distilled successfully[263] at temperatures as high as 162°/2 mm.

Copper, cuprous chloride, cupric acetate, bronze and other copper containing metals and salts cause violent polymerization. Other metals such as nickel, manganese and mercury also tend to promote polymerization. Inhibitors of vinyl polymerization, such as *p*-toluquinone, hydroquinone or *p-tert*-butylcresol, are probably satisfactory for the stabilization of triallyl cyanurate.

(4) Commercial Applications. (a) *Polymeric Products.* Triallyl cyanurate alone polymerizes[259, 264] to hard, clear, brittle, glassy materials which have been used in the preparation of laminated glass mats. Sheets of glass cloth impregnated with triallyl cyanurate monomer are pressed together and polymerization is initiated with heat and a latent catalyst. The mats so prepared have a high flexural strength which does not change over long periods of time even at temperatures above 230°.

Triallyl cyanurate is compatible with alkyd resins such as those from maleic anhydride, ethylene glycol and fumaric acid-ethylene glycol.[265] Copolymers may be made[259, 264] with styrene or other vinyl monomers. The resins can be cured speedily and anaerobically. They have excellent alkali, acid, and heat resistance.[264] Uses that have been suggested[259] for these resins include laminates, molding compounds, coating compositions, adhesives, and high temperature castings.

At temperatures of 100–140°, triallyl cyanurate undergoes trans-esterification[178, 262] reactions with a number of glycols. The products, which may be useful as platicizers for other resins, are obtained as clear gels, rubbery solids, or viscous oils.

Polytriallyl cyanurates may be polymerized further through the residual vinyl groups by the addition of another unsaturated monomer along with a suitable catalyst.[262] The reaction proceeds with a minimum of shrinkage giving hard, sometimes brittle resins possibly useful[262] for surface coatings and molding uses.

(b) *Plasticizing Agent.* Triallyl cyanurate and other low molecular weight alkyl esters of cyanuric acid may be used as platicizing, swelling, and softening agents in cellulose or phenol-formaldehyde resins [260, 266].

(c) *Insecticide.* Some promise has been shown in this field. A 0.1 % solution of triallyl cyanurate in 65 % acetone is effective[259] against Aphis runicis.

(5) Physiological Properties. Mild but only temporary irritation was caused by triallyl cyanurate in the conjunctival sacs of the eyes of albino rabbits, and after six successive daily applications to the shaven abdomens of albino rabbits. Occasionally death of mice has resulted from prolonged inhalation. In male mice, oral administration of a 10% solution of triallyl cyanurate in Wesson oil caused death in 50% of the subjects at a level of 575 mg./kg.[259]

In view of these incomplete and uncertain results, triallyl cyanurate should be handled carefully. Oral intake, excessive skin contact or prolonged inhalation of the vapor is to be avoided.[259] In addition to its limited toxicity, triallyl cyanurate is a moderately effective hypnotic

and anti-convulsant in mice.[263] Given orally, it abolished the seizures
which were artificially produced by electroshock or by the injection of
Metrozol.[259]

D. Other Alkyl Esters

A number of other alkyl esters of cyanuric acid have been synthesized and are listed in Table I-2. Included in this group are those
compounds which have been claimed to be mixed normal and iso
esters, and also others for which some reasonable evidence of existence
has been offered. A unique series of 2,4,6-dialkylaminoalkoxy-s-tri-
azines has recently been prepared[242a] together with their salts.

The methods of preparation commonly employed for these compounds are in order of frequency with which they have been used:
(1) The reaction of cyanuric chloride with an alkali alcoholate[177, 267]
and (2) the use of powdered sodium hydroxide, an alcohol, and cyanuric
chloride. In the latter procedure, sodium carbonate is preferred[178] to
moderate the vigorous reaction with low molecular weight alcohols,
where as sodium hydroxide is the more effective for preparation of the
higher esters. Sodium hydroxide is best used as a dry powder, but it
can also be added as a concentrated aqueous solution in some cases.
The dry powder dissolves rapidly at room temperature in the lower
alcohols and may easily be maintained in suspension in the higher
alcohols by mechanical stirring.

Occasionally special techniques are necessary to effect reaction
between cyanuric chloride and certain alcohols. Thus the addition of
a[178] pyridine acceptor to a cyanuric chloride-glycolonitrile suspension
resulted in an 81 % yield of 2,4,6-tris(cyanomethyl)-s-triazine (XXIII).

Another widely applicable method for trialkoxy-s-triazines is (3)
ester interchange, mentioned earlier as a preparative method for triethyl and triallyl cyanurates. Its advantage lies in the fact that only
catalytic amounts of alkali are necessary. For example, 2,4,6-tris-

(β-hydroxyethoxy)-s-triazine is readily prepared[178] by heating the corresponding trimethoxy compound with ethylene glycol for two hours at 100° in the presence of a small amount of sodium methoxide

$$\text{CH}_3\text{O}\underset{\underset{\text{OCH}_3}{}}{\overset{\text{N}}{\underset{\text{N}\quad\text{N}}{}}}\text{OCH}_3 + 3\ \text{HOCH}_2\text{CH}_2\text{OH} \xrightarrow[\text{2 hrs. 100°}]{\text{NaOCH}_3} \text{HOCH}_2\text{CH}_2\text{O}\underset{\underset{\text{OCH}_2\text{CH}_2\text{OH}}{}}{\overset{\text{N}}{\underset{\text{N}\quad\text{N}}{}}}\text{OCH}_2\text{CH}_2\text{OH} \quad (30)$$

(30). (4) Trialkyl cyanurates have been prepared[268, 269] by heating imino-carbonates at temperatures of 150–250° in the presence of catalytic amounts of salts of strong acids and weak bases.[268] Yields range from 50 to 100% and catalysts such as aluminum chloride, stannous chloride, ferric chloride, cuprous bromide, zinc chloride, and calcium chloride have been used to prepare tri-*n*-propyl, -allyl, -*n*-butyl, -*n*-decyl, and β-methoxyethyl cyanurates. The respective alcohols are by-products of the reaction (31). They are removed by distillation using vacuum for the higher boiling alcohols.

$$3\ \underset{\text{RO}}{\overset{\text{RO}}{>}}\text{C}=\text{NH} \xrightarrow[\text{150–250°}]{\text{AlCl}_2\ \text{or ZnCl}_2\ \text{or CaCl}_2,\ \text{etc.}} \text{RO}\underset{\underset{\text{OR}}{}}{\overset{\text{N}}{\underset{\text{N}\quad\text{N}}{}}}\text{OR} + 3\ \text{ROH} \quad (31)$$

An examination[263] of the physiological properties of a large number of alkyl cyanuric acid esters indicates that the trimethyl, tri-*n*-propyl, and triallyl esters are good anticonvulsants.

2. Aryl and Arylalkyl Esters

A. Triphenyl Ester

(1) **History.** The triphenyl ester of cyanuric acid, 2,4,6-tri-phenoxy-s-triazine (XXIV), has been known[229, 270] since 1870. It was prepared by the action of cyanogen chloride[270] or cyanogen bromide[270] on sodium phenolate and by destructive distillation of phenylurethan.[179]

(2) **Physical Properties.** Triphenyl cyanurate is a white crystal-line solid[179] melting at 235–236°. It may be recrystallized from benzene, methyl Cellosolve, or dioxane as fine needles or from acetic acid as prisms.

(3) Synthetic Methods.   Two excellent laboratory methods are available for the preparation of triphenyl cyanurate as well as several others which may be considered as possible but not optimal.

(1) Fusion of cyanuric chloride and phenol at reflux (185–210°) for five hours gives yields of 80–100%.[179, 271]

(2) Heating aqueous-acetone mixtures of cyanuric chloride, phenol and sodium hydroxide at 25° for three hours gives[179] yields of 95% (32).

$$(I) + 3\,C_6H_5OH + 3\,NaOH \xrightarrow[\text{(CH}_3)_2\text{CO aq.}]{3\text{ hrs. }25°}$$

$$
\begin{array}{c}
C_6H_5O \diagdown N \diagup OC_6H_5 \\
N \quad N \\
\diagdown \diagup \\
OC_6H_5
\end{array}
\qquad (32)
$$

(XXIV)

If the reaction period is cut to one hour, only two of the chlorines are replaced and 2,4-diphenoxy-6-chloro-*s*-triazine is obtained. It should be understood that the method is not a good preparative method for this compound, however; it is obtained in low yields and is difficult to purify.

(3) Triphenyl cyanurate may also be prepared directly from sodium phenolate and cyanuric chloride.[272]

(4) If cyanogen chloride or cyanogen bromide is used for the preparation,[229] the reaction proceeds in the following manner with[273] aqueous sodium phenolate (33). The intermediate is diphenyl

$$BrCN + 2\,NaOC_6H_5 + H_2O \longrightarrow \left[\begin{array}{c} C_6H_5C{=}NNa \\ | \\ Br \end{array} \right] \longrightarrow (C_6H_5O)_2C{=}NH \quad (33)$$

iminocarbonate which, on standing a day at room temperature, upon distillation, or in glacial acetic acid, forms triphenyl cyanurate.

$$3\,(C_6H_5O)_2C{=}NH \xrightarrow{\Delta} 3\,(XXIV) + 3\,C_6H_5OH$$

(5) Diethyl-N-phenyl iminocarbonate likewise gives[274] small amounts of the triphenyl ester upon thermal decomposition although ethylene, phenyl isocyanate, and carbanilide predominate.

(6) The synthesis of 2,4,6-triphenoxy-*s*-triazine has been accomplished by destructive distillation of phenylurethan,[270] but the product is difficult to free from such by-products as diphenylcarbamide and triphenylbuiret.

(4) Reactions. The triaryl esters in general are much more stable than the alkyl esters. Heating triphenyl cyanurate to the decomposition point effects no transformation to the iso compound. Heating with hydrochloric acid under pressure at 150° is required for hydrolysis to cyanuric acid and phenol.

(a) *Amines.* In contrast to the 2,4,6-trialkoxy-s-triazines, the 2,4,6-aryloxy-s-triazines react smoothly[229] with all classes of amines without the formation hydroxy triazines as by-products. The conditions required for the reaction depend to a large extent on the basicity of the amine used. The weaker the base, the higher is the temperature required or the longer is the heating period.

Triphenyl cyanurate reacts nearly quantitatively with 33–50% excess ethanolanine at 180–210°. A 75% yield of N^2, N^4, N^6,-tris-β-hydroxyethyl melamine (XXV) is obtained.[229] The weaker base,

$$(XXIV) \xrightarrow[\text{180–210° 5 hrs.}]{\text{H}_2\text{NCH}_2\text{CH}_2\text{OH, 50\% excess}}$$

HOCH$_2$CH$_2$NH——NHCH$_2$CH$_2$OH

NHCH$_2$CH$_2$OH

(XXV)

N-phenyl ethanolamine requires a temperature of 250°. Even after sixteen hours the reaction was incomplete and only a 43% yield[229] of N^2, N^4, N^6-hydroxyethyl-N^2, N^4, N^6-triphenyl melamine was obtained. With the very weak base, 1-aminoanthraquinone, very little reaction occurred at 250°, but at 350° an almost quantitative weight of phenol was evolved. The substituted melamine could not be recovered in pure form.

(b) *Nitration.* Triphenyl cyanurate is nitrated in all three para positions[275] when small portions of the ester are added to fuming nitric acid.

$$(XXIV) \xrightarrow{\text{fuming HNO}_3} O_2N\text{——}O\text{——}O\text{——}NO_2$$

O——NO$_2$

B. Trixylyl Ester

Tris(3,5-xylyl) cyanurate is a white crystalline solid, m.p. 268.5–269.5°, obtained in 80% yield by heating cyanuric chloride with a slight excess of *m*-xylenol at 185–210° for five hours under a reflux air condenser.[179]

C. Tris(p-diisobutylphenyl) Ester

This compound, m.p. 294–295°, is prepared by heating cyanuric chloride with *p*-diisobutylphenol under conditions[179] similar to those used[179] for triphenyl cyanurate and trixylyl cyanurate. Its structure was proved by degradation with sodium hydroxide, yielding the sodium salt of *p*-diisobutylphenol, m.p. 163–165°, from which the free phenol is easily obtained.

Tris(*p*-diisobutylphenyl) cyanurate forms a complex with aluminium chloride in nitrobenzene. The ester can be recovered quantitatively by alkali decomposition of the complex.

D. Tris(p-chlorophenyl) Ester

The *p*-chlorophenyl ester melts at 200–205°. It is made[179] in 84% yield by the fusion process from cyanuric chloride and *p*-chlorophenol.

E. p-Nitrophenyl Esters

(1) 2,4-Dichloro-6(p-nitrophenyl) cyanurate and 2-chloro-4,6-di(p-nitrophenyl) cyanurate. Attempts to prepare tris(*p*-nitrophenyl) cyanurate from cyanuric chloride and sodium *p*-nitrophenolate lead only to partial replacement of the chlorine atoms (33).

The chloro compounds have been isolated but have not been well characterized. The remaining chlorine atoms may be hydrolyzed with boiling water and the resulting hydroxy compounds readily reconverted[276, 277] to chloro compounds with $POCl_3$, PCl_5, etc.

(2) Tris(p-nitrophenyl) cyanurate. The tris(nitrophenyl) ester has been prepared by nitration of triphenyl cyanurate with fuming nitric acid (see IV 3.A (4) (b)). It is a yellow flocculate[275] melting at 191°, soluble in hot water, acetic acid, and dilute ethanol.

F. Haloaryloxy-s-triazines

(1) 2,4-Dichloro-4-phenoxy-s-triazine. This compound was prepared[275a] by Hirt and his workers in 50% yield by heating cyanuric chloride dissolved in chloroform with one equivalent of phenol for one hour at 50° with sufficient sodium hydroxide present to neutralize the liberated acid. The product may be recrystallized from toluene, whereupon crystals melting at 113–114° and boiling at 170° at 10 mm. are obtained.

(2) 2-Chloro-4,6-diphenoxy-s-triazine. It is a crystalline compound, m.p. 121–123° after recrystallization from heptane, in which it is slightly soluble. It was prepared by treating cyanuric chloride in acetone with two equivalents of aqueous sodium phenoxide; the reaction mixture, kept for one and one half hours at 15–20° and one hour at 25°, gave a 97% yield of the product.

(3) 2-Chloro-4,6-bis(pentachlorophenoxy)-s-triazine. This compound melts at about 300°. It is prepared[179] from pentachlorophenol and cyanuric chloride in the manner described for 2-chloro-4,6-diphenoxy-s-triazine.

It does not react with additional pentachlorophenol and sodium hydroxide in aqueous acetone at 25°, probably due either to the very low solubility of the triazine or to the high acidity of pentachlorophenol. The question could be better resolved if it were known whether the last chlorine atom reacted with aniline, for instance. It is seen that unusual factors such as those involved with pentachlorophenol may change the reactivity of the chlorine atoms on the triazine ring.

(4) 2,4-Dichloro-6(pentachlorophenoxy)-s-triazine. This triazine has not been isolated in a pure state.[179] It was prepared by treatment of cyanuric chloride with one equivalent of pentachlorophenol in the presence of sodium hydroxide in aqueous acetone solution.

If the crude dihalo ester is added to an allyl alcohol solution containing sodium hydroxide at 10° and heated to 50–60° for twenty minutes, 2,4-diallyloxy 6-pentachlorophenoxy-s-triazine is obtained in 72% overall yield. It forms crystals which melt at 94–95° after recrystallization from ethanol.

G. Other Aryl Esters

The esters described in the preceding paragraphs are typical of the known aryloxy-s-triazines. Other triaryl esters are listed in Table I-2 along with the physical properties which have been reported for them in the literature. These compounds were prepared by the methods described above. For the most part the reaction between cyanuric chloride and the respective sodium alcoholate or phenolate was used for their preparation. It is highly probable, however, that the phenol fusion process or the aqueous acetone-powdered sodium hydroxide method could be used successfully.

V. Acyloxy-s-triazines

Under certain conditions, the hydroxyl groups of cyanuric acid can be acetylated and benzoylated in a manner which, bears some resemblance to the acetylation of phenols.

1. Triacetoxy-s-triazine

Triacetoxy-s-triazine or triacetyl cyanurate (XXVI) is a colorless crystalline compound melting with decomposition[139] at 170°. It is soluble in acetic anhydride, slowly and difficulty soluble in chloroform, and insoluble in ether.

(XXVI), which is prepared by the action of acetyl chloride on trisilver cyanurate,[139] is usually written structurally as 2,4,6-triacetoxy-s-triazine. The method of preparation, however, indicates that acyla-

$$\text{AgO}\underset{\substack{N\ \ N\\ \diagdown\diagup \\ OAg}}{\overset{N}{\diagup\diagdown}}\text{OAg} \ + \ 3\ CH_3COCl \longrightarrow \ CH_3COO\underset{\substack{N\ \ N\\ \diagdown\diagup \\ OOCCH_3}}{\overset{N}{\diagup\diagdown}}OOCCH_3 \ + \ 3\ AgCl$$

(XXVI)

tion occurs at the nitrogen atoms. Indeed, it would be surprising if silver cyanurate were to give any oxygen substituted cyanuric acid derivatives at all. Thus the structure 1,3,5-triacetyl-2,4,6-trioxohexahydro-s-triazine (XXVII) is probably the more correct one.

Acetic anhydride is lost when the triacetyl compound is heated near its melting point.

$$O=\underset{\substack{CH_3CON\ \ \ NCOCH_3\\ \diagdown\diagup \\ O}}{\overset{\substack{COCH_3\\ N}}{\diagup\diagdown}}=O$$

(XXVII)

2. Tribenzoyl Cyanurate

Tribenzoyl cyanurate (XXVIII) was prepared[140] a year after triacetyl cyanurate by treating trisilver cyanurate with benzoyl chloride (34). It is obtained as colorless needles, slightly soluble in chloroform but insoluble in ether.

$$\text{AgO}\underset{\substack{N\ \ N\\ \diagdown\diagup \\ OAg}}{\overset{N}{\diagup\diagdown}}\text{OAg} \ + \ 3\ C_6H_5COCl \longrightarrow \ C_6H_5COO\underset{\substack{N\ \ N\\ \diagdown\diagup \\ OOCC_6H_5}}{\overset{N}{\diagup\diagdown}}OOC_6CH_5 \ + \ 3\ AgCl \quad (34)$$

(XXVIII)

TABLE I-2.   Esters of Cyanuric Acid and Chloroalkoxy and Chloroaryloxy-s-Triazines

R_1	R_2	R_3	M.p., °C	B.p., °C/mm.	Yield
—OC_2H_5	—OH	—OH	171–173		
—OCH_2 (4-NO_2 benzyl)	—OH	—OH	284		
—OCH_3	—OCH_3	—OH	186 and 220.5 reported		
—OC_2H_5	—OC_2H_5	—OH	152		
—OCH_3	—OCH_3	—OCH_3	135	265/760	98
(Compound)			105		
(Compound)			118		
—OC_2H_5	—OC_2H_5	—OC_2H_5	29–30	220/760 235/35–40 135/5	
—OC_3H_7	—OC_3H_7	—OC_3H_7	33–34	220/76 130–133/0.6 120/0.65	64
$R_1R_2R_3=$ n-C_4H_9O	—$OCH(CH_3)_2$		102–103	206–213/760 209/11 170–184/4–5 165–170/0.6 155–156/0.6	95.5

y	Form	Remarks	Ref.
			22
ethyl alc.			18
ter, ethyl alc., hot ic acid. Insol. ether	Long, flat needles		2, 3, 4
ter, S. sol. ethyl Insol. ether	Prisms from water	Solidifies at 161° (isomerization)	3, 8
ether, water	Long, rhombic or prismatic, colorless crystals		1, 3, 5, 6, 9, 10, 20, 21
nzene, ether		Steam volatile	6
		Steam volatile	6
ıyl alc., chloro-, carbon disulfide			3, 10, 21
		Dec. on vacuum distn. to resinous mass consisting mostly of iso ester.[a] Temp. with $ZnCl_2 \cdot H_2O$ 180°	3, 21, 26, 29
			13, 21
		Achromatic, scentless liquid	13, 14, 21, 28, 29, 30
		[a] Temp. with $CaCl_2$ 205–210°, yield 47 %	
		[a] Temp. with $ZnCl_2$ 205–210°, yield 66 %	
		[a] Temp. with $AlCl_3$ 180–195°, yield 54 %	

(Table continued)

TABLE I-2 (*continued*)

R_1	R_2	R_3	M.p., °C	B.p., °C/mm.	Yield
$-OCH(CH_3)CH_2CH_3$				168/5	
$-OCH_2CH(CH_3)_2$			44–45	146–155/1	62
$-OC(CH_3)_3$					
$n\text{-}OC_5H_{11}$				210–213/5	
mixed-OC_5H_{11}				180–188/2	68
$iso\text{-}OC_5H_{11}$				165–167/0.6	
$sec\text{-}OC_5H_{11}$				147–150/0.4	
$tert\text{-}OC_5H_{11}$				150 (dec.)/3	
$-OCH(C_2H_5)_2$				155/0.8	
$n\text{-}OC_6H_{13}$				210/1.7	63
$sec\text{-}OC_6H_{13}$				195/2.2	
$-OC_8H_{17}$					
$-OC_{10}H_{21}$					
$-OC_{12}H_{25}$					
$-OCH_2CH:CH_2$			31	161–162/760	85
				72/0.35	
$-OC_{18}H_{33}$ (oleyl)					
$-OCH_2CN$			158–159		81
$-OCH_2CH_2Cl$			154		
$-OCH_2CH_2OH$			130–132		
$-OCH_2CH_2OCH_3$				170/0.45	
$-OCH_2CH_2N(CH_3)_2$				183–185/3	27
$-OCH_2CH_2N(C_2H_5)_2$				195–197/3	39
$-OCH_2CH_2CH_2N(C_2H_5)_2$				245/3	36

ty	Form	Remarks	Ref.
			13, 20
			20, 21
			13
			11, 13, 21
			20
			21
			21
			21
			21
		Steam volatile	20, 21
			21
			14
		[a] Temp. with $ZnCl_2$ 180°	28
	Yellowish oil which gradually crystallizes		14
. aq. methyl and yl alc.		[a] Temp. with $FeCl_3 \cdot 6 H_2O$, yield 100 %	20, 21, 27, 28, 29
			14
methyl Cellosolve			20
, dioxane			20
, dioxane			20
		[a] Temp. with CuBr 150–210°, yield 75 %	28
		Salt with CH_3I in 84 % yield; M.p. 296–298 (dec.). Also 214–5	32, 33
		(dec.). Salt with C_2H_5I in 72 % yield, M.p. 271–3 (dec.)	33
		Salt with CH_3I in 81 % yield; M.p. 248–50 (dec.). Salt with C_2H_5I in 76 % yield; M.p. 243–4 (dec.)	32
		Salt with CH_3I in 86 % yield; M.p. 249–50 (dec.). Salt with C_2H_5I in 76 % yield; M.p. 251–3 (dec.)	32

(Table continued)

TABLE I-2 (*continued*)

R₁	R₂	R₃	M.p., °C.	B.p., °C/mm.	Yield
$-OCH_2CH_2CH_2-N\begin{smallmatrix}CH_2CH_2\\CH_2CH_2\end{smallmatrix}O$					
$-OC_6H_5$			235–236		80–
$-OC_6H_5$	—H	—H	59	140/15	
$o\text{-}CH_3C_6H_2O-$			152		
$m\text{-}CH_3C_6H_4O-$			225		
$p\text{-}CH_3C_6H_4O-$			207		
$-OCH_2C_6H_5$			101–102		
H₃C⟨⟩CH₃			268.5–269.5		80
$p\text{-}C_8H_{17}C_6H_4O-$ (C_8H_{17} = diisobutyl)			294–295		85
$(CH_3)_2HC$⟨⟩CH_3 (thymyl)			151		
⟨⟩OCH_3 $CH_2CH=CH_2$ (eugenyl)			122		
—OH $p\text{-}NO_2C_6H_4O-$	$p\text{-}NO_2C_6H_4O-$		194		
$p\text{-}ClC_6H_4O-$			200–205		84
Cl⟨⟩Cl Cl⟨⟩Cl Cl	$-OCH_2CH=CH_2$		94–95		72

ty	Form	Remarks	Ref.
		Hydrochloride salt only in 73 % yield. (dec.) 272–5°. Cryst. dry methyl alc. and dry isopropanol	33
nethyl Cellosolve, yl alc., benzene. sol. acid glacial tic acid	Needles from benzene; prisms from glacial acetic		3, 11, 10, 15, 16, 17, 20, 25, 26
pet. ether			31
ther, acetic acid. ol. ethyl alc.	Needles		17
ther, acetic acid. ol. hot water	Needles		17
cetic acid. S. sol. ether	Needles		17
			21
			25
			25
cetic acid. S. sol. yl alc., ether, hot er	Cryst. powder		17
cetic acid. S. sol. yl alc., ether, hot ter	Yellow scales		17
			24
ot water, dil. ethyl			17
			25
ethyl alc.			25

(Table continued)

TABLE I-2 *(continued)*

R_1	R_2	R_3	M.p., °C	B.p., °C/mm.	Yield
α-$OC_{10}H_7$ (naphthyl)			(dec.) 160–225		
β-$C_{10}H_7$(naphthyl)			dec. 220		
—OCH_3	—Cl	—Cl	88–90		58
—Cl	—Cl	C_6H_4O—	113–114	170/10	50
—Cl	—Cl	p-NO_2 C_6H_4O—			
—Cl	—Cl	n-C_4H_9O—		146/13	97
—Cl	—OCH_3	—OCH_3	75–76		74
—Cl	—OC_2H_5	—OC_2H_5	43–44	144–145/13–14	
—Cl		—$OCH_2CH:CH_2$	137–138		10
—Cl	—OC_6H_5	—OC_6H_5	121–123		97
—Cl		p-$NO_2C_6H_4O$—			
—Cl			ca. 300		93

[a] Temperature employed when prepared by the imino-carbonate method, yield obtained by this method, and catalyst.

1. A. Hofmann and O. Olshausen, *Ber.*, **3**, 371 (1870).
2. H. Schiff, *Ann.*, **291**, 371 (1896).
3. A. Hofmann, *Ber.*, **19**, 2063 (1886).
4. K. Slotta and R. Tschesche, *Ber.*, **60B**, 295 (1927).
5. J. Ponomarew, *Ber.*, **18**, 3261 (1885).
6. A. Hantzsch and H. Bauer, *Ber.*, **38**, 1005 (1905).
7. A. Wurtz, *Ann.*, **71**, 326 (1849).
8. A. Habich and H. Limpricht, *Ann.*, **109**, 101 (1859).
9. A. Wurtz, *Compt. rend.*, **26**, 368 (1848).
10. P. Klason, *J. Prakt. Chem.*, (2), **33**, 129 (1886).
11. A. Hofmann, *Ber.*, **19**, 2077 (1886).
13. E. Zappi, and J. Cagnoni, *Anales asoc. quim. argentina*, **36**, 58 (1948); through *Chem. Abstracts*, **43**, 9034 (1949).
14. W. Hentrich, E. Schirm and R. Endres, U.S. 2,306,440 (1941) to Patchem A–G.
15. A. Hofmann, *Ber.*, **18**, 764 (1885).

ity	Form	Remarks	Ref.
benzene, nitrobenzene, loroform, glacial acetic d, S. sol. ethyl alc., ler, hot water	Greenish, yellow powder		17
l. benzene, chloro- m	Light, gray powder		17
. heptane			20
. toluene			31
			23
			30
ether, benzene, glacial etic acid. S. sol. glacial etic acid, ether	Cryst. from benzene and petroleum		12, 20
ether, ethyl alc., ben- le. S. sol. glacial acetic id	Needles		12
l. water			20
l. heptane			25
			23
l. 1,1,2,2-tetra- loroethane			25

16. J. Nef, *Ann.*, **287**, 319, 321 (1895).
17. R. Otto, *Ber.*, **20**, 2236 (1887).
18. E. Lyons and E. Reid, *J. Am. Chem. Soc.*, **39**, 2986 (1917).
19. A. Senier, *Ber.*, **19**, 310 (1886).
20. J. Dudley et al., *J. Am. Chem. Soc.*, **73**, 2986 (1951).
21. M. Spielman, W. Close and I. Wilk, *J. Am. Chem. Soc.*, **73**, 1775 (1951).
22. P. Guha, S. Rao and A. Saletore, *J. Indian Chem. Soc.*, **6**, 565 (1929). through *Chem. Abstracts*, **24**, 113 (192).
23. Brit. 334, 887, (1929) to I.G. Farbenind.
24. W. Hentrich and J. Hilger, U.S. 1,904,229 (1933) to I.G. Farbenind.
25. F. Schaefer, J. Thurston and J. Dudley, *J. Am. Chem. Soc.*, **73**, 2990 (1951).
26. H. Tieckelmann and H. Post, *J. Org. Chem.*, **13**, 268 (1948).
27. J. Dudley, U.S. 2,510,564 (1950) to Amer. Cyanamid Co.
28. D. Kaiser, Can. 473, 960, (1951) to Amer. Cyanamid Co.
29. A. Hantzsch and L. Mai, *Ber.*, **28**, 2466 (1895).
30. H. Huemer, Ger. 854,801, (1952) to Deutsche Gold u. Silber-Scheidenstadt.
31. R. Hirt, H. Nidecker and R. Berchtold, *Helv. Chim. Acta*, **33**, 1365 (1950).
32. J. Hohmann, *Doctoral Dissertation*, State U. of Iowa 1953.
33. B. Horrom, *J. Am. Chem. Soc.*, **76**, 3032 (1954).

VI. Cyanuric Azides

1. Cyanuric Triazide

A. *Physical Properties*

The most important member of the cyanuric azides is the triazide (II). It is a colorless compound crystallizing in hexagonal prisms[241] and melting at 94°. It is soluble in acetone, ether, benzene, chloroform, and hot alcohol; slightly soluble in alcohol; and insoluble in water. The density has been reported as:

$$d_{13}^{13} = 1.54 \text{ g./cm.}^3$$

This azide is an exceedingly potent explosive, having even greater sensitivity than mercuric fulminate.[278] It decomposes when heated slowly, detonates when heated rapidly. Large crystals explode when merely broken up with a rubber policeman. A capillary tube of cyanuric triazide will explode if held in a flame; it will explode spontaneously if heated for a long time at 150–160°, a short time[279] at 170–180°, at once[280] at 205° or if struck a sharp blow. Bowden and Williams[283a] found that in the liquid state cyanuric azide can be initiated by the adiabatic compression of a gas bubble, although, even in the apparent absence of gas bubbles, the molten explosive is very sensitive to impact. After a careful study of the mechanism of explosion of cyanuric azide, Yoffe[295a] discovered that it may be melted in a vacuum without decomposition. Even at 112° (m.p. 94°) under as much as 170 mm. of argon, no decomposition occurred over several hours. At 150°, the rate of gas evolution was slow and the products were nitrogen and cyanogen. With a full atmosphere of inert gas, rapid decomposition occurs and an explosion results. Yoffe found that the inert gases act to prevent rapid evaporation of the liquid, and explosion occurs at only a certain pressure of inert gas. During the initial induction period of heating prior to explosion, nitrogen is the only gas evolved; therefore it follows that the explosion is thermal in origin and preceded by self heating of the azide. The effect of the inert gas on the explosion is to prevent escape from a region near the surface of the liquid of the hot products of reaction or of active nitrogen. This active nitrogen loses its energy to the surface of the molten azide by collision. During this period, the heat gained by the azide is greater than the heat lost by conduction and convection, and, as a result, a thermal explosion results.

B. Synthetic Methods

There are two methods for preparing cyanuric triazide only the first of which is important either commercially or in the laboratory.

(1) From cyanuric chloride. Ninety per cent yields[278-283] of cyanuric triazide may be obtained by treating cyanuric chloride (I) with sodium azide in an ice-cold aqueous solution over a period of twelve hours. Acetone solutions of each of the two components can also be used,[227] and Moulin reports[300a] 95 % yields after 24 hours at 36° in acetone.

(2) From 2,4,6-trihydrazino-s-triazine. (III) (Cyanuric trihydrazide). A less commonly used but feasible method is the action of nitrous acid on 2,4,6-trihydrazino-s-triazine.[284] Depending on the duration of

the reaction and the relative amount of nitrite used, the two intermediate azidohydrazino compounds 2-hydrazino-4,6-diazido and 2,4-dihydrazino-6-azido-s-triazine (IV and V), respectively, are obtained (1 and 2).

C. Structure

There is little doubt that the fundamental structure of cyanuric azide comprises a triazine ring. The side-chains have provided an interesting subject for X-ray diffraction analytical work on the arrangement of the three extranuclear nitrogen atoms attached to each carbon atom.

Sutton[241, 285] has claimed that the structure in crystalline azides, including cyanuric triazide, consists of a short chain of nitrogen atoms at right angles to the plane of the ring and joined to one of the carbon

(VI)   (VII)

atoms at the *central* nitrogen atom (VI). This strongly suggests a ring structure for the side-chain nitrogen atoms. Indeed, it is felt that in the case of liquid azides, the ring structure $R—N\big\langle\!\!\begin{smallmatrix}N\\ \|\\ N\end{smallmatrix}$ exists.

The work of Bragg[286] and others[287-289] has presented more convincing evidence that linear nitrogen chains exist, but that these are joined to the ring carbon atoms by a terminal nitrogen atom instead of the central one, and that the angle of the chain is oblique rather than at right angles (VII).

D. Reactions

(1) Hydrolysis. The triazide of cyanuric acid is rapidly and completely hydrolyzed[279] by dilute aqueous sodium hydroxide at 50° to cyanuric acid (3).

(2) Explosive decomposition. As mentioned above, cyanuric triazide is very sensitive to a blow or shock and will explode if heated at 150–160° for a short time. When exploded electrically or in vacuum, the decomposition products are cyanogen and nitrogen.[279]

$$2 \text{ (II)} \xrightarrow{\text{spark}} 3 \text{ (CN)}_2 + 9 \text{ N}_2$$

(3) Reduction. Cyanuric triazide can be directly reduced[291] to melamine by hydrogenation over palladium with ethanol as the solvent (4):

$$(II) \xrightarrow[\text{Pd–C}_2\text{H}_5\text{OH}]{[H]} \qquad \qquad \qquad (4)$$

Reduction (probably a replacement) proceeds[292] at only one of the azido groups when an ethereal solution of the triazide is treated with a stream of ammonia.

$$(II) \quad + 2\,NH_3 \longrightarrow \quad (X) \qquad \qquad (5)$$

(4) Reaction with triphenylphosphine. If a solution of cyanuric triazide in ether or in xylene is treated with triphenylphosphine, cyanuryl-bis(triphenylphosphinimine) monoazide (VIII), m.p. 243° (dec.) is formed.[256] It is not explosive, but burns quietly. The third

$$(II) \quad + P(C_6H_5)_3 \xrightarrow[\text{Xylene}]{\text{Ether or}} \quad (VIII) \quad \xrightarrow[170-180]{P(C_6H_5)_3} \quad (IX)$$

triphenylphosphine group can be introduced best by use of a high boiling solvent at 170–180° giving cyanuryl-tris(triphenylphosphin-imine) (IX) melting at 239°. Compound (IX) forms 1:1 addition compounds with ethyl benzoate or ethanol. It shows no reactivity toward carbon dioxide or carbon disulfide.

Attempts[300a] to form a triazole derivative by adding a reactive acetylene, 2-methylbutyne-3-ol, to the three nitrogens in the cyanuric azide side chain, resulted only in decomposition products.

E. Uses

Cyanuric triazide has found application as a booster explosive.[293] It has the greatest sensitivity of any explosive to a falling weight.[280] It is this very high sensitivity, however, which has prevented a wider use for the compound in the explosives field. Styrene and other vinyl monomers have been polymerized[302a] to high molecular weight without discoloration by means of a 0.3% concentration of cyanuric azide as catalyst.

2. 2-Amino-4,6-diazido-s-triazine

2-Amino-4,6-diazido-s-triazine forms dense colorless crystals which do not melt sharply but decompose above 200°, violently if heated suddenly to 210°. It is insoluble in most common solvents.

It is prepared[292] by the reducing action of a stream of ammonia on a solution of cyanuric triazide in ether, a reaction which may be as a replacement reaction.

Treatment with hydrogen sulfide effects reduction to melamine (6).

$$(X) + H_2S \longrightarrow (H_2NCN)_3 \tag{6}$$
$$\text{melamine}$$

3. 2,4-Dichloro-6-azido-s-triazine

This compound melts at 85° when recrystallized from alcohol.

The introduction of one azido group onto the s-triazine ring is accomplished by adding an aqueous solution of sodium azide to cyanuric chloride in acetone[292] and evaporating the solvent (7).

$$\tag{7}$$

4. Azidohydrazino-s-triazines

The two azidohydrazino-s-triazines are 2-azido-4,6-dihydrazino-s-triazine (V) and 2,4-diazido-6-hydrazino-s-triazine (IV). The former has a melting point of 85–87°. Its salts are completely hydrolyzed by water. The diazide melts at 87–88° and is insoluble in water and in mineral acids.

Both azidohydrazino compounds are prepared by regulation of the amounts of sodium nitrite added to 2,4,6-trihydrazino-s-triazine; and by the length of the reaction time used in converting this compound to the triazide.

The azidohydrazino-s-triazines are less sensitive to shock than the triazide and hence have specialized uses in the explosives industry.

VII. Thiocyanuric Acids

1. Monothiocyanuric Acid

Monothiocyanuric acid, or 2,4-dihydroxy-6-mercapto-s-triazine (XI), was prepared in 1903[176] by hydrolysis of the corresponding O,O'-dimethyl ester (XII). The free monothio acid forms hydrated prisms from hot water and melts at 316°. It is soluble in hot water, ethanol, acetic acid; slightly soluble in methanol; and not soluble in either ether, benzene, or petroleum ether.

Monothiocyanuric acid is obtained when the corresponding O,O'-dimethyl ester (XII) is hydrolyzed with hydrochloric acid.[176] It forms needles of a water insoluble barium salt with barium hydroxide, and characteristic needles of an addition compound with mercuric chloride.

A. 2,4-Dimethoxy-6-mercapto-s-triazine (XII)

The dimethyl ester of monothiocyanuric acid (XII) was also prepared[176] in 1903 by Diels and Liebermann and used to synthesize the free acid. It forms thick solid prisms from hot absolute alcohol which melt at 134°, resolidify and melt again at 194°. Probably there occurs an isomerization of the normal ester to an iso form which, in the case of the cyanuric acid esters at least, has a higher melting point. It is likely that a second melting point would be observed upon further heating past the initial transition stage. 2,4 Dimethoxy-6-mercapto-s-triazine is soluble in ether, benzene, and chloroform and slightly soluble in acetic acid, pyridine, and ethyl acetate.

It may be prepared from 2-chloro-4,6-dimethoxy-s-triazine and potassium hydrogen sulfide. Hydrolysis of (XII) yields monothio-cyanuric acid (XI).

2. Dithiocyanuric Acid

Dithiocyanuric acid (XIII) or 2,4-dimercapto-6-hydroxy-*s*-triazine forms scales which dehydrate at 100° and sublime.[215] It may be recrystallized from hot water.[215]

According to Klason,[215] dithiocyanuric acid monohydrate is formed together with other sulfur compounds by the evaporation of an alcoholic solution of thiocyanic acid. It forms a difficultly soluble barium salt, $C_3N_3(OH)S_2Ba \cdot 2 H_2O$, a potassium salt, $C_3N_3(OH)(SH)(SK)$, and a lead salt, $C_3N_3(OH)(S_2Pb)$.[215]

TABLE I–3.   Salts of Dithiocyanuric Acid

Formula	Hydrate	Solubility and Form	Ref.
$C_3N_3OHS_2HK$	none	Microscopic prisms No dec. at 200°	215
$C_3N_3OHS_2Ba$	$2 H_2O$	Insol. H_2O	215
$C_3N_3OHS_2Pb$	—	White amorphous ppt. Insol. HNO_3	215

When dithiocyanuric acid (XIII) is treated with iodine, oxidation occurs and a disulfide is formed which is easily decomposed by water (8).

(XCI)   (XCII)

The structure written is open to some question. Although admittedly less likely, structure (XIV) has not been eliminated.

(XIV)

A. 2-Ethoxy-4,6-dimercapto-s-triazine (XV)

2-Ethoxy-4,6-dimercapto-*s*-triazine (m.p. 150°) is the O-monoethyl ester of dithiocyanuric acid. It is made[258] by treating the condensation product of ammonium thiocyanate and ethyl chloroformate with thiourea (9).

$$NH_4SCN + ClCOOC_2H_5 \longrightarrow C_2H_5OOCNH\overset{\overset{\displaystyle S}{\|}}{C}OC_2H_5$$

$$C_2H_5OOCNH\overset{\overset{\displaystyle S}{\|}}{C}OC_2H_5 + NH_2CSNH_2 \longrightarrow$$

(XV)

(9)

The mechanism of the formation of this triazine is discussed with monoethyl cyanurate (see Sect. IV 1.B. (3)).

3. Trithiocyanuric Acid

Trithiocyanuric acid, or 2,4,6-trimercapto-s-triazine (XVI), was first identified in 1885 by Hofmann[202] who prepared it by the reaction of sodium sulfide with cyanuric chloride. It is obtained as fine yellow needles, which are reported to acquire strong electric charges by rubbing.[202] The compound does not melt below 300°, a temperature at which it suffers no decomposition.

Trithiocyanuric acid is soluble in sodium hydroxide solution, in 28% aqueous ammonia, in hot pyridine, and in hot Cellosolve. It is slightly soluble in the following solvents: cold Cellosolve, pyridine, hot acetone, hot ethanol and hot dioxane. It is almost completely insoluble in cold acetone, benzene, carbon disulfide, nitrobenzene, and chloroform.

A. Preparation

Trithiocyanuric acid may be readily prepared from cyanuric chloride. A mixture of cyanuric chloride and excess sodium sulfide is triturated at room temperature and the reaction is completed by gentle warming. The crude reaction product is dissolved in water, the surplus sodium sulfide is removed by cautious addition of hydrochloric acid, and the trisodium salt of the acid crystallizes from the solution. Excess acid precipitates free trithiocyanuric acid.

The reaction may also be conveniently run in xylene. Water extraction removes the sodium chloride and the free acid is precipitated with hydrochloric acid as a yellow insoluble solid. Yields are over 75 %. A similar procedure (10) is to substitute[215] a concentrated solution of potassium hydrogen sulfide for the sodium sulfide. The monopotassium

$$\text{(I)} \quad Cl \underset{N}{\overset{N}{\bigcirc}} Cl \quad + 4\ KSH \xrightarrow{\ \varDelta\ } HS \underset{N}{\overset{N}{\bigcirc}} SK \quad + 3\ KCl + H_2S \qquad (10)$$

salt of the acid can be obtained by this procedure because trithiocyanuric acid is a stronger acid than hydrogen sulfide and therefore displaces the latter during the reaction. The synthesis may also be accomplished by heating potassium bisulfate and potassium thiocyanate.[294] The mechanism for the formation of trithiocyanuric acid by the last method is one which undoubtedly involves the trimerization of thiocyanic acid, HS—CN, generated during the heating.

B. Salts of Thiocyanuric Acids

Salts of trithiocyanuric acid are prepared by routine methods; much of this work was done by Hofmann.[202] Table I-4 contains a list of metal trithiocyanurates together with their physical properties. The trisodium salt was probably prepared by Hofmann, but attempts to characterize it were not successful. The tripotassium salt of trithiocyanuric acid is not stable in water, undergoing hydrolysis to the dipotassium salt.

C. Reactions

(1) Pyrolysis. Trithiocyanuric acid is not altered by heating to 200° C. At higher temperatures carbonization and decomposition occur with the liberation of thiocyanic acid.[202] When dry thiocyanuric acid is heated in a boiling mercury bath, it decomposes[215] with the formation of melem, melon, and melam. Melem is the principal one of the three remaining as a residue in the retort; carbon disulfide and thiocyanic acid distill.

TABLE I–4.   Salts of Trithiocyanuric Acid

Formula	Hydrate	Solubility, Form and Properties	Ref.
$C_3N_3S_3H_2Na$	Hygroscopic	Sol. H_2O. S. sol. ethyl alc. Insol. ether. Large, glossy crystals	1
$(C_3N_3S_3H_2)_2Ba$	2 H_2O lost at 280°		1
$C_3N_3S_3HBa$	3 H_2O	Thick yellow crystals stable in boiling H_2O. Sol. hot H_2O	2, 3, 4
$C_3N_3S_3K_3$	3 H_2O lost at moderate heat in vacuum	Oil which crystallizes when washed with ethyl alc. M.p. ca. 350°	2
$C_3N_3S_3HCa$	5 H_2O	Yellow prisms. S. sol. H_2O	2
$C_3N_3S_3HSr$	5 H_2O	Yellow rhombic prisms. Sol. H_2O, s. sol. ethyl alc.	1, 2
$C_3N_3S_3HAg_2$	—	Canary yellow amorphous substance	1
$C_3N_3S_3HPb$	—	Amorphous	1
$C_3H_3S_3HCu$	—	Amorphous blue-green	1
$(C_3N_3S_3H_2)_4Ti$	—	—	4
[a] $C_3N_3S_3HCa$	—	S. sol. H_2O Sol. ethyl alc. Rhombic needles	1
[a] $C_3N_3S_3HMg$	—	Sol. H_2O, insol. ethyl alc. Needles	1
[a] $C_3N_3S_3HSn$	—	Fine white needles	1
[a] $C_3N_3S_3HFe$	—	Fine, aggregated, yellow needles	1
[a] $C_3N_3S_3HMn$	—	Thin, colorless platelets	1
[a] $C_3N_3S_3HZn$	—	White needles	1
[a] $C_3N_3S_3HCo$	—	Reddish colored groups of needles	1
[a] $C_3N_3S_3HBi$	—	Yellow, amorphous ppt.	1
[a] $C_3N_3S_3HNi$	—	Greenish, amorphous ppt.	1
[a] $C_3N_3S_3HPt$	—	Red-brown amorphous ppt.	1
[a] $C_3N_3S_3HAu$	—	Red-brown amorphous ppt.	1

[a] = Not well characterized; analytical data lacking.

1. A. Hofmann, *Ber.*, **18**, 2196 (1885).
2. P. Klason, *J. prakt. Chem.*, (2), **33**, 121 (1886).
3. F. Wohler, *Ann.*, **62**, 241 (1841).
4. A. Rosenheim and R. Cohn, *Z. angew. Chem.*, **28**, 167 (1901).

(2) Hydrolysis.   The boiling of trithiocyanuric acid in water[215] causes slight decomposition leading to formation of thiocyanic acid. At 130°, aqueous hydrochloric acid initiates an hydrolysis[215] which is complete at 200° giving cyanuric acid and hydrogen sulfide (11). Other mineral acids, such as nitric and sulfuric, also cause hydrolysis at elevated temperatures.[215] Alkaline permanganate does so at room temperature.

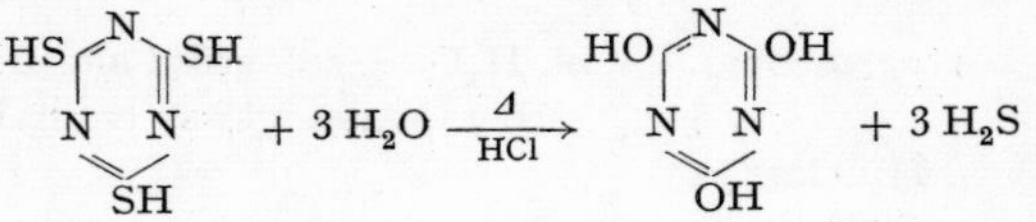

$$\text{(XVI structure)} \quad + 3\,H_2O \xrightarrow[HCl]{\Delta} \quad \text{(OH structure)} \quad + 3\,H_2S \tag{11}$$

(3) Oxidation with iodine. When thiocyanuric acid is treated with iodine,[215] it forms a disulfide analogous to the one formed from dithiocyanuric acid. The structure of the product requires reconsideration. It has been formulated as cyclic, but no real evidence exists for the structure (XVII) nor for any other structure of this tri-disulfide.

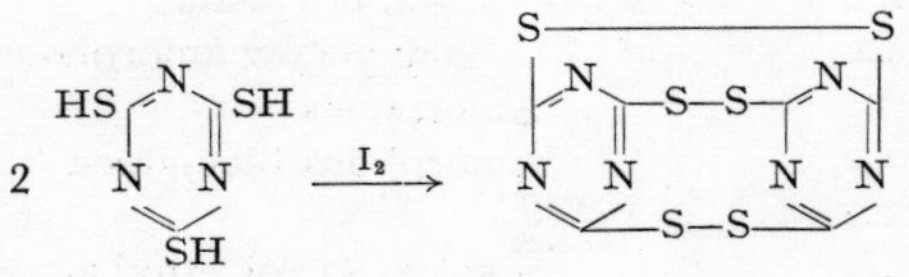

$$2 \quad \text{(XVI)} \quad \xrightarrow{I_2} \quad \text{(XVII)}$$

(XVI)   (XVII)

If correct, the condensed ring structure presents the sterically complex picture of two ten membered rings each containing four sulfur atoms as well as two nitrogen atoms. These are linked to the two s-triazine rings. There is a good possibility that the compound in question is a linear polysulfide.

(4) Reaction with ammonia. By the application of heat and ammonia under pressure, thiocyanuric acid can be converted to melamine, but yields are only 40%. The melamine so produced is contaminated with sulfur or sulfur compounds which are exceedingly difficult to remove.

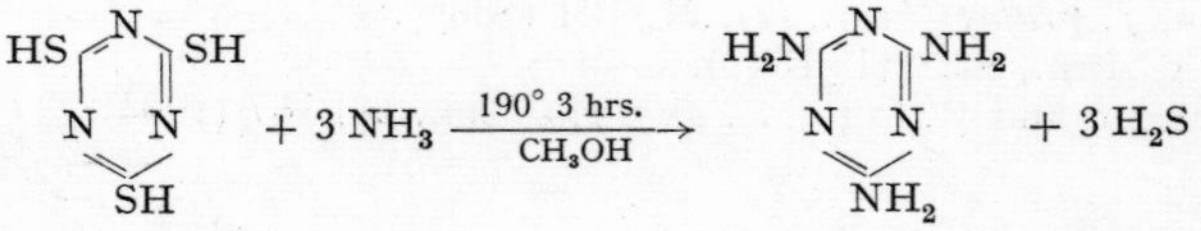

$$\text{(XVI)} \quad + 3\,NH_3 \xrightarrow[CH_3OH]{190^\circ \ 3\ hrs.} \quad \text{(melamine)} \quad + 3\,H_2S$$

(XVI)

D. Uses

Trithiocyanuric acid may find application[295] in photographic emulsions. It is a fair synthetic retarder for rubber.

4. Alkyl Thiocyanurates

Alkyl isocyanates are converted at ordinary or at elevated temperatures to alkyl isocyanurates. However, the behavior of alkyl thiocyanates in most respects is not analogous to that of the oxygen compounds. Alkyl thiocyanates on heating yield normal alkyl thiocyanurates, but much higher temperatures are required than for the oxygen analogs and no isothiocyanurates are formed even then.

A. Trimethyl Trithiocyanurate

Trimethyltrithiocyanurate, 2,4,6-trimethylthio-s-triazine (XVIII), was known in 1880 even before the time that trithiocyanuric acid was identified.[202] After crystallization from acetic acid it melts at 188°. Plots of melting points of mixtures of the normal and isothiomethyl esters have been made by Gillis.[296]

Two principal methods are available for preparing trimethyltrithiocyanurate. The first consists in treating[215] cyanuric chloride with sodium and methyl mercaptide. The result is a simple exchange reaction whereby the thiomethyl group is incorporated onto the ring and sodium

$$Cl-\underset{\underset{Cl}{\underset{(I)}{\parallel}}}{\overset{N}{\underset{N\quad N}{\bigcirc}}}-Cl \ + \ 3\ NaSCH_3 \ \longrightarrow \ CH_3S-\underset{\underset{SCH_3}{\underset{(XVIII)}{\parallel}}}{\overset{N}{\underset{N\quad N}{\bigcirc}}}-SCH_3 \ + \ 3\ NaCl$$

chloride is split out. Yields have not been reported. The second method involves trimerization of methylthiocyanate. When methylthiocyanate which is *not* pure or which contains a trace of acid is heated at 180–185° for several hours, a 50% yield of the normal trimethylthio ester is obtained.[202, 297, 298] Trimerization does not occur if very pure methylthiocyanate is used. Whether the catalyst is acid or some other impurity is not clear.

$$3\ CH_3SCN \ \xrightarrow[180-185°]{H^+} \ CH_3S-\underset{\underset{SCH_3}{\underset{(XVIII)}{\parallel}}}{\overset{N}{\underset{N\quad N}{\bigcirc}}}-SCH_3 \quad 50\%$$

The crude crystalline thiocyanuric ester has been purified by washing with alcohol, drying and vacuum distilling. Beautiful crystals can be made by dissolving it in alcohol under pressure at 120° and allowing the solution to cool slowly. No trimethyl isothiocyanurate is produced by this crystallization procedure. Thioammeline (2-mercapto-4,6-diamino-s-triazine) and dithioammelide (2,4-dimercapto-6-amino-s-triazine) can both be alkylated at the sulfhydryl group with alkyl sulfates or halides in the presence of strong alkali. It should therefore be possible to alkylate trithiocyanuric acid by a similar procedure, and this should be an alternate method of synthesis.

That the thioester (XVIII) is the normal and not the isothio-cyanuric compound is shown by its ready hydrolysis[299] to cyanuric acid which occurs with vigorous evolution of methyl mercaptan and without the formation of traces of methylamine and carbon oxy-sulfide or carbon dioxide and carbon disulfide.

$$CH_3S \underset{N \quad N}{\overset{N}{\diamond}} SCH_3 \quad + \; 3\,H_2O \; \xrightarrow{HCl} \; HO \underset{N \quad N}{\overset{N}{\diamond}} OH \; + \; 3\,CH_3SH$$
(XVIII) SCH₃   OH

In the absence of hydrochloric acid, trimethyl trithiocyanurate is stable when heated with water under pressure at a temperature of 180°; however, like a typical ester, it undergoes base-catalyzed hydrolysis. For example, treatment with sodium sulfide produces sodium cyanurate and sodium methyl mercaptide (12). Melamine can

$$CH_3S \underset{N \quad N}{\overset{N}{\diamond}} SCH_3 \quad + \; 3Na_2S \; \xrightarrow{\;\Delta\;} \; NaS \underset{N \quad N}{\overset{N}{\diamond}} SNa \; + \; 3\,NaSCH_3 \qquad (12)$$
(XVIII) SCH₃   SNa

be produced from trimethyl trithiocyanuric acid by heating at 180–190° with aqueous ammonia.[298,299] The reaction can also be controlled[299] by regulation of reaction time and temperature, so that isolation of the two intermediate compounds, the S-methyl esters of thioammelide and thioammeline, is possible (13).

$$CH_3S\underset{SCH_3}{\overset{N}{\diamond}}SCH_3 \xrightarrow[\Delta]{NH_3aq.} H_2N\underset{SCH_3}{\overset{N}{\diamond}}SCH_3 \xrightarrow[\Delta]{NH_3aq.} H_2N\underset{NH_2}{\overset{N}{\diamond}}SCH_3 \xrightarrow[\Delta]{NH_3aq.} H_2N\underset{NH_2}{\overset{N}{\diamond}}NH_2 \qquad (13)$$
(XVIII)

B. Other Alkyl Thiocyanurates

Triethyl trithiocyanurate crystallizes from acetic acid in large colorless plates[297], m.p. 27° and b.p. 150–152° at 0.7–0.8 mm.[297a] It is soluble in ether, carbon disulfide and acetic acid and may be distilled without decomposition at 350° and one atmosphere. Triallyltrithiocyanurate is a heavy clear yellow oil,[297a] and tri-n-amyltrithiocyanurate is a viscous yellow oil, not crystalline even at —18°. The triethyl ester has been prepared[297a] in 61% yield from cyanuric chloride and sodium ethyl mercaptide, while the triallyl ester was prepared in 78% yield from allyl chloride and trithiocyanuric acid, in ethanolic potassium hydroxide by heating for 40 minutes at 45°. Both the triethyl and tri-n-amyl esters may be prepared[202] by polymerization of the respective thiocyanic esters, if available, but yields are low. These and the other known trithio esters are best prepared[215] from cyanuric chloride and the corresponding alkali mercaptide.

5. Aryl Thiocyanurates and Aralkyl Thiocyanurates

Only two aromatic thioesters have been reported,[215] the triphenyl and the tri-p-tolyl esters, and one aralkyl thioester, the tribenzyl compound.[297a]

The triphenyl thioester crystallizes from glacial acetic acid in glistening crystals melting at 97°. The tri-p-tolyl thioester melts at 114° and is also crystallized from glacial acetic acid. The tribenzyl thioester crystallizes in long white needles melting at 76–79°. The first two esters are prepared from cyanuric chloride, using the corresponding sodium thiophenolate.[215] Potassium thiocyanurate reacts with benzyl chloride[297a] to give tribenzyl trithiocyanurate (78% yield). The synthesis is illustrated for the triphenyl derivative (13).

$$\text{(13)}$$

Esters of trithiocyanuric acid have been suggested[297a] as oil additives for corrosion inhibition.

6. 2,4,6-Tri(carbethoxythio)s-triazine (XIX)

This compound is the tricarbethoxy derivative of trithiocyanuric acid.[300] It forms yellow crystals which, when recrystallized from alcohol, melt above 200° at no definite point.

Chloroethylcarbonate and ammonium dithiocarbamate react in absolute alcohol at 0° to give S-carbethoxydithiocarbamate. If the reaction mixture is allowed to warm up, a sudden temperature rise is observed and some of the product consists of 2,4,6-tri(carbethoxythio)s-

$$3 \; ClCOOC_2H_5 + 3 \; H_2NCSSNH_4 \rightarrow 3 \; H_2NCSSCOOC_2H_5 + NH_4Cl \xrightarrow{\Delta}$$

triazine (XIX). Like many members of the thiocyanuric acid group, this compound has received only a limited amount of attention in regard to synthetic methods and almost none in regard to its reactions.

VIII. Triazinylthioglycolic Acids and Their Derivatives

1. 2,4,6-Tri(carboxymethylthio)s-triazine

This compound, and the ester from which it is prepared, were first synthesized by Heintz in 1865.[301] It melts at 199.5° and is soluble in ether, warm alcohol, and slightly soluble in water. Preparation of 2,4,6-tri(carboxymethylthio)s-triazine is accomplished by alkaline hydrolysis of the ethyl ester (14).[301,302] The structure is apparent from a

(14)

consideration of its hydrolysis products. When the free acid is heated with very dilute hydrochloric acid, attack takes place at the sulfur atoms giving cyanuric and thioglycolic acids.

Treatment of the free tricarboxylic acid with potassium hydroxide produces a tripotassium salt which is soluble in water, but insoluble in ether and in alcohol. Barium chloride forms two tertiary barium salts, a di- and a hexahydrate. Salts of silver, copper, iron, cobalt, cadmium, and zinc are also formed but have been incompletely characterized.[301,302]

2. 2,4,6-Tri(carbethoxymethylthio)s-triazine

Heintz was also the first to synthesize 2,4,6-tri(carbethoxymethyl-thio)s-triazine by trimerization of ethyl thiocyanatoacetate. The tri-ester, crystallized from ether, alcohol, or hot water, melts at 80.5–81°. The synthesis is best accomplished by slow vacuum distillation or treatment with dilute sulfuric and phosphoric acids of ethyl thiocyanato-acetate, which can be prepared from potassium thiocyanate and ethyl chloroacetate (15 and 16). The trimerization is not a simple one and the

$$KSCN + ClCH_2COOC_2H_5 \longrightarrow NC(S)CH_2COOC_2H_5 \tag{15}$$

$$NC(S)CH_2COOC_2H_5 \xrightarrow[\text{or dil. } H_2SO_4 \text{ or } H_3PO_4]{\text{slow vac. distn.}} \tag{16}$$

following compounds have also been obtained[302]: ethylcarbylamine, ethanol, propionitrile, ethyl thioglycollate, ethyl ether, acetyl thio-cyanate, aliphatic mercaptans, and cyanogen thiocyanate, NC—SCN.

Hydrolysis of the ester to the free carboxylic acid has been described above as a method of preparing the tricarboxylic acid.

IX. 2,4,6-Tri(acetonylthio)s-triazine

The triacetyl derivative of trimethyl trithiocyanurate is prepared[303] by trimerizing acetylmethyl thiocyanate (17). The compound is a deri-

$$3\ CH_3COCH_2SCN \longrightarrow \tag{17}$$

vative of trithiocyanuric acid, but because it has not been prepared by a direct reaction of that compound, it is listed separately in this section. The side-chain undergoes the expected reactions. Two of the carbonyl groups react readily with phenylhydrazine, p-tolylhydrazine, semi-carbazide and hydroxylamine and give typical carbonyl derivatives. With hot concentrated hydrochloric acid, rearrangement takes place, probably by the mechanism below.

The S-triacetyl derivative of thiocyanuric acid has not been prepared, but the most likely preparation would appear to be the reaction of acetyl chloride with tri-silver trithiocyanurate.

X. Triselenocyanuric Acid

The selenium analog of cyanuric acid may be obtained by treating cyanuric chloride with sodium selenide.[304] The acid has not been characterized, but treatment of the trisodium salt with methyl iodide

gave the trimethyl ester (18). 2,4,6-Triselenylmethyl-s-triazine, crystallized from alcohol, melts at 174°. Heating with ammonia produced melamine and selenyl methane.

XI. Esters of s-Triazine-2,4,6-triphosphonite

Cyanuric chloride reacts with organic phosphites according to Coover[303a] to give hexaalkyl or hexaaryl-s-triazine-2,4,6-triphosphonite. Butyl, ethyl, and phenyl derivatives of this class have been reported. The ethyl derivative melts at 82–84°. Cyclohexane has been found to be a useful recrystallization solvent.

XII. Uses and Industrial Applications of Cyanuric Chloride and Derivatives

1. Dyestuffs

The material described in the patent literature with rare exceptions, contains little conclusive proof of structure and gives almost no physical data on individual compounds. The greater portion of the chemistry of the s-triazine ring is concerned with the reaction of one or more of the chlorine atoms of cyanuric chloride with a primary amino group. The remainder involves the Organic Chemistry of Dyes, a subject which is outside the scope of this work.

Fierz-David and Matter[43] have studied the preparation and properties of dyes containing the s-triazine ring, which have appeared on the market since 1924 and which are the subject of numerous patents. The s-triazine ring has two important advantages over such condensing agents as phosgene in the preparation of dyes and dye intermediates.[305] It can be used (1) to link together derivatives such as 1,8-aminonaphthols that are not usually amenable to phosgenation, and (2) it enables the condensation of three different molecules through the same ring. The introduction of the s-triazine ring is usually accomplished by suitable condensations with cyanuric chloride and may be described as cyanuration. It is not merely a convenient procedure for combining azo or other dye units to form more complex dyes, but special properties have been claimed for cyanurated dyes. They have high tinctorial power and purity of shades (particularly on cotton and regenerated cellulose), increased affinity for cellulose fibers, and greater fastness. Ciba has included some of the cyanurated azo dyes in its range of Chlorantine Fast colors which are notable for their fastness; a few cyanurated anthraquinone vat dyes are also among the Cibanone colors. Venkataraman[306] feels that the cyanuric ring per se does not improve fastness.

Fierz-David[43] has shown that many patent procedures do not give products of the chemical structure claimed. In a number of instances not the pure compound, but a mixture of several compounds was obtained when the procedures were reinvestigated. It was shown that the aminonaphtholsulfonic acids react at the amino group only, and not at the hydroxyl group, and it was also reported that formation of a secondary condensation product of two amino groups with one cyanuric chloride molecule proceeds at a rate more rapid than that of the primary condensation. Since this phenomenon is observed only when the primary condensation product is soluble and the initial reactants are insoluble in the reaction medium, it can only be concluded that this was the case for the examples examined or that the procedures in the patents under examination were improperly described. At any rate, a number of claims in the patent literature of having joined two or three different amino derivatives onto the same s-triazine nucleus are in reality reports of mixtures. For example, the indicated product

$$2 \quad \underset{\underset{Cl}{\bigcirc}}{Cl \underset{N}{\bigcirc} Cl} + 2\,ANH_2 + 2\,BNH_2 \longrightarrow 2 \quad \underset{\underset{NHB}{\bigcirc}}{ANH \underset{N}{\bigcirc} Cl} + 4\,HCl \qquad (19)$$

of reaction (19), where A and B represent aryl groups, may actually be a mixture of the products of reaction (20).

$$2 \quad \underset{\underset{Cl}{\bigcirc}}{Cl \underset{N}{\bigcirc} Cl} + 2\,ANH_2 + 2\,BNH_2 \longrightarrow \quad \underset{\underset{NHA}{\bigcirc}}{ANH \underset{N}{\overset{H}{\bigcirc}} Cl} + \underset{\underset{NHB}{\bigcirc}}{BNH \underset{N}{\bigcirc}} + 4\,HCl \quad (20)$$

Under ordinary circumstances, it is possible, by operating at a low temperature, 0°, to isolate a primary condensation product of cyanuric chloride and an aminonaphtholsulfonic acid. At 40°; mainly the secondary product is produced and at 90–100°; all three chlorines will undergo reaction with amino derivatives. The linkage formed, s-triazine ring carbon to substituent nitrogen, is relatively stable to hydrochloric acid, but less so to sodium carbonate; it can be readily cleaved by sodium hydroxide.[43] This statement is a general one and does not hold true in every case. In some instances cleavage of this bond is best realized by hydrolyzing with acid under very vigorous conditions. The structure of the complex dyes is best investigated by reducing the azo linkages with sodium hydrosulfite to obtain the basic s-triazine compound and the amino fragment or fragments. Cyanuric chloride is the most commonly employed starting material for the preparation of cyanurated dyes. The primary condensation product with sodium methoxide is also a useful intermediate. Aniline and its nuclear substituted derivatives form primary, secondary and tertiary condensation products, the first type being useful intermediates. More complex amines undergo the third condensation with difficulty. The replacement of the first chlorine atom is carried out in a solvent such as benzene at 0°. If water-soluble amines are used; for example, the sodium salts of arylaminosulfonic acids, the condensation may be effected in aqueous solution. Higher temperatures are necessary for the second and third replacements. Cyanurated compounds have been obtained from intermediates such as H-acid, 1-amino-8-naphthol-3,6-disulfonic acid; J-acid, 2-amino-5-naphthol-7-sulfonic acid; and K-acid, 1-amino-8-naphthol-4,6-disulfonic acid; aminobenzoic acids; and aminosalicylic acid. When Fierz-David and Matter[43] condensed H-acid and J-acid with cyanuric chloride, according to the patents they obtained a mixture of primary and secondary condensation products; but pure primary, secondary or tertiary condensation products can be obtained under specific conditions. Some typical s-triazine dyes are presented below.

A. Azo Dyes

Four of the direct cotton dyes of the Ciba Chlorantine Fast series were identified by Fierz-David and Matter[43] by degradation and synthesis. Chlorantine Fast Blue 8G and 10GL are dyes in which only two of the chlorines of cyanuric chloride have been replaced, one by N-acyl-*p*-phenylenediamine in both dyes. The two dyes differ only in that the sodium-2-amino-5-nitrobenzene sulfonate residue of Chlorantine Fast Blue 8G is substituted with H-acid in the 10GL dye. Chlorantine Fast Rubine RLL is of interest as a copper complex and a dye in which the s-triazine residue replaces the carbonyl group in the commonly used urea of J-acid. Recent patent literature gives ample evidence of

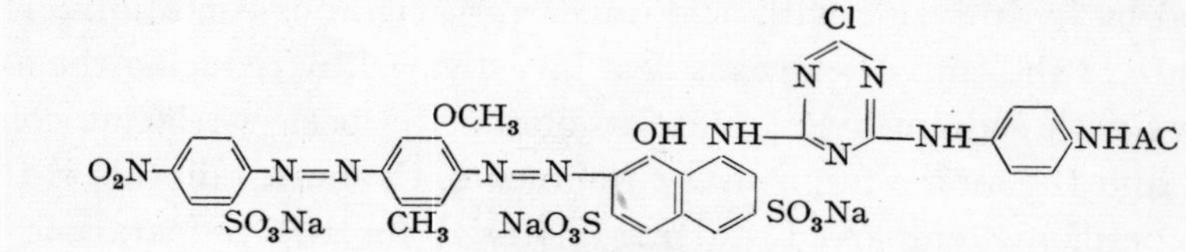

Chlorantine Fast Blue 8 G

the importance of this relatively new class of metalliferous, direct cotton dyes. Chlorantine Fast Green BLL is a good example of the use of cyanuric chloride in the production of synthetic dyes of desired

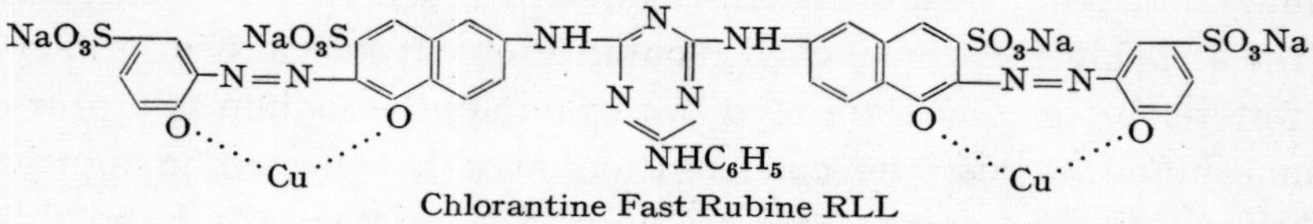

Chlorantine Fast Rubine RLL

shades. A blue and a yellow component can be joined by means of the s-triazine ring to give a pure green shade. Venkataraman has presented[307] the following typical procedure for the preparation of a dye such as Chlorantine Fast Green BLL.

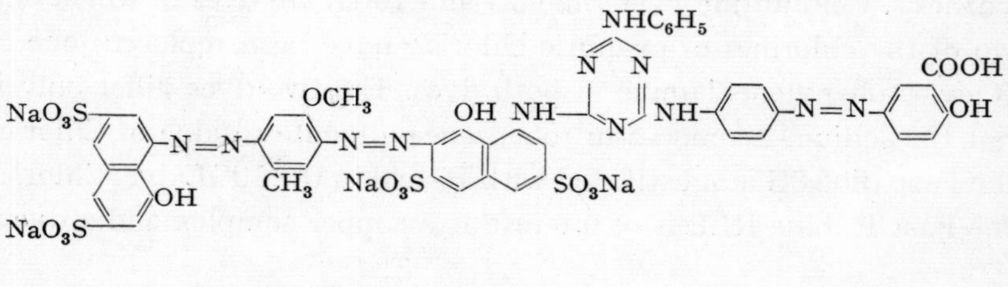

A solution of one mole of the diazo dye (H-acid → cresidine → H-acid) in the calculated amount of aqueous sodium carbonate is added gradually to a suspension of cyanuric chloride (one mole) in water at 0–5° with stirring. Simultaneously a 10% sodium carbonate solution is added so as to maintain the pH at about 6. After 4 hours, the suspension of the primary condensation product is treated with a neutral solution of one mole of sodium p-aminobenzeneazo-salicylate and stirred for 24 hours at 40°, sodium carbonate solution being added to neutralize the liberated hydrochloric acid. The third component, aniline (two moles, the extra mole serves as an acid-binding agent), is now added and the mixture heated at 90–95° for 2 hours. The solution is finally made alkaline with sodium carbonate and the dye salted out.

Copper complexes of cyanurated azo dyes containing groups conferring substantivity for cotton, figure in many patents. The complexes may be prepared in substance or the dyes applied to the fiber in the presence of a copper salt. For example anthranilic acid or an o-aminophenol may be diazotized and coupled with the condensation product of J-acid (one or two moles) with cyanuric chloride or a primary derivative of cyanuric chloride. Two typical dyes which yield copper complexes are (I) and (II)[308]; the latter confers great substantivity.

The presence of two salicylic acid residues in the green trisazo dye (III) enables the fastness to be increased by after-treatment with copper.[309] The few typical examples cited above do not begin to cover

the vast number of s-triazine containing dyes which have been patented,[310] many of them to The Society of Chemical Industry at Basle, but they are representative of the commercial members of the category.

B. Anthraquinone Vat Dyes

Condensations of aminoanthraquinones with cyanuric chloride provide a mode of acylation by which an aminoanthraquinone is converted into a vat dye.[311] The cyanuration of the soluble azo dyes is carried out in aqueous solution, but the aminoanthraquinones are condensed in a suitable organic solvent. Nitrobenzene was suggested in earlier patents with cuprous chloride sometimes used as a catalyst, but phenol is a much better solvent. While two equivalents of a substance such as α-aminoanthraquinone readily condense with one equivalent of cyanuric chloride, a third equivalent reacts only with great difficulty. The third chlorine may be replaced by one of several methods. The tertiary compound is obtained smoothly[312,314] and in excellent yield in phenolic solvents at temperatures from 100–180°. The third chlorine may be replaced by adding[313] cyanuric chloride to an aqueous suspension of aminoanthraquinone generated in situ by hydrolysis of 1-thionylaminoanthraquinone. Drastic conditions can be avoided by using more strongly basic amines to react with the third chlorine atom. Commercial representatives of this group are Cibanone Red G, Red 4B, and Orange 6R. Cibanone Red G is the condensation product of cyanuric chloride with two moles of 1 amino-4-methoxy-anthraquinone and one mole of ammonia. Cibanone Red 4B is the tertiary condensation product of cyanuric chloride with 1-amino-4-benzamidoanthraquinone[312] and Cibanone Orange 6R is the analog of Red 4B with methoxyl groups in place of the benzamido groups.

Cibanone Red G

Cibanone Red 4 B

The following anthraquinones, anthraquinone derivatives, or related substances have been incorporated into dye molecules with the s-triazine nucleus: diaminoanthraquinones,[315] anthraquinone acridone derivatives,[316,317] anthraquinone thioxanthone compounds,[318] pyrantho-nes,[319] and others. Nitrobenzene has proved a useful solvent. Hydrosul-fite is commonly used as a reducing agent and hypochlorites are reported to enhance the liveliness of the color.[320] The amino groups on the anthra-quinone dye molecules may be coupled or condensed with other compo-nents,[321] such as acylating or benzoylating reagents,[322] in order to modify the color effects of their prototypes. Combinations of aminoanthraqui-nones with azo substances similar to those discussed are often useful, particularly when the latter contain[322] solubilizing hydrophilic groups. Mixtures of 1-aminoanthraquinone with phenol, cresylic acid, chlorophe-nols, or α-naphthol and cyanuric chloride are reported to give excellent cotton dyes.[324]

C. Phenolic Dyestuffs

Phenols and naphthols can be condensed with cyanuric chloride in the presence of anhydrous aluminum chloride to give tertiary con-densation products.[325] α-Naphthol will react in the presence of aluminum chloride[326] or sulfuric acid[327] with cyanuric halides containing one or more residual halogen atoms. The reaction is carried out either with or without such inert solvents[328] as carbon disulfide, petroleum ether, tetrachloroethane, or nitrobenzene and gives nuclear substitution products. With α-naphthol, Fierz-David and Matter obtained 2,4,6-tris(4'-hydroxy)naphthyl-s-triazine, which is an energetic coupling component of the Naphthol AS type with good affinity for cotton. With simpler diazonium salts, bordeaux shades are produced, and fast black shades with diazotized amino- or diaminoazo compounds.[329]

D. Direct Dyeing

Cyanuric chloride reacts with alkali impregnated cotton cellulose and with some cellulose derivatives to impart changed dyeing charac-

teristics to the fiber. Cellulose[331] or cotton[332] is first impregnated with
alkali and then treated with cyanuric chloride or cyanuric bromide in
xylene.[333] The resulting product is in turn treated with a basic dye to
give a stable color. The colors of cyanurated cottons do not deteriorate
with age and are resistant to the action of dilute alkali, hot dye baths,
boiling sodium carbonate solutions, and mercerization. In these respects
they are superior to acylated intermediates. They are insoluble in the
usual solvents for cellulose esters and ethers.[334] Halogen present in the
product can be made to react with amines to impart the property of
taking up wool dyes or with aromatic diamines to make possible the
chemical attachment of a dye through diazotization and coupling.[334]
The reaction of cotton with cyanuric chloride is influenced by the type
of alkali pretreatment and by the choice of organic solvent. Substitution of the order of one triazine ring for every 1.9 anhydroglucose
residues and one chlorine atom per 3.4 anhydroglucose residues has
been reported.[334] The chlorinated product was stable to heating at 100°
and after several months storage it still maintained its activity in reactions with amines.

E. Dye Fixing Agents

Cyanuric halides have found application in the dyestuff industry
via their reaction with a miscellaneous group of substances. Basic
compounds of this type are used to insolubilize acid dyes which have
already been applied to the fiber. Some dye fixing agents include the
reaction product with quinazolone derivatives,[335] the water soluble
reaction products of cyanuric halides and polyethylene polyamines,[336]
$H_2N-(C_2H_4NH)_nC_2H_4NH_2$, the reaction product of dihaloethanes and
ammonium hydroxide, and the condensation product obtained by
heating m-sulfochlorobenzoic acid with the intermediate from cyanuric
chloride and aniline.[337] If the dyes derived from the polyethylene polyamines are further treated either with dimethyl sulfate, methyl-
chloride, methanol and hydrogen chloride, or benzyl chloride, tertiary
amines are formed.[338] The amines are converted into quaternary ammonium salts which, in aqueous solutions, are useful for treating
cellulose with a substantive dye to improve fastness to perspiration,
water, acids and washing.

2. Optical Bleaches

Optical bleaches, whitening agents or brighteners are fluorescent compounds that absorb ultraviolet light and emit visible light when they are applied to textile fibers. They may be classified as dyes if a dye is defined as a compound that is able to affix itself to a textile fabric and influence the apparent color of that fabric. Many dyestuffs containing the *s*-triazine ring have been synthesized in research laboratories, described in the patent literature, and offered commercially. Actually the market for optical bleaching agents derived from cyanuric chloride is greater than that for dyes derived from cyanuric chloride. Several examples of optical bleaches made from cyanuric chloride are presented below.

Incorporation[339] of bis-(2,4-dihydroxy-1,3,5-triazinyl-6)-diamino-diphenyl urea disulfonic acid (IV) into transparent wrapping materials not only prevents discoloration of the sheet but also provides an ultraviolet absorber which is not leached out by the moisture present in foods.

(IV)

One of the latest improvements in soaps and detergents is the incorporation of whitening agents for the purpose of making laundered fabrics whiter. The *s*-triazine ring is present in (V), a compound which

(V)

is a bluish fluorescing agent, substantive to cellulosic materials and useful as an additive to soaps and detergents.[340] Cyanuric chloride, ethanolamine, and 4,4'-diamino-2,2'-stilbenedisulfonic acid condense[341] to give the brightening agent 4,4'-bis(6-chloro-4-(2-hydroxyethyl-amino)-*s*-triazine-2-yl-amino)-2,2'-stilbenedisulfonic acid (VI). Other amines may be substituted for the ethanolamine group. The variety is considerable.[342] The amine may be aliphatic or aromatic, primary or secondary; it may contain hydroxy, acylamino, sulfo, sulfamido or

(VI)

alkoxy substituents. One chlorine may be retained in each s-triazine nucleus or they may both be replaced by amino residues, [343,345a] in which case the best quality products are obtained.

Fabrics washed with formulations of detergents containing these fluorescent agents appear much whiter in the case of whites and much brighter in the case of colors than fabrics which are washed with ordinary soaps or detergents. In addition to their use in paper or other wrapping materials to improve whiteness and to protect the contents from the action of ultraviolet light, they may also be incorporated in discharge pastes whereby the whites obtained upon discharge are decidedly whiter than in the absence of such materials.

3. Coloration of Hydrocarbons

Liquid hydrocarbons may often be identified by the characteristic coloration imparted to them by certain dyestuffs.[344] The dyestuffs can be obtained[344] by condensing cyanuric chloride with at least one equivalent of a polycyclic aromatic compound in the presence of anhydrous aluminum chloride. The condensation product of cyanuric chloride and pyrene colors petroleum hydrocarbons bluish-green and gives benzene a bluish fluorescence. The product using chrysene colors petroleum distillates dark bluish violet and benzene brownish-yellow. Similar materials are obtained when cyanuric chloride is condensed with N-ethylcarbazole or perylene. In addition to the color they lend to petroleum oils and benzene, the products give color to oils and waxes[2] by which they can be identified.

4. Pesticides

A number of substances containing the s-triazine structure are said to be effective as insecticides and as preservatives. Compounds of the aryloxyaminosulfonic acid type condensed with cyanuric chloride (1), are reported to produce useful mothproofers[346] and fur, feather, hair, and fibrous protectors.[347] To this list of compounds possessing pesticidal

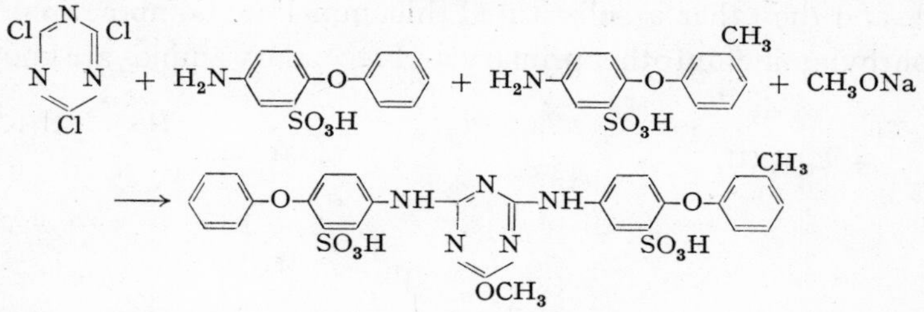

(1)

properties may be added their position isomers and also the analogous types in which oxygen links are replaced[348] by linkages such as sulfide, sulfoxide, sulfone and methylene. This group of compounds is derived from metanilic acid and cyanuric chloride. A number of other compounds also derived from metanilic acid are known.[349-351] An example of their group is the reaction product of cyanuric chloride and 2-amino-naphthol-5,7-disulfonic acid. It is a useful substitute for tannins, a reserve agent for silk and wool, and a wetting or emulsifying agent.[352] Mothproofing agents are obtained by the condensation[353] of cyanuric chloride with p-chlorophenyl mercaptan, 4,6-dichlorometanilic acid and 4,5-dichloro-orthanilic acid (2). This triazine derivative belongs to a

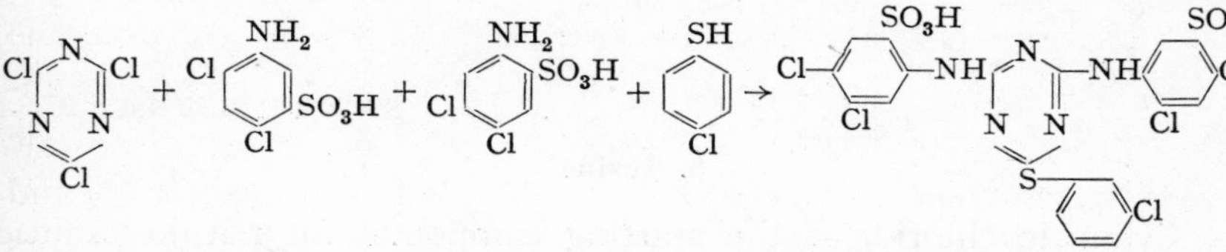

(2)

group of compounds in which the substituted benzene rings may or may not be alike. The substituents may be any alkyl, arylalkyl or benzene derivative with at least one chlorine and one sulfonic acid group and with an oxygen, sulfur or nitrogen linkage to the s-triazine ring.

5. Rubber Industry

Treating cyanuric chloride with one, two, or three equivalents of ammonia or with a primary or a secondary amine, and replacing the residual chlorine atoms with such groups as —OH, —SH, —NR, —OR, etc., gives compounds reported to be useful antioxidants[355] and vulcanization accelerators (3).[344] The following syntheses illustrate[356] the preparation of two examples of these compounds, one a substituted dithioammelide and the other a substituted thioammeline. Combinations using β-naphthylamine and other primary and secondary amines are known.[356]

$$(3)$$

Vulcanization accelerators which do not exhibit the unfavorable critical temperature characteristics of dialkylamine salts of dithiocarbamic acids are produced by condensing[357] a di-substituted dithiocarbamic acid or its salts with cyanuric chloride (4). The reaction proceeds readily, requires only slight warming and the final products are yellow, crystalline, high melting compounds.

6. Resins

Cyanuric chloride is the starting compound for trithiocyanuric acid. Trithiocyanuric acid and related compounds containing at least two functional groups form resins which may be used in "the treatment of paper, textiles, and leather, fruit juices, pectin, as absorbents for plant nutrients, and in nonaqueous media when condensed[358] with polyalkylenepolyamines."

7. Explosives

The explosive properties of cyanuric triazide and related compounds have been briefly discussed under (Section VI, 1) which deals with the chemistry of these compounds.

8. Metallurgy

Cyanuric acid has not found application as yet in this field. However, it has been found[359] that the addition of 0.01–1.0 oz. of trithiocyanuric acid per gallon of plating bath resulted in the production of bright silver plating from cyanide baths over a wide range of current densities.

9. Surface Active Agents

A surface active agent used in the textile, leather and paper industries has been prepared by treating cyanuric chloride and sodium dodecylaminoethyl sulfate, $C_{12}H_{25}NHCH_2CH_2OSO_3Na$, with a 50.% solution of sodium acetate in refluxing alcohol.[360] Aminostilbenes with one or more s-triazine rings per molecule have been prepared[361] and found useful as washing aids.

10. Medicine

A. s-Triazinylquinolines

Products useful as bactericides and in the treatment of diseases caused by protozoa are synthesized from cyanuric chloride and 4,6-diamino-2-methyl-7-methoxyquinoline.[362] Either one or two equivalents of the quinoline derivative may be used and the remaining halogen or halogens replaced by —NH$_2$, —NHR, —NR$_2$, —OH, —OR, etc.

(5)

Example (5) above illustrates the method of preparation used for the group of compounds listed in Table I-5. Cyanuric chloride is the starting compound.

TABLE I–5.   Triazinylquinolines

$$\begin{array}{c} R_6 \diagdown \overset{N}{\diagup} R_2 \\ N \diagdown N \\ R_4 \end{array} \qquad Q = \quad NH - \overset{N}{\diagup} CH_3 \\ NH_2$$

R_2	R_4	R_6	M.p., °C
—NH$_2$	Q	Q	245 (dec.)
—Cl	—Cl	Q	> 300
—NH$_2$	—NH$_2$	Q	267
—NH$_2$	—Cl	Q	> 300
—Cl	Q	Q	> 300
—NEt$_2$	Q	Q	215–220
—NHCH$_2$CH$_2$N Et$_2$	Q	Q	170 (dec.)
—OEt	Q	Q	235 (dec.)
—OH	7—OCH$_3$ Q	7—OCH$_3$ Q	290 (dec.)
—NH$_2$	Q	Q	> 305

B. Metallo-organic s-Triazines

A substantial number of metallo-organic medicinal compounds, principally those of arsenic and antimony, are reported in a series of patents issued to Friedheim. The chemistry of these compounds is mentioned only briefly in this section in connection with their usefulness as therapeutics. A more complete discussion of their chemistry and pharmacology is available in standard textbooks.[363,364]

(1) Arsenicals.   (a) *Types.*   The arsenic containing compounds, which are representative of these metallo-organics, comprise substances in which the s-triazine ring is linked through an amino or hydrazino linkage to an aromatic ring containing one of the following groups: arsine oxide, arsenic dichloride, arsonic acid or arsenobenzene. The aromatic ring is usually a substituted benzene, and the s-triazine ring may have a variety of substituents in the 4- and 6-positions.

(b) *Preparation; Synthetic Methods.*   (1) *Arsine Oxides.*   Halo or amino-s-triazines are condensed with either substituted or unsubstituted arsine oxides to give compounds of therapeutic value in the treatment of spirochetes or trypanosomes.[365] For example, the condensation of 3-amino-4-hydroxybenzenearsine oxide and cyanuric chloride produces 2,4-dichloro-6(2-hydroxy-4-arsine oxide phenylamino)-s-triazine (6).

$$\text{(6)}$$

Equation (6): reaction of cyanuric chloride with an amino-hydroxy-arsine oxide compound at 0°, anhyd.

(2) *Arsonic Acids*. Arsonic acids containing amino groups (arsanilic acids) may be used to produce a series of compounds. For example, cyanuric chloride and the disodium salt of *p*-aminobenzenearsonic acid react[366] in a one to one mole ratio in aqueous media to produce 4(4,6-dichloro-2(1,3,5-triazinyl)amino) benzenearsonic acid (7). The chlorine

$$\text{(7)}$$

Equation (7): cyanuric chloride + AsO_3Na_2-substituted aniline (NH_2 aq.) → triazinyl-NH-benzene-AsO_3HNa + $NaCl$

atoms on the *s*-triazine ring may be replaced[367] by other substituents by methods already discussed. If one amino group is introduced by treatment with 10% ammonia at 45° for one hour, an amphoteric compound insoluble in water, ethanol, benzene, and ether is obtained (8).

$$\text{(8)}$$

Equation (8): Cl,Cl-triazinyl-NH-benzene-AsO_3H_2 $\xrightarrow[\text{1 hr. 45°}]{\text{10\% NH}_4\text{OH}}$ Cl,NH$_2$-triazinyl-NH-benzene-AsO_3H_2

Condensation of cyanuric chloride and 4-amino-3,5-dinitrobenzene-arsanilic acid produces[368] a medicinal (9).

$$\text{(9)}$$

Equation (9): cyanuric chloride + O_2N,NO_2-AsO_3H_2-aniline (NH_2) → triazinyl-NH-benzene(NO_2, NO_2)-AsO_3H_2

Arsonic acid derivatives include position isomers containing benzene ring substituents such as (VI). The arsine oxides and the corresponding arseno compounds are also known.[369,370] Derivatives containing the arsonic acid group have been prepared from the diazonium

H_2N-triazinyl-NHR (NH_2)   where R = benzene-AsO_3H_2,OH or   benzene-AsO_3H_2,OH

(VI)

salt of *p*-aminobenzenearsine oxide and thioammeline at 70° with sodium carbonate.

Arsanilic acids may also be used as starting materials for the preparation of *s*-triazinylhydrazino compounds by the typical reaction[371] sequence (10). The chlorine atoms can be replaced by amino or hydrazino groups by treating the product with ammonia or hydrazine, respectively.

$$\text{(10)}$$

(*c*) *Arsenicals Tabulated.* Table I-6 contains a list of arsine oxides and dichlorides which have been prepared,[368,370] and Table I-7 contains a list of the derivatives[369] of *p*-aminobenzenearsonic acid.

In addition to the aminobenzenearsonic acids, some mercaptobenzenearsonic acids have been prepared.[372] These include the following:

m(4-amino-6-chloro-2-*s*-triazinyl-
mercapto)benzenenearsonic acid

m(4-amino-6-diethylamino-2-*s*-
triazinylmercapto)benzenearsonic acid

3(4-amino-6-methoxy-2-*s*-triazinyl-
mercapto)benzenearsonic acid

p(4,6-dichloro-2-*s*-triazinyl-
mercapto)benzenearsonic acid

(*d*) *Reactions.* The reactions of the *s*-triazinyl arsenicals discussed briefly here are the reactions of groups on the arsenic atom. These derivatives are all related to one another. The oxygen atom of arsine oxides may be replaced by —S, —X_2, or —SR_2 or, more commonly in this series, by two atoms of chlorine. The hydrochloride salts of arsenic

TABLE I–6. Triazinylarsine Oxides and Dichlorides

Benzene ring position	3	5	6
	—NH$_2$	—Cl	—
	—Cl	—Cl	—
	—NO$_2$	—NO$_2$	—
	—NH$_2$	—	—
	—	—	—NH$_2$
	—NH$_2$	—NH$_2$	—

TABLE I–7. Triazinyl-p-aminobenzenearsonic Acids

R	R$_1$
Cl	Cl
Cl	OH
OH	OH
NH$_2$	Cl
NH$_2$	OH
NH$_2$	NH$_2$
NH$_2$	CH$_3$NH
CH$_3$NH	CH$_3$NH
(C$_2$H$_5$)$_2$N	(C$_2$H$_5$)$_2$N
p-arsanilo	Cl
p-arsanilo	NH$_2$
p-sulfanilo	Cl
	Cl

dichlorides result when the oxides are treated with concentrated hydrochloric acid containing a trace of sodium iodide. Sulfur dioxide completes the reaction which is reversible[373] with base (11). Stannous chloride and hydrochloric acid reduce the oxide to a yellow solid believed to have structure (VII).

$$\text{(triazinyl)}\text{—NH—C}_6\text{H}_4\text{(AsO)(OH)} \xrightarrow[\text{then SO}_2]{\text{conc. HCl + trace NaI}} \text{(triazinyl)}\text{—NH—C}_6\text{H}_4\text{(AsCl}_2\cdot\text{HCl)(OH)} \tag{11}$$

$$\xleftarrow{\text{NaOH}}$$

$$\downarrow \begin{array}{c}\text{SnCl}_2\\ \text{HCl}\end{array}$$

$$\left(\text{Cl-triazinyl-Cl}\text{—NH—C}_6\text{H}_3\text{(OH)}\text{—AsH}\right)_2$$

Yellow Solid   (VII)

If an arsine oxide derivative is instead heated with a trace of copper after acidification and is then treated with stannous chloride and iodine, reduction to a substituted arsenobenzene occurs. This is illustrated for p-(4,6-diamino-2-s-triazinylmercapto) arsine oxide (12).

$$2\,\text{H}_2\text{N—(triazinyl)(NH}_2\text{)—S—C}_6\text{H}_4\text{—AsO} \xrightarrow[\text{then SnCl}_2 + \text{I}_2]{\text{H}^+ + \text{Cu} + \Delta} \text{H}_2\text{N—(triazinyl)(NH}_2\text{)—S—C}_6\text{H}_4\text{—As=As—C}_6\text{H}_4\text{—S—(triazinyl)(NH}_2\text{)—NH}_2 \tag{12}$$

The arsenobenzenes are cleaved by a combination of hydrogen chloride, hydrogen iodide and sulfur dioxide to arsenic dichlorides. The dichlorides may be hydrolyzed to the oxides by sodium hydroxide; the chlorides of

$$\text{H}_2\text{N—(triazinyl)(NH}_2\text{)—S—C}_6\text{H}_4\text{—As=As—C}_6\text{H}_4\text{—S—(triazinyl)(NH}_2\text{)—NH}_2 \xrightarrow[\text{then SO}_2]{\text{HCl + HI}} 2\,\text{H}_2\text{N—(triazinyl)(NH}_2\text{)—S—C}_6\text{H}_4\text{—AsCl}_2 \tag{13}$$

substituted thioammelines can be hydrolyzed by ammonia. Arsine oxides can be oxidized to pentavalent arsonic acids by means of hydrogen peroxide (14). If the triazine to phenyl linkage is sulfur instead of

$$\text{H}_2\text{N—(triazinyl)(NH}_2\text{)—NH—C}_6\text{H}_4\text{—AsO} \xrightarrow{\text{H}_2\text{O}_2} \text{H}_2\text{N—(triazinyl)(NH}_2\text{)—NH—C}_6\text{H}_4\text{—AsO}_3\text{H}_2 \tag{14}$$

nitrogen, oxidation at this point also occurs and sulfoxides and sulfones are obtained.

The pentavalent arsonic acids can be[374] reduced to trivalent arsenic dichlorides or arsine oxides by the following reagents: sulfur dioxide, phosphorous acid, phenylhydrazine, and stannous chloride with hydrochloric acid and a trace of sodium iodide.

(2) Cyclic Disulfides with Arsenic and Antimony. Friedheim[353a] recently prepared a series of compounds containing arsenic and antimony as part of a dithiocyclopentane ring. The general method used for synthesis in this series, consists in treating the reaction product from the condensation of sodium p-(4,6-diamino-s-triazinyl-2) aminostilbonate and ammonium thioglycollate with 2,3-dimercaptopropanol for ten minutes at room temperature. Yields are reported[353a] to exceed 90%. The product (VIIa) of the reaction reduces Fehling's solution

(VIIa)

slowly on heating in aqueous suspension. It shows a negative nitroprusside test which becomes faint if the compound has been treated with sodium carbonate and strong after treatment with caustic soda.

This class of compounds is reported to be effective in the T. equiperdum infection in mice, with a therapeutic index in the case of product (VIIa) of fifty.[353a] The compounds prepared in this series are listed in Table I-8.

TABLE I-8. Cyclic s-Triazinyl Disulfides Involving Arsenic and Antimony[111a]

M	R	Physical properties: solubility
Sb	CH$_2$OH	M.p. 175°–200° (dec.). Insol. water, ethyl alc., ether. Sol. 10% propylene glycol forming a sol'n. stable > 3 week at 80°
As	CH$_2$OH	Sol. propylene glycol. Insol. water, cold ethyl or methyl alc.
Sb	CH$_2$COOH	Sol. aq. Na$_2$CO$_3$. Insol. water, ethyl alc., ether.
As	CH$_2$OC$_2$H$_5$	Sol. warm propylene glycol. Insol. water.
As	O-glucoside	Sol. water. Insol. ether, chloroform, benzene
As	CH$_2$OH	Sol. propylene glycol. Insol. water
(2-OH group on C$_6$ ring; As in 5-position)		

(3) Antimony. Antimony has been used in much the same manner as arsenic to prepare medicinals containing the s-triazinyl group. Although the number of antimony compounds is not nearly so large, the chemistry and the structure of the compounds of the two series are very similar.

Cyanuric chloride and stilbonic acid react to give a 40% yield of p-(2,4-diamino-s-triazine-6-ylamino)-benzenestilbonic acid (15).[373] This

compound has a pronounced prophylactic effect on typansoma equiperdum. However, if its octahydrated sodium salt is heated in 40% urea, a polymeric sodium salt is obtained which shows a four fold increase in typanocidal activity and a seventeen fold decrease in toxicity, as compared with the original compound.

Methylamine instead of ammonia may be added to the intermediate giving[375] p-(2,4-dimethylamino-1,3,5-triazin-6-ylamino)-ben-

(VIII)

zenestilbonic acid (VIII), a compound effective in treating experimental mouse typanosomiasis.

(4) Other Metals. A number of related phosphorous, selenium and mercury compounds prepared by[376] the methods described above are listed in Table I-9. They are reported to be effective also against experimental trypanosomiasis.

TABLE I–9. Triazinyl Organo-Metallics
(Exclusive of Arsenic)
Group A-Amino Linkages

X	Y	R
Cl	Cl	SbO_3H_2
Cl	NH_2	SbO_3H_2
NH_2	NH_2	SbO_3H_2
Cl	Cl	HgCl
NH_2NH	NH_2NH	HgOAc
Cl	Cl	SeO_3H (meta position)

Group B-Hydrazino Linkages

X	Y	R
Cl	Cl	PO_3H_2
Cl	Cl	SbO_3H_2
Cl	Cl	HgCl

References

1. C. Scheele, *Samtliche physische und chemische Werke*, S. Fr. Hermbstädt, Vol. II, Berlin, 1793, p. 149; through *Beilstein*, 26, 239.
1a. C. Grundmann, and A. Kreutzberger, *J. Am. Chem. Soc.*, 76, 632 (1954).
2. L. Pauling and J. Sturdivant, *Proc. Acad. Sci.*, 23, 615 (1937).
3. H. Brandenberger and R. Brandenberger, *Helv. Chim. Acta*, 37, 2201 (1954).
4. K. Lonsdale, *Proc. Roy. Soc. London*, 1937, 149.
5. A. Pullman, *Rev. sci.*, 86, 219 (1948).
6. A. Chevallier and J-L. Lassaigne, *Ann. chim. phys.*, (2), 13, 159 (1820).
7. Serullas, *Ann. chim. phys.*, (2), 38, 379 (1828).
8. F. Wohler, *Ann. chim. phys.*, (2), 43, 76 (1830).
9. J. Liebig and F. Wohler, *Ann. Phys. Chem.*, 20, 369 (1835).
10. J. Liebig, *Ann.*, 95, 264 (1855).
11. E. Drechsel, *J. prakt. Chem.*, (2), 11, 289 (1875).
12. J. Liebig, *Ann.*, 10, 32 (1834).
13. A. Hantzsch and H. Bauer, *Ber.*, 38, 1005 (1905).
14. E. Billows, *Z. Krystallographie Mineral*, 46, 481 (1908).
15. H. Schiff, *Ann.*, 291, 375 (1896).
16. G. Beck, *Chem.-Ztg.*, 46, 18 (1943).
17. L. Trooste and P. Hautefeuille, *Compt. rend.*, 69, 50 (1869).
18. H. Schroder, *Ber.*, 13, 1072 (1880).

19. P. Lemoult, *Compt. rend.*, **121**, 351 (1895).
20. L. Trooste and P. Hautefeuille, *Jahr. Chem.*, **1869**, 59.
21. P. Lemoult, *Ann. chim. phys.*, (7), **16**, 338 (1849).
22. A. Hantzsch, *Ber.*, **39**, 145 (1906).
23. E. Wightman and H. Jones, *Am. Chem. J.*, **46**, 103 (1911).
24. J. Boeseken, *Rec. trav. chim.*, **37**, 147 (1917).
25. A. Dunstan and A. Mussell, *J. Chem. Soc.*, **97**, 1939 (1910).
26. M. Padoa, *Atti accad. nazl. Lincei*, **29**, II, 198 (1920).
27. S. Siddhauta and P. Ray, *J. Indian Chem. Soc.*, **20**, 359 (1943).
28. J. Maruha, *J, Chem. Soc. Japan*, Pure Chem. Sect., **71**, 627 (1950); through *Chem. Abstracts*, **45**, 9067 (1951).
29. Z. Kahovec and K. Kohlrausch, *Z. physik. Chem.*, **193**, 188 (1944).
30. A. Roosena, *Bull. soc. chim. Belges*, **59**, 377 (1950); through *Chem. Abstracts*, **45**, 4137 (1951).
31. E. Billows, *Z. Krystallographie Minerol.*, **46**, 481 (1908).
32. Voit, *Ann.*, **132**, 223 (1864).
33. Schabus, *Jahr. chem.*, **1854**, 375.
34. P. Groth, *Chemische Krystallographie*, Leipzig, **1910**, Part III, p. 563.
35. A. Hantzsch, *Z. physik. Chem.*, **61**, 281 (1908).
36. A. Hantzsch and K. Caldwell, *Z. physik. Chem.*, **61**, 232 (1908).
37. M. Gouy, *Ann. chim. phys.*, (8), **8**, 334 (1906).
38. R. Bader, *Z. physik. Chem.*, **6**, 310 (1890).
39. H. Schroeder, *Ber.*, 13, 1072 (1880).
40. C. Ichakawa, *J. Agr. Chem. Soc. Japan*, **12**, 898 (1936).
41. L. Wise and E. Walters, *J. Agr. Res.*, **10**, 85 (1917).
42. S. Kasugai and S. Ozaki, *J. Sci. Agr. Soc.* (*Japan*), **232**, 1 (1922).
43. H. Fierz-David and M. Matter, *J. Soc. Dyers* and *Colourists*, **53**, 424 (1937).
44. American Cyanamid Co., *Cyanuric Chloride*, New Product Bulletin.
45. A. Eghis, *Ber.*, **2**, 159 (1869).
46. L. Gatterman and A. Rossolymo, *Ber.*, **23**, 1192 (1890).
47. P. Klason, *J. prakt. Chem.*, (2), **33**, 129 (1886).
48. H. Williams, *Cyanogen Compounds*, 2nd Ed., Arnold & Co., London, **1948**, p. 74.
49. E. Werner, *J. Chem. Soc.*, **103**, 1010 (1913).
50. A. Senier and Walsh, *J. Chem. Soc.*, **81**, 290 (1902).
51. E. Werner and W. Fearon, *J. Chem. Soc.*, **117**, 1357 (1920).
52. E. Werner and W. Fearon, *J. Chem. Soc.*, **103**, 2275 (1913).
53. H. Werner and J. Gray, *Proc. Roy. Soc. Dublin*, **24**, 209 (1947).
53a. K. Suchy, *Sbornik Mezinarod. Polarog. Sjezdu Praze*, 1st Congr., 1951, Pt. 1, Proc. 718, through *Chem. Abstracts*, **46**, 10959 (1952).
54. C. Weltzein, *Ann.*, **132**, 222 (1864).
55. N. Sidgwick, *The Organic Chemistry of Nitrogen*, Oxford Univ. Press, Oxford, 1945, p. 323.
56. F. Wohler, *Ann. Physik. Chem.*, **15**, 622 (1829).
57. C. Weltzein, *Ann.*, **107**, 219 (1858).
58. C. Weltzein, *Ann.*, **107**, 220 (1858).
59. A. F. Holleman, *Textbook of Organic Chemistry*, 4th Ed., John Wiley & Sons, New York, p. 356.
60. J. Das Gupta, *J. Indian Chem. Soc.*, II, 207 (1934).
61. G. Roosler and H. Scheuermann, Ger. 865,306 (1953) to Badische Anilin-und Soda-Fabrik.
62. A. Werner and J. Gray, *Sci. Proc. Roy. Soc. Dublin*, **26**, 111 (1946).

63. R. Haworth and F. Mann, *J. Chem. Soc.*, **1943**, 603.
64. A. Wurtz, *Compt. rend.*, **24**, 436 (1847).
65. F. Koduris, *Ann. Physik. Chem.*, **19**, 11 (1830).
66. A. Wurtz, *Ann.*, **64**, 307 (1847).
67. A. Behal, *Bull. soc. chim.*, (4), **15**, 149 (1914).
68. E. de Vry, *Ann.*, **61**, 249 (1847).
69. H. Schiff, *Ann.*, **299**, 238 (1898).
70. R. von Walther, *J. prakt. Chem.*, (2), **79**, 126 (1909).
71. C. Hands and F. Whitt, *J. Soc. Chem. Ind.*, **67**, 66 (1948).
72. J. MacKay, U.S. 2,527,316, (1950) to American Cyanamid Co.
73. J. Boeseken and J. Langezaal, *Rec. trav. chim.*, **29**, 332 (1910).
74. K. Pfister, U.S. 1,752,998 (1930) to Rohm & Haas & Co.
75. J. Pelonze, *Ann.*, **44**, 106 (1842).
76. J. Pelonze, *Ann. chim. phys.*, (3), **6**, 69 (1842).
77. S. Wiedemann, *Ann. Physik.*, **74**, 67, 81 (1848).
78. S. Wiedemann, *J. prakt. chem.*, (1), **43**, 274 (1848).
79. C. Finckh, *Ann.*, **124**, 333 (1862).
80. C. Bamberger, *Ber.*, **23**, 1861 (1890).
81. E. Schmidt, *J. prakt. Chem.*, (2), **5**, 41 (1872).
82. F. Kruzer, *J. Chem. Soc.*, **1951**, 1258.
83. C. Venable and F. Moore, *J. Am. Chem. Soc.*, **39**, 1750 (1917).
84. C. Venable, *J. Am. Chem. Soc.*, **40**, 1099 (1918).
85. M. Scholtz, *Ber.*, **34**, 4130 (1901).
86. F. Moore and R. Thomas, *J. Am. Chem. Soc.*, **40**, 1124 (1918).
87. E. Theis, Fr. 769,920 (1934) to I.G. Farbenind.; Brit. 416,599 (1934) to I.G. Farbenind.; Ger. 607,663 (1935), to I.G. Farbenind.; U.S. 2,045,111 (1936), to I.G. Farbenind.
88. E. Steigerwald, Ger. 620,906 (1935) to I.G. Farbenind.; Brit. 443,119 (1936), to I.G. Farbenind.; Fr. 46,196 (1936), to I.G. Farbenind.
89. R. Slocombe, E. Hardy, J. Saunders and R. Jenkins, *J. Am. Chem. Soc.*, **72**, 1888 (1950).
90. V. Marecek, *Chem. Obzor*, **23**, 217 (1948).
91. D. Brundrit, and Imperial Chem. Ind. Ltd. Brit. 570,715 (1945).
92. G. Schroter and M. Lewinski, *Ber.*, **26**, 2173 (1893).
92a. S. Hartman and J. Fellig, *J. Am. Chem. Soc.*, **77**, 1051 (1955).
93. E. A. Werner and A. E. Werner, *Proc. Roy Soc. Dublin*, **23**, 137 (1943).
94. H. Freyermuth and C. Raiford, *Proc. Ia. Acad. Sci.*, **48**, 248 (1941).
95. F. Davis and C. Kidwell, *J. Am. Chem. Soc.*, **41**, 1004 (1919).
96. K. Schaum and H. Schneider, *Ber.*, **56B**, 2460 (1923).
97. H. Schiff and V. Monsacchi, *Ann.*, **288**, 316 (1885).
98. H. Bechurts and G. Frerichs, *J. prakt. Chem.*, **66**, 177 (1902).
99. J. Liebig, *Ann.*, **95**, 268 (1855).
100. W. Henneberg, *Ann.*, **73**, 243 (1850).
101. M. Striegler, *J. prakt. Chem.*, (2), **33**, 164 (1886).
102. J. Liebig, *Ann.*, **10**, 7 (1834).
103. F. Knapp, *Ann.*, **21**, 251 (1837).
104. M. Nencki, *Ber.*, **9**, 235 (1876).
105. A. Hofmann and O. Ehrhart, *Ber.*, **45**, 2735 (1912).
106. A. Gossmann, *Ann.*, **99**, 375 (1856).
107. A. Claus, *Ann.*, **179**, 160 (1875).
108. A. Goldberg, *J. prakt. Chem.*, (2), **63**, 475 (1901).
109. P. Klason, *J. prakt. Chem.*, (2), **33**, 286 (1886).

110. A. Pumier, *Ber.*, **14**, 1083 (1881).
111. H. Debus, *Ann.*, **72**, 18, 20 (1849).
112. M. Schenck, *Ber.*, **38**, 461 (1905).
113. M. Gomberg and H. Berger, *Ber.*, **36**, 1099 (1903).
114. J. Herzig, *Ber.*, **12**, 175 (1879).
114a. N. Gaylord and C. Sroog, *J. Org. Chem.*, **18**, 1632 (1953).
115. B. Bottcher and F. Bauer, *Ber.*, **84**, 289 (1951).
116. P. Pascal, *Compt. rend.*, **176**, 1887 (1923).
117. L. Troost and P. Hautefeuille, *Jahr. Chem.*, **1868**, 315.
118. L. Troost, *Compt. rend.*, **67**, 1347 (1868).
119. C. Weltzein, *Ann.*, **132**, 222 (1864).
120. W. Hartley, *J. Chem. Soc.*, **41**, 48 (1882).
121. W. Hartley, J. Dobbie and A. Lander, *J. Chem. Soc.*, **79**, 855 (1910).
122. H. Blitz, *Ber.*, **72B**, 807 (1939).
123. I. Klotz and T. Askonnis, *J. Am. Chem. Soc.*, **69**, 801 (1947).
124. A. Castille and E. Ruppol, *Bull. soc. chim. biol.*, **10**, 623 (1928).
125. E. Agallidis, H. Fromberg and A. Hartzmann, *Ber.*, **71B**, 1391 (1938).
126. R. Hirt, *Symposium on Molecular Structure and Spectroscopy*, The Ohio State U., June, 1950.
127. R. Hirt and R. Schmitt, *Spectrochemica Acta*, in press.
128. E. Hughes, *J. Am. Chem. Soc.*, **63**, 1750 (1941).
129. E. Wiebenga, *J. Am. Chem. Soc.*, **74**, 6156 (1952).
130. K. Lonsdale, *Proc. Roy. Soc. Dunlin*, **1941**, 272.
131. A. Pullman, *Rev. sci.*, **86**, 219 (1948).
132. A. Hantzsch, *Z. anorg. Chem.*, **209**, 218 (1932).
133. A. Hofmann and A. Fock, *Ber.*, **19**, 2065 (1886).
134. E. Drechsel, *J. prakt. Chem.*, (2), **16**, 207 (1877).
134a. M. Ito, *Bull. Chem. Soc. Japan*, **26**, 339 (1953).
135. A. Perret and A. Krawczynski, *Helv. Chim. Acta*, **15**, 1009 (1932).
136. F. Beilstein, *Ann.*, **116**, 357 (1860).
137. R. Haworth and F. Mann, *J. Chem. Soc.*, **1943**, 603.
138. Brit. 598,175, (1948) to American Cyanamid Co.
139. J. Ponomarew, *Ber.*, **18**, 3261 (1885).
140. A. Senier, *Ber.*, **19**, 311 (1886).
141. J. Ponomarew, *Ber.*, **18**, 3273 (1885).
141a. R. Newman and R. Badger, *J. Am. Chem. Soc.*, **74**, 3545 (1952).
142. W. Kaplan, U.S. 2,444,828 (1948) to Sun Chem. Co.
143. R. Kruger, *J. prakt. Chem.*, (2), **42**, 473 (1891).
144. R. Bonnet, *Compt. rend.*, **198**, 1880 (1934).
145. L. Trooste and P. Hautefeuille, *Compt. rend.*, **69**, 48 (1869).
146. L. Dieke, G. Allen and C. Richter, *J. Pharmacol.*, **90**, 260 (1947).
147. H. Schwarz, *India Rubber World*, **114**, 211, 219 (1946).
148. Brit. 420,525 (1934) to I.G. Farbenind.
149. E. Theis, Ger. 613,629 (1935) to I.G. Farbenind.
150. A. Reiche, W. Rudolph and R. Klar, U.S. 2,266,265 (1942) to I.G. Farbenind.
151. A. Gautier, *Ann.*, **141**, 122 (1867).
152. J. Liebig, *Pogg. Ann.*, **15**, 359, 622 (1829).
153. O. Diels, *Ber.*, **32**, 691 (1899).
154. F. Chattaway and J. Wadmore, *J. Chem. Soc.*, **81**, 191 (1902).
155. P. Lemoult, *Compt. rend.*, **123**, 1276 (1896).
156. G. Costa, R. Hirt and D. Salley, *J. Chem. Phys.*, **18**, 434 (1950).

157. H. Halverson and R. Hirt, *J, Chem. Phys.*, **19**, 711 (1951).
158. H. Finger, *J. prakt. Chem.*, (2), **75**, 103 (1907).
159. W. Oldham, U.S. 2,417,659 (1947) to American Cyanamid Co.
160. V. Migridichian, Can. 399,464 (1941) to American Cyanamid Co.
161. J. Thurston, U.S. 2,416,656 (1947) to American Cyanamid Co.
162. Brit. 602,816 (1948) to American Cyanamid Co.
163. T. Metcalfe and Imperial Chem. Ind. Ltd. Brit. 566,827 (1945).
164. H. Schulz and H. Huemer, *Research and Production, 1953*, 454.
165. R. Hartigan, U.S. 2,541,053 (1951) to Koppers Co.
165a. G. O'Neal, U.S. 2,668,152 (1945) to The Sherwin-Williams Co.
166. P. Klason, *J. prakt. Chem.*, (2), **34**, 157 (1886).
167. H. Fries, *Ber.*, **19**, 2056 (1886).
167a. C. Witschonke, *Anal. Chem.*, **26**, 562 (1954).
168. A. Cahours, *Ann.*, **61**, 95 (1847).
169. Riche, *Ann.*, **92**, 357 (1864).
170. W. James, *J. Chem. Soc.*, **1887**, 268 and *J. prakt. Chem.*, (2), **35**, 459 (1887).
171. E. Ott, *Ber.*, **52**, 656 (1919).
172. F. Chattaway and J. Wadmore, *J. Chem. Soc.*, **81**, 200 (1902).
173. E. von Mayer and F. Nabe, *J. prakt. Chem.*, (2), **82**, 521 (1916).
174. P. Klason, *J. prakt. Chem.*, (2), **34**, 152 (1886).
175. J. Liebig, *Ann.*, **10**, 1, 7 (1834).
176. O. Diels and M. Liebermann, *Ber.*, **36**, 3191 (1903).
177. A. Hofmann, *Ber.*, **19**, 2061 (1886).
178. J. Dudley et al., *J. Am. Chem. Soc.*, **73**, 2986 (1951).
179. F. Schaefer, J. Thurston and J. Dudley, *J. Am. Chem. Soc.*, **73**, 2990 (1951).
180. E. Ott, *Ber.*, **20**, 2236 (1887).
181. Fr. 687,301 (1930); through *Chem. Abstracts*, **25**, 812 (1931) to Ciba, Ltd.
181a. C. Grundmann and E. Beyer, *J. Am. Chem. Soc.*, **76**, 1948 (1954).
182. C. Banks, O. Gruhzit, E. Tillitson and J. Controulis, *J. Am. Chem. Soc.*, **66**, 1771 (1944).
183. W. Cuthbertson and J. Moffatt, *J. Chem. Soc.*, **1948**, 563.
184. E. Friedheim, *J. Am. Chem. Soc.*, **66**, 1725 (1944).
185. U.S. 2,295,574 (1942); through *Chem. Abstracts*, **37**, 1228 (1943); U.S. 2,390,092 (1945); through *Chem. Abstracts*, **41**, 162 (1947); U.S. 2,390,089 (1945); through *Chem. Abstracts*, **41**, 160 (1947); U.S. 2,390,090 (1945); through *Chem. Abstracts*, **41**, 162 (1947).
186. U.S. 2,390,529 (1945); through *Chem. Abstracts*, **40**, 5070 (1946).
187. U.S. 2,422,724 (1947); through *Chem. Abstracts*, **41**, 6900 (1947).
188. H. Fries, *Ber.*, **19**, 242 (1886).
189. A. Fritzsche, E. Krummenacher, H. Gubler and O. Kaiser, U.S. 1,625,530 (1927); through *Chem. Abstracts*, **21**, 2193 (1927).
190. J. Liebig, *Ann.*, **10**, 1 (1834).
191. A. Hofmann, *Ber.*, **18**, 2755 (1885).
192. Brit. 598,175 (1948) to American Cyanamid Co.
193. F. Naebe, *J. prakt. Chem.*, (2), **82**, 521 (1916).
194. G. D'Alelio, U.S. 2,393,755 (1946); through *Chem. Abstracts*, **40**, 2166 (1946).
195. G. D'Alelio and J. Underwood, U.S. 2,328,961 (1948); through *Chem. Abstracts*, **38**, 1305 (1944).
196. G. D'Alelio, U.S. 2,312,698 (1942); through *Chem. Abstracts*, **37**, 4831 (1943).
197. G. D'Alelio and J. Underwood, U.S. 2,295,565 (1942); through *Chem. Abstracts*, **37**, 1131 (1943).
198. G. D'Alelio, U.S. 2,394,042 (1946); through *Chem. Abstracts*, **40**, 3144 (1946).

199. J. Biechler, *Compt. rend.*, **203**, 568 (1936).
200. M. Dahlen and R. Pingree, P.B. Report 1576 Bibliography of Scientific and Industrial Reports 1, p. 174 (1946).
201. L. Sauere, *Ber.*, **83**, 335 (1950).
202. A. Hofmann, *Ber.*, **18**, 2196 (1885).
203. G. D'Alelio and J. Underwood, U.S. 2,295,561 (1942); through *Chem. Abstracts*, **37**, 1131 (1943).
204. G. D'Alelio and J. Underwood, U.S. 2,295,562 (1942); through *Chem. Abstracts*, **37**, 1131 (1943).
205. C. Taylor and W. Rinkenbach, *Bur. Mines Repts. of Invest. No. 2513* (1923).
206. H. Finger, *J. prakt. Chem.*, (2), **75**, 103 (1907).
207. W. Hentrich and W. Hardtmann, U.S. 1,911,689 (1933); through *Chem. Abstracts*, **27**, 3952 (1933).
208. R. Hirt, H. Nidecker and R. Berchtold, *Helv. Chem. Acta*, **33**, 1365 (1950).
209. A. Ostrogovitch, *Chem. Ztg.*, **36**, 738 (1912).
210. F. Krafft, *Ber.*, **22**, 1759 (1889).
211. P. Klason, *J. prakt. Chem.*, (2), **35**, 82 (1887).
212. G. Barsky and I. Giles, U.S. 1,734,029 (1929); through *Chem. Abstracts*, **24**, 381 (1930) to American Cyanamid Co.
213. K. Schmidt and O. Wahl, U.S. 2,232,871 (1941) to Gen'l Aniline and Film Co. through *Chem. Abstracts*, **35**, 7102 (1941).
214. W. Kolb, *J. prakt. Chem.*, (2), **49**, 90 (1894).
215. P. Klason, *J. prakt. Chem.*, (2), **33**, 121 (1886).
216. A. Burger and E. Hornbaker, *J. Am. Chem. Soc.*, **75**, 4579 (1953).
217. J. Thurston, F. Schaefer, J. Dudley and D. Holm-Hansen, *J. Am. Chem. Soc.*, **73**, 2992 (1951).
218. M. Goldblatt, *Brit. J. Ind. Med.*, **2**, 183 (1945).
219. Serullas, *Ann. Physik. Chem.*, (2), **34**, 100 (1828).
220. A. Eghis, *Ber.*, **2**, 159 (1869).
221. E. Mulder, *Rec. trav. chim.*, **5**, 84 (1886).
222. V. Merz and W. Weith, *Ber.*, **16**, 2893 (1883).
223. L. Gattermann and A. Rossolymo, *Ber.*, **23**, 1192 (1890).
224. A. Perret and R. Perrot, *Bull. soc. chim.*, **7**, 743 (1940).
225. L. Birkenbach and M. Linhard, *Ber.*, **63B**, 2528 (1930).
226. American Cyanamid Co., unpublished data.
227. H. Williams, *"Cyanogen Compounds"*, Edward Arnold and Co., London, 2nd Ed., 1948, p. 12.
228. P. Kailasam, *Proc. Indian. Acad. Sci.*, **14A**, 165 (1941); through *Chem. Abstracts*, **36**, 2493 (1942).
228a. H. Callomon and H. Thompson, F. Andersen and B. Bak, *J. Chem. Soc.*, **1953**, 3709.
229. A. Hofmann and O. Olshausen, *Ber.*, **3**, 369 (1870).
230. H. Wheeler, P. Walden and H. Metcalf, *Am. Chem. J.*, **20**, 68 (1898).
231. Swiss 106,407 (1924) to Ciba.
232. E. Bilmann and J. Bjerrum, *Ber.*, **50**, 503 (1917).
233. K. Slotta, and R. Tschesche, *Ber.*, **60**, 301 (1927).
233a. W. Huckel, *Nachr. Akad. Wiss. Gottingen Math.-Physik Klasse*, **1**, 36 (1946).
234. H. Schiff, *Ann.*, **291**, 371 (1896).
235. H. Slotta and R. Tschesche, *Ber.*, **60B**, 295 (1927).
236. Swiss 106,116 (1924) to Ciba.
237. N. Sidgwick, *The Organic Chemistry of Nitrogen*, New Edition, Oxford University Press, Oxford, 1945, p. 344.

238. A. Hantzsch, *Z. anorg. Chem.*, **209**, 213 (1932).
239. A. Hofmann, *Ber.*, **19**, 2082 (1883).
240. A. Hofmann, *Ber.*, **18**, 2796 (1885).
241. T. Sutton, *Phil. Mag.*, **15**, 1001 (1933).
242. A. Wurtz, *Compt. rend.*, **26**, 368 (1848).
242a. J. Hohmann, Doctoral Dissertation, State U. of Iowa, 1953.
243. E. Mulder, *Rec. trav. chim.*, **1**, 191 (1882).
244. E. Mulder, *Ber.*, **16**, 390 (1883).
245. E. Mulder, *Rec. trav. chim.*, **1**, 63 (1882).
246. E. Mulder, *Rec. trav. chim.*, **3**, 287 (1884).
247. E. Mulder, *Rec. trav. chim.*, **4**, 91, 148 (1885).
248. E. Mulder, *Ber.*, **15**, 70 (1882).
249. J. Ponomarew, *Ber.*, **15**, 513 (1882).
250. A. Wurtz, *Ann.*, **71**, 326 (1849).
251. A. Habich and H. Limpricht, *Ann.*, **109**, 101 (1859).
252. E. Mulder, *Ber.*, **16**, 2763 (1883).
253. E. Mulder, *Rec. trav. chim.*, **2**, 133 (1883).
254. C. Crymble, A. Stewart, R. Wright and F. Rea, *J. Chem. Soc.*, **99**, 1268 (1911).
255. A. Hofmann, *Ber.*, **19**, 2077 (1886).
256. W. Kesting, *J. prakt. Chem.*, (2), **105**, 242 (1923).
257. R. Otto and J. Troeger, *Ber.*, **23**, 767 (1890).
258. P. Guha, S. Rao and A. Saletore, *J. Indian. Chem. Soc.*, **6**, 565 (1929); through *Chem. Abstracts*, **24**, 1113 (1930).
259. American Cyanamid Company, New Product Bulletin, *"Triallyl Cyanurate"*.
260. J. Dudley, U.S. 2,510,564 (1950) to American Cyanamid Co.
261. H. Huemer, Ger. 854,801 (1952) to Deutsche Gold u. Silberscheidenstadt.
262. E. Kropa, U.S. 2,577,667 (1951) to American Cyanamid Co.
263. M. Spielman, N. Close and I. Wilk, *J. Am. Chem. Soc.*, **73**, 1775 (1951).
264. E. Kropa, U.S. 2,510,503 (1951) to American Cyanamid Co.
265. E. Kropa, U.S. 2,443,740 (1948) to American Cyanamid Co.
266. W. Hentrich, E. Schwim and R. Endres, U.S. 2,306,440 (1942).
267. A. Hofmann, *Ber.*, **19**, 2081 (1886).
268. D. Kaiser, Can. 473,960 (1951) to American Cyanamid Co.
269. A. Hantzsch and L. Mai, *Ber.*, **28**, 2466 (1895).
270. H. Schiff, *Ber.*, **3**, 650 (1870).
271. F. Schaefer, U.S. 2,560,824 (1951) to American Cyanamid Co.
272. A. Hofmann, *Ber.*, **18**, 764 (1885).
273. J. Nef, *Ann.*, **287**, 319, 321 (1895).
274. H. Tieckelmann and H. Post, *J. Org. Chem.*, **13**, 268 (1948).
275. R. Otto, *Ber.*, **20**, 2236 (1887).
275a. R. Hirt, H. Nidecker and R. Berchtold, *Helv. Chim. Acta*, **33**, 1365 (1950).
276. Brit. 334,887 (1929) to I.G. Farbenind.
277. W. Hentrich, U.S. 1,904,229 (1933) to I.G. Farbenind. through *Chem. Abstracts*, **27**, 3225 (1933).
278. C. Taylor and W. Rinkenbach, *Bur. Mines Repts. of Investig. No. 2513* (1923).
279. E. Ott and E. Ohse, *Ber.*, **54B**, 179 (1921).
280. H. Kast and A. Haid, *Zeit. Chem.*, **38**, 43 (1924).
281. E. Ott, U.S. 1,390,378 (1922).
282. Brit. 170,359 (1920 to Ciba).
283. E. Ott, Ger. 343,794 (1921); 346,811 (1921); 350,564 (1922); 352,223 (1922).
283a. F. Bowden and H. Williams, *Proc. Roy. Soc. London*, **A208**, 176 (1951).

284. E. Ott, Ger. 355,926 (1952).
285. T. Sutton, *Nature*, **128**, 872 (1931).
286. N. Bragg, *Nature*, **134**, 138 (1934).
287. E. Hughes, *J. Chem. Phys.*, **3**, 1 (1935).
288. I. Knaggs, *J. Chem. Phys.*, **3**, 241 (1935).
290. I. Knaggs, *Proc. Roy. Soc. London*, **A150**, 576 (1935).
292. C. Hart, *J. Am. Chem. Soc.*, **50**, 1922 (1928).
293. F. Olsen, *Army Ordnance*, **3**, 269 (1923).
294. L. Birckenbach, E. Buchner, K. Kraus and E. Kayser, *Ber.*, **73B**, 1153 (194).
295. K. Murofushi and R. Ashikawa, *J. Chem. Soc. Japan*, **52**, 12 (1949); through *Chem. Abstracts*, **45**, 1444 (1951).
295a. A. Yoffe, *Proc. Roy. Soc. London*, **A208**, 188 (1951).
296. J. Gillis, *Chem. Weekbl.*, **15**, 73 (1918).
297. A. Hofmann, *Ber.*, **13**, 1351 (1880).
297a. G. Loughran and E. Hook, U.S. 2,676,151 to American Cyanamid Co.
298. J. Obermeyer, *Ber.*, **20**, 2918 (1887).
299. A. Hofmann, *Ber.*, **18**, 2758 (1885).
300. E. Buchanan, A. Reims and H. Sargent, *J. Org. Chem.*, **6**, 764 (1941).
301. W. Heintz, *Ann.*, **136**, 223 (1865).
302. P. Klason, *Ber.*, **14**, 732 (1881).
302a. H. Park and H. Walter, U.S. 2,579,442 (1951) to Monsanto Chemical Co. through *Chem. Abstracts*, **46**, 3326 (1952).
303. A. Hantzsch and H. Schwaneberg, *Ber.*, **61B**, 1776 (1928).
303a. H. Coover, U.S. 2,685,581 to Eastman Kodak Co.
304. H. Stolte, *Ber.*, **19**, 1578 (1886).
305. J. Boyle, *Ind. Chemist*, **15**, 331 (1939).
306. K. Venkataraman, *The Chemistry of Synthetic Dyes*, Academic Press Inc., New York, 1952, p. 583.
307. K. Venkataraman, *The Chemistry of Synthetic Dyes*, Academic Press Inc., New York, 1952, p. 587.
308. M. Crossley, *Am. Dyestuff Reptr.*, **27**, 127 (1938). Swiss 228,371–374 to J. R. Geigy, A.-G. (1943). The following patents to Ciba: Swiss 217,958–967 (1942), Swiss 228,936 (1944), Swiss 232,296 (1944), Swiss 239,342–345 (1945), Swiss 240,225 (1946) and U.S. 2,460,618 (1949).
309. Brit. 541,968 to Ciba (1941).
310. An incomplete list of these patents is given below.
    To Ciba: Swiss patents: 103,430 (1924); 106,074–106,117, 119 (1924); 106,383–389, 394–399, 406–409 (1924); 131,494 (1929); 137,932–938 (1930); 217,948–949, 958–967 (1941), through *Chem. Abstracts*, **43**, 4479 (1949); 221,142–143, 148 (1942), through *Chem. Abstracts*, **43**, 4472 (1949); 221,205 (1942); 222,142–143 (1942); 225,560 (1943); 231,407 (1944); 232,296 (1944), through *Chem. Abstracts*, **43**, 4472 (1949); 233,845 (1944); 236, 428–531 (1945); 236,586 (1946); 237,397 (1945); 239,342–235 (1946); 240,115–126, 225 (1946); 242,159, 841,995 (1946); 244,053, 601 (1947); 245,576 (1947); 246,424–427 (1947). German patents: 485,185 (1929); 538,579 (1931); 632,752 (1936); 636,283 (1936). British patents: 546,710 (1942); 578,014 (1946), through, *Chem. Abstracts*, **42**, 4760 (1948); 558,103 (1947), through, *Chem. Abstracts*, **41**, 6055 (1947); 606,872 (1948); 608,897 (1948), through, *Chem. Abstracts*, **43**, 8159 (1949); 619,688 (1949), through, *Chem. Abstracts*, **43**, 8160 (1949). U. S. patents: 1,625,530–533 (1927); 1,667,312 (1928); 1,867,541 (1932); 2,041,829 (1936); O. Kaiser, 2,396,659 (1946), through, *Chem. Abstracts*, **40**, 3905 (1946); O. Kaiser, 2,387,997 (1945), through, *Chem. Abstracts*, **40**,

1041 (1946); E. Moser, 2,399,447 (1946), through, *Chem. Abstracts*, **40,** 2,467,621 (1949). French patent: 747,651 (1933).

J. R. Geigy Patents: Swiss patents: 239,758 (1946); 244,250, 253–254 (1946); 228,371–374 (1943). British patent: W. Graves, 543,182 (1942); 616,523 (1949), through, *Chem. Abstracts*, **44,** 10329 (1950). U. S. patents: E. Keller, 2,390,152 (1945), through, *Chem. Abstracts*, **40,** 2638 (1946). E. Keller and R. Zweidler, 2,368,844 (1945). E. Keller and R. Zweidler, 2,459,435 (1949), through, *Chem. Abstracts*, **44,** 4686 (1950).

I.G. Farbenindustrie Patent: Brit. 300,987 (1929).

Independent patent: R. Schmid and E. Moser, U. S. 2,399,066 (1946), through, *Chem. Abstracts*, **41,** 6055 (1947).

311. *Ciba patents:* Swiss 97,059 (1924); 100,397 (1924); 101,405 (1924); 104,011–014,713 (1924); 108,210–216,856–857 (1925); 112,533–537 (1925); 114,1834 (1925); 116,076–077 (1926). Ger. 390,201 (1924); 399,485 (1925). Brit. 205,525 (1923); 223,911 (1923); 231,688 (1924); 234,086 (1924); 237,872 (1924).

I.G. Farbenindustrie patents: Ger. 590,163 (1933); Brit. 350,575 (1930).

312. K. Venkataraman, *The Chemistry of Synthetic Dyes*, Academic Press Inc., New York 1952, p. 892.

313. H. Lecher and D. Eberhart, U.S. 2,479,943 (1949) to American Cyanamid Co.

314. D. Graham, U.S. 2,373,826 (1945) to Dupont.

315. U.S. 1,523,308 (1925) to Ciba.

316. Swiss 11,502 (1925) to Ciba.

317. Brit. 234,086 (1925) to Ciba.

318. U.S. 1,568,627 (1926) to Ciba.

319. Ger. 507,830 (1930).

320. U.S. 1,663,474 (1928) to Ciba.

321. Ger. 390,201 (1924) to Ciba.

322. Ger. 399,485 (1924) to Ciba.

323. Brit. 466, 886 (1937) to Ciba.

324. Brit. 375,056 (1932) to I.G. Farbenind.

325. *Ciba patents:* Ger. 433,100 (1923). U.S. 1,155,095 (1915). Swiss 107,619 (1924); 108,191 (1924); 111,500 (1925); 119,363,366 (1927).

326. Swiss 108,191–202 (1924) to Ciba.

327. H. Fritzsche and P. Schaedli, U.S. 1,551,095 (1925) to Ciba.

328. Brit. 220,302 (1924) to Ciba.

329. Swiss 111,123 (1925) to Ciba; Swiss 111,497–499 (1925) to Ciba.

330. Brit. 375,056 (1932) to I.G. Farbenind.

331. Swiss 144,228 (1931) to Ciba.

332. Ger. 554,781 (1932) to Ciba.

333. Ger. 560,035 (1932) to Ciba.

334. J. Warren, J. Reid and C. Hamalainen, *Textile Research J.*, **XXII,** 584 (1952).

335. Brit. 237,872 to Ciba.

336. Brit. 423,864 to I.G. Farbenind.

337. Fr. 828,532 to Ciba.

338. Brit. 326,791 to I.G. Farbenind.

339. J. Eggert and B. Wendt, U.S. 2,171,427 (1939) to I.G. Farbenind.

340. W.Wallace and W.Williams, U.S. 2,658,064 (1953) to Gen'l Aniline & Film Co.

341. D. Adams, R. Wilson and Imperial Chem. Ind., Brit. 623,849 (1949) through *Chem. Abstracts*, **44,** 9692 (1950).

342. D. Adams and R. Wilson, Brit. 624,051,052 (1949) to Imperial Chemical Ind. through *Chem. Abstracts*, **44,** 5606 (1950).

343. E. Keller and R. Zweidler, U.S. 2,526,668 (1950) to J. R. Geigy, A.-G.
344. Brit. 480,604 (1938) to I.G. Farbenind.
345. K. Schmidt and O. Wahl, U.S. 2,325,803 (1944) to Gen'l. Aniline & Film Corp.
345a. W. Williams and W. Wallace, U.S. 2,660,578 (1953) to Gen'l. Aniline & Film Corp.
346. Swiss 213,707 (1941) to J. R. Geigy A.-G.
347. Swiss 205,408 (1939) to J. R. Geigy A.-G.
348. H. Martin and H. Zaeslin, U.S. 2,298,971 (1943) to J. R. Geigy through *Chem. Abstracts*, **37**, 270 (1943).
349. Swiss 211,490 (1940) to J. R. Geigy A.-G.
350. W. Hentrich and E. Schirm, U.S. 2,401,155 (1946) (Alien Prop. Custod.).
351. Swiss 230,836 (1944) to J. R. Geigy A.-G.
352. Fr. 702,556 (1930) to I.G. Farbenind.
353. Brit. 511,143 (1939) to J. R. Geigy A.-G.
353a. E. Friedheim, U.S. 2,662,079 (1953).
354. Brit. 290,178 (1929) to Ciba.
355. Brit. 318,275 (1930) to Ciba.
356. Fr. 697,599 (1931) to Ciba.
357. L. Orthner and M. Bogemann, U.S. 2,061,520 (1936) to I.G. Farbenind.
358. J. Dudley, U.S. 2,467,523 (1949) to American Cyanamid Co.
359. Brit. 585,107 (1947) to Imperial Chem. Ind. Ltd.
360. W. Hentrich and E. Schirm, U.S. 2,394,306 (1946) (Vested in Alien Prop. Custod).
361. B. Wendt, Ger. 731,558 (1943) to I.G. Farbenind.
362. Ger. 606,497 (1934) to I.G. Farbenind., through *Chem. Abstracts*, **29**, 1587 (1935).
363. A. Burger, *Medicinal Chemistry, Vol. II*, Interscience Publishers Inc., New York, 1951.
364. D. Belding, *Clinical Paristology*, 2nd Ed., Appleton-Century-Crofts, Inc., New York, 1952, p. 1040–1041.
365. E. Friedheim, U.S. 2,422,724 (1947).
366. E. Friedheim, Swiss 214,093 (1941) through *Chem. Abstracts*, **40**, 177 (1946).
367. E. Friedheim, U.S. 2,295,544 (1943).
368. E. Friedheim, U.S. 2,390,089 (1945).
369. E. Friedheim, *J. Am. Chem. Soc.*, **66**, 1775 (1944).
370. E. Friedheim, U.S. 2,390,090; 2,390,091 (1941).
371. E. Friedheim, U.S. 2,390,529 (1945).
372. E. Friedheim, U.S. 2,415,556 (1947).
373. E. Friedheim, U.S. 2,386,204 (1945).
374. E. Friedheim, U.S. 2,400,547 (1946); through *Chem. Abstracts*, **40**, 5459 (1946).
375. E. Friedheim, U.S. 2,418,115 (1947).
376. E. Friedheim, U.S. 2,415,555 (1947).

CHAPTER II

Alkyl(Aryl)-*s*-Triazines

I. Introduction

This chapter is concerned with the group of *s*-triazines in which the substituents on the triazine ring are joined to that ring by carbon-carbon bonds only. For convenience, these are referred to as "alkyl or aryl *s*-triazines," although there are a few compounds which meet the above definition but cannot be correctly given the common name (e.g. 2,4,6-tricyano-*s*-triazine).

The parent member of this class of compounds is *s*-triazine (I) the trimer of HCN whose identity has only recently been recognized (see Introduction).

Only one mono-substituted and one di-substituted *s*-triazine of this category has been reported in the literature at this writing. These are 2-phenyl-*s*-triazine prepared in 1953 by Grundmann and 2,4-

(I)   (II) C_6H_5

diphenyl-*s*-triazine, first prepared in 1890 by Kraft and Koenig. The trialkyl (or aryl)-*s*-triazines containing like groups in the 2,4 and 6 positions may be considered as trimers of nitriles, and indeed many of these compounds have been synthesized by the trimerization of nitriles, or nitrile precursors under a variety of conditions.

The nomenclature which has appeared in the literature in reference to these substituted *s*-triazines has usually been straightforward except for the following trivial naming system. In the early literature, the compound most frequently studied was 2,4,6-triphenyl-*s*-triazine (II) which was referred to as *cyaphenin* (variously *kyaphenin, kyaphenine,* etc.). Accordingly, the names cyabenzin (tribenzyl-s-triazine), cyamethin (trimethyl-s-triazine), etc. have been used by some workers. In this volume, the unambiguous 2,4,6-substituted-s-triazine nomenclature employed by Chemical Abstracts will be used.

The earliest preparations of these "trimeric nitriles" were recorded about 1860. Cloez[1] heated benzoyl chloride with potassium cyanate and obtained a stable, high melting (224°) compound to which he gave the

$$3 \, C_6H_5COCl + 3 \, KCNO \longrightarrow \quad \begin{array}{c} C_6H_5 \diagdown N \diagup C_6H_5 \\ | \quad | \\ N \quad N \\ \diagdown \diagup \\ C_6H_5 \end{array} \quad + 3 \, KCl + 3 \, CO_2$$

name "cyaphenine." In 1856, Limpricht[2] had heated salicylic acid amide to 270° and obtained a high melting compound which he called "salicylimid," and which was shown many years later[3] to be 2,4,6-tris(2′-hydroxyphenyl)-s-triazine (III). While studying the chlorination

$$3 \; \begin{array}{c} \diagup OH \\ \diagdown C \diagdown NH_2 \end{array} \quad \xrightarrow{\Delta} \quad \begin{array}{c} (o)HOC_6H_4 \diagdown N \diagup C_6H_4OH(o) \\ | \quad | \\ N \quad N \\ \diagdown \diagup \\ C_6H_4OH(o) \end{array}$$

$$(III)$$

of propionitrile in 1860, Otto[4] obtained two products, a liquid and a solid. It was eventually shown that this "festen dichlorpropionitrile" was in reality the trimer, 2,4,6-tris(α,α-dichloroethyl)-s-triazine.

It was not until the 1880's that the relationship of these nitrile trimers to the long known cyanuric halides and cyanuric acid was shown by the synthesis of some triaryl-s-triazines with cyanuric bromide as a starting material.

The trialkyl and triaryl-s-triazines are in general rather stable compounds (especially the triaryl derivatives). They are, with few exceptions, solids and in the case of the aryl derivatives, high melting and rather difficultly soluble in the common organic solvents. These compounds show only faintly basic properties and, in most cases, do not form stable salts. The chemistry of the alkyl (aryl)-s-triazines has been studied only sparsely.

II. General Synthetic Methods

A rather large number of methods have been used for the preparation of this group of compounds, but many of them have been used only for one compound and will be referred to in the discussion of that derivative.

1. Trimerization of Nitriles

The trimerization of nitriles has been used extensively in preparing the simple substituted *s*-triazines. Until recently, it was believed that only nitriles having no α-hydrogen underwent this trimerization. However, it has now been shown[5] that under extreme pressures, nitriles with one and two α-hydrogens, such as acetonitrile, butyronitrile etc., will trimerize to the *s*-triazine derivatives

$$3\ CH_3CN \longrightarrow$$

$$
\begin{array}{c}
CH_3 \quad N \quad CH_3 \\
\diagdown \quad \diagdown \\
N \quad N \\
\diagdown \quad \diagup \\
CH_3
\end{array}
$$

It has also recently been demonstrated that dichloroacetonitrile and dibromoacetonitrile will trimerize under mild conditions to yield the 2,4,6-tris(dihalomethyl)-*s*-triazines[6,7] (IV). Earlier workers had believed that the product from dichloroacetonitrile was a dimer.[8,9]

$$3\ CHCl_2CN$$
$$(CHBr_2CN) \longrightarrow$$

$$
\begin{array}{c}
CHCl_2 \quad N \quad CHCl_2 \\
(CHBr_2) \quad \quad (CHBr_2) \\
N \quad N \\
\diagdown \quad \diagup \\
CHCl_2 \\
(IV) \quad (CHBr_2)
\end{array}
$$

Another example of the trimerization of a nitrile containing an α-hydrogen is that postulated as the intermediate reaction product involved in the conversion of tetrafluorethylene to 2,4,6-tris(difluoromethyl)-*s*-triazine (V) by reaction with ammonia.[10] Aside from these exceptions, the formation of *s*-triazines from nitriles, proceeds much more readily with nitriles containing no α-hydrogen.

$$CF_2 = CF_2 + NH_3 \longrightarrow (CHF_2CN) \longrightarrow$$

$$
\begin{array}{c}
CHF_2 \quad N \quad CHF_2 \\
\diagdown \quad \diagup \\
N \quad N \\
\diagdown \quad \diagup \\
(V) \quad CHF_2
\end{array}
$$

The trimerization of nitriles has been effected under a variety of conditions and with many different catalysts both acidic and basic.

The formation of an s-triazine from α,α-dichloropropionitrile in the presence of hydrogen chloride and hydrogen bromide was observed as early as 1860.[4,11-17] The use of the hydrogen halides as catalysts for trimerization has been extended to other nitriles, especially α-halogenated nitriles. The trimerization of trichloroacetonitrile has been reported to afford excellent yields of 2,4,6-tris(trichloromethyl)-s-triazine (VI)

$$3 \ CCl_3CN \xrightarrow[\substack{800 \ \text{atm.} \\ \text{Room temp.}}]{\text{HCl}}$$

when carried out in the presence of anhydrous hydrogen chloride under pressure.[18-22] Fineman[23] obtained 2,4,6-triphenyl-s-triazine as a byproduct in the preparation of benzonitrile by reaction of benzotrichloride with ammonia. It is probable that HCl catalyzed the trimerization of the nitrile here. The preparation of unsymmetrically substituted triazines by the trimerization of mixtures of nitriles in the presence of hydrogen chloride has been reported.[24,7]

$$2 \ CCl_3CN + CH_3CN \xrightarrow[-15°]{\text{HCl}}$$

Among the most satisfactory conditions of acidic catalysis is the use of chlorosulfonic acid at 0° C. This was reported to afford excellent yields of 2,4,6-triphenyl-s-triazine, 2,4,6-tris(p-tolyl)-s-triazine, 2,4,6-tris(m-tolyl)-s-triazine, and 2,4,6-tris(β-naphthyl)-s-triazine.[24,26] A very low yield of the o-tolyl derivative was obtained under similar conditions. In the earlier literature the use of concentrated or fuming sulfuric acid is mentioned without much detail as to yields and scope. Bromine has

$$3 \ C_2H_5OC{-}CN \xrightarrow[100°]{Br_2}$$

also been reported as a catalyst in the trimerization of ethyl cyanoformate to 2,4,6-tris(carboethoxy)-s-triazine[27] (VII) (ethyl ester of paracyanoformic acid).

Basic catalysts have been used to effect the trimerization of nitriles to a lesser extent than acids. As early as 1868, Hofmann[28] isolated a small amount of 2,4,6-triphenyl-s-triazine from the reaction of sodium metal with benzonitrile. This was confirmed later by Lottermoser in 1896[29] who also obtained 2,4,6-triphenyl-s-triazine by heating benzonitrile with sodium in benzene solution for several days. Besides the tri-substituted triazine, Lottermoser also obtained a compound which he showed to be 2,2,4,6-tetraphenyl-1,2 dihydro-s-triazine (VIII).

$$4 \ C_6H_5CN + 2 \ Na \longrightarrow NaCN +$$

(VIII)

The structure of (VIII) was revealed by hydrolysis with KOH at 150° which yielded benzhydrol in addition to benzoic acid and ammonia. Frankland and Evans[30] obtained 2,4,6-triphenyl-s-triazine by heating benzonitrile with diethyl zinc at 150°. Other basic reagents which have been ussed to trimerize benzonitrile include sodium hydride,[31] Grignard reagents,[31] sodium triphenylmethyl,[32] sodium dicyclohexyl phenyl methyl,[33] and alkali metal salts of amines.[31]

Pinner[34] found 2,4,6-tribenzyl-s-triazine as a by-product in the preparation of benzyl cyanide from benzyl chloride and KCN. In the high pressure triazine synthesis of Cairns and coworkers,[5] the use of ammonia or ammonium acetate gives somewhat better conversions. The high pressure trimerizations were carried out at 60–150° in methanol at pressures of 5,000 to 12,000 atmospheres. In this manner nitriles such as acetonitrile, propionitrile, and butyronitrile, having α hydrogens, were successfully trimerized to the 2,4,6-trialkyl-s-triazines in yields of 15–50%. Benzonitrile also undergoes trimerization normally under these conditions.

Grundmann and coworkers[7] have attempted to elucidate the mechanism of the nitrile trimerization to s-triazines. Noting that catalysis for this polymerization has usually been by hydrogen halides or materials capable of forming hydrogen halides, they attempted and were able to isolate an intermediate reaction product of easily tri-merizable nitriles with hydrogen halides. The empirical formula of these "primary products" was $(RCN)_2 \cdot HCl$.[35] In the presence of additional nitrile (either the same one or a different one), HCl is evolved and the triazine derivatives formed. This is formulated as follows:

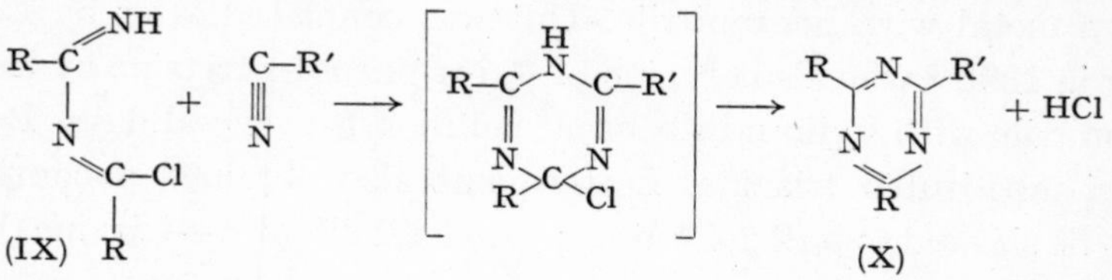

In this scheme, the reaction was visualized as a "diene" condensation. However, some of their experimental results indicate that this explana-tion is an oversimplification. For example, when the HCl-trichloro-acetonitrile adduct (IX, $R = CCl_3$) was treated with acetonitrile, no 2-methyl-4,6-bis(trichloromethyl)-s-triazine (X, $R = CCl_3$, $R' = CH_3$) was obtained, whereas when a mixture of trichloroacetonitrile and acetonitrile was treated with hydrogen chloride, a 90% yield of (Xa) was formed.

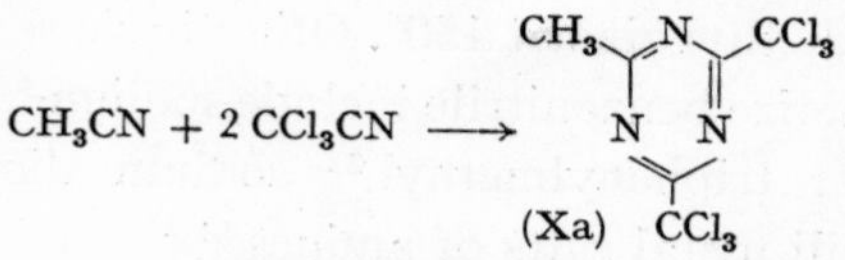

Variations of the nitrile synthesis which probably involve the nitrile as an intermediate include the following. In 1865, Engler[36] obtained a small yield of triphenyl-s-triazine from the reaction mixture obtained when bromobenzonitrile was heated with lime. Henry[37] ob-tained a low yield of triphenyl-s-triazine by heating benzamide with P_2S_5; benzonitrile was the major product. Reaction of N-methyl benz-amide with phosphorus pentachloride and phosphorus pentabromide is reported to yield small amounts of triphenyl-s-triazine in addition to benzonitrile.[38-40]

Limpricht[1] heated salicylic acid amide to 270° and obtained a high melting compound which he called salicylimide. Henry,[41] a few years, later believed this reaction gave him o-hydroxybenzonitrile. However, Miller[3] later prepared some of the monomeric o-hydroxybenzonitrile by dehydration of salicylaldehyde oxime and showed that its properties (M.p. 96°) were different from the high melting compounds of Limpricht and Henry. Miller also obtained some of the high melting product when he heated the oxime with acetic anhydride. He showed that on treatment with concentrated hydrochloric acid, the compound yielded phenol, carbon dioxide, and ammonia; and on treatment with sodium hydroxide it gave salicylic acid. Cousin and Volmar[42] showed that o-hydroxybenzonitrile and o-hydroxybenzamide are easily converted by heat to 2,4,6-tris(o-hydroxyphenyl)-s-triazine (XI). He proved the

structure by reduction to the glyoxaline (XII). Einhorn and Schmidlin[43] also believed they obtained the triazine by heating o-hydroxybenzamide with urea; however, the melting point of their compound, does not agree with that of the other workers.

2. From Iminoethers and Related Compounds

Closely related to the trimerization of nitriles is the preparation of trisubstituted-s-triazines by the cyclization of iminoethers. This was first observed by Pinner[44, 45] in 1877. While attempting to prepare benzamidine by the reaction of isobutyl benziminoether with ammonia,

he obtained a high melting compound which he later identified as 2,4,6-triphenyl-s-triazine. Several years later Glock[46] observed a high melting compound which was formed when ethyl p-toluiminoether was allowed to stand for a long period of time. Pinner[47] later developed a practical method of preparing 2,4,6-triphenyl-s-triazine which involves an iminoether as an intermediate. Benzonitrile is treated with alcohol and dry HCl. After standing for 48 hours, the solid reaction mixture (the iminoether hydrochloride) is treated with concentrated sodium hydroxide to yield the triazine.

An interesting variation is the preparation of 2,4,6-triphenyl-s-triazine by the action of sodium hydroxide on ethyl and benzyl benzimino thioethers.[48]

The preparation of triazines from iminoethers has found little application due to the fact that iminoethers are usually made from nitriles which can yield the triazines directly.

3. From Cyanuric Halides and Cyanogen Halides

The preparation of 2,4,6-trisubstituted-s-triazines from cyanuric halides or cyanogen halides has been used to a great extent and in many cases is the most convenient synthesis of these compounds.

The Friedel-Crafts reaction of cyanuric chloride with benzene in the presence of aluminum chloride was tried unsuccessfully by Klason in 1887.[49] Several years later Scholl and Norr[50] obtained good yields of triaryl-s-triazines by treating an aromatic hydrocarbon with cyanogen bromide and aluminum chloride. These workers showed that the reaction probably consisted in a trimerization of cyanogen bromide to

$$3 C_6H_6 + 3 CNBr \xrightarrow{AlCl_3} \qquad + 3 HBr$$

cyanuric bromide followed by a Friedel-Crafts reaction of the latter with benzene. Thus, cyanogen bromide afforded good yields of cyanuric bromide in the presence of aluminum chloride, while the other possible intermediate, benzonitrile, gave only small amounts of 2,4,6-triphenyl-s-triazine under the reaction conditions. The reaction was successful with toluene, o- and m-xylene. However, the expected triazine was not obtained in the case of p-xylene and p-cymene. Anisole yielded a mixture of bromoanisole and cyanoanisole.

Meyer and Nabe[51] used cyanuric bromide in the Friedel-Crafts reaction with various aromatic compounds and obtained excellent yields of the triaryl-s-triazines using aluminum chloride in carbon disulfide.

The successful use of cyanuric chloride in the Friedel-Crafts reaction to yield triaryl-s-triazines has been reported in the patent literature.[52, 53] Thus, in a typical example for the preparation of mixed triaryl-s-triazines, Fritzsche and Schadeli treated cyanuric chloride with two moles of naphthol and the resulting product was heated with m-xylene to yield 2,4-bis(4'-hydroxynaphthyl)-6-m-xylyl-s-triazine (XIII). Barksy and Gillis[54] claimed excellent yields of 2,4,6-triphenyl-

s-triazine from the reaction of cyanuric chloride with benzene at reflux in the presence of an excess of aluminum chloride. The present commercial availability of cyanuric chloride should result in a more detailed study of this method of preparation for substituted s-triazines.

The Wurtz-Fittig reaction of cyanuric chloride with bromobenzene in the presence of sodium was used by Klason[49] in 1887. He obtained mainly 2,4-diphenyl-6-chloro-s-triazine (XIV) and a low yield of 2,4,6-triphenyl-s-triazine. Kraft[55] obtained a similar result using

iodobenzene. Diels and Lieberman[56] prepared 2,4,6-tris(4'-ethoxyphenyl)-s-triazine (XV) from cyanuric chloride and p-bromophenetole in the presence of sodium.

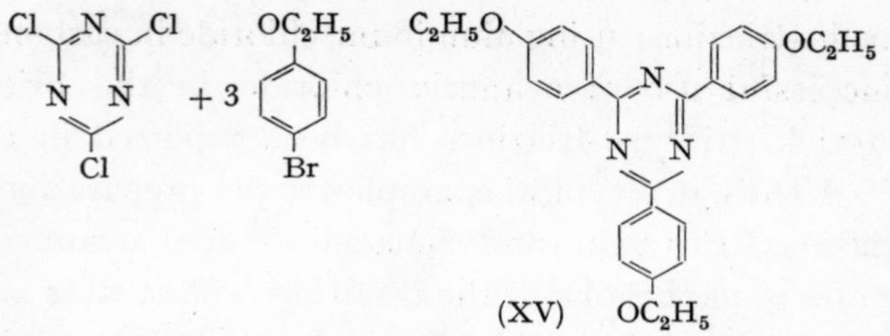

(XV) OC$_2$H$_5$

An aliphatic substituted triazine, 2,4,6-triethyl-s-triazine, was obtained by heating cyanuric bromide with ethyl magnesium iodide.[51]

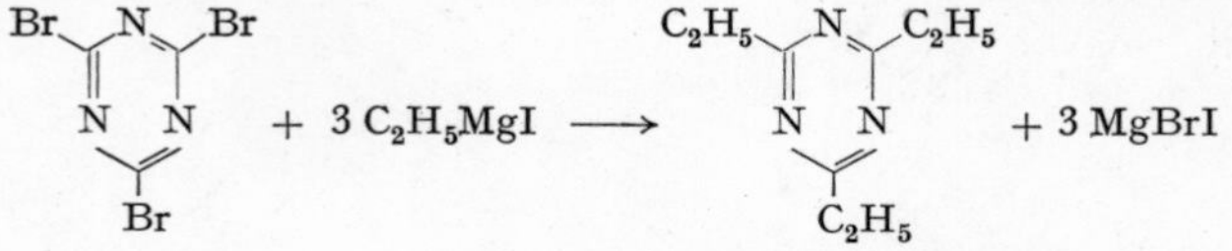

4. Reaction of Acid Chlorides with Nitriles

In 1889, Krafft and Von Hansen[57] attempted to prepare palymityl p-cyanophenyl ketone, C$_{15}$H$_{31}$COC$_6$H$_4$CN, by the Friedel-Crafts reaction of palymitoyl chloride with benzonitrile. Instead of the desired product, they obtained a compound which had a high nitrogen content and was unaffected by alkali. Investigating the reaction further, they treated benzonitrile with acetyl chloride in the presence of aluminum chloride. The resulting reaction product had faintly basic properties. On heating with sulfuric acid, benzoic and acetic acids were obtained in addition to ammonia. These facts together with an elementary analysis and a molecular weight determination led Krafft and von Hansen to propose the s-triazine structure, 2-methyl-4,6-phenyl-s-triazine. The generality of the reaction was shown by the preparation of a series of 2-alkyl-4,6-diphenyl s-triazines[48,59] (XVI). From succinoyl

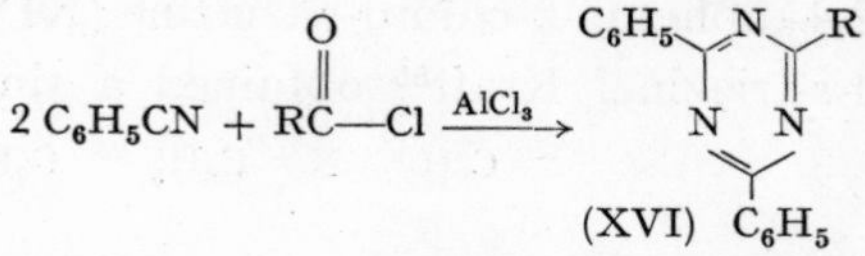

(XVI) C$_6$H$_5$

chloride, they obtained the 2,2'-ethylenebis (4,6-diphenyl-s-triazine) (XVII).

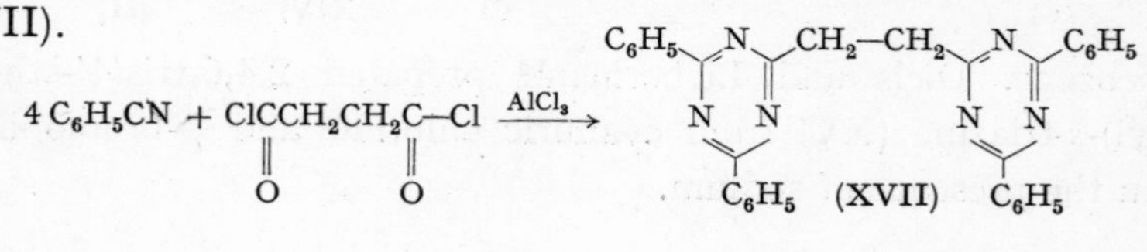

No aliphatic nitriles were used in this work, but there is no indication that they will not participate in the reaction. Aromatic acid chlorides react to yield triaryl-s-triazines. In attempting to prepare 2,4,6-triphenyl-s-triazine from benzonitrile and benzoyl chloride, Eitner and Krafft[60] obtained a poor yield, but when they added ammonium chloride, the yield was improved greatly. To explain this, they treated pure benzonitrile and benzoyl chloride with aluminum chloride and obtained a crystalline hygroscopic material to which they assigned the formula (XVIIa). When this product was treated with ammonia, 2,4,6-triphenyl-s-triazine was obtained.

$$
\begin{array}{c}
C_6H_5 \\
| \\
C \\
\diagdown \\
N \qquad Cl \cdot AlCl_3 \\
| \\
(XVIIa) \quad C_6H_5 - C = N - C \diagup C_6H_5 \\
\diagdown O
\end{array}
$$

The acid chloride—nitrile synthesis was employed by Cook and Jones[26] in preparing various nitro substituted 2,4,6-triphenyl s-triazines, using nitrobenzoyl chloride with benzonitrile and nitrobenzonitrile

$$p\text{-}NO_2C_6H_4COCl + 2\ C_6H_5CN \xrightarrow{\ NH_4Cl,\ AlCl_3\ }$$

$$C_6H_5COCl + 2\ p\text{-}NO_2C_6H_4CN \longrightarrow$$

with benzoyl chloride. The reaction failed to give the desired product when o-nitrobenzonitrile and 2,4,6-trinitrobenzonitrile were used. Also an attempt to prepare 2,4,6-tris(p-nitrophenyl)-s-triazine by reaction of p-nitrobenzonitrile with p-nitrobenzoyl chloride was unsuccessful, yielding instead the Friedel-Crafts product.

5. Reaction of Amidines with Anhydrides

In the course of his classical work on iminoethers and amidines, Pinner[61] studied the reaction of aromatic amidines with anhydrides, and

$$
\overset{NH}{\overset{\|}{2\ C_6H_5CNH_2}} + (CH_3CO)_2O \longrightarrow \overset{NH\ \ NH}{\overset{\|\ \ \ \|}{C_6H_5CNHC-C_6H_5}} + CH_3CONH_2 + CH_3COOH
$$

at first believed that the reaction led to compounds which he named "diimidines" as formulated below. Several years later,[62] however, when he reacted furamidine with acetic anhydride, he obtained a compound which at first he postulated as an aminopyrimidine (XVIII). However, the weakly basic character of the product led him to revise his formula-

(XVIII)

tion to that of a "mixed kyanidine"-2-methyl-4,6-difuryl-s-triazine (XIX). Pinner proposed the following mechanism for the formation of

(XIX)

the triazine. Better evidence for the s-triazine structures came when the properties of the "diimidine" which he had prepared earlier were in-

vestigated.[63] Thus, the compound previously called "dibenzimidine" was found to have the properties of 2-methyl-4,6-diphenyl-s-triazine which had been described in the meantime by Krafft and von Hansen.[57] Similarly, the erroneously named "ditolylimidine" and "di-β-naphthylimidine" were reformulated as the corresponding 2-methyl-4,6-diaryl-s-triazines.

This general method of synthesis for mixed triazines has found very little use, probably due to the relative inaccessability of the amidines; the only references to its application are those of Pinner and his co-workers,[64-66] aside from a recent preparation of 2-trichloromethyl-4,6-bis(p-chlorophenyl)-s-triazine.[67] In certain specific instances variations of this method have been useful, as discussed below.

Closely related to this method was the preparation of 2,4-diphenyl-6-(2'-hydroxyphenyl)-s-triazine (XX) by Pinner[68] from the reaction of benzamidine with ethylsalicylate. Pinner had believed that the reaction

went further with cyclization to yield a benzoxazine derivative (XXI).
However, the structure of Pinner's compound was shown to be the

(XXI)

s-triazine by Titherley and Hughes[69] who obtained the same product
by the reaction of 2-phenyl-1,3-benzoxazine-4-one (XXII) with benz-

amidine. The triazine was also obtained from the reaction of salicyl
benzamidine (XXIII) with benzamidine, which may have been the
intermediate stage in the Pinner preparation.

The preparation of triazines from benzal derivatives of amidines
is an interesting variation. Pinner[47] reported that when benzal benzamidine (XXIV) (prepared from benzamidine and benzaldehyde) was

$$\underset{(XXIV)}{2 \; C_6H_5\overset{NH}{\overset{\|}{C}}-N=CH-C_6H_5} \quad \xrightarrow{\;\Delta\;} \quad C_6H_5-\underset{N-N}{\overset{N}{\diagdown\diagup}}-C_6H_5 \atop C_6H_5$$

heated above its melting point, it yielded 2,4,6-triphenyl-s-triazine. Later, Bougault and Robin[70] reported that benzhydramide (XXV), heated with sodium carbonate yielded triphenyl triazine. These authors

$$\underset{(XXV)}{C_6H_5CH\diagdown{N=CHC_6H_5 \atop N=CHC_6H_5}} \rightarrow \underset{(XXVI)}{C_6H_5CH\diagdown{N=C\diagdown{C_6H_5 \atop O} \atop N=C\diagdown{C_6H_5}} + NH_3} \rightarrow \underset{C_6H_5}{C_6H_5-\overset{H}{\overset{N}{\diagdown}}-C_6H_5 \atop HN \quad N} \xrightarrow{H_2} \underset{C_6H_5}{C_6H_5-\overset{N}{\diagdown}-C \atop N \quad N}$$

postulated a diazoxaline (XXVI) as an intermediate. Sachs and Steinert[71] obtained 2,4,6-tris(4'-dimethylaminophenyl)-s-triazine in poor yields by heating (XXVIa).

$$\underset{(XXVIa)}{(CH_3)_2NC_6H_4-CH=N\diagdown{\atop CH-C_6H_4-N(CH_3)_3} \atop (CH_3)_2NC_6H_4-CH=N\diagup}$$

6. Reaction of Nitrogen Sulfide with Aldehydes

A rather interesting and unusual preparation of trisubstituted s-triazines is that discovered by Francis and Davis.[72] In a study of the reactions of sulfur nitride (S_4N_4), they heated benzaldehyde with S_4N_4, and obtained as the main product, 2,4,6-triphenyl-s-triazine. The

$$3\, C_6H_5CHO + N_4S_4 \;\longrightarrow\; \underset{C_6H_5}{C_6H_5\diagdown{N \atop N}\diagup C_6H_5 \atop N \quad N} + SO_2 + H_2O + NH_4SO_4 + S$$

reaction proceeded similarly with p-tolylaldehyde, p-methoxybenz-aldehyde, p-nitrobenzaldehyde, m-nitrobenzaldehyde, p-chlorobenz-aldehyde, and piperonal. It failed with cinnamaldehyde, salicylaldehyde, p-isopropylbenzaldehyde, and aliphatic aldehydes.[73,74] In the reaction of p-methoxybenzaldehyde with sulfur nitride, a small amount of p-methoxybenzamidine was isolated, and it was believed that this might be an intermediate in the formation of the triazines. However, it was not possible to isolate any benzamidine from the reaction with benzaldehyde. Benzonitrile plus nitrogen sulfide did not yield 2,4,6-

triphenyl-*s*-triazine; this rules out the nitrile as a possible intermediate. In a somewhat related reaction, Schenk[75] had isolated triphenyl-*s*-triazine by heating benzylamine and sulfur nitride. Other than this original work, no other references to these reactions have appeared.

The other methods which have been used for the preparation of individual trisubstituted triazines do not involve the synthesis of the triazine ring system, but are merely substitution reactions on the side chain of an *s*-triazine and many of these will be discussed under reactions of trisubstituted triazines.

Mono- and disubstituted triazines (i.e. with no functional group attached to the ring) have received very little attention until recently. The only example of a monosubstituted triazine of this type is 2-phenyl-*s*-triazine (XXVIII) prepared by Grundmann and co-workers in 1952.[76]

Two methods were used, the most satisfactory of which started with the condensation of phenyl magnesium bromide with cyanuric chloride to yield 2-phenyl-4,6-dichloro-*s*-triazine (XXVII). This was then converted to the dithiol with sodium hydrosulfide followed by methylation with methyl iodide. Treatment of the dithioether with Raney nickel resulted in desulfurization with the formation of the desired phenyl-*s*-triazine in fair yields. Direct reduction of 2-phenyl-4,6-dichloro-*s*-triazine was unsuccessful.

In the alternate method, 2-phenyl-4,6-bis(trichloromethyl)-*s*-triazine (XXIX) (prepared by mixed trimerization of benzonitrile and trichloroacetonitrile) was reduced to 2-phenyl-4,6-dimethyl-*s*-triazine. The dimethyl derivative was oxidized in poor yield to 2-phenyl-4,6-dicarboxy-*s*-triazine which was then decarboxylated to yield 2-phenyl-s-triazine. The product was identical with that prepared by the previous scheme.

(XXIX)

2,4-Diphenyl-s-triazine is the only disubstituted nonfunctional s-triazine which has been reported*. It was first prepared in 1890 by Krafft and Koenig[58] using a method similar to that described above. 2-Methyl-4,6-diphenyl-s-triazine was oxidized to 2-carboxy-4,6-diphenyl-s-triazine and this acid was decarboxylated. Grundmann[76]

obtained the same compound by the Raney nickel desulfurization of 2-methylthio-4,6-diphenyl-s-triazine (prepared in a manner analogous to the corresponding monophenyl compound described above).

III. Reactions

Few reactions of the trisubstituted s-triazines (i.e. trialkyl or triaryl) have been studied, are especially reactions which involve the triazine ring system.

Only three reactions have been reported which do concern the triazine ring. The first of these is a hydrolysis—acid or base catalyzed—which splits the ring into a carboxylic acid and ammonia. This reaction

has been used as a diagnostic tool in proving the structure of several

* Note added in proof: The preparation of 2,4-dimethyl-s-triazine has been reported recently (Schroeder and Grundmann, J. Am. Chem. Soc., 78, 2447 (1956)).

of the trisubstituted s-triazines. In his original paper on the preparation of 2,4,6-triphenyl-s-triazine, Cloez[1] observed that when the compound was heated with sodium hydroxide, ammonia was evolved. This was disputed a few years later by Engler,[77] but the fact that triarylated s-triazines will cleave to the corresponding acids in the presence of alkali hydroxides was shown in subsequent reports.[3,27] The acid hydrolysis has been used most extensively, and numerous examples of cleavage of triazines to carboxylic acids by this procedure have been recorded.[3,16,27,30,51,57,72]

In general, drastic conditions are employed—concentrated hydrochloric acid at 150–225°—sometimes in a sealed tube. Hydrogen iodide and sulfuric acid have also been used. The only compound which

$$\text{(XXX)} \quad + 6\,H_2O \longrightarrow 3\,NH_3 + \begin{array}{c} COOH \\ | \\ COOH \end{array}$$

appears to be cleaved readily is 2,4,6-tricarboxy-s-triazine (XXX) (paracyanoformic acid) which yields ammonia and oxalic acid on treatment with hot water.[27]

Closely related to the hydrolysis of the s-triazine ring system is alcoholysis which yields the corresponding ester. This has been reported only for 2,4,6-tris(trifluoromethyl)-s-triazine (XXXI) and provides a very convenient synthesis for esters of trifluoroacetic acid.[79]

$$\text{(XXXI)} \quad + 3\,ROH + 3\,HCl \longrightarrow 3\,CF_3COOR + 3\,NH_4Cl$$

The second reaction of the trialkyl(aryl)-s-triazines is the reduction—with loss of nitrogen—to form the five-membered glyoxaline derivative (XXXII).

$$\xrightarrow{H_2} NH_3 + \quad \text{(XXXII)}$$

This transformation of the triazine ring was first observed by Radziszewski[80] in 1882 when he treated 2,4,6-triphenyl-s-triazine with

zinc in alcoholic alkali or with zinc in acetic acid. The product he
obtained was the known "lophin", 2,4,5-triphenylglyoxaline (XXXIII).

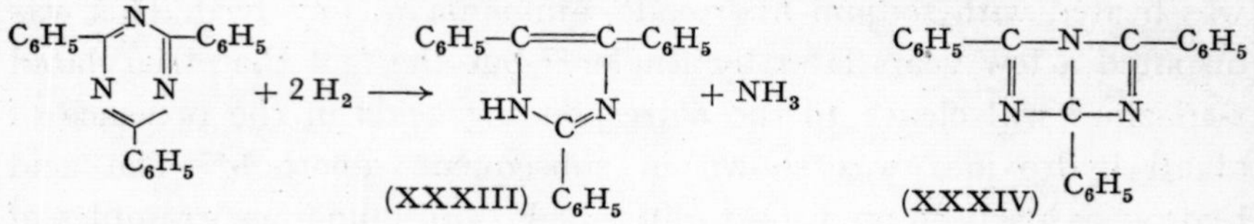

(XXXIII) C_6H_5 (XXXIV) C_6H_5

This led Radziszewski to propose the erroneous structure (XXXIV)
for 2,4,6-triphenyl-s-triazine with the tertiary N being the one removed
in the reduction process.

The cleavage of the triazine ring system to the glyoxaline systems
appears general for substituted s-triazines. Among the aryl triazines
which have been converted to the corresponding lophin analogues are
the 2,4,6-tri-p-tolyl-,[81] 2,4,6-tris(o-hydroxyphenyl)-,[42] and 2,4,6(tris-p-
chlorophenyl)-s-triazines.[26]

In the reduction of 2,4,6-tris(α,α-dichloroethyl)-s-triazine Otto and
Voigt,[16] and Troeger[82] obtained, in addition to 2,4,6-triethyl-s-triazine,
a lesser quantity of a basic compound which was probably the glyoxaline (XXXV).

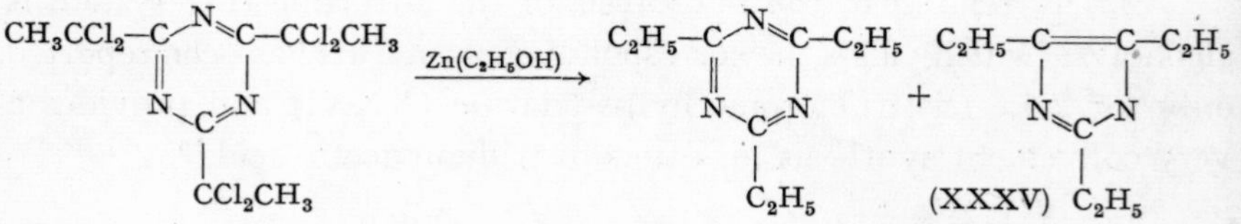

(XXXV) C_2H_5

A third reaction involving the s-triazine ring structure is that
reported recently by Cairns, Larcher, and McKusick[5] who found that
2,4,6-triethyl-s-triazine rearranged partially to 4-amino-2,6-diethyl-5-
methyl-pyrimidine (XXXVI) when heated in ammoniacal methanol at

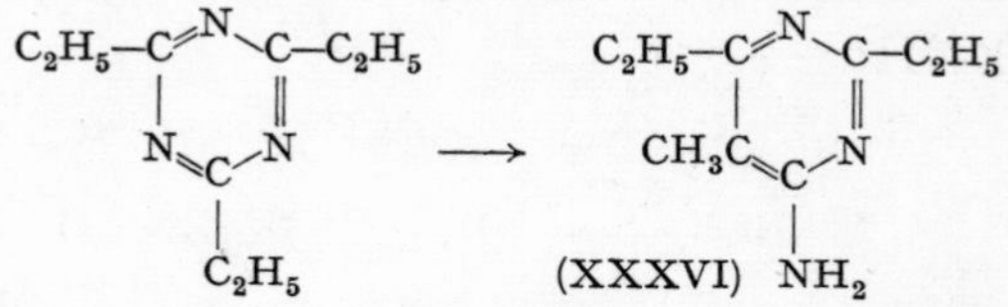

(XXXVI) NH_2

150° C. under 8500 atmospheres. Under similar conditions, 2,4,6-tri-
methyl-s-triazine rearranged to a limited extent to 4-amino-2,6-di-
methyl-pyrimidine. The latter compound was also encountered as a by-

product when 2,4,6-trimethyl-s-triazine was prepared by trimerization of acetonitrile under extreme pressures.

IV. Trialkyl-s-Triazines

The number of trialkyl-s-triazines which have been prepared and positively identified is relatively small. Those reported through 1954 are listed in Table II-1.

Aside from the halogenated compounds 2,4,6-tris(trichloromethyl)-s-triazine and 2,4,6-tris(α,α'-dichloroethyl)-s-triazine, very little information concerning this class of s-triazines is available. This is due to the difficulty of preparation of the trialkyl-s-triazines. The trimerization of nitriles having two α-hydrogens to s-triazines is very difficult and has been accomplished only recently under conditions of extremely high pressures[5] (above 1000 atmospheres). The only nitriles with one α-hydrogen which have been successfully converted to s-triazines are dichloroacetonitrile and dibromoacetonitrile.[5,6] It is well known that nitriles with α-hydrogens can and usually do polymerize by alternate methods to yield either iminonitriles (XXXVII) or aminopyrimidines

$$2\ R_2CHCN \longrightarrow \underset{\underset{R}{\overset{(XXXVII)}{\mid}}}{R_2CHC} \overset{\overset{NH\ R}{\overset{\|}{\underset{}{\mid}}}}{\underset{}{-C-CN}}$$

$$3\ RCH_2CN \longrightarrow \underset{(XXXVIII)}{RCH_2-\underset{N}{C}\underset{N}{\overset{R-C\overset{NH_2}{\mid}\diagdown N}{}}C-CH_2R}$$

(XXXVIII).[83] Aliphatic nitriles with no α-hydrogens, such as trichloroacetonitrile, αα-dichloropropionitrile, and ethyl cyanoformate, can be trimerized easily to the s-triazine derivatives.

1. 2,4,6-Trimethyl-s-triazine

2,4,6-Trimethyl-s-triazine is an extremely weakly basic, low melting solid (m.p. 59–60°) which forms a dihydrochloride in ether and a monopicrate. It is very water soluble and is also soluble in most organic solvents. It can be sublimed and is steam volatile. Hydrolysis with concentrated hydrochloric or sulfuric acid yields acetic acid and the ammonium salt of the organic acid. The methyl groups are apparently activated similarly to that of α-picoline, as the compound

TABLE II-1.   Trialkyl-s-Triazines

A. Like Substituents

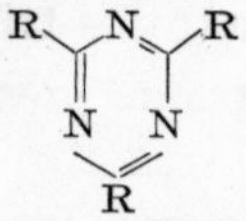

R	M.p., °C. (Recrystallization solvent)	B.p., °C./mm.	Method of preparation[a]	Ref.
CH_3	59–60° (hexane)	156°/760	A	1
	55–56°	—	B	2
C_2H_5	29°	193–195°	B	3
	30°	—	C	4
	25–26°	198°	A	1
C_4H_9		284–7/760	A	1
		85–91/0.5		
CHF_2	24.5°	73/9	A	17
$CHCl_2$	69–70° ($CHCl_3$)		A	5a, 2b
$CHBr_2$	127–129°	—	A	5b
CF_3	—24.8	98.3–98.5°	F	6
CCl_3	91–92° (alcohol)	—	D	7
	96°	—	A	6, 8
CBr_3	129–130° (alcohol)	—	A	9
$CHClCH_3$	identity dubious		B	3b
CCl_2CH_3	74.5 (alcohol)		A	1, 3, 10
CN	119° (benzene)	262/771	G	11
$CONH_2$	amorphous		H	11, 12
COOH	>250 (dec.)		I	12, 13
$COOCH_3$	154° (alcohol)		J	12
$COOC_2H_5$	165° (alcohol)		A	12, 13, 2b
$COOC_4H_9$ (iso)	158° (alcohol		A	12
$CONHCH_3$	>250 (dec.)		H	12
$CONHC_6H_5$	—		H	12
C—CH$_3$ ‖ S	dubious		K	15

[a] *Methods of Preparation*

A   Trimerization of nitrile.
B   Reduction of chlorine containing side chain.
C   Cyanuric Halide plus Grignard Reagent.

D $+ PCl_5$

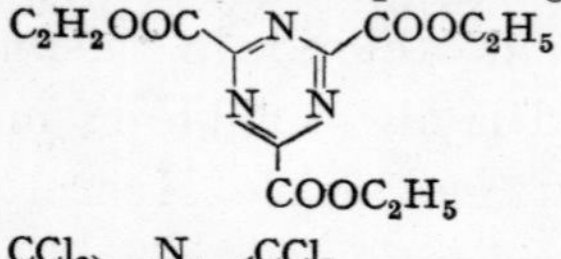

F $+ HF \xrightarrow{SbF_5}$

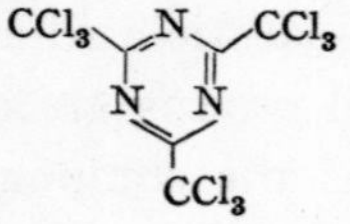

G 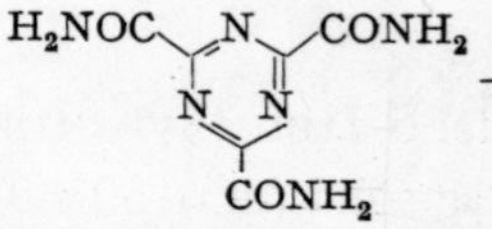 $\xrightarrow{P_2O_5}$

H   Ester + NH_3 or amine.
I   Hydrolysis of ester.
J   Silver salt plus methyl iodide.
K   R—CCl_2CH_3 + KSH.

B. Unlike Substituents

$$R_1 \diagdown \overset{N}{\underset{N}{\diagup}} \diagup R_1$$
$$R_2$$

R_1	R_2	M.p., °C. (Recrystallization solvent)	B.P., °C.	Method of preparation[a]	Ref.
CCl_3	CH_3	96–97° (alcohol)		A	2b, 16
CF_3	CF_2Cl	—51	119	F	6
CF_xCl_y	CF_xCl_y	where x + y = 3 in various combinations			6
CCl_3	$COOC_2H_5$	40°		A	2b
$COOC_2H_5$	CCl_3	112° (alcohol)		A	2b
$\overset{CCH_3}{\underset{S}{\|}}$	$\overset{CCH_3}{\underset{O}{\|}}$	dubious		K	15
CCl_3	$—C_{17}H_{35}$	oil		A	16

1a. T. Cairns, A. Larcher, and B. McKusick, U.S. 2,503,999 (1950).
  b. T. Cairns, A. Larcher, and B. McKusick, *J.Am. Chem. Soc.*, **74**, 5633 (1952).
2a. C. Grundmann and G. Weisse, *Ber.*, **84**, 684 (1951).
  b. C. Grundmann, G. Weisse, and S. Seide, *Ann.*, **577**, 77 (1952).
3a. R. Otto and K. Voigt, *J. prakt. Chem.*, (2), **36**, 78 (1887).
  b. J. Troeger, *ibid.*, (2), **50**, 446 (1894).
4. V. Meyer and Fr. Nabe, *ibid.*, (2) **82**, 537 (1910).
5a. N. Tscherven-Iwanoff, *ibid.*, (2), **46**, 142 (1892).
  b. E. Ghigi, *Gazz chim ital.*, **71**, 641–5 (1941) through *Chem. Zentr.*, 1942, II, 37.
6. E. T. McBee, O. R. Pierce and R. O. Bolt, *Ind. Eng. Chem.*, **39**, 391–2 (1947).
7. A. Weddige, *J. prakt. Chem.*, (2), **28**, 188 (1883).
8a. A. Weddige, *ibid.*, (2), **33**, 76 (1886).
  b. K. Dauchlauer, Germ. 699,493 (1940).
  c. T. Norton, U.S. 2,525,714 (1950).
9. C. Broche, *J. prakt. Chem.*, (2), **47**, 304 (1893).
    C. Broche, *J. prakt. Chem.*, (2), **50**, 114 (1894).
10a. R. Otto, *Ann.*, **116**, 195 (1860).
  b. R. Otto, *Ann.*, **132**, 181 (1864).
  c. H. Beckurts and R. Otto, *Ber.*, **9**, 1593 (1876).
  d. H. Beckurts and R. Otto, *Ber.*, **10**, 263, 2040 (1877).
  e. R. Otto and G. Holst, *J. prakt. Chem.*, (2), **41**, 461 (1890).
  f. J. Troeger, *J. prakt. Chem.*, (2), **46**, 353 (1892).
11. E. Ott, *Ber.*, **52**, 656 (1919).
12. A. Weddige, *J. prakt. Chem.*, (2), **10**, 208 (1874).
13. G. D. Lander, *J. Chem. Soc.*, **83**, 411 (1903).
14a. A. Hantzch and H. Bauer, *Ber.*, **38**, 1010 (1905).
  b. O. Diels, *ibid.*, **38**, 1186 (1905).
15. J. Troeger and V. Hornung, *J. prakt. Chem.*, (2), **57**, 357 (1898).
16. K. Dachlauer, Ger. 682,391 (1939).
17. D. Coffman, M. Rassch, G. Rigby, P. Barrick, W. Hanford, *J. Org. Chem.*, **14**, 747 (1949). See also U.S. 2,484,528.

condenses readily with benzaldehyde in the presence of base to yield
2,4,6-tristyryl-s-triazine (**XXXIX**).[84]

2. 2,4,6-Tris(trichloromethyl)-s-triazine

2,4,6-Tris(trichloromethyl)-s-triazine is a crystalline solid melting
at 96°. No investigation of its basicity or other physical characteristics
appears to have been made. It is readily available from the trimerization of trichloroacetonitrile in the presence of hydrogen chloride or
hydrogen bromide.[18, 21] The rate of trimerization is speeded up considerably by the use of aluminum chloride.[79] The allylic nature of the
chlorine atoms in this molecule make their replacement by fluorine
relatively simple. This has been studied by McBee and coworkers.[19]
Using HF and antimony pentafluoride, a variety of mixed tris(chloro-
fluoromethyl)-s-triazines were obtained all the way up to 2,4-6-tris-(trifluoromethyl)-s-triazine. 2,4,6-Tris(trichloromethyl)-s-triazine is more

resistant to hydrolysis by acids than other trialkyl-s-triazines, being
recovered unchanged after treatment with dilute hydrochloric or sulfuric
acid at 150–170°. At 200° with concentrated hydrochloric acid, hydrolysis
to ammonium chloride and trichloroacetic acid takes place slowly.

The —CCl$_3$ groups in 2,4,6-tris(trichloromethyl)-s-triazine are
rather labile and are replaced by means of various reagents.[85] On
heating with alkali, chloroform is evolved and the —CCl$_3$ grouping is

replaced by —OH. After prolonged treatment with alcoholic KOH, Weddige was able to obtain cyanuric acid, which served to characterize the starting material as an s-triazine. By using ammonia or amines, one or two of the trichloromethyl groups can be replaced; the third is resistant to attack by the amine, but can then be replaced by hydroxyl.

The replacement of the first —CCl_3 group occurs at room temperature, while the second group is attacked at 110°. Treatment of 2,4,6-tris-(trichloromethyl)-s-triazine with zinc in formamide does not result in simple reduction of the chlorines to hydrogen, but replacement of one of the trichloromethyl groups with —NH_2 occurs.[84] It is not clear in this case whether the ammonia comes from the formamide or from concurrent ring cleavage. Reduction of 2-methyl-4,6-bis(trichloromethyl)-s-triazine yields 2,4,6-trimethyl-s-triazine.[84]

3. 2,4,6-Tricarboxy-s-triazine

2,4,6-Tricarboxy-s-triazine and its derivatives form a very interesting group of s-triazines. The name "paracyanoformic acid" has used as a trivial name for these compounds. 2,4,6-Tricarboethoxy-s-triazine (XL) was first prepared by Weddige in 1874[27] by the trimerization

of ethyl cyanoformate in the presence of anhydrous hydrogen chloride or bromine in a sealed tube at 100°. Ott[86] later obtained quantitative yields of the compound by the use of dry hydrogen chloride at —15°, with a reaction period of two to three weeks. The same product has been obtained by heating the half ester, half iminoether of oxalic acid.

The triester is a solid (M.p. 165°) which is unstable above its melting point. It is insoluble in water, ether and benzene, and may be recrystallized from hot alcohol. Treatment with alkali, in the cold, results in hydrolysis to 2,4,6-tricarboxy-s-triazine. With hot alkali or acid, it is degraded to oxalic acid. Reaction of the triester with ammonia or amines gives good yields of the corresponding amides (XLI).

When the ester is heated with phosphorous pentachloride, it is converted to 2,4,6-tris(trichloromethyl)-s-triazine, a reaction which served to characterize the "paracyanoformates" as s-triazine derivatives.

Attempts to decarboxylate 2,4,6-tricarboxy-s-triazine to s-triazine were not successful.[88] Ott was able to prepare 2,4,6-tricyano-s-triazine in poor yield by treatment of 2,4,6-tricarboxamido-s-triazine with

phosphorous pentoxide. The product, which is a trimer of cyanogen (sometimes called hexacyanogen), could not be prepared by direct trimerization of cyanogen. 2,4,6-Tricyano-s-triazine was obtained as a crystalline solid (M.p. 119°) from benzene. It distils at 262° at atmospheric pressure. Its vapor is decomposed over platinum to yield cyanogen quantitatively. The triazine reacts rapidly with water and somewhat more slowly with methanol to yield cyanuric acid and trimethyl cyanurate, respectively, with the formation of HCN. In the later case, the intermediate products with one and two cyano groups replaced were also isolated.

The few mixed alkyl s-triazines which have been prepared were made by the mixed polymerization of nitriles. This was first carried out by Dachlauer[24] and later extended by Grundmann and co-workers.[7] Dachlauer treated a mixture of trichloroacetonitrile and acetonitrile with HCl for several hours at room temperature and obtained good yields of 2-methyl-4,6-bis(trichloromethyl)-s-triazine. This was confirmed by Grundmann, et al, who also noted that none of the other

$$2 \ CCl_3CN \ + \ CH_3CN \ \longrightarrow$$

possible products (trimethyl, dimethyl-trichloromethyl, or tris(trichloromethyl)-) were isolable. The cotrimerization of trichloroacetonitrile with ethyl cyanoformate yields all of the four possible products, but either the mono- or diester can be made to predominate by suitable choice of reaction conditions. Thus, when trichloroacetonitrile is treated with HCl to form the primary addition product $(CCl_3CN)_2 \cdot HCl$, and this is then treated with ethylcyanoformate, the major product is 2-carboethoxy-4,6-bis(trichloromethyl)-s-triazine, whereas, when HCl is added to a mixture of the two nitriles, 2-trichloromethyl-4,6-bis-(carboethoxy)-s-triazine is the principal product. It is interesting to note that acetonitrile did not cotrimerize with ethyl cyanoformate.

V. Triaryl-s-Triazines

As can be seen from the listings in Tables II-2 and II-3, the number and variety of triaryl-s-triazines and mixed alkyl aryl triazines which have appeared in the literature is much greater than for the trialkyl-s-triazines. This is due to the greater ease of preparation of these compounds. The general synthetic methods and common properties have been covered in an earlier section of this chapter. Some of the individual compounds which have been studied to a greater degree are discussed below.

TABLE II-2. Triaryl s-Triazines

A. Symmetrical Triaryl-s-Triazines

Ar	M.p., °C. Crystalline form, solvent	Method of preparation[a]	Ref.
C_6H_5	232 (needles-toluene, benzene, acetic acid)	A	1,2,3,4
		B	5,6,7,8,8a
		C	9
		D	10, 11
		E	12, 13
		F	14
		G	15
		H	2, 16, 17, 18, 19
$o\text{-}CH_3C_6H_4$	110 (rods, acetic acid)	A	1
$m\text{-}CH_3C_6H_4$	152–153	A	1, 4
$p\text{-}CH_3C_6H_4$	278–9° (needles, toluene + alcohol)	A	1, 4
		D	10, 11
		F	20
		G	15
		H	21
$C_6H_5CH_2$	221 (needles-acetic acid)	B	22
$C_6H_5CH{=}CH$		I	23
$o\text{-}CNC_6H_4$	296 (acetic acid)	A	24
$o\text{-}HOC_6H_4$	296–299 (needles-nitrobenzene)	A	15, 25, 26, 27, 28, 29
$p\text{-}HOC_6H_4$	357° (needles-acetic acid-pyridine)	J	30
$p\text{-}(CH_3)_2NC_6H_4$	357° (nitrobenzene + alcohol)	H	31
$o\text{-}CH_3OC_6H_4$	158°	G	32
		H	18
$p\text{-}CH_3OC_6H_4$	—	D	11
	217° (benzene)	G	15, 17
	224°	H	33
$p\text{-}C_2H_5OC_6H_4$	171°	F	30
$m\text{-}NO_2C_6H_4$	342° (nitrobenzene)	G	32
$p\text{-}NO_2C_6H_4$	> 360° (nitrobenzene)	G	32
$p\text{-}ClC_6H_4$	335° (needles-decalin)	A	1
		G	32
$2,4\text{-}(CH_3)_2C_6H_3$	154–5° (flakes-acetone)	D	10, 11
$3,4\text{-}(CH_3)_2C_6H_3$	210 (benzene)	D	10, 11
	266 (benzene)	G	32
		H	18

(Table continued)

TABLE II-2A (*continued*)

Ar	M.p., °C. Crystalline form, solvent	Method of preparation[a]	Ref.
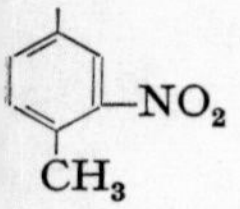 (2-CH₃, NO₂ phenyl)	305–7° (nitrobenzene)	A K	1 1
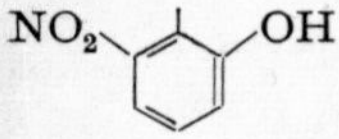 (NO₂, OH phenyl)	> 340°	A	34
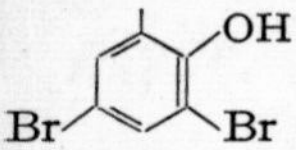 (Br, OH, Br phenyl)	> 355°	A	34
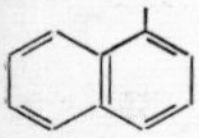 (naphthyl)	190–200°	D A	11 4
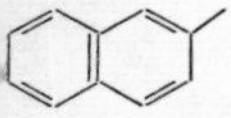 (methylnaphthyl)	290° (needles)	A	4

B. Unsymmetrical Triaryl-s-Triazines

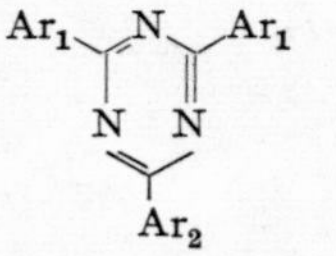

$$\begin{array}{c} \text{Ar}_1 \diagup\!\!\!\diagup N \diagdown\!\!\!\diagdown \text{Ar}_1 \\ N \qquad N \\ \text{Ar}_2 \end{array}$$

Ar₁	Ar₂	M.p., °C. Crystalline form, solvent	Method of preparation[a]	Ref.
C₆H₅	p-CH₃C₆H₄	182–3° (acetic acid)	A	4
C₆H₅	o-HOC₆H₄	245° (yellow needles)	H	35, 36
C₆H₅	o-CH₃OC₆H₄	140–141°	L	36
C₆H₅	m-NH₂C₆H₄	214° (needles-decalin)	M	1
C₆H₅	p-NH₂C₆H₄	273° (needles-decalin)	M	1
C₆H₅	p-CH₃CONHC₆H₄	315° (needles-decalin)	L	1
C₆H₅	(SO₃Ba)	—	N	37
C₆H₅	m-NO₂C₆H₄	206° (needles-acetic acid)	F	1
C₆H₅	p-NO₂C₆H₄	218° (needles-acetic acid)	F	1
C₆H₅	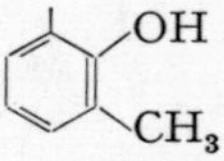 (OH, CH₃ phenyl)	214°	H	36
C₆H₅	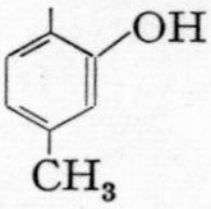 (OH, CH₃ phenyl)	235°	H	36

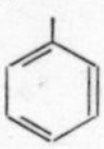

(Table continued)

TABLE II-2B (*continued*)

Ar$_1$	Ar$_2$	M.p., °C. Crystalline form, solvent	Method of preparation[a]	Ref.
C$_6$H$_5$	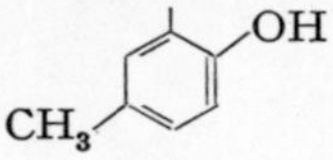 [structure: CH$_3$-substituted phenol with OH]	202°	H	36
p-CH$_3$C$_6$H$_4$	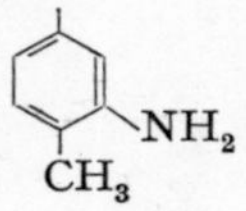 [structure: NH$_2$, CH$_3$-substituted benzene]	231° (decalin)	M	1
p-CH$_3$C$_6$H$_4$	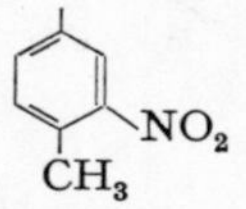 [structure: NO$_2$, CH$_3$-substituted benzene]	239° (decalin)	K	1
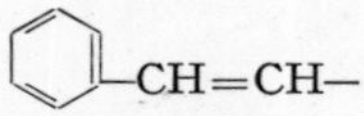 [structure: phenyl–CH=CH–]	C$_6$H$_5$	167.5–168.5°	O	38
m-NO$_2$C$_6$H$_4$	C$_6$H$_5$	253° (nitrobenzene)	F	1
p-NO$_2$C$_6$H$_4$	C$_6$H$_5$	297° (yellow plates-nitrobenzene)	F	1
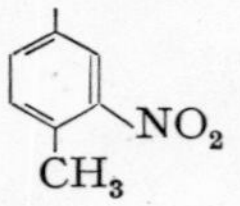 [structure: NO$_2$, CH$_3$-substituted benzene]	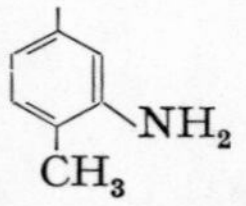 [structure: NH$_2$, CH$_3$-substituted benzene]	261° (decalin)	M	1
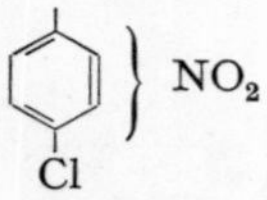 [structure: Cl-substituted benzene] } NO$_2$ [structure: Cl-substituted benzene]	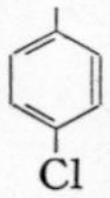	348° (nitrobenzene)	K	1
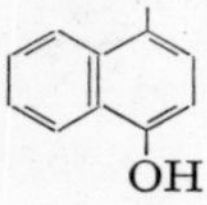 [structure: naphthalene with OH]	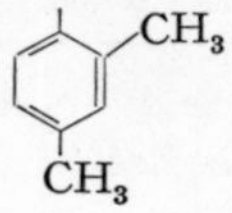 [structure: CH$_3$, CH$_3$-substituted benzene]	red-brown powder	D	39
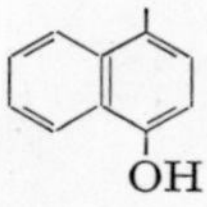 [structure: naphthalene with two OH]	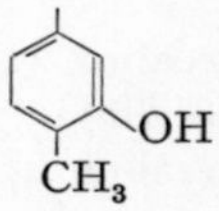 [structure: OH, CH$_3$-substituted benzene]		D	39
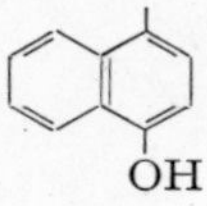 [structure: naphthalene with two OH]	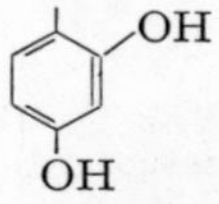 [structure: OH, OH-substituted benzene]		D	39
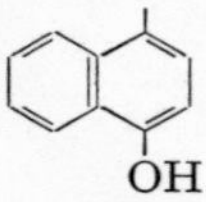 [structure: naphthalene with two OH]	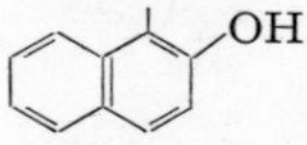 [structure: naphthalene with OH]		D	39
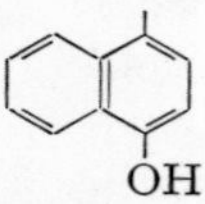 [structure: naphthalene with OH]	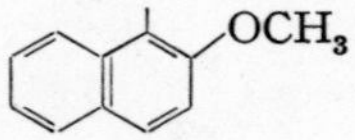 [structure: naphthalene with OCH$_3$]		D	39

(*Table continued*)

TABLE II-2B (continued)

Ar'	Ar²	M.p., °C. Crystalline form, solvent	Method of preparation[a]	Ref.
			D	39
			D	39
C_6H_5	H	75° (alcohol) 88.5°		40, 38
H	C_6H_5	63.5° (needles-alcohol)		38

[a] *Methods of Preparation*

A   Trimerization of nitrile-acid catalysis.
B   Trimerization of nitrile-basic catalysis.
C   Trimerization under high pressures.
D   Cyanuric halide (or cyanogen halide) plus aromatic compound in presence of $AlCl_3$.
E   Cyanuric halide plus aromatic halide in presence of Na.
F   Nitrile + acid chloride — with $AlCl_3$ and NH_4Cl.
G   Aromatic aldehyde plus N_4S_4.
H   From amidines or related compounds.
I   Trimethyl-s-triazines plus benzaldehyde.
J   Hydrolysis of ethoxy derivative.
K   Nitration of aromatic ring.
L   Acetylation of OH or NH_2 compound.
M   Reduction of nitro compound.
N   Sulfonation of aromatic ring
O   Reaction of methyl groups with benzaldehyde.

1. A. H. Cook and D. G. Jones, *J. Chem. Soc.*, **1941**, 278–82.
2. A. Pinner, *Ber.*, **22**, 1610 (1889).
3. A. Pinner and Fr. Klein, *Ber.*, **11**, 764 (1878).
4. M. Kunz, K. Koberle, E. Berthold, U.S. 1,989,042 (1932).
5. R. M. Anker and A. H. Cook, *J. Chem. Soc.*, **1941**, 323.
6. F. Swamer, G. Reynolds and C. Hauser, *J. Org. Chem.*, **16**, 43 (1951).
7. A. Hofmann, *Ber.*, **1**, 194 (1868).
8. A. Lottermoser, *J. prakt. Chem.*, (2), **54**, 132 (1896).
8a. O. Neunhoeffer and F. Nerdel, *Ann.*, **526**, 47 (1936).
9. T. Cairns, A. Larcher and B. McKusick, *J. Am. Chem. Soc.*, **74**, 5633 (1952).
10. R. Scholl and W. Norr, *Ber.*, **33**, 1052 (1900).
11. V. Meyer and Fr. Nabe, *J. prakt. Chem.*, (2), **82**, 537 (1910).
12. P. Klason, *J. prakt. Chem.*, (2), **35**, 83 (1887).
13. F. Krafft, *Ber.*, **22**, 1759 (1889).
14. P. Eitner and F. Krafft, *Ber.*, **25**, 2266 (1892).

15. F. Francis and O. Davis, *J. Chem. Soc.*, **85**, 259 (1904).
16. A. Pinner and Fr. Klein, *Ber.*, **10**, 1896 (1877), **11**, 4 (1878).
17. F. Francis and O. Davis, *J. Chem. Soc.*, **85**, 1535 (1904).
18. J. Bougault and P. Robin, *Compt. rend.*, **169**, 978 (1919).
19. B. Holmberg, *Arkiv Kemi, Mineral Geol.*, **A20**, No. 1, 14 pp. (1945) – through *Chem. Abstracts*, **41**, 1217g.
20. J. Piepes-Poratynski, *Bull de l'Acadamie des Sciences de Cracovie*, **1900**, through *Chem. Zentr.*, 1900, **II**, 477.
21. Glock, *Ber.*, **21**, 2652 (1888).
22. A. Pinner, *Ber.*, **17**, 2010 (1884).
23. C. Grundmann and G. Weisse, *Ber.*, **84**, 684 (1951).
24. S. Ross and M. Fineman, *J. Am. Chem. Soc.*, **72**, 3302 (1950).
25. H. Limpricht, *Ann.*, **98**, 258 (1856).
26. L. Henry, *Ber.*, **2**, 490 (1869).
27. J. Miller, *Ber.*, **22**, 2797 (1889).
28. Cousin and Volmar, *Bull. Soc. Chem.*, (4), **15**, 416 (1914).
29. A. Einhorn and Schmidlin, *Ber.*, **35**, 3653 (1902).
30. O. Diels and M. Liebermann, *Ber.*, **36**, 3191 (1903).
31. F. Sacks and P. Steinert, *Ber.*, **37**, 1737 (1904).
32. O. Davis, *J. Chem. Soc.*, **87**, 1831 (1905).
33. P. Robin, *Ann. Chim.*, (9), **16**, 117.
34. H. Lindemann and H. Thiele, *Ann.*, **449**, 63 (1926).
35. A. Titherley, and E. Hughes, *J. Chem. Soc.*, **99**, 1493 (1911).
36. A. Pinner, *Ber.*, **23**, 2934, 3824 (1890).
37. A. Pinner, *Ber.*, **17**, 2515 (1884).
38. C. Grundmann, H. Ulrich and A. Kreutzberger, *Ber.*, **86**, 181 (1953).
39. H. Fritzsche and P. Schadeli, U.S. 1,566,742 (1925).
40. F. Krafft and G. Koenig, *Ber.*, **23**, 2382 (1890).

TABLE II-3.   Mixed Alkyl-Aryl *s*-Triazines

R_1	R_2	M.p., °C. Crystalline form, solvent	Method of preparation[a]	Ref.
CH_3	C_6H_5	36–37°	A	1
CCl_3	C_6H_5	97–98° (alcohol)	B	2, 3
CCl_3	p-ClC_6H_4	142° (ethanol)	D	
CCl_3		210–212°	B	2
COOH	C_6H_5	170–180° (not pure)	C	1
C_6H_5	CH_3	110° (Ligroin, alcohol)	D	4
			E	5
C_6H_5	COOH	192° (prisms, dil. alcohol)	C	6
C_6H_5	C_2H_5	67°	E	5
C_6H_5	C_3H_7	78.5°	E	5

(*Table continued*)

TABLE II-3 (*continued*)

R_1	R_2	M.p., °C. Crystalline form, solvent	Method of preparation[a]	Ref.
C_6H_5	C_6H_{13}	44°	E	5
C_6H_5	$C_7H_{15}(n)$	28° (alcohol)	E	6
C_6H_5	$C_8H_{17}(n)$	43° (alcohol)	E	6
C_6H_5	$C_9H_{19}(n)$	38° (alcohol)	E	5
C_6H_5	$C_{15}H_{31}(n)$	64° (isobutyl alcohol)	E	5
C_6H_5		245° (nitrobenzene)	E	6
p-$CH_3C_6H_4$	CH_3	152–3°	D	7
p-iso $C_3H_7C_6H_4$	CH_3	68° (needles-dil. alcohol)	D	8
o-$CONH_2C_6H_4$	CH_3	—	D	13
m-$NO_2C_6H_4$	CH_3	185° (yellow needles-alc.)	D	9
p-$NO_2C_6H_4$	CH_3	280° (needles)	D	10
	CH_3	195 (prisms acetic acid)	D	11
	CH_3	138°	D	12

a Methods of Preparation

A   Reduction of trichloromethyl analog.
B   Mixed trimerization of nitriles.
C   Oxidation of methyl analog.
D   Amidines plus anhydrides.
E   Acid chloride and nitriles – in presence of aluminum chloride.

1.   C. Grundmann, H. Ulrick and A. Kreutzberger, *Ber.*, **86**, 181 (1953).
2.   K. Dachlauer, Ger. 682,391 (1939).
3.   C. Grundmann, G. Weisse and S. Seide, *Ann.*, **577**, 77 (1952).
  a. C. Grundmann and G. Ottman, U.S. 2,671,085 (1954).
4a. A. Pinner, *Ber.*, **17**, 2512 (1884).
  b. A. Pinner, *Ber.*, **25**, 1624 (1892).
5.   F. Krafft and A. von Hansen, *Ber.*, **22**, 803 (1889).
6.   F. Krafft and G. Koenig, *Ber.*, **23**, 2382 (1890).
7.   G. Glock, *Ber.*, **21**, 2156 (1888).
8.   P. Flatow, *Ber.*, **30**, 2009 (1897).
9.   A. Pinner, *Ber.*, **28** 482 (1895).
10. T. Rappeport, *Ber.*, **34**, 1989 (1901).
11. A. Pinner, *Ber.*, **25**, 1434, 1624 (1892).
12. A. Pinner, *Ber.*, **25**, 1414 (1892).
13. G. Luchenbach, *Ber.*, **17**, 1434 (1884).

1. 2,4,6-Triphenyl-s-triazine

2,4,6-Triphenyl-s-triazine, which has been prepared by at leas eight different methods (see Table II-2), has been the most studiec of the nonfunctional trisubstituted s-triazines. The most convenien method of preparation appears to be the reaction of benzonitrile witl chlorosulfonic acid at 0°.[25,26] After standing for several hours, th reaction mixture is poured onto ice. The precipitated product is obtainec in yields above 75%. The compound forms small white needles, m.p 233° C., when recrystallized from toluene. Triphenyl-s-triazine is a very stable compound and is reported to distill at temperatures in excess o 350° C. at one atmosphere pressure without decomposition. It is in soluble in water and dilute acids. If the compound has any basi characteristics, they have gone unnoticed in the literature. Attempts t prepare stable salts with mineral acids have not been successful. It i not soluble in ether, alcohol or ethyl acetate, but is soluble in carbo disulfide, hot acetic acid, benzene, and toluene and can be recrystallizec from these latter solvents. The stability of the compound is illustratec by the conditions required to cleave the s-triazine ring to form benzoi acid and ammonia—concentrated hydrochloric or hydriodic acid a 250° C. in a sealed tube. This triazine is inert to boiling caustic anc dilute acids. At water bath temperature, fuming sulfuric acid gives monosulfonate of uncertain structure.[61] Nitration with fuming nitri acid yields a trinitro derivative for which the structure 2,4,6-tris(m nitrophenyl)-s-triazine has been proposed due to the fact that m-nitro benzoic acid was obtained on hydrolysis.[1,89] However, a later prepara tion of the tri-m-nitrophenyl derivative from m-nitrobenzaldehyde anc nitrogen sulfide,[24] and the work of Cook and Jones[26] are not in agree ment with the above structure. The conversion of the triazine ring t the 5 membered glyoxaline system has been discussed previousl (see Section III).

The other triaryl-s-triazines have not been studied as thoroughl as the triphenyl derivative, but, in general, they are high-meltin stable compounds which exhibit chemical behavior similar to that o the triphenyl derivatives.

Aside from hydrolysis of the s-triazine ring system, and reductio to the glyoxaline structure, only a few chemical reactions of the triaryl *s*-triazines have been reported. The sulfonation and nitration of 2,4,6-triphenyl-*s*-triazine have been reported (v.s.). The nitration of substituted aryl *s*-triazines and the reduction of various nitro-substituted aryl *s*-triazines has been reported by Cook and Jones.[26] They were able to prepare 2-(*m*-nitro, *p*-tolyl)-4,6-diphenyl-*s*-triazine (XLII) and

2,4,6-tris(*m*-nitro *p*-tolyl)-*s*-triazine (XLIII) by the nitration of 2,4,6-tris(*p*-tolyl)-*s*-triazine. They were not able to isolate a dinitro derivative. The nitration of tris(*p*-chlorophenyl)-*s*-triazine yielded only a dinitrated product.

The phenylhydrazine reduction of the nitro groups to amino groups was carried out in good yield on 2-*m*-nitrophenyl-4,6-diphenyl-*s*-triazine, 2-*p*-nitrophenyl 4,6-diphenyl-*s*-triazine, and 2-(*m*-nitro, *p*-tolyl)-4,6-di(*p*-tolyl)-*s*-triazine. In the case of 2,4,6-tris(*m*-nitro, *p*-tolyl)-*s*-triazine, only one of the nitro groups could be reduced.

VI. Alkyl-Aryl-*s*-Triazines

Quite a variety of mixed alkyl, aryl *s*-triazines have been prepared, but very little study of their chemical properties has been made. Krafft and von Hansen have indicated that some of these compounds form HCl and PtCl$_4$ double salts of the structure (C·HCl)$_2$ PtCl$_4$.[57] The compounds of this classification are listed in Table II-3.

VII. Alkyl-Aryl-Dihydro-*s*-Triazines

Lottemoser[29] first observed the formation of a nonfunctional dihydro-*s*-triazine as a by-product in the formation of 2,4,6-triphenyl-*s*-triazine by reaction of benzonitrile with sodium metal. He formulated the reaction as with the product, after acidification, being 2,2,4,6-tetra-phenyl-1,2-dihydro-s-triazine (XLIV). Its hydrolysis to yield benz-

$$4\,C_6H_5CN + 2\,Na \longrightarrow NaCN +$$

(XLIV) C_6H_5

hydrol, ammonia, and benzoic acid was cited as evidence for the proposed structure.

Many years later, Anker and Cook[32] studied the reactions of nitriles with basic reagents in greater detail. They had also observed the formation of 2,2,4,6-tetraphenyl-1,2-dihydro-s-triazine in the reaction of benzonitrile with sodium in boiling benzene, and believed that the first step in the reaction involved the formation, at elevated tempera-tures, of phenyl sodium, which acted as the condensing agent. Ac-cordingly, they investigated the reaction of benzonitrile with various metallo-organic compounds at lower temperatures.

In the presence of sodium triphenylmethane, benzonitrile was simply trimerized to 2,4,6-triphenyl-s-triazine. When lithium com-pounds were used, the reaction took one of two courses. The ketimines first formed by reaction of the nitrile with the metallo-organic compound subsequently reacted with either one or two moles of nitrile. In the first case (in the presence of benzyl lithium, and sodium diphenyl-methane) the products were shown to be substituted pyrazolines. In the latter instance, 2,2,4,6-tetrasubstituted 1,2-dihydro-s-triazines were obtained in good yields. This was true when methyl, ethyl, n-propyl, isopropyl, n-butyl, and phenyl lithium were the organic bases.

The structure of these products was deduced from the following facts. The ultraviolet absorption spectra were all similar, and different from the pyrazolines. The compounds were strong bases and gave no ammonia on treatment with caustic. On heating with dilute sulfuric acid, ketones were formed.

The possibility that the products were asymmetrical triazines was disproved when their behavior on heating was studied. The methyl, ethyl, n-propyl, and butyl derivatives all lost ammonia on heating at

250–300° C. to yield crystalline products which were shown by synthesis to be 2,4,6-triphenyl pyrimidines (XLV). The unsymmetrical triazines

$$R = H, CH_3, C_2H_5, C_3H_7 \qquad (XLV)$$

$$(XLVI)$$

would have given the 2,4,5-triphenyl pyrimidines (XLVI). Alkylation of the salt of 2-methyl-2,4,6-triphenyl-1,2-dihydro-*s*-triazine with methyl iodide yielded 1,2-dimethyl-2,4,6-triphenyl-1,2-dihydro-*s*-triazine (XLVII). When this compound was heated, methyl amine was liberated with the formation of 2,4,6-triphenyl pyrimidine (XLVIII).

Swamer, Reynolds and Hauser[31] observed the formation of 2,4,6-triphenyl-1,2-dihydro-*s*-triazine (XLIX, B=H) in the reaction of benzo-

$$C_6H_5CN + BM \longrightarrow C_6H_5C=NM \xrightarrow{C_6H_5CN} C_6H_5C=NM$$

(XLIX) C_6H_5

B = H, alkyl, aryl;　M = Na, Li

nitrile with sodium hydride. They proposed the above as a mechanism for the condensation. In their case B=H, M=Na, while in the work of Anker and Cook alkyl and aryl lithiums yielded the tetra-substituted compound (XLIX, B=alkyl, aryl).

2,4,6-Triphenyl-1,2-dihydro-s-triazine was easily converted to the aromatic s-triazine by heating in refluxing nitrobenzene or xylene.

A listing of the dihydro s-triazines which have been reported is given in Table II-4.

TABLE II-4.   Dihydro-s-Triazines

R_1	R_2	R_3	M.p., °C. Crystalline form, solvent	Ref.
H	C_6H_5	H	171–2/toluene	1
H	C_6H_5	C_6H_5	190–1	2
			192	3
H	C_6H_5	CH_3	143	3
H	C_6H_5	C_2H_5	155	3
H	C_6H_5	C_3H_7	116	3
H	C_6H_5	C_3H_7 (iso)	184	3
H	C_6H_5	C_4H_9	117	3
CH_3	C_6H_5	CH_3	156	3

1. F. Swamer, G. Reynolds and C. Hauser, *J. Org. Chem.*, **16**, 43 (1951).
2. A. Lottermoser, *J. prakt. Chem.*, **54**, 132 (1896).
3. R. Anker and A. Cook, *J. Chem. Soc.*, **1941**, 323.

VIII. Applications

No commercial or pharmacological applications of the compounds covered in this chapter have as yet come to light. The preparation of trifluoroacetic acid esters from 2,4,6-tris(trifluoromethyl)-s-triazine may be of some limited commercial importance.

References

1. S. Cloez, *Ann.*, **115**, 23 (1860).
2. H. Limpricht, *Ann.*, **98**, 258 (1856).
3. J. Miller, *Ber.*, **22**, 2797 (1889).
4. R. Otto, *Ann.*, **116**, 195 (1860).
5. T. Cairns, A. Larcher and B. McKusic, *J. Am. Chem. Soc.*, **74**, 5633 (1952), also U.S. 2,503,999 (1950).
6. E. Ghigi, *Gazz chim. ital.*, **71**, 641 (1941), through *Chem. Zentr.*, 1942, II, 37.
7. C. Grundmann, G. Weisse and S. Seide, *Ann.*, **577**, 77 (1952).
8. A. Weddige and M. Korner, *J. prakt. Chem.*, (2), **31**, 148 (1885).
9. N. Tscherven-Iwanoff, *J. prakt. Chem.*, (2), **46**, 176 (1892).
10. D. Coffman, M. Raasch, G. Rigby, P. Barrich and W. Hanford, *J. Org. Chem.*, **14**, 747 (1949).
11. R. Otto, *Ann.*, **132**, 181 (1864).
12. H. Beckurts and R. Otto, *Ber.*, **9**, 1593 (1876).
13. H. Beckurts and R. Otto, *Ber.*, **10**, 263, 2040 (1877).
14. R. Otto, *Ber.*, **23**, 836 (1890).
15. R. Otto and Holst, *J. prakt. Chem.*, (2), **41**, 461 (1890).
16. R. Otto and K. Voigt, *J. prakt. Chem.*, (2), **36**, 78 (1887).
17. J. Troeger, *J. prakt. Chem.*, (2), **46**, 353 (1892).
18. K. Dachlauer, Ger. 699,493 (1940).
19. E. McBee, O. Pierce, and R. Bolt, *Ind. Eng. Chem.*, **39**, 391 (1947).
20. T. Norton, U.S. 2,525,714 (1950).
21. N. Tscherven-Iwanoff, *J. prakt. Chem.*, (2), **46**, 142 (1892).
22. C. Broche, *J. prakt. Chem.*, (2), **47**, 304 (1893).
23. P. Fineman, *J. Am. Chem. Soc.*, **52**, 2951 (1930).
24. K. Dachlauer, Ger. 682,391 (1939).
25. M. Kunz, K. Koberle and E. Berthold, U.S. 1,989,042 (1932).
26. A. Cook and D. Jones, *J. Chem. Soc.*, 1941, 278.
27. A. Weddige, *J. prakt. Chem.*, (2), **10**, 208 (1874).
28. A. Hofmann, *Ber.*, **1**, 194 (1868).
29. A. Lottermoser, *J. prakt. Chem.*, (2), **54**, 132 (1896).
30. E. Frankland and J. Evans, *J. Chem. Soc.*, **37**, 563 (1860).
31. F. Swamer, G. Reynolds and C. Hauser, *J. Org. Chem.*, **16**, 43 (1951).
32. R. Anker and A. Cook, *J. Chem. Soc.*, 1941, 323.
33. O. Neunhoeffer and F. Nerdel, *Ann.*, **526**, 47 (1936).
34. A. Pinner, *Ber.*, **17**, 2010 (1884).
35. J. Troger and O. Lunning, *J. prakt. Chem.*, (2), **69**, 354 (1904).
36. C. Engler, *Ann.*, **133**, 146 (1865).
37. L. Henry, *Ber.*, **2**, 305 (1869).
38. H. von Pechmann, *Ber.*, **28**, 2368 (1895).
39. H. von Pechmann, *Ber.*, **33**, 611 (1900).
40. J. Braun and C. Miller, *Ber.*, **39**, 2018 (1906).
41. L. Henry, *Ber.*, **2**, 490 (1869).
42. Cousin and Volmar, *Bull. soc. chim.*, (4), **15**, 416 (1914).
43. A. Einhorn and Schmidlin, *Ber.*, **35**, 3653 (1902).
44. A. Pinner and Fr. Klein, *Ber.*, **10**, 1896 (1877).
45. A. Pinner and Fr. Klein, *Ber.*, **11**, 4 (1878).
46. G. Glock, *Ber.*, **21**, 2652 (1888).
47. A. Pinner, *Ber.*, **22**, 1610 (1889).
48. B. Holmberg, *Arkiv. Kemi. Mineral. Geol.*, **A20**, No. 1, 14 (1945).

49. P. Klason, *J. prakt. Chem.*, (2), **35**, 83 (1887).
50. R. Scholl and W. Norr, *Ber.*, **33**, 1052 (1900).
51. V. Meyer and Fr. Nabe, *J. prakt. Chem.*, (2), **82**, 537 (1910).
52. H. Fritzsche and P. Schadeli, U.S. 1,566,742 (1925).
53. K. Schmidt and O. Wahl, U.S. 2,232,871 (1941).
54. G. Barsky and I. Gillis, U.S. 1,734,029 (1929).
55. F. Krafft, *Ber.*, **22**, 1759 (1889).
56. O. Diels and M. Liebermann, *Ber.*, **36**, 3191 (1903).
57. F. Krafft and A. von Hansen, *Ber.*, **22**, 803 (1889).
58. F. Krafft and G. Koenig, *Ber.*, **23**, 2382 (1890).
59. F. Krafft and G. Koenig, *Ber.*, **23**, 2388 (1890).
60. P. Eitner and F. Krafft, *Ber.*, **25**, 2266 (1892).
61. A. Pinner, *Ber.*, **17**, 2512 (1884).
62. A. Pinner. *Ber.*, **25**, 1414 (1892).
63. A. Pinner, *Ber.*, **25**, 1624 (1892).
64. A. Pinner, *Ber.*, **28**, 482 (1895).
65. P. Flatow, *Ber.*, **30**, 2009 (1897).
66. T. Rappeport, *Ber.*, **34**, 1989 (1901).
67. C. Grundmann and G. Ottman, U.S. 2,671,085 (1954).
68. A. Pinner, *Ber.*, **23**, 2934, 3824 (1890).
69. A. Titherley and E. Hughes, *J. Chem. Soc.*, **99**, 1493 (1911).
70. J. Bougault and P. Robin, *Compt. rend.*, **169**, 978 (1919).
71. F. Sachs and P. Stienert, *Ber.*, **37**, 1737 (1904).
72. F. Francis and O. Davis, *J. Chem. Soc.*, **85**, 259 (1903).
73. F. Francis and O. Davis, *J. Chem. Soc.*, **85**, 1535 (1903).
74. O. Davis, *J. Chem. Soc.*, **87**, 1831 (1905).
75. R. Schenk, *Ann.*, **290**, 181 (1896).
76. C. Grundmann, H. Ulrick and A. Kreutzberger, *Ber.*, **86**, 181 (1953).
77. C. Engler, *Ann.*, **149**, 310 (1869).
78. G. Luckenbach, *Ber.*, **17**, 434 (1884).
79. T. Norton, *J. Am. Chem. Soc.*, **72**, 3527 (1950).
80. B. Radziszewski, *Ber.*, **15**, 1493 (1882).
81. J. Piepes-Poratynski, *Bull. de l'Acadamie des Science de Cracovie*, **1900**, through *Chem. Zentr.*, **1900**, II, 477.
82. J. Troeger, *J. prakt. Chem.*, (2), **50**, 446 (1894).
83. V. Migrdichian, *The Chemistry of Organic Cyanogen Compounds*, Reinhold, New York, 1947, p. 351.
84. C. Grundmann and G. Weisse, *Ber.*, **84**, 684 (1951).
85. A. Weddige, *J. prakt. Chem.*, (2) **33**, 76 (1886).
86. E. Ott, *Ber.*, **52**, 656 (1919).
87. G. Lander, *J. Chem. Soc.*, **83**, 411 (1903).
88. A. Hantzsch, and H. Bauer, *Ber.*, **38**, 1010 (1905).
89. A. Claus, *J. prakt. Chem.*, (2), **51**, 399 (1895).

CHAPTER III

Monohydroxy, Hydroxyamino, Dihydroxy-*s*-Triazines and Related Compounds

I. Monohydroxy-*s*-Triazines

The simplest monohydroxy-*s*-triazine, 2-hydroxy-*s*-triazine (I), has not been reported. Attempts to prepare it from 2-amino-*s*-triazine (II) by hydrolysis or reaction with nitrous acid were unsuccessful.[1,2] Grundmann and co-workers also heated formylguanidine with formylurea but did not obtain the desired 2-hydroxy-*s*-triazine.

The closest approach to 2-hydroxy-*s*-triazine appears to have been 2-phenoxy-*s*-triazine (III) which Hirt, Nidecker, and Berchtold[3] prepared by hydrogenation of 2,4-dichloro-6-phenoxy-*s*-triazine.

A number of 2-hydroxy-4,6-diaryl-*s*-triazines were prepared by Pinner and collaborators. In 1894, Pinner[4] observed that when he condensed benzamidine with acetylmalonic ester in the presence of calcium carbonate he obtained, in addition to 2-phenyl-4-hydroxy-6-methyl pyrimidine (IV), the benzamidine salt (V). When the latter compound

was heated at 170–200°, carbon dioxide and acetone were evolved and a compound formulated as 2-hydroxy-4,6-diphenyl-*s*-triazine was produced. Pinner believed that the intermediate was the substituted

urea (VI) which cyclized with loss of ammonia under the reaction conditions.

That this postulate was at least possible, was shown shortly thereafter when he reported[5] two other preparations of this triazine. The
reaction of benzamidine with phosgene yielded 2-hydroxy-4,6-diphenyl-
s-triazine directly in addition to the urea. When the urea was heated
at its melting point (229° C.), it lost ammonia and gave the hydroxy-
s-triazine.

The reaction of benzamidine with ethyl chloroformate yielded a
substituted urethane (VII), which, on heating, lost alcohol and urethane
to give the same triazine (VIII). This latter method is the most convenient synthesis of 2-hydroxy-4,6-diphenyl-s-triazine.

$$2 C_6H_5C(=NH)NH_2 + 2 ClCOOC_2H_5 \longrightarrow 2 C_6H_5C(=NH)NHCOOC_2H_5 \xrightarrow{\Delta\,160°}$$

(VII)

There has been very little reported concerning the chemistry of
2-hydroxy-4,6-diphenyl-s-triazine and analogous compounds. Pinner
noted the amphoteric properties—solubility in dilute alkali and concentrated hydrochloric acid. The replacement of the hydroxyl group
with chlorine has been accomplished by reaction with phosphorous
oxychloride.[6] The nitration of the compound has been reported in the

patent literature[7] to yield 2-hydroxy-4,6-di(3'-nitrophenyl)-s-triazine.

The reaction of amidines with phosgene to yield 2-hydroxy-4,6-diaryl-s-triazines was extended by Pinner and co-workers to include the p-tolyl,[8] p-iso-propylphenyl,[9] m- and p-nitro,[10,11] and the α-furyl[8] homologs. With β-naphthamidine the reaction proceeded only as far as the urea stage and this could not be converted to the s-triazine. When aliphatic amidines were used, the triazines were not obtained.*

Somewhat related to the monohydroxy-s-triazines is 2-methoxy-4,6-dicyano-s-triazine (IX). It was prepared[12] by reaction of 2,4,6-tricyano-s-triazine with absolute methanol at room temperature.

$$\underset{\text{CN}}{\underset{|}{\overset{\text{NC}\quad\text{N}\quad\text{CN}}{\bigcirc}}} + CH_3OH \longrightarrow \underset{\text{CN}\quad\text{(IX)}}{\underset{|}{\overset{\text{NC}\quad\text{N}\quad\text{OCH}_3}{\bigcirc}}} + HCN$$

II. Monochloro-s-Triazines

Related to the monohydroxy-s-triazines are the monohalo-s-triazines. The earliest example of this structure was 2-chloro-4,6-diphenyl-s-triazine which was prepared in 1893 by Ephraim[6] by the reaction of the corresponding hydroxy compound with phosphorous oxychloride. A similar procedure has been used to prepare the m-nitrophenyl homolog.[13]

The reaction of cyanuric chloride with phenylmagnesium bromide was first studied by Ostrogovich.[14,3,15] The major product was 2-chloro-4,6-diphenyl-s-triazine with minor amounts of the monophenylated compound whose formation can be minimized by the use of excess Grignard reagent.

$$\underset{\text{Cl}}{\underset{|}{\overset{\text{Cl}\quad\text{N}\quad\text{Cl}}{\bigcirc}}} + 2\,C_6H_5MgBr \longrightarrow \underset{\text{C}_6\text{H}_5}{\underset{|}{\overset{\text{C}_6\text{H}_5\quad\text{N}\quad\text{Cl}}{\bigcirc}}}$$

Diels and Lieberman[16] treated cyanuric chloride with p-ethoxyphenyl bromide in the presence of sodium and obtained a small amount of 2-chloro-4,6-bis(p-ethoxyphenyl)-s-triazine as a by-product in addition to the triaryl derivative.

$$\underset{\text{Cl}}{\underset{|}{\overset{\text{Cl}\quad\text{N}\quad\text{Cl}}{\bigcirc}}} + C_2H_5OC_6H_4Br \xrightarrow{\text{Na}} \underset{C_6H_4OC_2H_5(p)}{\underset{|}{\overset{(p)C_2H_5OC_6H_4\quad\text{N}\quad\text{Cl}}{\bigcirc}}} + \underset{C_6H_4OC_2H_5(p)}{\underset{|}{\overset{(p)C_2H_5OC_6H_4\quad\text{N}\quad C_6H_4OC_2H_5(p)}{\bigcirc}}}$$

* Note added in proof: Schroeder and Grundmann (J. Am. Chem. Soc., **78**, 2447 (1956)) have extended the reaction to halogenated aliphatic amidines.

The replacement of a chlorine by an amino group in the *s*-triazine series has been mentioned elsewhere (Chapter I). It was used by Ephraim[6] to prepare some monoamino-*s*-triazines (see Chapter IV).

Grundmann and co-workers[15] treated 2-chloro-4,6-diphenyl-*s*-triazine with sodium hydrosulfide to prepare 2-mercapto-4,6-diphenyl-*s*-triazine, which was subsequently methylated with methyl iodide.

A listing of monohydroxy-*s*-triazines and related compounds is found in Table III-1.

TABLE III-1.   Monohydroxy-*s*-Triazines and Related Compounds

X	R_1	R_2	M.p., °C. Recrystallization solvent	Ref.
OH	C_6H_5	C_6H_5	289 (ethyl alc.)	1
OH	$C_6H_4CH_3(p)$	$C_6H_4CH_3(p)$	290 (ethyl alc.)	2
OH	$C_6H_4CH(CH_3)_2(p)$	$C_6H_4CH(CH_3)_2(p)$	253 (ethyl alc.)	3
OH	$C_6H_4NO_2(m)$	$C_6H_4NO_2(m)$	238–40	4, 5
OH	$C_6H_4Cl(p)$	$C_6H_4Cl(p)$	374	14
OH	$C_6H_4NO_2(p)$	$C_6H_4NO_2(p)$	> 305	6
OH	C_4H_3O	C_4H_3O	Dec. > 250	7
Cl	C_6H_5	C_6H_5	138–139 (ethyl alc.)	8, 9
Cl	$C_6H_4NO_2(m)$	$C_6H_4NO_2(m)$	180 (xylene)	10
Cl	$C_6H_4OC_2H_5(p)$	$C_6H_4OC_2H_5(p)$	149	11
OCH$_3$	CN	CN	86.5	12
SH	C_6H_5	C_6H_5	196–7	13
SCH$_3$	C_6H_5	C_6H_5	145	13
Cl	$C_6H_4Cl(p)$	$C_6H_4Cl(p)$	213	14

1. A. Pinner, *Ber.*, **23**, 161 (1890).
2. A. Pinner, *Die Imidoather und Seine Derivate*, Robert Oppenheimer, Berlin, 1892, pp. 185, 259.
3. P. Flatow, *Ber.*, **30**, 2006 (1897).
4. A. Pinner, *Ber.*, **28**, 483 (1895).
5. W. Hentrich and J. Hilger, U.S. 1,841,440 (1932).
6. T. Rappeport, *Ber.*, **34**, 1983 (1901).
7. A. Pinner, *Ber.*, **25**, 1414 (1892).
8. J. Ephraim, *Ber.*, **26**, 2226 (1893).
9. A. Ostrogovich, *Chem. Zeit.*, **36**, 739 (1912).
10. Brit. 334,887 (1930).
11. O. Diels and M. Lieberman, *Ber.*, **36**, 3191 (1903).
12. E. Ott, *Ber.*, **52**, 656 (1919).
13. C. Grundmann, H. Ulrick and A. Kreutzberger, *Ber.*, **86**, 181 (1953).
14. C. Grundmann and H. Schroeder, *Ber.*, **87**, 747 (1954).

III. Hydroxyamino-s-Triazines

Compounds with the general structural formula (X) have been called *guanides* in most of the past and current literature. This name is convenient for classification purposes to workers in the field, but to the

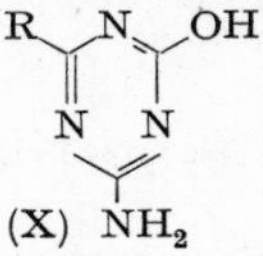

R N OH

N N   R=H, alkyl, aryl

(X) NH$_2$

average organic chemist, the systematic 2-hydroxy-4-amino-6-alkyl (or aryl)-s-triazine nomenclature is less misleading and easier to visualize. The name "guanide" originated because of the earliest preparation of this type of compound from the "guanamines" (2,4-diamino-s-triazines) (see Chapter IV) by Nencki.[17] Thus, hydrolysis of 2,4-diamino-6-methyl-s-triazine (acetoguanamine) (XI) with hot sodium hydroxide solution, yielded a compound (XII) in which one —NH$_2$ group was replaced by —OH. (The structure of these compounds will

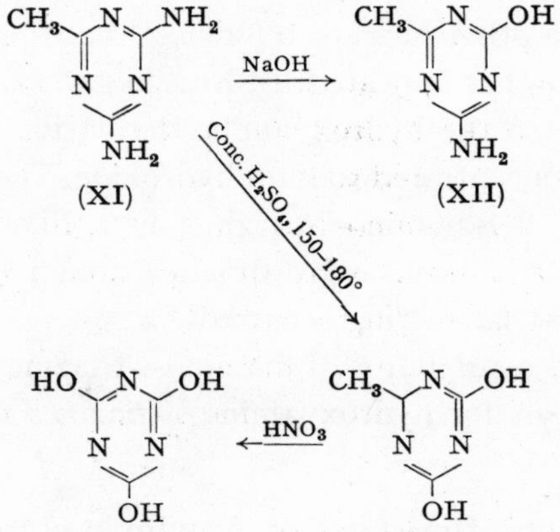

CH$_3$ N NH$_2$ CH$_3$ N OH

N N $\xrightarrow{\text{NaOH}}$ N N

NH$_2$ NH$_2$

(XI)   (XII)

Conc. H$_2$SO$_4$, 150–180°

HO N OH   CH$_3$ N OH

N N $\xleftarrow{\text{HNO}_3}$ N N

OH   OH

(XIII)

be discussed below.) This was called "guanid" by Nencki. Stronger hydrolysis yielded the dihydroxy compound (XIII) which was called "guanamide." In the more specific guanide-guanamide nomenclature, the compounds are named as derivatives of the acids containing one more carbon atom than the alkyl (or aryl) substituent on the rings. The relationship of these compounds to the more common s-triazines was shown by the oxidative degradation of (XIII) to cyanuric acid.[17]

Aside from the work of Ostrogovich in Italy, the hydroxyamino-s-triazines have received rather limited attention. In recent years, some industrial interest in these derivatives has been stimulated by the growing importance of other s-triazines.

1. 2-Hydroxy-4-Amino-6-Alkyl(or aryl)-s-Triazines (Guanides)

A. Methods of Preparation

(1) Hydrolysis of Diamino-s-Triazines. The hydrolysis of 2,4-diamino-6-methyl-s-triazine (XIV) by Nencki[17] in 1876 afforded the earliest preparation of a compound of this class. However, aside from

this work and one other obscure reference[18] no other mention of this preparative method has appeared. In Nencki's work, conversion of the diamino-s-triazine to the hydroxyamino derivative was accomplished by heating with concentrated sodium hydroxide. The hydrolysis of the parent compound, 2,4-diamino-s-triazine, in a like manner, was not successful. When conditions were drastic enough to effect reaction, destruction of the triazine ring occurred.

The increased availability of diamino-s-triazines might make this method of synthesis for hydroxyamino-s-triazines more attractive in the future.

(2) Cyclization of an Acyl or Aroylguanylurea. A more convenient method of preparation for the hydroxyamino-s-triazines is the cyclization of an acylated guanylurea. Thus, in 1909, Ostrogovich[19] reacted guanylurea with acetyl chloride and obtained acetylguanylurea hydrochloride (XV). When he attempted to prepare the free base (XVI) by neutralization with alkali, he obtained, instead, a good yield of 2-hydroxy-4-amino-6-methyl-s-triazine (XVII).

$$\underset{NH_2CNHCNH_2}{\overset{O\quad\ NH}{\overset{\|\quad\ \|}{}}} + CH_3COCl \longrightarrow \underset{NH_2CNHCNHCCH_3}{\overset{O\quad\ NH\ O}{\overset{\|\quad\ \|\quad\ \|}{}}} \cdot HCl$$

(XV)

$$\big\downarrow OH^-$$

$$\underset{NH_2}{\underset{(XVII)}{\overset{CH_3\diagdown\ N\diagup OH}{\overset{N\ N}{\bigcirc}}}} \xleftarrow{\ -H_2O\ } \left[\ \underset{NH_2CNHCNHCCH_3}{\overset{O\quad\ NH\ O}{\overset{\|\quad\ \|\quad\ \|}{}}}\ \right]$$

(XVII)   (XVI)

In similar work, Ostrogovich[20] heated benzamidine hydrochloride with guanylurea acetate at 160–200° and obtained a fair yield of 2-hydroxy-4-amino-6-phenyl-s-triazine. When he used guanylurea hydrochloride or sulfate, he did not obtain the desired product.

$$\underset{}{\overset{NH}{\overset{\|}{C_6H_5C}}}-NH_2\cdot HCl + \underset{NH_2CNHCNH_2}{\overset{NH\ O}{\overset{\|\quad\ \|}{}}}\cdot CH_3COOH \rightarrow \underset{NH_2}{\overset{C_6H_5\diagdown\ N\diagup OH}{\overset{N\ N}{\bigcirc}}} + NH_4Cl + NH_4OOCCH_3$$

(XVIII)

Ostrogovich believed these reactions to be general, but did not study them further. Several years later, renewed interest in the chemistry of cyanoguanidine lead to improved methods for the preparation of acylated guanylureas[21] and several other 2-hydroxy-4-amino-6-substituted s-triazines were prepared by cyclizing these compounds.[22,23]

$$(a)\ \underset{}{\overset{O}{\overset{\|}{RC}}}-Cl + \underset{NH_2CNHCN}{\overset{NH}{\overset{\|}{}}} \longrightarrow \underset{RCNHCNHCN}{\overset{O\quad\ NH}{\overset{\|\quad\ \|}{}}}$$

(XIX)

$$(b)\ \underset{RCNHCNHCN}{\overset{O\quad\ NH}{\overset{\|\quad\ \|}{}}} + H_2O \xrightarrow{\ HCl\ } \underset{RCNHCNHCONH_2}{\overset{O\quad\ NH}{\overset{\|\quad\ \|}{}}}$$

(XX)

$$(c)\ \underset{RCNHCNHCONH_2}{\overset{O\quad\ NH}{\overset{\|\quad\ \|}{}}} \xrightarrow{\ NaOH\ } \underset{NH_2}{\overset{R\diagdown\ N\diagup OH}{\overset{N\ N}{\bigcirc}}} + H_2O$$

The process as developed by Kaiser and Thurston involved three steps: (a) reaction of an acid chloride (or other acylating agent) with cyanoguanidine to yield an acylcyanoguanidine (XIX); (b) hydrolysis of this compound to the acylguanylurea (XX); and (c) cyclization by treatment with dilute caustic at room temperature. The cyclization step can also be carried out by adding the acylguanylurea to excess aqueous sodium hydroxide. The solution is heated to boiling, cooled, and filtered. On acidification, the hydroxyamino-s-triazines are obtained in yields of better than 90%.[24]

(3) From Cyanoguanidine. A procedure closely related to the above was first reported by Andreasch.[25] He obtained 2-hydroxy-4-amino-6-methyl-s-triazine in a single step by reaction of acetic anhydride with cyanoguanidine. Similar results were obtained when

$$(CH_3CO)_2O + CN\overset{\overset{\displaystyle NH}{\|}}{N}HCNH_2 \longrightarrow \underset{NH_2}{\overset{CH_3\diagdown\diagup N\diagdown\diagup OH}{N\diagdown\diagup N}} + CH_3COOH$$

benzoic anhydride was used.[26] When a substituted cyanoguanidine, N³-isopropylcyanoguanidine, was treated with acetic anhydride, 2-hydroxy-4-isopropylamino-6-methyl-s-triazine was the product.[27]

$$(iso)\ C_3H_7NH\overset{\overset{\displaystyle NH}{\|}}{C}NHCN + (CH_3CO)_2O \longrightarrow \underset{(XXI)\quad NHC_3H_7\ (iso)}{\overset{CH_3\diagdown\diagup N\diagdown\diagup OH}{N\diagdown\diagup N}} + CH_3COOH$$

This synthesis was studied further by Adams and co-workers.[24] They showed that acylated cyanoguanidines (see previous section) which they formulated as (XXII) were readily converted to hydroxy-

$$R\overset{\overset{\displaystyle O}{\|}}{C}NH\overset{\overset{\displaystyle NH_2}{|}}{C}=NCN \longrightarrow \underset{(XXII)\quad NH_2}{\overset{R-C\diagdown\diagup O\diagdown\diagup C=NH}{N\diagdown\diagup_C N}} \overset{\Delta}{\longrightarrow} \underset{NH_2}{\overset{R\diagdown\diagup N\diagdown\diagup OH}{N\diagdown\diagup N}}$$

amino-s-triazines by heating alone or in the presence of amine salts. The preparation of the s-triazines was accomplished by heating 50%

aqueous methoxyethanol solutions of the acylated cyanoguanidines. The less soluble hydroxyamino-*s*-triazines precipitated from the reaction mixture in good yields.

A convenient synthesis of hydroxyamino-*s*-triazines is that reported by Nagy.[28] He treated cyanoguanidine with carboxylic acids in the presence of oleum to obtain salts of acylated carbamylguanidines

$$
\underset{\substack{\parallel \\ \text{NCNHCNH}_2}}{\overset{\text{NH}_2}{}} + \text{RCOOH} \xrightarrow{\text{oleum}} \underset{\substack{\parallel\ \ \parallel\ \ \parallel \\ \text{RCNHCNHC-NH}_2 \cdot \text{H}_2\text{SO}_4}}{\overset{\text{O}\ \ \text{O}\ \ \text{NH}}{}} \xrightarrow{\text{NaOH}} \begin{array}{c} \text{R} \quad \text{N} \quad \text{OH} \\ \diagdown \diagup \\ \text{N} \quad \text{N} \\ \diagdown \diagup \\ \text{NH}_2 \end{array} + \text{H}_2\text{O}
$$

(XXIII)

(XXIII). Like the isomeric acylated guanylureas (see Section B), these compounds cyclized readily to the hydroxyamino-*s*-triazines on neutralization and warming of the aqueous solution of the free base.

(4) Oxidation of 2-Mercapto-4-Amino-6-Alkyl(Aryl)-*s*-Triazines (Thioguanides). Ostrogovich developed another method of synthesizing hydroxyamino-*s*-triazines from cyanoguanidine.[29,30] This involves first the reaction of a thioacid with cyanoguanidine to yield a mercaptoamino-*s*-triazine (XXIV) (see below) which is easily oxidized to the

$$
2\ \underset{\substack{\parallel \\ \text{O}}}{\text{RC}}{-}\text{SH} + \text{NC}{-}\text{NH}{-}\underset{\substack{\parallel \\ \text{NH}}}{\text{C}}{-}\text{NH}_2 \longrightarrow \begin{array}{c} \text{CH}_3 \quad \text{N} \quad \text{SH} \\ \diagdown \diagup \\ \text{N} \quad \text{N} \\ \diagdown \diagup \\ \text{NH}_2 \end{array} + \text{H}_2\text{S} + \text{RCOOH}
$$

(XXIV)

$$
\Bigg\downarrow \begin{array}{c} \text{H}_2\text{O}_2 \\ \text{HNO}_3 \\ \text{KMnO}_4 \end{array}
$$

$$
\begin{array}{c} \text{R} \quad \text{N} \quad \text{OH} \\ \diagdown \diagup \\ \text{N} \quad \text{N} \\ \diagdown \diagup \\ \text{NH}_2 \end{array}
$$

hydroxyamino-*s*-triazine. The oxidation is best carried out in aqueous potassium hydroxide solution with hydrogen peroxide. Ostrogovich prepared many homologs of the hydroxyamino-*s*-triazines by this procedure and the yields were usually quite good. The utility of the method, however, is dependent upon the accessibility of the thioacids.

(5) Reaction of Guanidine with Acetylurethane. The first method for preparing 2-hydroxy-4-amino-6-methyl-s-triazine employed by Ostrogovich[31] consisted of heating acetylurethane with guanidine

$$CH_3CNHCOOC_2H_5 + NH_2C-NH_2 \cdot H_2CO_3 \longrightarrow \quad + C_2H_5OH + 2 H_2O + CO_2$$

carbonate at 140° C. The reaction probably involves the intermediate formation of acetyl guanylurea. The yields were poor, however, and the reaction was not studied extensively.

B. Physical and Chemical Properties

The compound in this class which has been studied most is 2-hydroxy-4-amino-6-methyl-s-triazine (acetoguanide) and a full description of its properties and chemical reactions, which follows, will indicate what can be expected of its homologues.

2-Hydroxy-4-amino-6-methyl-s-triazine does not possess a definite melting point, but decomposes in the neighborhood of 300° C. Most of the other members of this series are crystalline solids which melt above 270° C. These compounds are usually only slightly soluble in hot water and insoluble in the common neutral organic solvents. The hydroxy-amino-s-triazines are amphoteric in nature and, as such, are readily soluble in strong inorganic acids and bases with salt formation. Thus, the hydrochloride, neutral sulfate, sodium, potassium, and silver salts of 2-hydroxy-4-amino-6-methyl-s-triazine have been prepared. Due to the weakly acidic and basic properties of the free compound, the salts are readily hydrolyzed in water. Stable picrates are formed and these are the best derivatives for identification purposes. They usually melt considerably lower than the parent compound.

The structural formulae which have been written for the hydroxy-amino-s-triazines with hydroxy and amino groups attached to the s-triazine ring are for convenience only and probably do not represent the true structures. In common with other amino and hydroxy-s-triazines, the tautomeric structures with imino and/or oxo groupings are also present to a greater or lesser degree, depending upon the particular groups present. In order to conveniently differentiate these compounds from dihydro and tetrahydro-s-triazines, we prefer to use

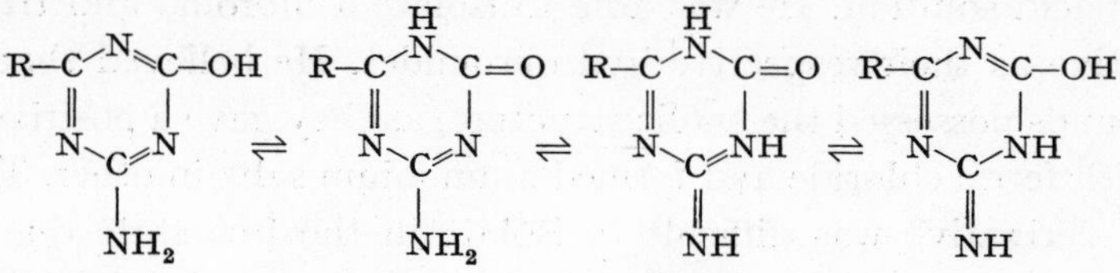

$$
\underset{\substack{| \\ NH_2}}{\overset{\substack{H \\ N}}{R-C}} \rightleftharpoons \underset{\substack{| \\ NH_2}}{\overset{\substack{H \\ N}}{R-C}} \rightleftharpoons \underset{\substack{\| \\ NH}}{\overset{\substack{H \\ N}}{R-C}} \rightleftharpoons \underset{\substack{\| \\ NH}}{\overset{\substack{N}}{R-C}}
$$

(XXV)

the most aromatic structure in classifying these compounds, recognizing the fact that both in the free state and in solution the other tautomeric forms might better represent the true structure.

Ostrogovich[32] favored the oxo-imino structure (XXV) as best representing the reactions and properties of "acetoguanide." Thus, the compound did not give a ferric chloride test and did not form a stable ammonium salt. No benzoyl derivative was obtained by the Schotten-Baumann procedure with benzoyl chloride. Also, this triazine did not react with benzenesulfonyl chloride. When 2-hydroxy-4-amino-6-methyl-s-triazine was acetylated with acetic anhydride, the resulting monoacetate showed an increase in acidic properties over the parent compound and was believed to have the enolic structure (XXVI),

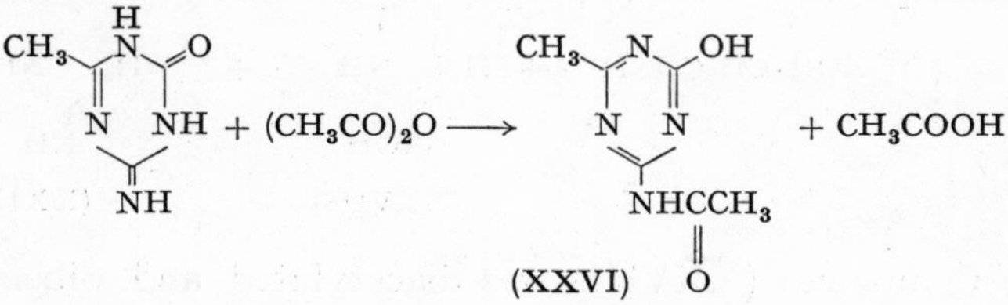

CH₃ structure + (CH₃CO)₂O ⟶ CH₃ structure + CH₃COOH

(XXVI)

The chemical reactions of the hydroxyamino-s-triazines have been very sparsely studied. Salt formation and acetylation have been

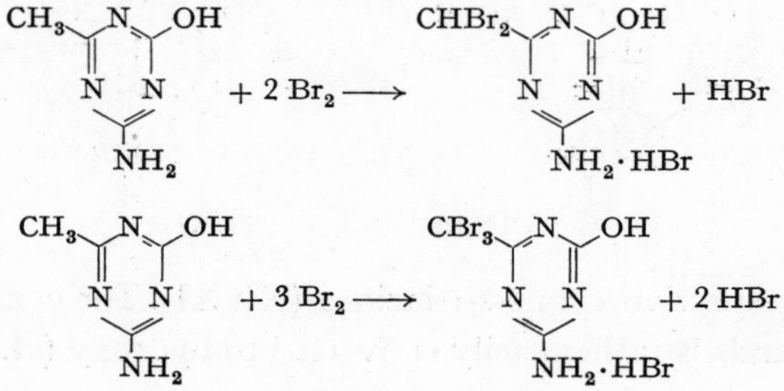

CH₃ structure + 2 Br₂ ⟶ CHBr₂ structure + HBr

CH₃ structure + 3 Br₂ ⟶ CBr₃ structure + 2 HBr

mentioned above. Ostrogovich[32] studied the bromination of 2-hydroxy-4-amino-6-methyl-s-triazine in glacial acetic acid and in aqueous hydrobromic acid solution. He was able to isolate a dibromo and tribromo derivative as their respective hydrobromides. He believed that these compounds possessed the enolic structure, as they gave a positive color test with ferric chloride and formed ammonium salts in ether. The tribromo derivative was difficult to isolate in the free state due to its tendency to react with water to yield bromoform and 2,4-dihydroxy-6-amino-s-triazine (ammelide) (XXVII).

The reaction of 2-hydroxy-4-amino-6-dibromomethyl-s-triazine with hydroxylamine acetate was carried out by Ostrogovich and Cadariu.[33] Instead of the expected mono-oxime, the principal product proved to be 6-oxo-4-isonitroso,3,4,5,6,tetrahydro-2-carboxaldoxime-s-triazine (XXVIII) with only a small amount of the mono-oxime

(XXIX). Compound (XXVIII) was diacetylated and dibenzoylated readily, and, on treatment with pyridine, these derivatives (XXX)

formed the respective cyano-s-triazines (XXXI). The cyano group in these compounds is rather easily converted to hydroxy (cf. Chapter II,

Section IV). The reaction with hydroxylamine to give the amidoxime (XXXII) was also carried out.

The reduction of the original isonitroso oxime (XXVIII) with stannous chloride gave the amino derivative (XXXIII). Reaction with phenylhydrazine yielded the phenylhydrazone (XXXIV).

The mono-oxime (XXXV) obtained in low yield by the reaction of hydroxylamine with 2-hydroxy-4-amino-6-dibromomethyl-s-triazine was studied briefly by Ostrogovich and Cadariu.[33] This compound formed both a mono- and diacetate. The diacetate was converted to the cyano-s-triazine (XXXVI) by reaction with pyridine. Treatment of

the oxime with phenylhydrazine yielded the phenylhydrazone (XXXVII) which was also obtained by reaction of the dibromomethyl-s-triazine with phenylhydrazine. Reduction with stannous chloride yielded the amino compound (XXXVIII).

Andreasch[25] briefly studied the reactions of 2-hydroxy-4-amino-6-methyl-*s*-triazine. Hydrolysis with concentrated sulfuric acid afforded 2,4-dihydroxy-6-methyl-*s*-triazine and reaction with chlorosulfonic acid at 150° yielded the sulfonate (XXXIX).

$$\underset{\text{(XXXIX)}}{\underset{\text{NH}_2}{\text{HSO}_3-\text{CH}_2}} \xleftarrow{\text{ClSO}_2\text{H}} \underset{\text{NH}_2}{\text{CH}_3} \xrightarrow{\text{H}_2\text{SO}_4} \underset{\text{OH}}{\text{CH}_3}$$

2. 2-Mercapto-4-Amino-6-Alkyl(Aryl)-*s*-Triazines (Thioguanides)

Closely related to the hydroxyamino-*s*-triazines are the mercapto-amino-*s*-triazines (thioguanides) (XL). As nearly as can be ascertained, these compounds have been studied only by Ostrogovich and co-

$$2\,\text{R}-\overset{\text{O}}{\underset{\|}{\text{C}}}-\text{SH} + \text{NC}-\text{NH}-\overset{}{\underset{\underset{\text{NH}}{\|}}{\text{C}}}-\text{NH}_2 \longrightarrow \underset{\underset{\text{(XL)}}{\text{NH}_2}}{\text{R}\quad\text{N}\quad\text{SH}} + \text{H}_2\text{S} + \text{RCOOH}$$

workers. The mercaptoamino-*s*-triazines have been prepared by the reaction of thioacids with cyanoguanidine. This reaction was discovered by Ostrogovich in 1912.[29] He was attempting to prepare acetyl-thioureidioguanidine

$$\underset{\text{O}\quad\ \text{S}\quad\ \text{NH}}{\overset{}{\text{CH}_3\text{CNHCNHCNH}_2}}$$

by addition of thioacetic acid to the nitrile group of cyanoguanidine with the hope that this compound could be cyclized to the *s*-triazine derivative with loss of water similar to the cyclization of acetyl-guanylurea. Instead, he obtained the triazine directly without being able to isolate any intermediate compounds. Since hydrogen sulfide is liberated, Ostrogovich believed that the reaction involved first an acylation, followed by an addition of thioacetic acid (the order of these steps might be reversed). Cyclization then occurs with elimination of acetic acid. In the case of thioacetic acid and aromatic thioacids, the

reaction is best carried out by adding a hot alcoholic solution of cyanoguanidine to a solution of the potassium salt in alcohol, followed by

$$CH_3CSH + NCNHCNH_2 \longrightarrow NCNHCNHCCH_3 + H_2S$$

$$CH_3CNHCNHCNHCCH_3 \xrightarrow{+CH_3C-SH} CH_3CNHCNHCNHCCH_3$$

$$+ CH_3COOH \longleftarrow$$

acidification with sulfuric acid. On standing, the "thioguanide" and
potassium sulfate precipitate. The triazine is dissolved in potassium
hydroxide and reprecipitated with acetic acid. For the higher aliphatic
derivatives, an alcoholic solution of cyanoguanidine is added to a solution of the free thioacid in ether. After a heating period, the solvents
are removed by distillation and the residue recrystallized from water or
alcohol. The yields by both procedures are generally good.

The mercaptoamino-substituted *s*-triazines have much the same
properties as the analogous hydroxy compounds. They are high melting
and soluble in acids and bases. Unlike the hydroxy analogs, they
dissolve easily in dilute ammonium hydroxide.

The chemistry of these compounds has not been investigated to any
great extent. One member of the series, 2-mercapto-4-amino-6-phenyl-
s-triazine, has been treated with dimethyl sulfate to form a monomethyl
derivative of uncertain structure. All of the other members have been
oxidized with hydrogen peroxide or alkaline permanganate to yield the
corresponding hydroxy compounds. The hydrogen peroxide oxidation

$$\xrightarrow{H_2O_2}$$

is carried out in aqueous potassium hydroxide solution at room temperature. After a standing period of several hours, the addition of acetic
acid precipitates the hydroxyamino-*s*-triazine in quantitative yield.

The hydroxyamino- and mercaptoamino-*s*-triazines which have
been characterized in the literature are found in Table III-2.

TABLE III-2.   A. 2-Hydroxy-4-Amino-6-Alkyl(Aryl)-*s*-Triazines

R	M.p., °C.	Method of preparation[a]	Ref.	Salt or derivative	M.p., °C.	Ref.
CH_3	Dec. > 300	A	1	Picrate	224	3
		B	2, 3	N^4 Acetyl		3
		C	4	N^4 Isopropyl	271	12
		E	5			
		J	17			
$CHBr_2$		G	3	Picrate	180–181	3
CBr_3	204–5	G	3	Picrate	177–178	3
CH_2SO_3H		H	5a			
C_2H_5	277–8	E	6	Hydrochloride	214–216	
		J	17	Picrate	191–192	6
C_3H_7	274–5	E	6	Picrate	195–196	6
		J	17			
C_4H_9 (iso)	263–4	E	7	Picrate	217–218	7
C_5H_{11}	240–241	D	8			
		J	17			
$C_{11}H_{23}$	229–230	D	8			
		J	17			
$C_6H_5CH_2$	277–8 (dec.)	E	9	Hydrochloride	220–210	
				Picrate	208–210	9
$C_6H_5CH=CH$	308–9 (dec.)	E	9	Picrate	271–273	9
HO—[triazine]—$CH_2CH_2CH_2CH_2$ ... NH_2	> 320	D	8			
C_6H_5	334–5	E	10	Hydrochloride	295–296	
		J	17	Picrate	296–297	10
o-$CH_3C_6H_4$	292–3	E	10	Picrate	255–256	10
m-$CH_3C_6H_4$	217–9	E	10	Picrate	297–298	10
p-$CH_3C_6H_4$	233–4	E	10	Hydrochloride	94–6 (dec.)	
		G	11	Picrate	304–5 (dec.)	10
p-$CH_3OC_6H_4$	327–8 (dec.)	E	10	Hydrochloride	290–192	
				Picrate	308–9	10
p-ClC_6H_4		E	11			
p-$NO_2C_6H_4$	300	D	8			
p-$NH_2C_6H_4$	320–325	D	8			
o-$HOOCC_6H_4$	295	D	8			
m-HOC_6H_4	235–240	D	8			
p-HOC_6H_4	326	D	8			

B. 2-Mercapto-4-Amino-6-Alkyl(Aryl)-s-Triazines

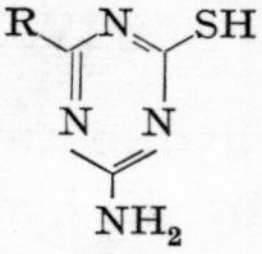

R	M.p., °C.	Salt or derivative	M.p., °C.	Ref.
CH$_3$	Dec.	Picrate	196–7 (dec.)	5, 13, 14
C$_2$H$_5$	257–8 (dec.)	Picrate	188–9 (dec.)	14
C$_3$H$_7$	262 (dec.)	Picrate	153 (dec.)	
C$_4$H$_9$ iso	269–270 (dec.)	Picrate	174–5	7
C$_6$H$_5$CH$_2$	270–271 (dec.)	Picrate	187–8 (dec.)	15
C$_6$H$_5$CH=CH	284–5 (dec.)	Picrate	221–2	15
C$_6$H$_5$	281–2 (dec.)	Picrate	193–4	16
o-CH$_3$C$_6$H$_4$	243–4 (dec.)	Picrate	224–5	16
m-CH$_3$C$_6$H$_4$	272–3	Picrate	210–11	16
p-CH$_3$C$_6$H$_4$	278–80	Picrate	191–2	16
p-CH$_3$OC$_6$H$_4$	282–3	Picrate	198–9	16

a Methods of Preparation:

A Hydrolysis of a diamino-s-triazine.
B Acyl urethane plus guanidine carbonate.
C Guanylurea plus acetyl chloride.
D Cyclization of an acylguanylurea.
E Oxidation of mercapto analogue.
F Cyanoguanidine, plus anhydride or acid chloride.
G Bromination of methyl derivative.
H Chlorosulfonation of methyl derivative.
J Cyclization of acylcyanoguanidine.

1. M. Nencki, *Ber.*, 9, 232 (1876).
2. A. Ostrogovich, *Gazz. chim. ital.*, 27, I, 222 (1897).
3. A. Ostrogovich, *Bul. Soc. Stunte Bucuresti*, 14, 288 (1905).
4. A. Ostrogovich, *Gazz. chim. ital.*, 39, I, 540 (1909).
5. A. Ostrogovich, *Bul. Soc. Stunte Bucuresti*, 21, 27 (1912).
5a. R. Andreasch, *Monatsh.*, 48, 145 (1927).
6. A. Ostrogovich and V. Galea, *Gazz. chim. ital.*, 65, 349 (1935).
7. A. Ostrogovich and V. Galea, *Gazz. chim. ital.*, 67, 664 (1937).
8. D. Kaiser and J. Thurston, U.S. 2,418,944 (1947).
9. A. Ostrogovich, and V. Galea, *Gazz. chim. ital.*, 65, 367 (1935).
10. A. Ostrogovich and V. Galea, *Gazz. chim. ital.*, 65, 357 (1935).
11. W. Hentrich and M. Hardtmann, Ger. 543,122 (1930).
12. F. King, R. Acheson and P. Spensley, *J. Chem. Soc.*, 1948, 1366.
13. A. Ostrogovich, *Rend. acca. nazl. Lincei*, (5), 21, 213 (1912).
14. A. Ostrogovich, *Rend. acca. nazl. Lincei*, (6), 11, 1012 (1930).
15. A. Ostrogovich, *Rend. acca. nazl. Lincei*, (6), 12, 162 (1931).
16. A. Oostrogovich, *Rend. acca. nazl. Lincei*, (6), 11, 1108 (1930).
17. P. Adams, D. Kaiser, D. Nagy, G. Peters, R. Sperry and J. Thurston, *J. Org. Chem.*, 17, 1162 (1952).

IV. Dihydroxy-s-Triazines

Like the hydroxyamino-s-triazines, a dihydroxy-s-triazine was first prepared by the hydrolysis of a diamino-s-triazine. This was accomplished by Nencki[17] in 1876 when he heated 2,4-diamino-6-methyl-s-triazine with concentrated sulfuric acid at 180° C. The name "aceto-guanamide" was used by Nencki for the product and the "guanamide" nomenclature has been used in much of the published work on these compounds (see Section C).

The parent compound of this class, 2,4-dihydroxy-s-triazine was unknown until the recent work of Brandenberger,[34,35,36] who studied the oxidation of uric acid with alkaline peroxide and permanganate using isotopically labelled uric acid. Earlier workers had shown that the first product (oxonic acid) was formed with loss of one carbon and one nitrogen of the uric acid molecule, and a second product (allantoxaidin) resulted from the loss of another carbon as carbon dioxide. The structures previously proposed for these compounds are (XLI) and (XLII) respectively.

(XLI)   "oxonic acid"   (XLII)   "allantoxaidin"   (XLIII)

Using uric acid (XLIII) labelled with C^{14} in the 2, 4, 6, and 8 positions successively, Brandenberger showed that the carbon atom lost in forming oxonic acid was C-6 of uric acid, and in going to allantoxaidin, C-5 is lost. This meant that neither of the oxidation products had the imidazole ring system as previously believed. From a study of the infrared and ultraviolet spectra of the oxidation products, and comparison with cyanuric acid, Brandenberger proposed s-triazine structures for these compounds. Thus, oxonic acid is 2,4-dihydroxy-6-carboxy-s-triazine (XLIV) and allantoxaidin, formed by

(XLIV)   (XLV)

decarboxylation, is 2,4-dihydroxy-s-triazine (XLV). Confirmatory evidence for the correctness of these structures was given by Hartmann and Fellig.[36]

As is true of the hydroxyamino-s-triazines, much of the work on the dihydroxy-s-triazines was done by Ostrogovich.

1. 2,4-Dihydroxy-6-Alkyl(Aryl)-s-Triazines (Guanamides)

A. Preparative Methods

(1) Hydrolysis of Diamino-s-Triazines. Although the hydrolysis of 2,4-diamino-6-methyl-s-triazine was used for the first preparation of a dihydroxy-s-triazine, only one other reference to this synthetic method has appeared. This was the work of Bandrowski[37] who reported the preparation of 2,4-dihydroxy-6-isobutyl-s-triazine. Very drastic treatment—concentrated sulfuric acid at 180° C.—was required to effect the hydrolysis.

(2) Cyclization of Acylbiurets and Related Methods. The most generally applicable method for the preparation of the 2,4-dihydroxy-6-substituted s-triazines is the cyclization of an acylbiuret. The first approach to this method was in work done by Ostrogovich[38] in the 1890's. He obtained 2,4-dihydroxy-6-methyl-s-triazine in 30%

$$CH_3CONHCOOC_2H_5 + NH_2CONH_2 \xrightarrow[150°]{\Delta}$$

$$+ C_2H_5OH + H_2O$$

$$CH_3CONHCONH_2 + NH_2COOC_2H_5$$

yield by heating urea with acetylurethane. Similarly, the reaction of acetylurea with urethane gave a 25% yield of the s-triazine. A few years later, he studied the reaction further[39] and showed that acetylurea and acetylbiuret were by-products. He believed that acetylbiuret was an intermediate in the formation of the triazine, but when he heated acetylbiuret to 190°, he did not obtain 2,4-dihydroxy-6-methyl-s-triazine.

Many years later, Ostrogovich showed that benzoylbiuret cyclized easily in the presence of cold, dilute potassium hydroxide to yield

2,4-dihydroxy-6-phenyl-s-triazine (XLVI).[40, 41] The cyclization of the acetyl derivative under similar conditions gave a poorer yield due to its greater susceptibility to hydrolysis.

$$C_6H_5CONHCONHCONH_2 \xrightarrow{OH^-}$$

$$\begin{array}{c} C_6H_5 \diagdown \quad N \diagup OH \\ \quad \parallel \\ N \quad N \\ \diagdown \diagup \\ OH \end{array} + H_2O$$

(XLVI)

No extensive study of the conditions for the cyclization of the acylbiurets has been made. Aside from the acetyl- and benzoylbiuret cyclizations, the method has been applied to phenylacetylbiuret[42] and a few aroylbiurets.[43] In the latter case, the biurets were synthesized by the reaction of an amide with allophanyl chloride (XLVII).

$$\begin{array}{cc} O \quad O \\ \parallel \quad \parallel \\ NH_2CNHC{-}Cl + C_6H_5CONH_2 \end{array} \longrightarrow \begin{array}{ccc} O \quad O \quad O \\ \parallel \quad \parallel \quad \parallel \\ C_6H_5CNHCNHCNH_2 + HCl \end{array}$$

(XLVII)

$$\Big\downarrow NaOH$$

$$\begin{array}{c} C_6H_5 \diagdown \quad N \diagup OH \\ \quad \parallel \\ N \quad N \\ \diagdown \diagup \\ OH \end{array}$$

During the course of Ostrogovich's work, he heated acetylbiuret with acetyl chloride and obtained a compound which he believed to be 2-hydroxy-4,6-dimethyl-s-triazine. However, he later showed[44, 45] that he had actually obtained 2,4-dihydroxy-6-methyl-s-triazine. The

$$CH_3CONHCONHCONH_2 + CH_3COCl \longrightarrow \begin{array}{c} CH_3 \diagdown \quad N \diagup OH \\ \quad \parallel \\ N \quad N \\ \diagdown \diagup \\ OH \end{array} + HCl + CH_3COOH$$

reaction proceeded in fairly good yield, but is not as clean cut as indicated above, since ammonium chloride and CO_2 were obtained as by-products. In contrast to this, the cyclization of benzoyl biuret by heating with benzoyl chloride did not take place.[40] The potential commercial availability of biuret should make this route to dihydroxy-s-triazines attractive in the future.

(3) Miscellaneous Methods.   A few scattered references have appeared describing the synthesis of dihydroxy-s-triazines by methods which involve the conversion of other functional groups present on a triazine ring to hydroxyls. Tschewen-Iwanoff prepared 2,4-dihydroxy-6-trichloromethyl-s-triazine (yield not given) by the hydrolysis of 2-amino-4,6-bis(trichloromethyl)-s-triazine with concentrated hydrochloric acid.[46] One would not expect good yields, since some of the

monohydroxy compounds and some cyanuric acid would probably be obtained as by-products.

Kolb[47] reacted cyanuric chloride with sodium diethylmalonate in alcoholic solution and was able to isolate only the monosubstituted derivative 2,4-dihydroxy-s-triazin-6-ylmalonic ester (XLVIII). This

compound was hydrolyzed and decarboxylated to 2,4-dihydroxy-6-carboxymethyl-s-triazine. Treatment of the silver salt of this acid with methyl iodide supposedly gave 2,4-dihydroxy-6-methyl-s-triazine.

B. Physical and Chemical Properties

There has been no general study made of the chemistry of the dihydroxy-substituted s-triazines. The little work which has been done has been confined principally to the 6-methyl derivative.

2,4-Dihydroxy-6-methyl-s-triazine is a high melting (276–277°) crystalline compound. It is very water soluble and somewhat soluble in common organic solvents. The compound is amphoteric. It forms salts with the mineral acids and also a variety of metal salts have been prepared. The fact that the metal salts contain a single equivalent of the metal atom led Ostrogovich[35] to propose that the structure was mainly the monoenolic form (XLIX).

(XLIX)

The halogenation of 2,4-dihydroxy-6-methyl-s-triazine was studied briefly by Nencki[17] and Ostrogovich,[38] but neither obtained well characterized products. It is probable that mixtures of the di- and tri-halomethyl derivatives were obtained. On hydrolysis, the reaction products yielded cyanuric acid and the haloform.

The reaction of 2,4-dihydroxy-6-aryl-s-triazines with phosphorous pentachloride[48] or thionyl chloride[49] gives the corresponding 2,4-di-chloro-s-triazines in excellent yield.

Ostrogovich hydrogenated 2,4-dihydroxy-6-methyl-s-triazine in the presence of platinum at room temperature. Absorption of one mole of hydrogen took place with the formation of 2,4-dihydroxy-6-methyl-5,6-dihydro-s-triazine (L),[50] which is the "trigenic acid" of Leibig and Wohler (see Section V, 2).

The reaction of the silver salt of 2,4-dihydroxy-6-methyl-s-triazine with methyl iodide resulted in an N-methyl derivative (LI).[39] Hydrolysis of the product yielded methylamine and ammonia. The reaction apparently involved a tautomeric keto form of the parent compound. Alkylation with ethyl iodide gave similar results.

Ostrogovich and Crasu[51, 52] studied the reaction of 2,4-dihydroxy-6-methyl-*s*-triazine with mixtures of nitric oxide and nitrogen dioxide and with amyl and isobutyl nitrites. The product of the reactions was believed to be 2,4-dihydroxy-*s*-triazin-6-yl formaldoxime (LII). The

acid salts and the mono-, di-, and trisodium salts of the oxime were prepared as well as several other metal salts. The reaction with acetic anhydride did not lead directly to an acetate, but in the presence of pyridine an acetyl derivative of the pyridine salt was obtained. In

pyridine solution, this product was converted to 2,4-dihydroxy-6-cyano-*s*-triazine (LIII). The oxime (LII) was reduced by the action of stannous chloride to the aminomethyl derivative (LIV); reaction with hydrogen sulfide produced the thioamide (LV).

2,4-Dihydroxy-6-benzyl-*s*-triazine was also converted to an oxime (LVI) by treatment with amyl nitrite in acid solution.[53] Various salts of the product were prepared and characterized. The iron and copper salts were believed to be complex salts containing two s-triazine rings.

$$HO-N-CH_2C_6H_5 \xrightarrow{C_5H_{11}ONO} HO-N-C\begin{smallmatrix}C_6H_5\\\ \ \ NOH\end{smallmatrix}$$

$$\overset{N\ N}{\underset{OH}{\ }} \qquad \overset{N\ N}{\underset{OH}{\ }} \quad (LVI)$$

The Beckmann rearrangement of the ketoxime in the presence of PCl$_5$ yielded 2,4-dihydroxy-6-benzoylamino-s-triazine (LVII) indicating an anti-configuration.

$$HO-N-C\begin{smallmatrix}C_6H_5\\\ \ \ N-OH\end{smallmatrix} \xrightarrow{PCl_5} HO-N-NHCC_6H_5$$

$$\overset{N\ N}{\underset{OH}{\ }} \qquad \overset{N\ N\ \ O}{\underset{OH}{\ }} \quad (LVII)$$

Block and Sobotka[41] studied the action of diazomethane on 2,4-dihydroxy-6-phenyl-s-triazine. They obtained two products which each contained two methyl groups. One of these compounds showed the presence of a methoxyl group by analysis. On treatment with dilute acid, the methoxyl group was hydrolyzed to yield compound (LX). Treatment of (LX) with diazomethane again gave the original mixture

$$C_6H_5-N-OH \xrightarrow{2CH_2N_2} C_6H_5-N-O \xrightarrow{NaOH} C_6H_5COOH + 2CH_3NH_2$$

$$\overset{N\ N}{\underset{OH}{\ }} \qquad CH_3N\ \ NCH_3$$

$$\qquad\qquad\qquad \overset{}{\underset{O\ \ (LVIII)}{\ }}$$

$$\Big\downarrow 2CH_2N_2$$

$$C_6H_5-C\overset{N}{\diagdown}C-OCH_3 \qquad C_6H_5-C\overset{N}{\diagdown}C-OH$$

$$CH_3N\diagdown_{C}\diagdown N \xrightarrow{H^+} CH_3N\diagdown_{C}\diagdown N \xrightarrow{CH_2N_2} (LVIII)+(LIX)$$

$$\overset{}{\underset{O\ \ (LIX)}{\ }} \qquad \overset{}{\underset{O\ \ (LX)}{\ }}$$

of compounds. The second of the dimethylated products, showing no —OCH$_3$ by analysis, gave benzoic acid and more than one equivalent of methylamine. The two diazomethane reaction products are thus formulated as the di-N-methylated derivative (LVIII), and the N and O methylated derivative (LIX), respectively. This is believed to be the first example of a mixed ether in the s-triazine series.

V. Hydrogenated Derivatives

Because of their relationship in structure to the 2-hydroxy-4-amino-6-substituted-s-triazines and the 2,4-dihydroxy-6-substituted s-triazines, the group of s-triazines of the structure (LXI) and (LXIII), which in their tautomeric forms (LXII) and (LXIV) are dihydro-hydroxyamino-, and dihydrodihydroxy-s-triazines, are discussed in

(LXI)   (LXII)   (LXIII)   (LXIV)

this chapter. In form (LXIII) these compounds are correctly named as 2,4-dioxo-6-substituted hexahydro-s-triazines, whereas the tautomer (LXIV) is a 2,4-dihydroxy-6-substituted dihydro-s-triazine. In most cases, the dioxo structure probably most correctly represents the true structure, but this has not been established for all members of the group.

1. Imino-oxohexahydro-s-Triazines

The only reported work on this type of molecule is that of Ostrogovich. In 1909, he observed[54] that the reaction of benzaldehyde with guanylurea sulfate at room temperature yielded "benzilidine guanylurea" to which he assigned structure (LXV). Twenty years later[55] he

prepared several other derivatives using various substituted benzaldehydes. The products were not unequivocably proven to contain the s-triazine ring system, but the analogy from the similar synthesis of the dioxo-hexahydro-s-triazines presents a strong argument for the proposed structures.

The compounds were basic in nature, forming stable salts with inorganic acids. Various picrates and platinic chloride-hydrogen chloride complexes were also prepared and characterized. Alkali metal

salts also formed, leading Ostrogovich to believe that the imino-oxo-
s-triazines existed to some extent in the enolic form. He was unable
to obtain acetyl derivatives and thus concluded that the $\diagdown$C=NH
grouping was present rather than the amino structure. The compounds
prepared by Ostrogovich are listed in Table III-3.

TABLE III-3.   2-Imino-4-Oxo-6-Aryl-
               Hexahydro-s-Triazines

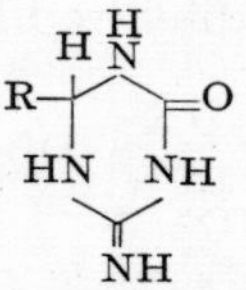

R	M.p., °C.	Hydrochloride, M.p., °C.	Picrate, M.p., °C.
C_6H_5	183–4	—	211–12
o-$NO_2C_6H_4$	208–9	235–6	213–15
m-$NO_2C_6H_4$	222	268	210–11
p-$NO_2C_6H_4$	180	250	212–13
p-$(CH_3)_2NC_6H_4$	220–221	212	220

2. Dioxohexahydro-s-Triazines

The first compound of this series dates back to 1846 when Liebig
and Wohler[56] treated cyanic acid with acetaldehyde and obtained a
product to which they gave the name "trigenic acid." In 1881, Herzig[57]
studied this compound further. He noted its ease of oxidation to cyanuric
acid and its thermal decomposition to carbon dioxide, ammonia, and
"acetaldehyde ammonia." Herzig proposed two ethylidine biuret
structures, an open-chain form (LXVI) and the cyclic structure

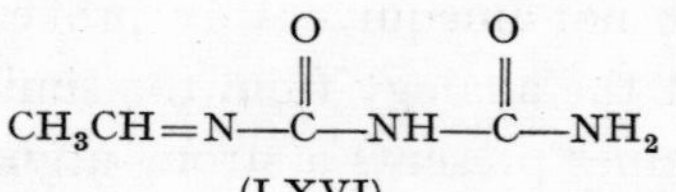

$$CH_3CH=N—\overset{O}{\overset{\|}{C}}—NH—\overset{O}{\overset{\|}{C}}—NH_2$$

(LXVI)

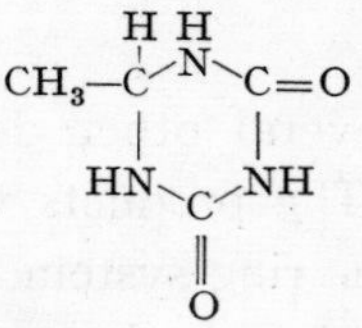

(LXVII)

(LXVII). That the latter was correct was demonstrated by Ostrogovich[50] who showed that the hydrogenation product of 2,4-dihydroxy-
6-methyl-s-triazine (enolic form of (LXVIII)) was identical with the

o-called "trigenic acid" prepared by the method of Liebig and Wohler. The compound shows no acidic properties according to Ostrogovich. He was able to prepare several salts with hydrogen chloride, $HAuCl_4$,

$$CH_3 \underset{HN \quad NH}{\overset{N \quad O}{\diagdown}} \xrightarrow{\; H_2 \;} CH_3 \underset{HN \quad NH}{\overset{H \; N \; H}{\diagdown}} O$$

(LXVIII)

and picric acid; also a basic mercuric salt and a silver salt. The compound forms a diacetate which on treatment with ammonia was converted to acetamide and the parent compound. The mechanism of the formation of "cycloethylidinebiuret" from cyanic acid has not been elucidated.

The corresponding aromatic derivatives were prepared by condensing benzaldehyde with urea[58] or biuret[54, 59] and by the reaction of benzal chloride[60] with urea. The product, 2,4-dioxo-6-phenyl-hexa-

$$C_6H_5CHO + NH_2CNHCNH_2$$

$$C_6H_5CHO + 2\,NH_2CNH_2 \longrightarrow C_6H_5 \underset{HN \quad NH}{\overset{H \; H \; N}{\diagdown}} O$$

$$C_6H_5CHCl_2 + 2\,NH_2CNH_2$$

hydro-s-triazine has been called "benzilidine biuret" in much of the literature. The reaction of benzaldehyde with urea was believed by Schiff to involve a condensation with two moles of urea to form a benzylidine bisurea (LXIX), which then cyclized with the loss of

$$C_6H_5CHO + 2\,NH_2CNH_2 \longrightarrow C_6H_5CH \underset{NHCNH_2}{\overset{NHCNH_2}{\diagup}} \xrightarrow{\; -NH_3 \;} C_6H_5 \underset{HN \quad NH}{\overset{H \; H \; N}{\diagdown}} O$$

(LXIX)

ammonia. In substantiation of this path, Schiff was able to isolate benzilidine bismethylurea by the reaction of methylurea with benzaldehyde. Heating the bisurea at 250° gave a low yield of 2,4-dioxo-3-

methyl-6-phenyl-hexahydro-s-triazine (LXX) identical with that obtained by the methylation of the phenyl derivative.

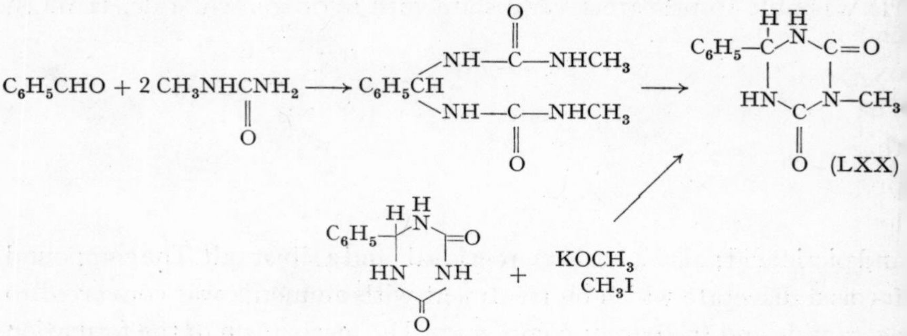

$$C_6H_5CHO + 2\ CH_3NHCNH_2 \longrightarrow C_6H_5CH \begin{array}{c} NH-C-NHCH_3 \\ \\ NH-C-NHCH_3 \end{array} \longrightarrow$$

(LXX)

$$+ \begin{array}{c} KOCH_3 \\ CH_3I \end{array}$$

Brodsky[61] heated benzaldehyde with ammonium thiocyanate at 135–165° and obtained a compound which he formulated as 2,4-dimercapto-6-phenyl-5,6-dihydro-s-triazine (LXXI). A few years later,

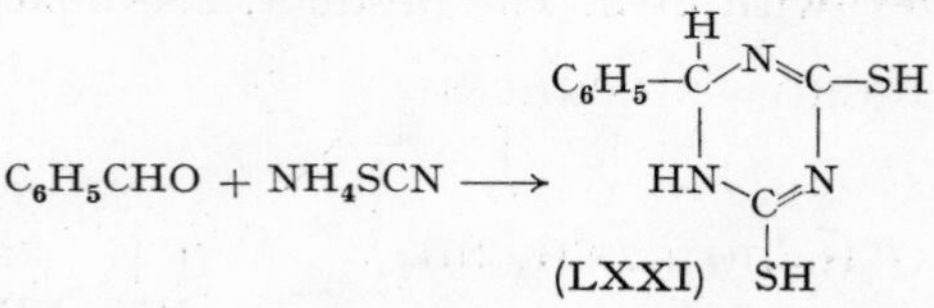

$$C_6H_5CHO + NH_4SCN \longrightarrow$$

(LXXI)

Abel[60] attempted to prepare the same compound by the reaction of benzal chloride with thiourea (cf. reaction with urea above) but isolated a chlorine containing compound of undetermined structure.

No systematic study of the chemistry of the "arylidine-biurets" has been made. Hydrolysis with sodium hydroxide yields benzaldehyde and ammonia; with barium hydroxide, urea and carbon dioxide can also be identified.

The parent member of this group, 2,4-dioxo-hexahydro-s-triazine, was synthesized by Diels and Lichte[62, 63] by the acid cyclization of methylene bisurea (LXXII). The same compound has been prepared recently by the reduction of 2,4-dihydroxy-s-triazine (cf. p. 202) with

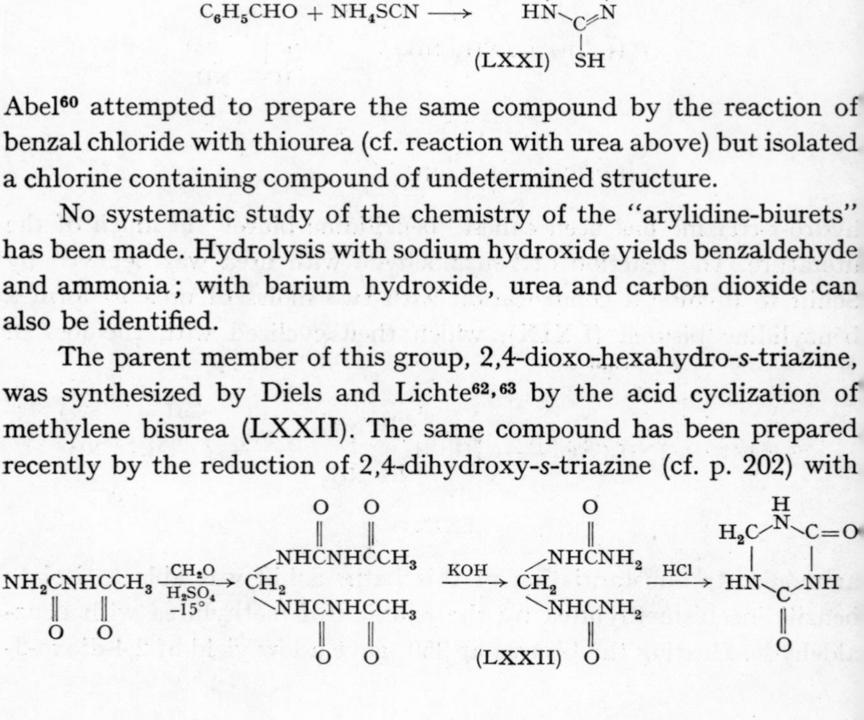

$$NH_2CNHCCH_3 \xrightarrow[\substack{H_2SO_4 \\ -15°}]{CH_2O} CH_2 \begin{array}{c} NHCNHCCH_3 \\ \\ NHCNHCCH_3 \end{array} \xrightarrow{KOH} CH_2 \begin{array}{c} NHCNH_2 \\ \\ NHCNH_2 \end{array} \xrightarrow{HCl}$$

(LXXII)

sodium amalgam.[36] A similar sequence starting with thiourea led to the corresponding dithiono derivative. The cyclization of methylene bis-urea has also been accomplished by heating at 100–230° C.[64] The chemistry of these compounds has been practically neglected. The oxygenated compound is weakly basic, forming salts with strong acids. The sulfur derivative is acidic (probably due to the prevalence of the thiol tautomer) and silver, copper, and mercurous salts have been prepared. The alkylation of the mercurous salt with methyl and ethyl iodides has been described.

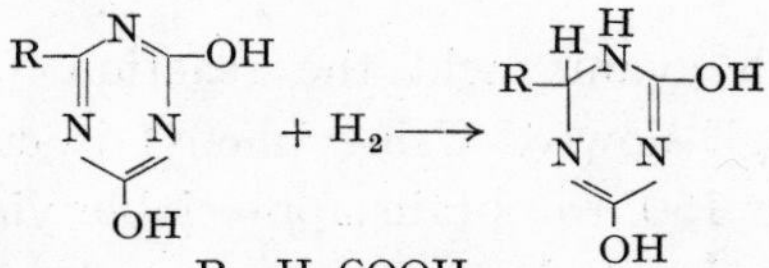
R—
—OH
N
N N
+ H2 ⟶
OH
H H
R—
N
—OH
N N
OH

R=H, COOH

Pinner and Lifschutz[65] reported that on heating α,α,β-trichloro-butyraldehyde cyanohydrin with urea they obtained a small yield of 2,4-dioxo-6-(α,α,β-trichloropropyl)-hexahydro-*s*-triazine (LXXIII). This structure for their reaction product is very doubtful.

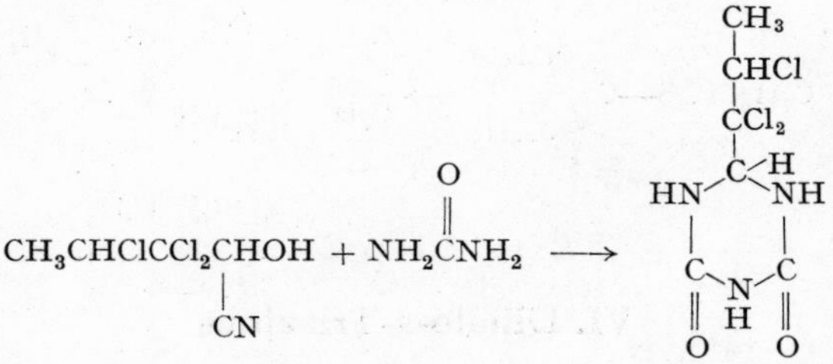
CH3CHClCCl2CHOH + NH2CNH2 ⟶
CN
O
CH3
CHCl
CCl2
C
H
HN
NH
C
N
C
H
O O

(LXXIII)

Some more highly substituted 2,4-dioxo-hexahydro-*s*-triazines were prepared in the work of Lange and co-workers on the condensation of Schiff's bases of benzaldehyde with cyanic acid and phenyl iso-

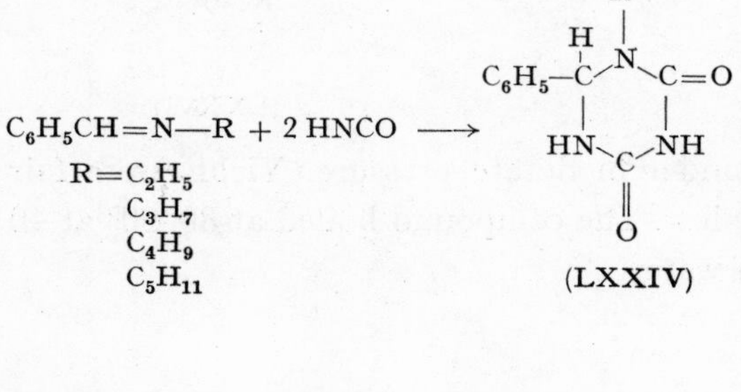
C6H5CH=N—R + 2 HNCO ⟶
R=C2H5
C3H7
C4H9
C5H11
R
H
N
C6H5—C
C=O
HN
NH
C
O

(LXXIV)

cyanate.[63,67,68] The reaction with cyanic acid yielded a 2,4-dioxo-1-alkyl-6-phenyl-hexahydro-s-triazine (LXXIV) and with phenyl isocyanate, a 2,4-dioxo-1-alkyl-3,5,6-triphenylhexahydro-s-triazine (LXXV)

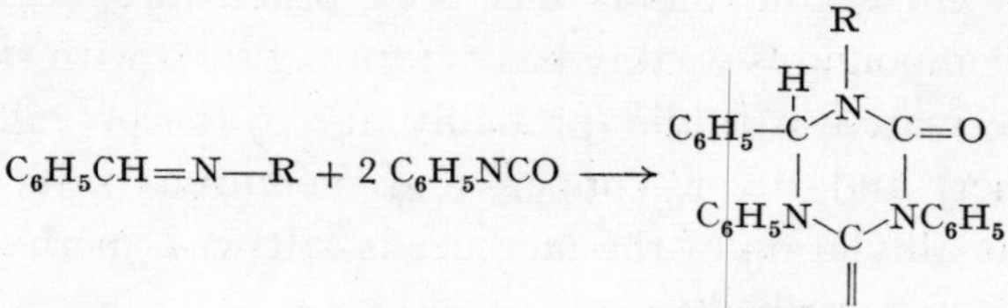

$$C_6H_5CH=N-R + 2\ C_6H_5NCO \longrightarrow$$

(LXXV)

was obtained. With cyanic acid the reaction proceeded at room temperature although slowly. Using phenyl isocyanate necessitated prolonged heating at 150° to obtain appreciable yields. With aromatic Schiff bases, the triazine derivatives were not obtained.

The reaction of benzoyl isothiocyanate with the benzyl ether of phenylthiourea yielded a compound which was formulated as an s-triazine derivative.[69] A similar interpretation was given to the reaction product of the methyl ether of phenylthiourea.[68]

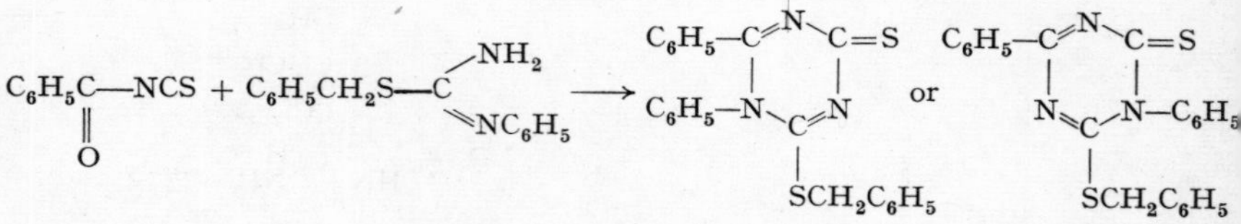

VI. Dihalo-s-Triazines

The preparation of the simplest dihalo-s-triazine, 2,4-dichloro-s-triazine (LXXVI) has been reported recently. It was synthesized by the cotrimerization of cyanogen chloride with hydrogen cyanide[71] (cf.

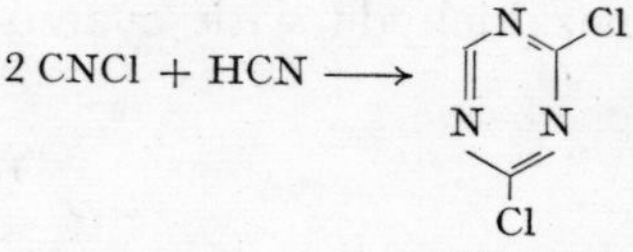

$$2\ CNCl + HCN \longrightarrow$$

(LXXVI)

Chapter II) under moderate pressure. Yields were fair but the conversions were low. The compound boiled at 80–90° at 40 mm. and was reactive with water.

The reaction of dihydroxy-s-triazines with phosphorous penta-chloride[48] and thionyl[49] chloride ahs been used to prepare 2,4-dichloro-6-aryl-s-triazines.

A poor yield of 2,4-dichloro-6-phenyl-s-triazine was obtained by the reaction of phenyl magnesium bromide with cyanuric chloride.[14]

The dihalo-s-triazines have been condensed with amines to yield 2,4-diamino-s-triazines.[71] Particularly important applications of this reaction are in the preparation of dye stuffs.[48,72] For this purpose, amines such as amino-anthraquinone have been reacted with various 2,4-dichloro-6-aryl-s-triazines.

References

1. A. Burger and E. Hornbaker, *J. Am. Chem. Soc.*, **75**, 4579 (1953).
2. C. Grundmann, L. Schwenicke and E. Beyer, *Ber.*, **87**, 19 (1954).
3. R. Hirt, H. Nidecker and R. Berchtold, *Heli. chim. acta.*, **33**, 1365 (1950).
4. A. Pinner, *Ber.*, **23**, 161 (1890); see also A. Pinner, Die *Imidoather and Seine Derivative*, Robert Oppenheimer, Berlin, 1892, pp. 185, 259–65.
5. A. Pinner, *Ber.*, **23**, 2919 (1890).
6. J. Ephraim, *Ber.*, **26**, 2226 (1893).
7. W. Hentrick and J. Hilger, U.S. 1,841,440 (1932); see also Ger. 501,087 (1930).
8. A. Pinner, *Ber.*, **25**, 1414 (1892).
9. P. Flatow, *Ber.*, **30**, 2006 (1897).
10. A. Pinner, *Ber.*, **28**, 483 (1895).
11. T. Rappeport, *Ber.*, **34**, 1983 (1901).
12. E. Ott, *Ber.*, **52**, 656 (1919).
13. Brit. 330,583 (1929); Brit. 334,887 (1930).
14. A. Ostrogovich, *Chem. Zeit.*, **36**, 739 (1912).
15. C. Grundmann, H. Ulrich and A. Kreutzberger, *Ber.*, **86**, 181 (1953).
16. O. Diels and M. Liebermann, *Ber.*, **36**, 3191 (1903).
17. M. Nencki, *Ber.*, **9**, 232 (1876).
18. Elzanowski, Thesis, Freiburg 1892.
19. A. Ostrogovich, *Gazz. chim. ital.*, **39**, I, 540 (1909).
20. A. Ostrogovich, *Rend. Acca. Lincei*, (6), **11**, 843 (1930).
21. D. Kaiser and J. Thurston, U.S. 2,397,667 (1946).
22. D. Kaiser and J. Thurston, U.S. 2,418,944 (1947).

23. J. Thurston, U.S. 2,444,013 (1945).
24. P. Adams, D. Kaiser, D. Nagy, G. Peters, R. Sperry and J. Thurston, *J. Org. Chem.*, **17**, 1162 (1952).
25. R. Andreasch, *Monatsh.*, **48**, 145 (1927).
26. W. Hentrick and M. Hardtmann, Ger. 543,112 (1930).
27. F. King, R. Acheson and P. Spensley, *J. Chem. Soc.*, **1948**, 1366.
28. D. Nagy, U.S. 2,481,526 (1949).
29. A. Ostrogovich, *Rend. Acca. Lincei*, (5), **21**, 213 (1912).
30. A. Ostrogovich, *Bull. Soc. Stunte Bucuresti*, **21**, 27 (1912), through *Chem. Zentr.*, 1912, II, 607.
31. A. Ostrogovich, *Gazz. chim. ital.*, **27**, I, 222 (1897).
32. A. Ostrogovich, *Bull. Soc. Stunte Bucuresti*, **14**, 288 (1905).
33. A. Ostrogovich and J. Cadariu, *Gazz. chim. ital.*, **71**, 505, 515, 524 (1941).
34. H. Brandenberger, *Helv. Chim. Acta*, **37**, 641 (1954).
35. H. Brandenberger and R. Brandenberger, *Helv. Chim. Acta*, **37**, 2207 (1954).
36. S. Hartman and J. Fellig, *J. Am. Chem. Soc.*, **77**, 1051 (1955).
37. E. Brandrowski, *Ber.*, **9**, 242 (1876).
38. A. Ostrogovich, *Ann.*, **288**, 318 (1895).
39. A. Ostrogovich, *Gazz. chim. ital.*, **27**, II, 416 (1897).
40. A. Ostrogovich, *Bull. Soc. Stunte Cluj*, **4**, 521 (1929).
41. E. Block and H. Sobotka, *J. Am. Chem. Soc.*, **60**, 1656 (1938).
42. A. Ostrogovich, and I. Tansilau, *Gazz. chim. ital.*, **64**, 824 (1934).
43. Fr. 785,458, 790,454 (1935).
44. A. Ostrogovich, *Gazz. chim. ital.*, **41**, II, 70 (1911).
45. A. Ostrogovich, *Gazz. chim. ital.*, **44**, II, 562 (1914).
46. N. Tscherven-Iwanoff, *J. prakt. Chem.*, (2), **46**, 145 (1892).
47. W. Kolbe, *J. prakt. Chem.*, (2), **49**, 90 (1894).
48. W. Hentrick, U.S. 1,897,428 (1933).
49. A. Joyce and W. Munro, U.S. 2,691,018 (1954).
50. A. Ostrogovich and G. Ostrogovich, *Gazz. chim. ital.*, **66**, 48 (1936).
51. A. Ostrogovich and V. Crasu, *Gazz. chim. ital.*, **64**, 800 (1934).
52. A. Oostrogovich and V. Crasu, *Gazz. chim. ital.*, **66**, 653 (1936).
53. A. Ostrogovich and I. Tanislau, *Gazz. chim. ital.*, **66**, 662 (1936).
54. A. Ostrogovich, *Gazz. chim. ital.*, **39**, I, 540 (1909).
55. A. Ostrogovich and V. Median, *Gazz. chim. ital.*, **59**, 189 (1929).
56. J. Liebig and F. Wohler, *Ann.*, **59**, 291 (1846).
57. J. Herzig, *Monatsh.*, **2**, 398 (1881), through *Chem. Zentr.*, **1881**, 627.
58. H. Schiff, *Ann.*, **291**, 361 (1896).
59. P. Biginelli, *Rend. Acca. Lincei*, (5), **3**, 195 (1894).
60. J. Abel, *Am. Chem. J.*, **13**, 114 (1891).
61. M. Brodsky, *Monatsch.*, **8**, 28 (1887).
62. O. Diels and R. Lichte, *Ber.*, **59**, 2778 (1926).
63. O. Diels, German 479,349 (1929).
64. H. Fahrenhorst and H. Schwermann, Ger. 694,829 (1941).
65. A. Pinner and J. Lifschutz, *Ber.*, **20**, 2345 (1887).
66. W. Hale and N. Lange, *J. Am. Chem. Soc.*, **41**, 379 (1919).
67. W. Hale and N. Lange, *J. Am. Chem. Soc.*, **42**, 107 (1920).
68. N. Lange, *J. Am. Chem. Soc.*, **48**, 2440 (1926).
69. T. Johnson and M. Elmer, *Am. Chem. J.*, **30**, 169 (1903).
70. J. Douglas and F. Dains, *J. Am. Chem. Soc.*, **56**, 719 (1934).
71. I. Hechenbleikner, *J. Am. Chem. Soc.*, **76**, 3032 (1954).
72. R. Gadea and W. Munro, U.S. 2,691,020 (1954).

CHAPTER IV

Monoamino- and Diamino-s-Triazines

I. Monoamino-s-Triazines

Amino-substituted s-triazines have been extensively studied, especially compounds containing two or three amino groups attached to the s-triazine ring. Only a few s-triazines containing one amino (and no other functional group) group have been reported.

1. 2-Amino-s-triazine and Derivatives

The earliest monosubstituted s-triazine prepared was 2-amino-s-triazine (I) reported by Diels[1] in 1899. Until the recent work of Grundmann on s-triazine itself, this was the simplest known s-triazine

derivative. Diels prepared 2-amino-s-triazine by the reduction of 2-amino-4,6-dichloro-s-triazine with a hydrogen iodide-phosphorous iodide mixture. The yield was poor, and, aside from noting its melting point (225°), solubility in dilute acids, and the preparation of a chloroplatinate, Diels made no further study of the compound.

English and Paden[2] reported the preparation of 2-amino-s-triazine by heating formylguanidine with formamide at 160° C. followed by distillation at 250° C.

217

In 1950 Hirt, Nidecker, and Berchtold,[3] in a search for possible antihistamine activity in the amino-s-triazines series, prepared 2-amino-s-triazine and several other monoamino-s-triazines by two procedures. The first method was the reduction of a dichloroamino-s-triazine with

R=H, CH$_3$, C$_2$H$_5$, C$_3$H$_7$, C$_4$H$_9$

hydrogen in the presence of a palladium catalyst. Some difficulties were encountered here due to the insolubility of the starting material and, in general, yields were poor. A better scheme was the reduction of 2,4-dichloro-6-phenoxy-s-triazine to 2-phenoxy-s-triazine. This went well because of the improved solubility of the starting material. It was found that reaction of the phenoxy-s-triazine with ammonia and amines gave the desired amino-s-triazines in good yield. With aliphatic

R=H, alkyl, aryl

amines and ammonia, replacement of the phenoxy group proceeded at relatively low temperatures (30–70°), while with aromatic amines heating at 120–150° was required.

Very little of the chemistry of 2-amino-s-triazine has been described. Burger and Hornbaker[4] tried several of the common amine reactions with this compound and were able to obtain only inorganic salts as products. They concluded that there was no primary amine group present in the compound, but that it could best be represented by the iminodihydro-s-triazine structure (II). This was borne out by the ultraviolet spectrum which does not show the characteristic absorption peak at 236 mμ that is found in melamine.

An attempt to prepare 2-hydroxy-s-triazine by reaction of 2-amino-s-triazine with nitrogen oxides was unsuccessful because the triazine ring system was destroyed.[5]

Hirt and co-workers[3] were able to alkylate monosubstituted amino-

TABLE IV-1.   Monoamino-s-Triazines

$$\begin{array}{c} N \stackrel{N-R_1}{\diagdown_{R_2}} \\ \parallel \quad \parallel \\ N \quad N \end{array}$$

R_1	R_2	M.p., °C. (Recrystallization solvent)	B.p., °C./P(mm.)
H	H	224 (dec.)/(hot H_2O)	—
H	CH_3	110/(benzene-pet. ether)	—
H	C_2H_5	64/(benzene-pet. ether)	—
H	C_3H_7	52	140–142/15
H	C_4H_9	62–3/(benzene)	—
H	C_6H_5	148–50/(benzene)	—
H	$C_6H_5CH_2$	105	183–5/13
$(CH_3)_2NCH_2CH_2$	$C_6H_5CH_2$	(HCl salt-153)	190–195/15
$(C_2H_5)_2NCH_2CH_2$	$C_6H_5CH_2$	—	170–175/1
H	$(p)CH_3OC_6H_4CH_2$	118–119	—
$(CH_3)_2NCH_2CH_2$	$(p)CH_3OC_6H_4CH_2$	(HCl salt 173–175)	225/15
H	$(p)C_2H_5OC_6H_4CH_2$	117/(alcohol)	—
$(CH_3)_2NCH_2CH_2$	$(p)C_2H_5OC_6H_4CH_2$	(HCl salt 155–156)	222/12

s-triazines by treating them with sodium amide followed by reaction with a dialkylaminoethyl chloride. The amino-s-triazines prepared in this work are summarized in Table IV-1. None of these compounds possessed appreciable antihistamine activity.

$$\begin{array}{c} N \quad NHR \\ \parallel \quad \parallel \\ N \quad N \end{array} \xrightarrow[(R_1)_2NCH_2CH_2Cl]{NaNH_2} \begin{array}{c} R \\ N \quad NCH_2CH_2N(R_1)_2 \\ \parallel \quad \parallel \\ N \quad N \end{array}$$

2. 2-Amino-4-alkyl-s-Triazines

A few monoamino-s-triazines having one other substituent (non-functional) group on the triazine ring also appear in the work of Hirt and co-workers.[3] They treated cyanuric chloride with methyl and ethyl magnesium bromide to obtain 2,4-dichloro-6-methyl-s-triazine and the corresponding ethyl derivative. This was then reacted with benzyl-amine to replace one chlorine atom with a benzylamino group. The other chlorine was then replaced with hydrogen by catalytic hydrogenation. Alkylation of the monosubstituted amine with dimethylaminoethyl chloride was also carried out. The compounds prepared are listed in Table IV-2.

TABLE IV-2.   Mononuclear Substituted
              Amino-s-Triazines

R_1	R_2	R_3	M.p., °C. (Recrystallization solvent)	B.p., °C.
H	$C_6H_5CH_2$	CH_3	68 (pet. ether)	—
H	$C_6H_5CH_2$	C_2H_5	48 (pet. ether)	—
$(CH_3)_2NCH_2CH_2$	$C_6H_5CH_2$	CH_3		161–3/0.6 mm.
$(CH_3)_2NCH_2CH_2$	$C_6H_5CH_2$	C_2H_5		170–173/0.4 mm.

3. 2-Amino-4,6-Alkyl(aryl)-s-Triazines

2-Amino-s-triazines with two alkyl (aryl) or substituted alkyl (aryl) groups also present on the triazine ring have been prepared by replacement of a —Cl, —CCl$_3$, or —CBr$_3$ group by reaction with ammonia or an amine.

As described earlier, the —CCl$_3$ and —CBr$_3$ groupings attached to the s-triazine ring are easily replaced by amino groups. Weddige[6] reported the preparation of 2-amino-4,6-bis(trichloromethyl)-s-triazine by reaction of 2,4,6-tris(trichloromethyl)-s-triazine with alcoholic ammonia at room temperature. Substitution of methyl amine for ammonia gave the homologous methylamino derivative. Broche[7] obtained similar results with 2,4,6-tris(tribromomethyl)-s-triazine, and also preparared 2-phenylamino-4,6-bis(tribromomethyl)-s-triazine by the use of aniline.

Ephraim[8] prepared some 2-amino-4,6-diphenyl-s-triazines by the reaction of 2-chloro-4,6-diphenyl-s-triazine with ammonia, aniline and phenylhydrazine at elevated temperatures.

$$C_6H_5 \diagdown \quad N \diagup Cl \quad + RNH_2 \xrightarrow{110-180°} \quad C_6H_5 \diagdown \quad N \diagup NHR$$

$$R = H, C_6H_5, C_6H_5NH$$

The simplest compound of this group, 2-amino-4,6-dimethyl-s-triazine, was obtained in 1892 by Tscherven-Iwanoff[9] who reduced 2-amino-4,6-bis(trichloromethyl)-s-triazine with zinc dust in alcoholic solution. Grundmann and Weisse[10] obtained the same compound when they attempted to prepare 2,4,6-trimethyl-s-triazine by the reduction of 2,4,6-tris(trichloromethyl)-s-triazine with zinc and formamide. Apparently the facile replacement of one —CCl$_3$ by —NH$_2$ occurred before reduction.

Grundmann[5] noted that the amino group of 2-amino-4,6-dimethyl-s-triazine does not condense with aromatic sulfonyl chlorides. Acetylation with acetyl chloride was also unsuccessful. He suggested that the compound might be best represented by the imino dihydro-s-triazine

(III)

structure (III). When Grundmann attempted the preparation of 2-hydroxy-4,6-dimethyl-s-triazine by alkaline hydrolysis of the "amino"

$$\xrightarrow{\text{Con. KOH}} \quad CH_3CO-NHC-NHCOCH_3$$

compound the only isolable product was diacetyl urea. With concentrated sulfuric acid, degradation of the triazine ring to ammonia, carbon dioxide and acetic acid occurred. These results are quite different in the case of 2,4-diamino-6-methyl-s-triazine which yields the mono- and dihydroxy substituted derivatives on hydrolysis.

The hydrolysis of 2-amino-4,6-bis(trichloromethyl)-s-triazine with concentrated hydrochloric acid at 95° yielded 2,4-dihydroxy-6-trichloromethyl-s-triazine.[9] With alcoholic potassium hydroxide, the amino group is retained and the product is ammelide (IV).[6]

Broche[7] treated 2-amino-4,6-bis(trichloromethyl)-s-triazine with nitrous acid and obtained a compound which he thought might have been 2-hydroxy-4,6-bis(trichloromethyl)-s-triazine. Later Grundmann and co-workers[5] showed that he had obtained bistrichloroacetyl urea, cleavage of the triazine ring having occurred.

II. Diamino-s-Triazines

The amino substituted s-triazines have received much attention because of their resin-forming properties. In this category, the compounds having two amino groups and one alkyl (or aryl) group attached to the s-triazine ring are of considerable interest. The name "guanamines" has been used for these compounds in much of the literature. Since the term "guanamine" is non-descriptive and misleading, we prefer to use the systematic s-triazine nomenclature.

The term "guanamine" was originated by Nencki[11] in 1874. He heated guanidine acetate and obtained a new organic base (V) which he named "acetoguanamine." Since then, these 2,4-diamino-s-triazines have been named as derivatives of the carboxylic acid having one carbon atom more than the substituent attached to the 6-position. Thus, 2,4-diamino-6-methyl-s-triazine (V) has been called "aceto-guanamine" and 2,4-diamino-6-phenyl-s-triazine (VI) was named "benzoguanamine."

Soon after the first preparation of a 2,4-diamino-s-triazine by heating carboxylic acid salts of guanidines, Nencki showed the relationship of the products to other members of the s-triazine family.[12] Thus, hydrolysis of "acetoguanamine" with one mole of water yielded a new compound which he called "guanide." More drastic hydrolysis gave a compound in which two nitrogens were lost as ammonia—"guanamide." On oxidation with dilute nitric acid "guanamide" was converted to cyanuric acid. Nencki compared this behavior with melamine, which on hydrolysis can yield successively ammeline, ammelide and finally cyanuric acid. In modern terms we may formulate these transformations in equations 1 and 2.

The characterization of these new organic bases as s-triazine derivatives was further established by the work of Diels in 1899.[1,13] He showed that the reduction of 2,4-diamino-6-chloro-s-triazine (obtained by amination of cyanuric chloride) led to 2,4-diamino-s-triazine which was identical with the "formoguanamine" of Nencki.

Since Nencki's work many other synthetic methods for the preparation of diamino-s-triazines have been developed; many of these are
more convenient than the use of guanidine salts. Several hundred
derivatives have been prepared and evaluated for various applications,
and the chemistry of certain members of this class has been explored
fairly extensively.

1. Preparative Methods

A. From Guanidine or Guanidine Derivatives

The formation of 2,4-diamino-6-methyl-s-triazine from guanidine
acetate was observed by Nencki in 1874.[11] The path of this reaction
was not correctly interpreted at first,[14] as he postulated structures
containing two vicinal nitrogen atoms in a ring and three external
imino groups. He later recognized the structural relationship with the
s-triazines, cyanuric acid, and melamine. Weith[15] and Claus[16] proposed
mechanisms for the reaction which involved the condensation of two
moles of guanidine with one of the carboxylic acid; the former pre-
ferring the diimino structure (VII) and the latter the diamino formulation (VIII).

Several years later Bamberger and Dieckman[17] showed that diamino-s-triazines could be prepared by heating salts of biguanide, and
suggested that Nencki's reaction involved first a self-condensation of

guanidine to biguanide followed by acylation and cyclization at the elevated temperature.

$$\underset{NH_2\overset{\displaystyle NH}{\overset{\|}{C}}-NH_2}{} + \underset{NH_2-\overset{\displaystyle NH}{\overset{\|}{C}}-NH_2}{} \xrightarrow{-NH_3} \underset{NH_2\overset{\displaystyle NH}{\overset{\|}{C}}-NH-\overset{\displaystyle NH}{\overset{\|}{C}}-NH_2}{} \xrightarrow{RCOOH} \underset{R\overset{\displaystyle O}{\overset{\|}{C}}-NH\overset{\displaystyle NH}{\overset{\|}{C}}-NH-\overset{\displaystyle NH}{\overset{\|}{C}}-NH_2}{}$$

$$\downarrow$$

The preparation of diamino-s-triazines from guanidine salts is accomplished by heating at 200–230° C. The guanamine is obtained as the acid salt and the free base generated by addition of base. This method has been applied to the simple aliphatic acids from formic through caproic.[11,12,14,18,19,20] Above caproic, s-triazines are not obtained; the principal product is the amide. The yields in general are poor and aside from the original work this method has found little favor.

Certain variations on the synthesis of diamino-s-triazines from guanidine derivatives have been made. Thus, Simons and Weaver[21] prepared a series of s-triazines in good yield by heating acyl guanidines

$$2\ R\overset{\displaystyle O}{\overset{\|}{C}}{-}NH\overset{\displaystyle NH}{\overset{\|}{C}}{-}NH_2 \xrightarrow{190-210°} \text{[triazine]} + H_2O + R\overset{\displaystyle O}{\overset{\|}{C}}{-}NH_2$$

(IX)

(IX) at 190–210°. Included in the compounds prepared were 2,4-diamino-6-phenyl-s-triazine, and 2,4-diamino-6-benzyl-s-triazine in addition to the simple aliphatic derivatives. Earlier workers[22] had heated acetyl methylguanidine (X) to obtain 2,4-bis(methylamino)-6-methyl-

$$2\ CH_3\overset{\displaystyle O}{\overset{\|}{C}}{-}NH{-}\overset{\displaystyle NH}{\overset{\|}{C}}{-}NHCH_3 \longrightarrow \text{[triazine]} + CH_3\overset{\displaystyle O}{\overset{\|}{C}}{-}NH_2 + H_2O$$

(X)

s-triazine. The extension of this work to other N-substituted diamino-s-triazines has not been reported.

In 1903 Korndorfer,[23] in studying the reaction of guanidine salts with acid chlorides and anhydrides, reported, in addition to the mono- and diacylguanidines, the formation of compounds which he called "anhydrodiacidylguanidines." These were shown later by Grundmann and Beyer,[24] to be the diacyl derivatives of the corresponding diamino-s-triazines (XI). The course of this reaction is postulated as proceeding through an intermediate diacyl biguanide.

$$2 (CH_3CO)_2O + 2 NH_2\overset{\overset{\displaystyle NH}{\|}}{C}NH_2 \longrightarrow \left[\begin{array}{c} CH_3\overset{\overset{\displaystyle O}{\|}}{C}-NH-\underset{\substack{NH\ NH \\ \diagdown C \diagup \\ | \\ NH \\ C=O \\ | \\ CH_3}}{\overset{\diagup NH}{C}} \end{array} \right] + 2 CH_3COOH + NH_3$$

$$\downarrow CH_3COOH$$

$$CH_3\overset{\overset{\displaystyle O}{\|}}{C}-NH-\underset{\substack{N\ \ N \\ \diagdown Y \diagup \\ NH \\ CO \\ | \\ CH_3}}{\underset{N}{C}}\underset{N}{C}CH_3$$

(XI)

More recently Austerweil[25] prepared aliphatic diamino-s-triazines by heating guanidine salts with cyanoguanidine. As described in the patent, the guanidine salt was prepared in situ, by heating cyano-guanidine with an ammonium salt of the acid, followed by addition of a second mole of cyanoguanidine.

$$NH_2\overset{\overset{\displaystyle NH}{\|}}{C}-NH_2 \cdot HOOCR + CNNH-\overset{\overset{\displaystyle NH}{\|}}{C}-NH_2 \longrightarrow \underset{\substack{N\ \ N \\ \diagdown Y \diagup \\ NH_2}}{\overset{R\diagup N\diagdown NH_2}{N}} + 2 NH_3 + CO_2$$

B. From Biguanide and Derivatives

The preparation of diamino-s-triazines from biguanide and its derivatives was first observed by Bamberger and co-workers in

1892.[17,26] While attempting to dry a chloroform solution of piperyl biguanide by allowing it to stand in the presence of potassium hydroxide at 0°, they observed, on evaporation of the solvent, a new compound which they identified as 2-amino-4-piperyl-s-triazine (XII). The same

$$NH_2C—NH—C—N \overset{CH_2—CH_2}{\underset{CH_2—CH_2}{<}} CH_2 + CHCl_3 \longrightarrow \text{(XII)} + 3\ HCl$$

compound was prepared by heating the formic acid salt of piperyl-biguanide to 160°. The generality of the reaction was shown by the preparation of unsubstituted diamino-s-triazines by heating biguanide salts with carboxylic acids at 150–200°. The reaction of chloroform with biguanide gave 2,4-diamino s-triazine.

Several years later Rachmann[27] showed that derivatives of carboxylic acids—esters and acid chlorides—would react with biguanide to yield diamino-s-triazines under milder conditions than the free acids. In

$$NH_2C—NHC—NH_2 + HCOOC_2H_5 \xrightarrow[alcohol]{refluxing} + C_2H_5OH$$

$$NH_2C—NHC—NH_2 + C_6H_5COCl \xrightarrow[temp.]{room} + H_2O + HCl$$

1927, Andreasch[28] prepared 2,4-diamino-6-methyl-s-triazine by heating biguanide acetate with acetic anhydride.

Very little interest was shown in the preparation of diamino-s-triazines from biguanide and substituted biguanides until the early 1940's when industrial research, principally in the laboratories of the American Cyanamid Company, resulted in the issuance of many patents describing the reactions of biguanide and phenylbiguanide with numerous esters and other carboxylic acid derivatives. The synthesis was shown to be applicable to lactones,[29] imides,[30,31] amides,[32] ortho esters,[33] and amidines,[33] as well as esters, acid chlorides, and anhydrides. The reaction probably involves an acylation of biguanide followed by a ready cyclization with the loss of water to yield the s-triazine.

Improvements in yield and reaction rates in the reaction of esters with biguanide were obtained when a full equivalent of a base such as sodium hydroxide or sodium methoxide was used.[34,35,36] Good yields are obtained by merely allowing an alcoholic solution of biguanide and an ester to stand at room temperature for several hours.

The use of a non-caustic alkali as an acid acceptor results in good yields when acid chlorides are reacted with biguanide and substituted biguanides.[37,38]

The presence of negative substituents on the acid chain of the ester favors the reaction, resulting in better yields with shorter reaction times, and in some cases, the use of base is unnecessary.[39,40]

When esters of dibasic acids are used, either the carboxy substituted diamino-s-triazine or a bisdiamino-s-triazine (XIII) is the predominant product depending upon whether one or two moles of biguanide are used.[38, 41, 42, 43] The use of the half sodium salt—half ester provides a good method of obtaining the carboxy-substituted derivatives.

(XIII)

The lower molecular weight alcohols are the preferred solvents for the biguanide-ester reaction. When α,β-unsaturated esters are used in the presence of sodium alkoxides, the diamino-s-triazines formed are those which result from the addition of the elements of alcohol across the double bond. This reaction has been studied by Bradley,[44] Thurston,[45] and Overberger and Shapiro.[46]

$$CH_2{=}CH{-}COOR + \underset{\underset{NH}{\|}}{NH_2C}{-}\underset{\underset{NH}{\|}}{NHC}{-}NH_2 \xrightarrow[R^1OH]{NaOR^1}$$

The wide variety of diamino-s-triazines which have been prepared from biguanide and substituted biguanides is apparent in the tables at the end of this chapter.

C. From Nitriles and Cyanoguanidine

A method of growing importance, due to the increasing availability of nitriles, is the preparation of diamino-s-triazines by the reaction of cyanoguanidine with a nitrile. This synthesis was discovered by Ostrogovich[48] in 1911. He heated acetonitrile and benzonitrile with cyanoguanidine at 200–230° for several hours and obtained good yields (50–60%) of 2,4-diamino-6-methyl-s-triazine and 2,4-diamino-6-phenyl-s-triazine. In later work he used m- and p-toluonitrile and phenylacetonitrile successfully.[48, 49] He was not successful in obtaining diamino-s-triazines from o-toluonitrile, isovaleronitrile or isocapronitrile. The reaction probably involves a condensation of the —NH₂ group of the cyanoguanidine with the —CN group of the nitrile to form an amidine linkage, followed by cyclization.

$$RCN + \underset{\underset{NH}{\|}}{NH_2{-}C}{-}NHCN \longrightarrow$$

Ostrogovich had some difficulty in reproducing the high yields he had obtained in some of his early experiments and believed that some impurity in the nitrile was responsible for this. Several years later it was shown that catalytic amounts of base improved the yields and purity of the products.[50, 51] Thus yields of better than 80–85% were claimed when piperidine was used. Several patents have described the use of various substituted nitriles,[52] dinitriles,[53, 54, 55, 56] and trinitriles[57] in the preparation of the corresponding diamino-s-triazines. With dinitriles it is possible to react either one or both nitrile groups. An interesting variation was the use of α,α-dialkoxyacetonitriles by Wystrach and Erickson.[58] Attempts to hydrolyze the acetal linkage in the resulting diamino-s-triazines were unsuccessful.

$$(RO)_2CHCN + NH_2\overset{\overset{\displaystyle NH}{\|}}{C}\!\!-\!\!NHCN \longrightarrow$$

The use of sodium or potassium hydroxide in an alcoholic solvent is the preferred method in the most recent work.[53, 55, 59, 60] A laboratory procedure for the preparation of 2,4-diamino-6-phenyl-s-triazine from benzonitrile and cyanoguanidine by reaction in a methoxyethanol solution of potassium hydroxide has been published recently.[61]

Closely related to the reaction of nitriles with cyanoguanidine is the reaction of amidines with cyanoguanidine. Ostrogovich[62] showed that good yields of diamino-s-triazines could be obtained by heating acetamidine hydrochloride or benzamidine hydrochloride with cyanoguanidine at 200–230°. This reaction has received little interest since

amidines are prepared from nitriles which themselves give excellent yields of the diamino-s-triazines. Ostrogovich and Gheorghui were successful in preparing 6-isobutyl- and 6-isoamyl-2,4-diamino-s-triazines from the amidines, whereas the nitriles did not give the desired products.[49]

D. Miscellaneous Methods

Several other methods, which have been used for preparing diamino-s-triazines, have as yet received only sparse attention.

Birtwell[63] obtained diamino-s-triazines by heating amidines with dicyanimide (XVI) at temperatures of 150–200°. When N-p-chloro-phenylacetamidine was used, instead of the desired ring N-substituted

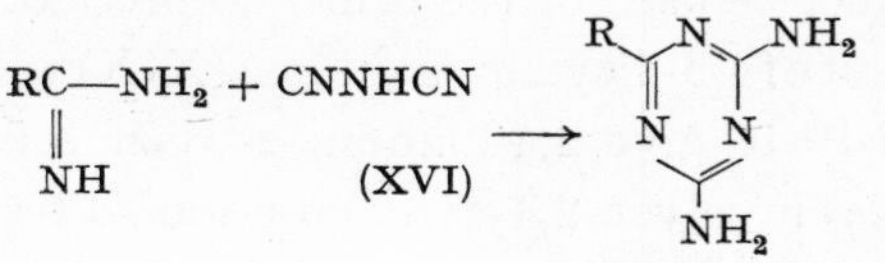

$$RC{-}NH_2 + CNNHCN \longrightarrow \underset{(XVI)}{} \quad$$

s-triazine (XVII), the product was 2-amino-4-p-chloroanilino-6-methyl-s-triazine (XVIII). This was formed presumably by fission and re-cyclization to the more stable configuration at the reaction temperature.

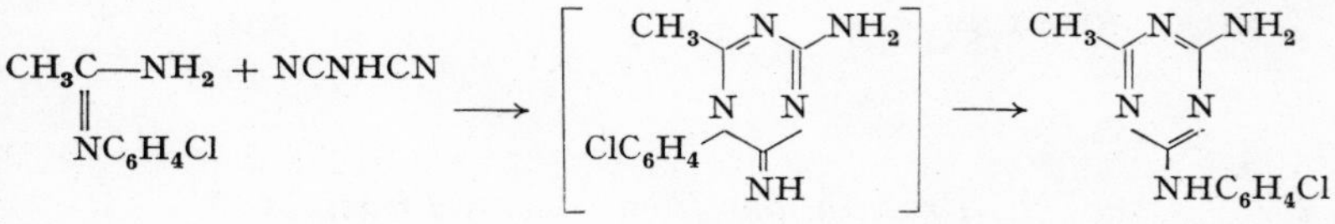

$$CH_3C{-}NH_2 + NCNHCN \longrightarrow$$

(XVII)   (XVIII)

Adams[64] reacted an acylated cyanoguanidine (XIV) with cyanamide and water and obtained diamino-s-triazines. Bindler[65] reported a similar

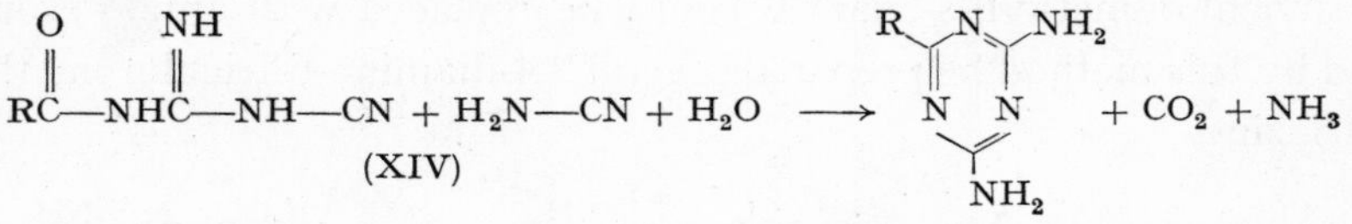

$$RC{-}NHC{-}NH{-}CN + H_2N{-}CN + H_2O \longrightarrow \quad + CO_2 + NH_3$$

(XIV)

reaction in which an acylated cyanoguanidine was heated with an amine. In this case the product was an N^2-substituted diamino-s-triazine (XV).

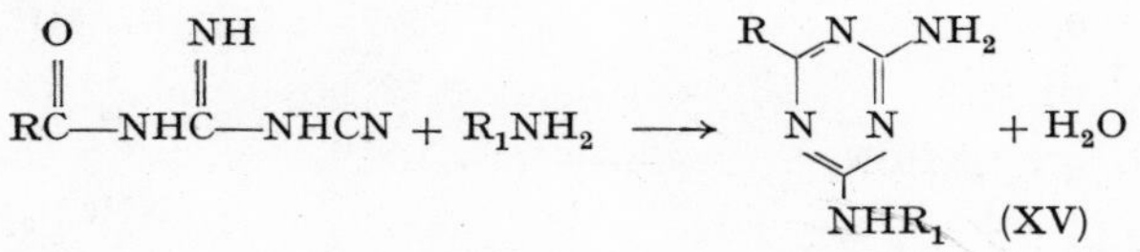

$$RC{-}NHC{-}NHCN + R_1NH_2 \longrightarrow \quad + H_2O$$

(XV)

2-p-Chloroanilino-4-amino-6-ethyl-s-triazine was obtained as a by-product by Birtwell[66] in the reaction of ethyl magnesium iodide with p-chlorophenylbiguanide at elevated temperatures.

Mackay[67] reacted urea with nitriles, amides, and acids in the pre-sence of ammonia at elevated temperatures under pressure and reported fair yields of the diamino-s-triazines. This process probably involves an intermediate formation of the nitrile (and/or amidine) followed by reaction with cyanoguanidine or similar species formed from urea. An excess of urea must be used or the principal product is the nitrile.

The treatment of 1,3-dicyanoguanidine (XIX) with excess hydrogen iodide is reported[68] to give 2,4-diamino-s-triazine in poor yield. This reaction probably involves 2,4-diamino-6-iodo-s-triazine as an intermediate which is then reduced by hydrogen iodide.

E. Preparations from Other s-Triazines

A scattering of 2,4-diamino-s-triazines have been prepared by methods which start with another s-triazine derivative.

Weddige[69] showed that one or two of the —CCl$_3$ groups in 2,4,6-tris(trichloromethyl)-s-triazine could be replaced with amino groups, and by this method he prepared several 2,4-diamino-6-trichloromethyl-s-triazines.

Several years later, Broche[7] carried out similar reactions with 2,4,6-tris(tribromomethyl)-s-triazine. The reaction of ethylenimine with 2,4,6-tris(trichloromethyl)-s-triazine was reported[70] to yield 2,4-bis(β-aziridinylethylamino)-6-trichloromethyl-s-triazine (XX).

A similar synthesis is the reaction of a 2,4-dihalo-s-triazine with an amine. This is illustrated in the preparation of certain dyestuffs.[71]

Diels[1] obtained 2,4-diamino-s-triazine by treating 2,4-diamino-6-chloro-s-triazine with hydrogen iodide and phosphorous triiodide.

A series of N²- and N²,N⁴-substituted 2,4-diamino-s-triazines has been prepared by the reduction of 2,4-diamino-6-chloro-s-triazines.[72] The chlorine was removed by the use of hydrogen iodide and phosphorous triiodide, stannic chloride and zinc dust, or catalytically in the presence of palladium.

The reaction of 2-amino-4-hydroxy-6-substituted-s-triazines with ammonia under pressure has been reported to yield the 2,4-diamino-s-triazines.[73] This reaction is accompanied by some ring cleavage giving nitriles as by-products.

2. Reactions of 2,4-Diamino-s-Triazines

A. Salt Formation

The 2,4-diamino-s-triazines are weak bases and readily yield stable, easily crystallizable salts with acids in aqueous solution. It is merely necessary to dissolve the s-triazine in hot acid and cool the solution. The formation of salts has been studied most extensively with 2,4-diamino-s-triazine, 2,4-diamino-6-methyl-s-triazine, and 2,4-diamino-6-phenyl-s-triazine. Table IV-3 lists the salts of these compounds which have been reported, and gives an indication of what can be expected of other members of this class.

B. Hydrolysis

The parent compound 2,4-diamino-s-triazine is resistant to hydrolysis by acids or bases.[12] When reaction does occur with concentrated potassium hydroxide, the ring is cleaved to carbon dioxide and am-

TABLE IV-3.   Salts of Various 2,4-Diamino-s-Triazine

2,4-Diamino-s-Triazine (C^1)		2,4-Diamino-6-methyl-s-triazine (C^2)		2,4-Diamino-6-phenyl-s-triazine (C^3)	
Salt	Ref.	Salt	Ref.	Salt	Ref.
$C^1 \cdot HCl$	1	$C^2 \cdot HCl \cdot 2\,H_2O$	2	$C^3 \cdot$ picric acid	4, 5
$C^1 \cdot 2\,HCl \cdot PtCl_4$	1	$C^2 \cdot 2\,HCl \cdot PtCl_4$	2	$C^3 \cdot HCl \cdot H_2O$	5, 6
$C^1 \cdot HNO_3$	1	$C^2 \cdot HNO_3$	2	$C^3 \cdot 2\,HCl \cdot PtCl_4$	5
$C^1 \cdot (COOH)_2$	1	$2\,C^2 \cdot H_2SO_4 \cdot 2\,H_2O$	2	$C^3 \cdot H_2CrO_4$	5
$3\,C^1 \cdot 2(COOH)_2$	7	$C^2 \cdot CH_3COOH$	2	$C^3 \cdot C_{10}H_{14}O_4S$	7
$C^1 \cdot C_{10}H_{13}O_4BrS$	7	$4\,C^2 \cdot (COOH)_2$	3	(thymo-p-	
		$2\,C^2 \cdot (COOH)_2$	3	sulfonate)	
		$2\,C^2 \cdot 3\,(COOH)_2$	3		
		$C^2 \cdot$ picric acid	3		
		$2\,C^2 \cdot H_2SO_4$	3		
		$C^2 \cdot H_2SO_4$	3		
		$C^2 \cdot HOBr$	3		
		$C^2 \cdot AgNO_3$	2		

1. M. Nencki, *Ber.*, **7**, 1584 (1874).
2. M. Nencki, *Ber.*, **7**, 775 (1894).
3. A. Ostrogovich, *Bull. Soc. Sci. Bucharest*, **14**, 49 (1905).
4. K. Rackmann, *Ann.*, **376**, 163 (1910).
5. A. Ostrogovich, *Atti. Accad. Lincei*, (5), **20**, 182 (1911).
6. F. Nachod and E. Steck, *J. Am. Chem. Soc.*, **70**, 2818 (1948).
7. K. Rehnelt, *Monatsch.*, **84**, 809 (1953).

monia. The "amino" groups of the 6-substituted s-triazines are more readily hydrolyzed. Thus, on heating 2,4-diamino-6-methyl-s-triazine with strong sodium hydroxide, Nencki[12] observed the elimination of one mole of ammonia with the formation of 2-amino-4-hydroxy-6-methyl-s-triazine (XXI). With sulfuric acid at 150–180° both amino

groups were removed. Ostrogovich[74] was able to hydrolyze 2,4-diamino-6-phenyl-s-triazine stepwise to the mono- and dihydroxy derivatives with alkali.

C. Acylation

The 2,4-diamino-s-triazines are readily converted into mono- and diacylated derivatives by reaction with acid anhydrides.[24,48,75,76]

D. Reaction with Aldehydes

The reaction of amino-s-triazines with formaldehyde is the basis for many of the resin uses of these compounds. This reaction has been discussed at length elsewhere (Chapter VI) and it will be merely mentioned here. The primary reaction involved is the formation of various methylol derivatives which are then condensed further to a variety of polymeric materials. Modifications which can be applied include the reaction of the methylolated compounds with alcohols and amines. It has been reported that other aldehydes can replace formaldehyde, but the latter is the compound used principally in making these resinous materials. Some references concerning the preparation and uses of resins from 2,4-diamino-s-triazines are presented at the end of the chapter. [77-84]

A different type of reaction with aldehydes has been described[76] for 2,4-diamino-6-methyl-s-triazine and benzaldehyde. In the presence of sulfuric acid the product is 2,4-diamino-6-styryl-s-triazine (XXII).

$$CH_3 \underset{N \quad N}{\overset{N \quad NH_2}{\bigcirc}} + C_6H_5CHO \longrightarrow C_6H_5CH=CH \underset{N \quad N}{\overset{N \quad NH_2}{\bigcirc}}$$
$$NH_2 \qquad\qquad (XXII) \quad NH_2$$

E. Reaction with Amines

Substitution on the N^2 and N^4 nitrogens of 2,4-diamino-s-triazines has been accomplished by heating with salts of primary and secondary amines.[85,86] Phenol has been used as a solvent for this reaction.

$$R \underset{N \quad N}{\overset{N \quad NH_2}{\bigcirc}} + R_1NH_2 \cdot HCl \longrightarrow R \underset{N \quad N}{\overset{N \quad NHR_1}{\bigcirc}} + NH_4Cl$$
$$NH_2 \qquad\qquad\qquad NH_2$$

F. Reaction with Nitrourea

It has been reported[25,87] that 2,4-diamino-s-triazines react readily with nitrourea to yield compounds in which the amino groups have been replaced by ureido radicals.

$$R \underset{N \quad N}{\overset{N \quad NH_2}{\bigcirc}} + 2\,H_2NC-NHNO_2 \longrightarrow R \underset{N \quad N}{\overset{N \quad NHCNH_2}{\bigcirc}} + 2\,N_2O + 2\,H_2O$$
$$NH_2 \qquad\qquad\qquad\qquad NH$$
$$| \qquad\qquad C=O \qquad | \qquad\qquad NH_2$$

G. Reaction with Phosphorous Oxychloride

The reaction of 2,4-diamino-s-triazine with phosphorous oxychloride has been reported.[88] The product after hydrolysis was the phosphoric acid amide (XXIII).

H. Reaction with Chlorosulfonic Acid

Andreasch[28] reacted 2,4-diamino-6-methyl-s-triazine with chlorosulfonic acid at 150° C and obtained the sulfomethyl compound (XXIV). The corresponding 6-n-propyl- and 6-isopropyl-diamino-s-triazines also were used and yielded the α-sulfonic acid derivatives.

I. Reaction with Sodium Chloroacetate

When 2,4-diamino-s-triazine was heated with sodium chloroacetate in the presence of sodium carbonate the reported product was 2-amino-4-carboxymethylamino-s-triazine (XXV).[89] Similarly, reaction

with other derivatives of chloroacetic acid, such as chloroacetamide, and substituted chloroacetamides, yielded the corresponding substituted methylamino-s-triazines.

J. Reaction with Olefin Oxides

Diamino-s-triazines have been reported[90, 91, 92] to react with a number of olefin oxides such as ethylene oxide and glycidol to yield polyglycol derivatives of uncertain structures. The condensates with several moles of ethylene oxide are water soluble.

K. Cyanoethylation

The reaction of acrylonitrile with 2,4-diamino-6-phenyl-s-triazine in the presence of potassium hydroxide yields the tetracyanoethylated product.[93] This has been hydrolyzed to the tetracarboxylic acid.

L. Halogenation

The halogenation of 2,4-diamino-6-methyl-s-triazine has been studied.[64, 75] In aqueous solution, Nencki obtained a dichloro derivative which was not well characterized. Ostrogovich studied the bromination reaction more completely, and was able to obtain the dibromo and tribromo derivatives; bromination took place on the methyl group. The 2,4-diamino-6-tribromomethyl-s-triazine loses its —CBr$_3$ side chain as bromoform (cf. Chapter II) under hydrolytic conditions to give 2,4-diamino-6-hydroxy-s-triazine.

M. Miscellaneous

Several reactions have been carried out on various 2,4-diamino-s-triazines which involve reaction of a substituent on the group attached to the 6 position, or a substituent on the 2 amino group. Thus, various 2,4-diamino-s-triazines with aromatic nucleii present have been sulfonated.[37] The bromination of an aromatic ring on a diamino-s-triazine has been reported.[46, 94] Nitro groups present on an aromatic substituent have been reduced using stannous chloride.[95, 96] The diazotization and coupling of the resulting amines has been reported.

The reduction of halomethyl groups on diamino-s-triazines has been carried out using sodium iodide in acetone, and catalytically on palladium.[94]

3. 2,4-Diamino-s-Triazines

The repeated number of 2,4-diamino-s-triazines which carry no substituent in the 6 position of the ring is not extensive but includes a fair variety of compounds. These are listed in Table IV-4A. In much of the literature this type of compound has been named as a derivative of formoguanamine. Thus the parent compound (XXVI) was called "formoguanamine" and (XXVII) was named N^2-phenylformoguanamine.

The most general method for preparation of these compounds is the reaction of a formic acid derivative (the free acid, amide, or ester) with biguanide or a substituted biguanide. The only other preparative route of any general application is the reduction of a 2,4-diamino-6-chloro-s-triazine.

A. 2,4-Diamino-s-triazine (Formoguanamine)

2,4-Diamino-s-triazine is a high melting (> 350°) stable solid. It is a very weak base ($K_b = 7.6 \times 10^{-9}$) which forms salts readily in dilute acid (see Section 2). It is soluble in hot water and crystallizes from water as rhombic needles.

2,4-Diamino-s-triazine is more stable to hydrolytic reactions than its homologues containing substituents in the 6 position. Prolonged heating with concentrated sulfuric acid results in degradation to carbon dioxide and ammonia. Similar results occur with strong alkali. Chlorine and bromine have no effect at ordinary temperatures, and at elevated temperatures degradation results. Treatment with nitric acid leads to complete oxidation when reaction occurs.

4. 2,4-Diamino-6-substituted-s-Triazines

A wide variety of diamino-s-triazines having substituents on the 6 position have been prepared and reported. The synthetic routes to these compounds include many of the methods which have been discussed earlier in this chapter. The processes, which are most generally applicable and most widely used, are (1) the reaction of a nitrile with cyanoguanidine and (2) the reaction of a carboxylic acid derivative (i.e. ester, acid chloride, amide etc.) with biguanide. The latter synthesis lends itself most readily to the preparation of N^2-substituted derivatives —use of a substituted biguanide. In many instances the N^2- and N^2,N^4-substituted compounds have been prepared by various substitution reactions on the amino groups of the parent derivatives.

A list of the 2,4-diamino-6-alkyl (aryl)-s-triazines is presented in Table IV-4-B.

A. 2,4-Diamino-6-methyl-s-triazine

2,4-Diamino-6-methyl-s-triazine (acetoguanamine) is a white crystalline solid which is now produced on a pilot plant scale. It is a high melting compound (ca. 270° dec.) and is sparingly soluble in most organic solvents in the cold. It is soluble in hot water and hot alcohol. The most convenient laboratory preparation is probably the condensation of acetonitrile with cyanoguanidine in the presence of piperidine or sodium hydroxide. When the reaction is carried out in an alcoholic solvent (particularly the ethylene glycol mono-ethers), the crystalline product is obtained easily from the reaction mixture on cooling. The infrared and ultraviolet absorption spectra, and optical properties have been described.[97] The dissociation constant of 2,4-diamino-6-methyl-s-triazine is 4.0×10^{-10}.[98] Salts, which are readily formed in aqueous acid have been listed earlier in this chapter.

The chemical reactivity of 2,4-diamino-6-methyl-s-triazine is similar to that of other members of this series. The condensation with benzaldehyde indicates an activation of the methyl group α to a ring nitrogen, similar to that encountered in other nitrogen heterocycles.

B. 2,4-Diamino-6-phenyl-s-triazine

2,4-Diamino-6-phenyl-s-triazine (benzoguanamine) is another diamino-s-triazine which is available commercially. The laboratory preparation of this compound has been described.[6] The infrared and ultraviolet spectra, and optical properties have been published.[97] It is a weaker base ($k_b = 1.4 \times 10^{-10}$) than the methyl homologue. In general the phenyl derivative is slightly more soluble in organic solvents, but less soluble in water than the methyl compound.

Nachod and Steck[99] have studied the ultraviolet spectra of 2,4-diamino-6-phenyl-s-triazine at various pH's. The observed batho- and hypochromic shift at pH 1 was interpreted as being due to the pre-

dominance of the least conjugated structure (XXVIII) in strongly acidic solutions. In the crystalline state they believe that the structures (XXIX) and (XXX) are most likely.

TABLE IV-4. Diamino-s-Triazines

A. 2,4-Diamino-s-Triazines (no substitution in 6 position)

$$\begin{array}{c} H \quad N \quad NR_1R_2 \\ N \quad N \\ NR_3R_4 \end{array}$$

R₁	R₂	R₃	R₄	M.p., °C. solvent	Method of prepn.[a]	Yield %
H	H	H	H	—	1	Fair
				325	16	—
				—	2, 3	—
				—	3a	Quant.
				—	3f	73
				—	5b	65
C_2H_5	H	H	H	197.5	2, 3, 18	—
C_3H_7	H	H	H	168	3a, f, 18	—
$CH_2CH=CH_2$	H	H	H	152.5	3a, f, 18	—
C_4H_9	H	H	H	122, 144	3a, f, 18	—
C_5H_9 (cyclopentyl)	H	H	H	164	3a, f	—
CH_2COOH	H	H	H	230 dec.	21	—
CH_2CONH_2	H	H	H	—	21	—
$CH_2C-N\begin{smallmatrix}CH_2-CH_2\\CH_2-CH_2\end{smallmatrix}CH_2$ (O=)	H	H	H	—	21	—
$CH_2NHCONH_2$	H	H	H	—	21	—
$C_5H_4N(\alpha)$	H	H	H	273–4	3a	—
C_6H_5	H	H	H	237, 236 230–32	3	70–73
				—	3a, c	—
				—	3f	91
$C_6H_4CH_3(p)$	H	H	H	165–6	3	67
$CH_2C_6H_5$	H	H	H	182	3a, f, 18	—
CHC_6H_5 (CH_3)	H	H	H	138	3a, f, 18	—
$C_6H_4NH_2(p)$	H	H	H	—	23	—
$C_6H_4N(CH_3)_2(p)$	H	H	H	225–6	3	76
$C_6H_4OCH_3(p)$	H	H	H	242–3	3	70
$C_6H_4OC_2H_5(p)$	H	H	H	209–10	3	81
$C_6H_4NO_2(p)$	H	H	H	325 (dec.)	3a	65

(Table c

LE IV-4A (*continued*)

	R₂	R₃	R₄	M.p.,°C. solvent	Method of prepn.ᵃ	Yield %	Ref.
l(p)	H	H	H	277 (HCl salt)	3	66	18
				200	3a, f	—	26
3r(p)	H	H	H	282–4 (HCl salt)	3	85	18
				260–61	3a	71	19
CH₃)₃ (2, 4, 5)	H	H	H	192–4 (HCl salt)	3	93	18
Br)₃ (2, 4, 6)	H	H	H	232–3	3	80	18
–C₆H₅(o)	H	H	H	206	3	55	18
α-Naphthyl)	H	H	H	246–7	3	63	18
				199	3f	Quant.	6
N=N—C₆H₃(OH)(COOH)(3, 4)				—	14	—	25
—N=N—C₆H₃(OH)(C₆H₅)(2, 5)				—	14	—	25
	CH₃	H		189–90	3	68	18
				192	3f	55	6
	C₂H₅	H	H	164–5	3	87	18
				170	3a, f, 18	—	27, 28
	C₆H₅	H	H	185–6	3	80	18
	CH₂C₆H₅	H	H	86	3a, f, 18	—	29, 30
	C₆H₁₁	H	H	145	3a, f, 18	—	31, 32
CH₂(CH₂CH₂)(CH₂CH₂)	H	H		194.5	2, 3	—	33
O(CH₂CH₂)(CH₂CH₂)	H	H		223	3f	40	6
	H	CH₃	H	204	3a, f, 18	—	36, 37
OOH	H	CONH₂	H	—	21	—	16
OOH	H	CH₂COOH	H	—	21	—	16
OOH	H	CH₂CONH₂	H	—	21	—	16
NH₂	H	CONH₂	H	—	21	—	16
HCONH₂	H	CONH₂	H	—	21	—	16
N(C₄H₈O)	H	CONH₂	H	—	21	—	16
I₅	H	COC₆H₅	H	—	6	—	38
	H	PO₃H	H	250–60	17	64	39
	CH₃	CH₃	H	193–4	3	76	18
	CH₃	C₆H₄Cl(p)	H	191–2	3	60	18
CH₂—CH₂		CH₂—CH₂		147–8/benzene heptane	5d	59	40

B. 2,4-Diamino-6-alkyl(aryl)-s-Triazines

1.

$$R \underset{\underset{NH_2}{\underset{|}{N}}}{\overset{N}{\underset{N}{\nearrow}}} NH_2$$

R	M.p., °C. solvent	Method of preparation[a]	Yield	Ref.
CH$_3$	265	1a	Fair	41, 42,
	252–5	1c	—	2
	265	2f	61	44, 45
	271–3	3a	96.5	46, 47,
	—	3b	65–70	49
	—	4	—	50
	—	4a	—	51
C$_2$H$_5$	> 300	1a	—	52
	—	1c	—	2
C$_3$H$_7$(n)	210–230 (subl.)	1a	Poor	41, 53
	195	1c	—	2
	—	4	41	50
C$_3$H$_7$ (iso)	—	1a	Poor	53
C(CH$_3$)=CH$_2$	246–7/ethyl acetate	2b	61	54, 55,
C$_4$H$_9$(n)	172–3	1a	Poor	57
	168	1c	—	—
C$_5$H$_{11}$	168–70	3d	—	58
C$_5$H$_{11}$ (iso)	177–8	1a	Poor	57
	174–5/H$_2$O	3b	30	59
	176	2a	—	3
CH=CH—CH=CH—CH$_3$	220	2b	80	60, 55
C$_6$H$_{13}$	130	1a	Poor	52
C$_7$H$_{15}$	174–5/methanol	3a	75	46
		4	—	50
CH(C$_2$H$_5$)C$_4$H$_9$	108–9.5	2b	82	61, 62
CH(C$_2$H$_5$)CH$_2$CH$_2$CH(CH$_3$)$_2$	97–101	2b	—	62
CH(C$_4$H$_9$)$_2$	—	2b	—	62
C$_9$H$_{19}$	118–19/acetone	2b	78	61
		2c	—	63
CH=CH—CH(C$_2$H$_5$)C$_4$H$_9$	99–101	2b	93	55
C$_{11}$H$_{23}$	118–19	2b	88	63, 64,
	115–16	2c	—	63
	280–290	1c	—	2
C$_{13}$H$_{27}$	114–116.5	2c	53	63, 45
C$_{15}$H$_{31}$	113–118	2c	—	63
C$_{17}$H$_{31}$	94/acetone	2c	90	63, 65
C$_{17}$H$_{33}$	—	2b, c	88	63, 61

(Table co

LE IV-4B1 (*continued*)

	M.p., °C. solvent	Method of preparation[a]	Yield	Ref.
	116–117	2b	65	63, 61
	112–117	2c	—	63
	115–118	3a	92.5	46, 66
laneous fatty acid vatives	—	2b	—	65
2	—	6b	—	43
	235–6	3a, 5a	72	46, 67
	210 (> 300)	5a, 6b	—	68, 43
CH(CH$_3$)$_2$	196–7/acetone	2b	57	69, 70
Br	143–4	2b	81	69, 70
$_{16}$H$_{33}$	—	2b, c	40	63, 61, 69, 70
CHBrCHBrC$_8$H$_{17}$	93–6	2b	—	69
OOH	—	2b	80	69, 71
H$_2$COOH	"Infusible"	2b, c, f	62	72, 45
H$_2$COOCH$_3$	159	2b	—	72, 69, 71
CH—COOH	335	2b, c	87	72, 69, 73
CH(SO$_3$H)COOH	—	2b	95	74
C—COOH || CH$_2$	—	2b	11	72, 69, 73
CH(OC$_2$H$_5$)COOH	253–5	2b	21	69
$_3$COOH	223–5	2b	75	72, 69, 71
$_3$COOC$_4$H$_9$	90–92	6i	—	71
H$_2$CON(C$_4$H$_9$)$_2$	150–2/alcohol	2b	—	75
H$_2$CONHC$_6$H$_5$	202–3	2g	93	76, 75
H(OCH$_3$)CONHC$_8$H$_{17}$	146–8	2b	—	69, 75
N	273/H$_2$O	2b	72	69
H$_2$CN	247–8	3a	96	46
$_4$CN	256–7	3a	87	46, 77
$_3$CN	213–4/Cellosolve	3a	74	46
OCH$_3$	330	2b	20	78
H$_2$COCH$_3$	184–5/ethanol	2b	40	78, 69
$_{10}$COCH$_3$	158–9/acetone	2b	93	78, 69
H)CH$_3$	254/H$_2$O	2b	51	69
H$_2$CH$_2$OH	—	2b	—	79
H$_2$	258–9/H$_2$O	2b	61	80
HC$_6$H$_5$	232–3	3a	—	46
(CH$_2$C$_6$H$_5$) (C$_6$H$_5$)	188–9/methanol	2b	61	80
H$_2$NHCH$_2$CH=CH$_2$	229–30	2b	—	80
H$_2$NHC$_4$H$_9$	211–12	8	73	80
H$_2$N(C$_5$H$_{10}$)$_2$	225–6	2b	89	80
H$_2$NHC$_6$H$_5$	200–2	3a	98	46

(Table continued)

TABLE IV-4B1 (*continued*)

R	M.p., °C solvent	Method of preparation[a]	Yield	Ref.
$CH_2CH_2NHCH_2C_6H_5$	209–10 (dec.)	2b	90	80
$CH_2CH_2NHC_{18}H_{37}$	120–2/methanol	2b	60	80
$CH_2N(C_6H_5)COCH_3$	215–6/dioxane	3a	90	46
$CH_2NHCOC_{17}H_{35}$	165	6a	—	80
$CH_2NHSO_2C_6H_5$	212–3	6a	—	80
$CH_2CH_2NHCOCH_3$	238–9/H_2O	3a	94	46
$CH_2CH_2NC_4H_9(COCH_3)$	222–3/H_2O	2b, 3a, 6a	81–95	46, 80
$CH_2CH_2NCH_2C_6H_5(COC_9H_{19})$	147–9	6a	—	80
$(CH_2)_5NHCOC_6H_5$	230	2b	78	80
$CH_2OC(CH_3)_3$	236–7 (dec.)	3a	83	81
$CH_2CH_2OC_2H_5$	164–5	3a	80	69, 56
$CH_2CH_2OC_5H_{11}$	119–20	2b	90	69, 56
$CH_2CH_2OC_{18}H_{37}$	108–10	3a	86	56
$CH_2CH(CH_3)OCH_3$	187–8	2b	73	54, 55
$CH_2CH(CH_3)OC_2H_5$	197–9	2b	50	54, 55, !
$CH(CH_3)CH_2OCH_3$	166	2b	—	54, 55, !
$CH_2OCH_2OC_2H_5$	177–178	3a	Quant.	81
$CH_2OCH_2OCH_2CH(CH_3)_2$	175–8	3a	67	81
$CH(OCH_3)_2$	208–9/H_2O	3a	89	82
$CH(OC_2H_5)_2$	194/aq. ethanol	3a	94	82
$CH(OC_4H_9)_2$	166–7/ethanol	3a	87	82
$CH(OC_8H_{17})_2$	115–6/hexane	3a	96	82
CH_2SO_3H	—	6h	—	44
$CH_2CH_2SO_3H$	255–60	2f	82	74
$CH_2CH_2SO_3Na$	280 (dec.)	3a	84	46
$CH(C_2H_5)SO_3H$	—	6h	—	44
$C(CH_3)_2SO_3H$	300	6h	—	44
$(CH_2)_9SO_3Na$	—	2b	Quant.	74
$CH_2CH_2CH(CH_3)NO_2$	—	2b	98	69
C_6H_5	215–18	1c	—	2
	222	2c	83	45, 4
	—	2e	Poor	47
	224–5	3a	93	46, 47, 4
	225	3b	70	49
	224–6	3d	—	58
	—	5c	53	83
	—	4	67	50
	—	4a	—	51
$C_6H_4CH_3(m)$	239–40	3a	18–20	84
$C_6H_4CH_3(p)$	240	3a	—	84
$CH_2C_6H_5$	237–8	2b	80	60

(*Table con*

LE IV-4B1 (*continued*)

	M.p., °C. solvent	Method of preparation[a]	Yield	Ref.
H₅	241–2	3a	95	46, 84, 48
	185–90	1c	—	2
CHC₆H₅	276	2b	90	55
	260	6d	—	38
Br)(CH₃) (3, 4)	235	2b	71	70
OOH(o)	248–9	2b, 2f	94	45, 85
SO₃Na)(COOH) (2, 3)	—	2b	—	85
SO₃H)(OH) (3, 4)	—	2b	10	86
ONH₂(o)	264–6/H₂O	2g	60	76, 75
ONHC₈H₁₇(o)	171/dil. alc.	2b	61	75
N(o)	229–30	3a	99	46
H₂OH(o)	218	2b	45	61, 79, 86
OH(o)	267	2b	58	86
CHC₆H₄(OH)(o)	296	2b	15	61,79,86,60,55
OH)(NO₂) (2, 3)	296	2b	10	86
NO₂(m)	243–5	2b	—	58
CHC₆H₄NO₂(p)	336	2b	71	55
NH₂(m)	212–3	11	—	87
NH₂(p)	206/H₂O	2b	67	61, 88
CHC₆H₄NH₂(p)	256–7	6g	66	88
NHCOCH₃(m)	278	3a	75	87
NHCOCH₃(p)	268/alc. H₂O	2b, 3a	50	87, 88
NHCOC₆H₅(m)	252–3	3a	60	87
NHCH₂COOH(m)	—	6e	—	87
OCH₃(p)	228	3a	—	87
OH)N=NC₆H₄SO₃H (2, 5)	326	6m	—	89
a)	276	2b	58	60
β)	240	3a	Quant.	48
COOH	—	2b	—	85
OH (2, 3)	317/butanol	2b	70	60
(OH)N=N—C₆H₅ (2, 3, 4)	213	6m	—	89
(OH)N=NC₆H₄SO₃H (2, 3, 4)	312 (dec.)	6m	—	89
	248–50	3a	—	48
	266/H₂O	2b	85	90
CH=CH—	254	2b	85	86, 90
	—	2b	86	90
N	—	2b	63	90

(*Table continued*)

TABLE IV-4B1 (*continued*)

R	M.p., °C. solvent	Method of preparation[a]	Yield	Ref.
	318–22	1c, 1d	—	91
	240	2b	65	90
	227	2b	57	92, 73
	225–6	3d	40	92
	261	2b	20	61, 80
	70–95	2f	64	92
	275	2b	65	79, 70
	326	2b	84	88

NH_2-substituted s-triazine (positions R, R$_1$, R$_2$)

R	R$_1$	R$_2$	M.p., °C. solvent	Method of preparation[a]	Yield	Ref.
CH_3	$CH_2CH_2CH_2$ / CH_2CH_2		177–9	2a	—	33
CH_3	C_6H_5	H	176–7	2a	60	18
CH_3	$C_6H_4Cl(p)$	H	179	2b	61	93, 64
$COCH_3$	$COCH_3$	H	179–80	3a	73	46
CH_2Cl	C_6H_4	H	178–80	6k	—	94
$CHCl_2$	C_6H_5	H	195–6	2f, 4a, 6f	Good	51, 95, 96
CCl_3	CH_3	H	284–5	6a, 6f	—	97, 43
CCl_3	C_6H_5	H	145–6	2b	54	94
	C_6H_5	H	154–5	2b	60	94
	C_6H_5	H	153–5	5a	—	67
	C_6H_5	H	170–172	2b	1	94
$COOH$	C_6H_5	H	232–3	2b	62	19
$COOCH_3$	C_6H_5	H	204–5/methanol	2b	92	19
$COOC_2H_5$	C_6H_5	H	197–9/acetonitrile	2b, 6i	—	19
$COOC_3H_7$	C_6H_5	H	194–5/propyl alc.	2b, 6i	34	19
$COOCH_2CH_2N(CH_3)_2$	C_6H_5	H	197–8	6i	31	19
$COOCH_2CH_2N(C_2H_5)_2$	C_6H_5	H	172–3	6i	—	19
$CONHNH_2$	C_6H_5	H	245–7	—	—	19
C_2H_5	$CH_2CH=CH_2$	H	85–7	2b	77	61
C_2H_5	C_6H_5	H	157–8	2a, b	68	18, 93
C_2H_5			158–60	6k	—	98
C_2H_5	$C_6H_4Cl(p)$	H	174–5	2c, 3e	—	99
C_2H_5	$C_6H_4Br(p)$	H	179–181/acetonitrile	2b, 6b	44	98

(*Table continued*)

TABLE IV-4B2 (*continued*)

R	R₁	R₂	M.p., °C. solvent	Method of preparation^a	Yield	Ref.
CH=CH₂	C₆H₅	H	180–1/EtOH	2c	37	98
C₃H₇	C₆H₅	H	155–6	2b	60	93
C₃H₇	C₆H₄OH(p)	H	205–6	2b	38	93
C₃H₇	C₆H₄NH₂(m)	H	200–5	2b	23	93
C₃H₇	C₆H₄—C₆H₄OH($p;p'$)	H	270	2b	60	93
CH₂CH(CH₃)₂	COCH₃	H	129–30	6a	—	59
C₅H₁₁	CH₃	CH₃	—	6c	—	100
C₅H₁₁	CH₂OCH₂ / —CH₂—CH₂		124	2b	60	93
C₅H₁₁	N–C-CH₃ / S (thiazole)	H	231–2	6c	—	17
CH(C₂H₅)C₄H₉	C₄H₉	H	131–2	2b	30	61
C₁₁H₂₃	C₆H₅	H	—	2c	93	101
C₁₇H₃₅	C₆H₅	H	113–4	2c	Quant.	101
C₁₇H₃₅	C₆H₅	CH₃	—	2c	—	101
C₁₇H₃₅	C₆H₃(CH₃)₂ (2, 5)	H	—	3d	—	102
CHBrCH₃	C₆H₅	H	135–6/methanol-H₂O	2b	18	94
CH₂CH₂SO₃H	C₆H₅	H	—	2b	—	74
			>410	3a	—	103
CH₂CH₂OH	C₆H₅	H	159–60/methanol	2b	18	98
CH₂CH₂CN	C₁₂H₂₅	H	76–7/hexane	3a	Quant.	46
CH₂CH₂CN	C₆H₅	H	169–70	3a	79	46
CH₂COCH₃	C₆H₅	H	259–60	2a	—	78
CH₂COCH₃	C₆H₄Cl(p)	H	162–4	2b	20	96
CH₂CH₂OCH₃	C₆H₅	H	119–20/ethanol	2b	50–60	93, 98, 69
CH₂CH₂OC₂H₅	C₆H₅	H	120–21	2b	31	98
CH₂CH₂OC₃H₇	C₆H₅	H	117–8	2b	41	98

			M.p., °C.	Method of preparation	Yield	Ref.
C6H5	C4H9	H	—	6c	—	100
C6H5	C6H5	H	199–201	2b	37	93, 64, 60
C6H5	CH2—O—CH2 / CH2 CH2		142–3	2b	—	93, 60
C6H4CH3(m)	COCH3	H	248	6a	—	84
C6H4CH3(p)	COCH3	H	273–4	6a	—	84
CH2C6H5	COCH3	H	239–40	6a	—	84
(furfuryl)	C6H5	H	—	2b	58	90

3.

R	R1	R2	M.p., °C. solvent	Method of preparation[a]	Yield	Ref.
CH3	CH3	CH3	241	1b	—	104
CH3	2 CH2OH(N,N-di-)	CH2OH	163–4	6d	—	105
CH3	2 CH2OH(N,N-di-)	2 CH2OH(N,N-di-)	127	6d	—	105
CH3	COCH3	COCH3	212–13	1a, 6a	—	97, 43
CH3	COC2H5	COC2H5	157–8	1a	—	97
CH3	COC6H5	COC6H5	153–4	6a	—	38
CH3	C6H4Cl(p)	COCH3	269–71	2f	Low	95
CH3	C6H4Cl(p)	CH(CH3)2	173–4	6f	—	106
CH3	C6H4Cl(p)	CH2CH2N(C2H5)2	145–6/pet. ether	2f	Good	95
CH3	C6H4Cl(p)	CH2CH2CH2N(C2H5)2	125/pet. ether	2f	Good	95

(Table continued)

TABLE IV-4B3 (continued)

R	R₁	R₂	M.p., °C. solvent	Method of preparation[a]	Yield	Ref.
CH_3	$C_6H_4Cl(p)$	$(C_2H_5)_2$	112/pt. ether	2f	—	95
CCl_3	CH_3	CH_3	206–7	5a	—	67
CCl_3	$CH_2CH_2N(CH_2CH_2)$	$CH_2CH_2N(CH_2CH_2)$	169–70/alc.	5a	—	107
CBr_3	CH_3	CH_3	263–4	5a	—	68
CBr_3	C_6H_5	C_6H_5	280	5a	—	68
CH_2COCH_3	$C_6H_4Cl(p)$	$CH(CH_3)_2$	121	2b	—	106
$CH_2CH(CH_3)_2$	$COCH_3$	$COCH_3$	129–30	6a	—	59
C_6H_5	$CH_2{-}CH_2$	$CH_2{-}CH_2$	142 (dec.) benzene heptane	5d	40	40
C_6H_5	C_4H_9	C_4H_9	—	6c	—	100
C_6H_5	$2\ CH_2CH_2CN(N,N\text{-di-})$	$2\ CH_2CH_2CN(N,N\text{-di-})$	162–3	6j	98	108
C_6H_5	$2\ CH_2CH_2CN(N,N\text{-di-})$	$2\ CH_2CH_2CN(N,N\text{-di-})$	195–6	6f	—	108
$C_6H_4CH_3(m)$	$COCH_3$	$COCH_3$	232–3	6a	—	84
$CH_2C_6H_5$	$COCH_3$	$COCH_3$	145	6a	—	84
$CH{=}CH{-}C_6H_5$	COC_6H_5	COC_6H_5	146	6a	—	38

C. Bis-2,4-diamino-s-triazines

R	M.p., °C.	Method of preparation[a]	Yield	Ref.
CH_2	—	2b	5	69, 71
	410	3a	—	109
CH_2CH_2	335	2b	75	72, 69, 110, 71

	m.p.	Type	Yield	Refs.
(CH$_2$)$_3$	340	2b	50	69, 110
	355 (dec.)	3a	82	103
CH$_2$—C(=CH$_2$)	—	2b	42	72, 69, 110
(CH$_2$)$_4$	301	2b	80	69, 110
	295/benzyl alc.	3a	84	111
	300	3a	76	109
(CH$_2$)$_5$	258	3a	89	111
(CH$_2$)$_7$	218–19	3a	—	103
(CH$_2$)$_8$	308	2b	100	69, 110
	307	3a	79	109
CH$_2$CH$_2$OCH$_2$CH$_2$	295–6	3a	93	46
CH$_2$—CH(OC$_2$H$_5$)	271–3	3a	77	103
CH$_2$—CH$_2$C(CH$_3$)(COCH$_3$)CH$_2$CH$_2$	310	2b	75	69, 56
CH$_2$—CH$_2$C{C(CH$_3$)(=CH$_2$)}{COCH$_3$} CH$_2$CH$_2$	—	2b	65	69
C$_6$H$_4$(o)	—	3a	65	103
	273–4	3a	—	103
C$_6$H$_4$(p)	345–50	3a	32	111
	354/glycol	3a	74	109
	300	2b	40	85, 90
	382	3a	68	111
C$_6$H$_4$—C$_6$H$_4$(p,p')	405–6/glycol	3a	84	109
C$_6$H$_4$—O—C$_6$H$_4$(p,p')	390–92	3a	86	112
C$_{10}$H$_6$(1,2)	290	3a	49	112
	376–80	3a	79	112
fluorene-9,9-diyl bis(CH$_2$CH$_2$)	—	3a	62	103
CH$_2$C$_6$H$_4$CH$_2$	316/acetic acid	3a	76	109

D. N²-Substituted Bis-2,4-diamino-s-triazines

R	R$_1$	M.p., °C.	Method of preparation^a	Yield	Ref
$(CH_2)_4$	C_6H_5	232–5	3a	60	11
$CH_3C-C-(CH_3)-(CH_2CH_2)_2=$ (with $\overset{\parallel}{O}$)	C_6H_5	—	3a	65	11
$(CH_3)_2C=CH-COCH(CH_2CH_2)_2=$	C_6H_5	273–4	3a	—	11
(fluorene structure) $(CH_2CH_2)_2$	C_6H_5	—	—	—	11

E. Tris-2,4-diamino-s-triazines

R	M.p., °C.	Method of preparation^a	Yield	Ref
$CH_3CC(CH_2CH_2)_3\equiv$ (with $\overset{\parallel}{O}$)	378 (dec.)	3a	—	10
$C_6H_5C(CH_2CH_2)_2=$ (with $\overset{|}{}$)	320/dimethyl formamide	3a	—	10

^{a} *Methods of Preparation:*

1. *From Guanidine*
   - 1a. Guanidine salt heated.
   - 1b. Acyl guanidine heated.
   - 1c. Acyl derivative of substituted guanidine heated.
   - 1d. Nitrile plus guanidine.

2. *From Biguanide*
   - 2a. Reaction with carboxylic acid.
   - 2b. Reaction with ester.
   - 2c. Reaction with acid chloride.
   - 2d. Reaction with amide.

2e. Reaction with amidine.
2f. Reaction with anhydride.
2g. Reaction with imide.
2h. Reaction with chloroform.

3. *From Cyanoguanidine*

3a. Reaction with nitriles.
3b. Reaction with amidines.
3c. Reaction with guanidine salt.
3d. Reaction of an acyl cyanoguanidine with cyanamide or amine.
3e. Reaction of substituted cyanoguanidine with Grignard reagent.

4. *Reaction of Urea with Nitrile, Acid, or Amide and Ammonia*

4a. Reaction of amidine with dicyanamide.

5. *From Other* s-*Triazines (excluding diamino-*s-*triazines)*

5a. Replacement of —CX_3 group with ammonia or amine.
5b. Reduction of 2,4-diamino-6-halo-*s*-triazine.
5c. Reaction of 2-amino-4-hydroxy-6-substituted-*s*-triazine with ammonia.
5d. Reaction of dihalo-*s*-triazine with ammonia or amines.

6. *From Other 2,4-Diamino-*s-*Triazines*

6a. Acylation of —NH_2 group.
6b. Halogenation of side chain.
6c. Reaction with amine hydrochloride.
6d. Reaction with aldehyde.
6e. Reaction of —NH_2 group with chloro acid.
6f. Miscellaneous hydrolysis reactions.
6g. Reduction of nitro group.
6h. Reaction of side chain with chlorosulfonic acid.
6i. Esterification or transesterification.
6j. Cyanoethylation of NH_2 group.
6k. Hydrogenation.
6l. Reaction of ester with ammonia.
6m. Coupling of diazo compound.

1. M. Nencki, *Ber.*, **7**, 1584 (1874).
2. J. Simons and W. Weaver, U.S. Patent 2,408,694 (1946).
3. E. Bamberger and W. Dieckman, *Ber.*, **25**, 534 (1892).
4. K. Rackmann, *Ann.*, **376**, 163 (1910).
5. Swiss Patent 255,408 (1949).
6. W. Oldham, U.S. Patent 2,320,882 (1943).
7. O. Diels, *Ber.*, **32**, 691 (1899).
8. Swiss Patent 261,811 (1949).
9. Swiss Patent 254,538 (1949).
10. Swiss Patent 261,819 (1949).
11. Swiss Patent 261,829 (1949).
12. Swiss Patent 261,812 (1949).
13. Swiss Patent 261,822 (1949).
14. Swiss Patent 252,530 (1948).
15. Swiss Patent 261,821 (1949).
16. Swiss Patent 249,374 (1948).

17. J. Thurston, U.S. Patent 2,474,194 (1949).
18. O. Clauder and G. Bulscu, *Magyar Kem. Folyoirat*, **57**, 68 (1951), through *Chem. Abstracts*, **46**, 4023g (1952).
19. C. Overberger and S. Shapiro, *J. Am. Chem. Soc.*, **76**, 93 (1954).
20. E. Wagner, *J. Org. Chem.*, **5**, 133 (1940).
21. Swiss Patent 261,813 (1949).
22. Swiss Patent 261,823 (1949).
23. Swiss Patent 261,814 (1949).
24. Swiss Patent 261,824 (1949).
25. J. Thurston and D. Kaiser, U.S. Patent 2,493,703 (1949).
26. Swiss Patent 261,830 (1949).
27. Swiss Patent 261,815 (1949).
28. Swiss Patent 261,825 (1949).
29. Swiss Patent 261,816 (1949).
30. Swiss Patent 261,826 (1949).
31. Swiss Patent 261,817 (1949).
32. Swiss Patent 261,827 (1949).
33. E. Bamberger and L. Seeberger, *Ber.*, **25**, 525 (1892).
34. Swiss Patent 261,820 (1949).
35. Swiss Patent 261,831 (1949).
36. Swiss Patent 261,818 (1949).
37. Swiss Patent 261,828 (1949).
38. V. Hunnicki, *Anzeiger Akad. Wiss. Krakau*, **1907**, 16, through Chem. Zentr., **1907**, II, 706.
39. Swiss Patent 243,738 (1948).
40. D. Kaiser and F. Schaefer, U.S. Patent 2,653,934 (1953).
41. Brit. Patent 639,218 (1950), see also French Patent 930,681 (1950).
42. M. Nencki, *Ber.*, **7**, 775 (1874).
43. A. Ostrogovich, *Bull. soc. sci. Bucharest*, **14**, 49 (1905).
44. R. Andreasch, *Monatsh.*, **48**, 145 (1927).
45. D. Nagy, U.S. Patent 2,446,980 (1948).
46. British Patent 642,409 (1950).
47. A. Ostrogovich, *Rend. Acca. Lincei*, (5), **20**, 249 (1929).
48. W. Zerweck and W. Brunner, U.S. Patent 2,302,162 (1942).
49. A. Ostrogovich, *Rend. Acca. Lincei*, (5), **20**, 182 (1929).
50. J. Mackay, U.S. Patent 2,527,314 (1950).
51. S. Birtwell, *J. Chem. Soc.*, **1952**, 1279.
52. C. Haaf, *J. prakt. Chem.*, (2), **43**, 75 (1891).
53. M. Nencki, *Ber.*, **9**, 228 (1876).
54. M. Bradley, U.S. Patent 2,309,624 (1943).
55. J. Thurston, U.S. Patent 2,461,943 (1949).
56. J. Thurston and M. Bradley, U.S. Patent 2,309,681 (1943).
57. E. Bandrowski, *Ber.*, **9**, 240 (1876).
58. P. Adams, U.S. Patent 2,397,396 (1946).
59. A. Ostrogovich and G. Gheorghiu, *Gazz. chim. ital.*, **62**, 317 (1932).
60. J. Thurston, U.S. Patent 2,427,314 (1947).
61. J. Thurston, U.S. Patent 2,309,679 (1943).
62. J. Thurston, U.S. Patent 2,321,052 (1943).
63. A. Grun, U.S. Patent 2,447,175 (1948).
64. W. Oldham, U.S. Patent 2,344,784 (1944).
65. J. Thurston, U.S. Patent 2,483,986 (1949).
66. D. Kaiser, U.S. Patent 2,606,904 (1952).

67. A. Weddige, *J. prakt. Chem.*, (2), **33**, 76 (1886).
68. C. Broche, *J. prakt. Chem.*, (2), **50**, 97 (1894).
69. J. Thurston, U.S. Patent 2,394,526 (1946).
70. J. Thuston, U.S. Patent 2,463,471 (1949).
71. J. Thurston, U.S. Patent 2,427,315 (1947).
72. A. Grun, U.S. Patent 2,447,176 (1948).
73. J. Thurston, and D. Nagy, U.S. Patent 2,427,316 (1947).
74. J. Thurston, U.S. Patent 2,390,476 (1945).
75. J. Thurston and D. Nagy, U.S. Patent 2,333,452 (1943).
76. D. Nagy, U.S. Patent 2,309,661 (1943).
77. J. Castle, U.S. Patent 2,548,772 (1951).
78. J. Thurston, U.S. Patent 2,305,118 (1943).
79. J. Thurston and D. Kaiser, U.S. Patent 2,309,680 (1943).
80. J. Thurston, U.S. Patent 2,459,397 (1949).
81. W. Gresham, U.S. Patent 2,491,658 (1949); see also British Patent 583,720 (1946).
82. V. Wystrach and J. Erickson, *J. Am. Chem. Soc.*, **75**, 6345 (1953); U.S. Patent 2,619,486 (1952).
83. J. Mackay and J. Paden, U.S. Patent 2,459,710 (1949).
84. A. Ostrogovich and G. Gheorghiu, *Gazz. chim. ital.*, **60**, 648 (1930).
85. J. Thurston and D. Nagy, U.S. Patent 2,425,287 (1947).
86. J. Thurston, U.S. Patent 2,386,517 (1945).
87. W. Brunner and E. Bertsch, *Monatsh.*, **79**, 106 (1948).
88. J. Thurston, U.S. Patent 2,447,440 (1948).
89. J. Thurston and D. Kaiser, U.S. Patent 2,425,286 (1948).
90. J. Thurston and D. Kaiser, U.S. Patent 2,535,968 (1950).
91. P. Russell and G. Hitchings, *J. Am. Chem. Soc.*, **72**, 4923 (1950).
92. J. Thurston, U.S. Patent 2,423,071 (1947).
93. W. Oldham, U.S. Patent 2,309,663 (1943).
94. S. Shapiro and C. Overberger, *J. Am. Chem. Soc.*, **76**, 97 (1954).
95. F. Curd, J. Landquist and F. Rose, *J. Chem. Soc.*, **1947**, 154.
96. F. Curd and F. Rose, *J. Chem. Soc.*, **1946**, 362.
97. C. Grundmann and E. Beyer, *Ber.*, **83**, 452 (1950).
98. C. Overberger and S. Shapiro, *J. Am. Chem. Soc.*, **76**, 1061 (1954).
99. S. Birtwell, *J. Chem. Soc.*, **1949**, 2561.
100. J. Thurston, U.S. Patent 2,385,766 (1945).
101. A. Grun, U.S. Patent 2,437,691 (1948).
102. J. Bindler, U.S. Patent 2,451,432 (1948).
103. J. Simons, U.S. Patent 2,510,761 (1950).
104. W. Traube and K. Gorniak, *Z. angew. chem.*, **42**, 379 (1929).
105. W. Zerweck, K. Keller and H. Salkowski, Ger. Patent 870,110 (1953).
106. G. Fraser and W. Kermack, *J. Chem. Soc.*, **1951**, 2682.
107. H. Bestian, et al., *Ann.*, **566**, 210 (1950).
108. W. Niederhauser, U.S. Patent 2,577,477 (1951).
109. British Patent 685,840 (1951).
110. J. Thurston, U.S. Patent 2,423,353 (1947).
111. J. Simons, U.S. Patent 2,684,366 (1954).
112. J. Simons, U.S. Patent 2,532,519 (1950).

5. Applications

Diamino-s-triazines have been used in a wide variety of applications. As mentioned earlier, one of the principal uses of these compounds is as intermediates in the preparation of resinous materials. As such they are useful in surface coatings, adhesives, molding compounds, textile finishing agents, and paper treating materials. Many of these applications have been summarized recently.[97] As a chemical intermediate the diamino-s-triazines have found uses in surface active agents, dyestuff preparations, and chemotherapeutic agents.

The diuretic action of various diamino-s-triazine has been the subject of considerable study.[100,101,102,103] The effect of structure upon activity has been studied.[104] The compounds with no substituent in the 6 position are the most active. 2,4-Bis(acetylamino)-s-triazine is a very potent diuretic, but its toxicity precludes its use in human beings.

III. Diamino dihydro-s-Triazines

A diamino-s-triazine system of considerable interest was encountered during the research on the metabolic transformations of the antimalarial drug, "chloroguanide" (proguanil) (XXXI).

$$p\ ClC_6H_4 \cdot NHC \cdot NH \cdot C{-}NH{-}CH \underset{CH_3}{\overset{CH_3}{<}}$$
$$\quad\quad\quad\ \ \underset{NH}{\|}\quad\ \underset{NH}{\|}$$

(XXXI)   (XXXII)   (XXXIII)

Early in 1951 Crounse[105] reported the isolation of a biologically inactive compound from the urine of monkeys which had received dosages of chloroguanide. He showed that this inactive metabolite, containing two hydrogens less than the drug, had the structure, 2-p-chloroanilino-4-amino-6,6-dimethyl-1,6-dihydro-s-triazine (XXXII). It was synthesized by the reaction of p-chlorophenylbiguanide (XXXIV) with acetone in the presence of acetic acid. The same compound had been prepared several years earlier by Birtwell[106] employing the same reagents with piperidine as the catalyst, and alternately by the reaction of 2-amino-4-methylthio-6,6-dimethyl-1,6-dihydro-s-triazine (**XXXV**) with *p*-chloroaniline.

$(p)\text{ClC}_6\text{H}_5\text{NHCNHCNH}_2$ + $(\text{CH}_3)_2\text{CO}$ $\xrightarrow[\text{acetic acid}]{\text{piperdine}}$

NH NH (**XXXIV**)

+ (*p*) ClC$_6$H$_4$NH$_2$

NH$_2$ (**XXXV**)

Not long after the work of Crounse had appeared, Carrington and co-workers[107] in England reported the isolation of an *active* metabolite. This compound was isomeric with that isolated by Crounse, and in the presence of alkali was converted to the inactive isomer. They believed the structure of the *active* metabolite to be 1-*p*-chlorophenyl-2,4-di-amino-6,6-dimethyl-1,6-dihydro-s-triazine (**XXXIII**). Synthesis was accomplished by the reaction of *p*-chlorophenylbiguanide with acetone in neutral solution, or better, in the presence of excess acid.

The detailed account of the excellent work on the structure of the two isomers has been published recently.[108] The structure of the in-active isomer was deduced principally on the basis of a study of the products obtained by condensing N[1]-aryl-N[1]-methylbiguanides with acetone. This reaction cannot lead to structures of the type (**XXXIII**) because of the substitution on the aryl-bearing nitrogen. When the reaction was carried out in the presence of either piperidine or hydro-chloric acid, the same product (**XXXVI**) was obtained. The ultraviolet spectrum of this compound was similar to that of the inactive isomer

(p) ClC$_6$H$_4$N—CNHCNH$_2$ + $(\text{CH}_3)_2\text{CO}$ $\xrightarrow[\text{or HCl}]{\text{piperidine}}$

CH$_3$ NH NH

NH$_2$ (**XXXVI**)

and different from that of the active compound. Evidence in favor of the s-triazine structure for the inactive isomer was the resolution of an analogous compound with two unlike substituents in the 6 position

(XXXVII). This was synthesized by condensing *p*-chlorophenyl-biguanide with methyl ethyl ketone. Other possible structures for

$$ClC_6H_4NHCNHCNH_2 + CH_3COC_2H_5 \longrightarrow$$
$$\underset{NH\ \ NH}{\overset{\|\ \ \|}{}}$$

(structure XXXVII shown with CH_3, H, N, C_2H_5, NHC_6H_4Cl, NH_2) (XXXVII)

reaction products of aryl biguanides and ketones, i.e. a Schiff's base or a 4-membered ring structure, would not be resolvable. On the basis of these facts the 2-anilino-*s*-triazine structure (XXXII) for the inactive metabolite was believed fairly well estblished.

Definitive chemical proof for the structure of the active isomer was more difficult to obtain. The ease of reversibility of the synthetic reaction between *p*-chlorophenylbiguanide and acetone made it appear unlikely that a hydrogen of the benzene ring was involved in the metabolic dehydrogenation. The formulation (XXXIII) appeared to be the most likely, but the Schiff's base (XXXVIII) and the cyclic structure (XXXIX) also seemed possible. The failure of the active isomer to

$$ClC_6H_4NHCNHCN{=}C{\overset{CH_3}{\underset{CH_3}{}}}$$
$$\underset{NH\ \ NH}{\overset{\|\ \ \|}{}}$$

(XXXVIII)

$$ClC_6H_4NH{-}C{-}NH{-}C{-}NH$$
$$\underset{NH}{\overset{\|}{}}\qquad \underset{N{-}C{-}CH_3}{\overset{\|}{}}$$
$$CH_2$$

(XXXIX)

form a complex with ammoniacal copper sulfate was considered evidence against an open chain compound. As in the case of the inactive isomer, a compound prepared by reaction with an unsymmetrical ketone should be resolvable due to the dissimilar substituents in the 6 position. However, attempts to resolve the products obtained by condensation (acidic conditions) of *p*-chlorophenylbiguanide with unsymmetrical ketones or aldehydes were not successful.

Carrington and co-workers studied the reaction of various aryl biguanides containing additional substituents in the N^2, N^4 and N^5 positions in an attempt to obtain additional evidence for the proposed structure. The reaction of N^1-*p*-chlorophenyl-N^5,N^5-dimethylbiguanide (XL) with acetone took place readily under acidic and basic conditions yielding the expected 1-aryl (XLI) and 2-arylamino- (XLII) *s*-triazines,

respectively. In this case the formation of a four-membered ring structure similar to XXXIX is not possible.

$$ClC_6H_4NHCNHC\!\!-\!\!N(CH_3)_2 + CH_3CCH_3 \xrightarrow{\ H^+\ }$$

$$\underset{NH\ \ NH}{} \qquad \underset{O}{}$$

(XL) (XLI)

$$\Big\downarrow OH^-$$

$$ClC_6H_4NHCNHC\!\!-\!\!N(CH_3)_2 + CH_3CCH_3 \xrightarrow{\ OH^-\ }$$

$$\underset{NH\ \ NH}{} \qquad \underset{O}{}$$

(XLII)

N¹-p-Chlorophenyl-N²,N²-dimethylbiguanide, and N¹-p-chloro-
phenyl-N²,N⁴,N⁵-trimethylbiguanide did not condense with acetone
under either acidic or basic conditions. N¹-p-Chlorophenyl-N⁴,N⁵-di-
methylbiguanide (XLIII) reacted only with difficulty under acidic
conditions to yield a product which appeared to be the 2-aryl-amino-
s-triazine (XLIV).

$$ClC_6H_5NHCNHCNHCH_3 + CH_3COCH_3 \longrightarrow$$

$$\underset{NH\ \ NCH_3}{}$$

(XLIII) (XLIV)

When the condensation reaction was applied to N¹,N²-disubstituted
biguanides very interesting results were obtained. Two products were
obtained from the reaction of acetone with N¹-p-chlorophenyl-N²-
methylbiguanide (XLV) by the usual procedures. When each of these
products was submitted to caustic alkali treatment the same mixture
of the two forms (XLVI) and (XLVII) resulted. These results show that
the two types of reaction are distinct, i.e. the base catalyzed reaction
does not involve the formation of an aryldihydrotriazine which then
rearranges to the anilino derivative. If this were the case the above

reaction (base-catalyzed) would have yielded a mixture rather than a distinct product.

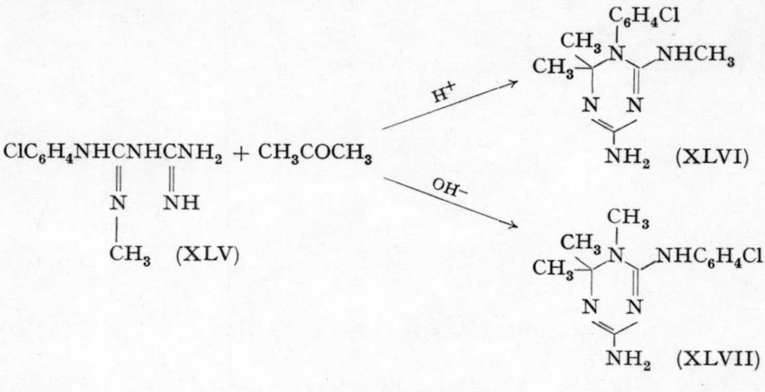

$$ClC_6H_4NHCNHCNH_2 + CH_3COCH_3$$
$$\underset{N}{\overset{\|}{}} \quad \underset{NH}{\overset{\|}{}}$$
$$\underset{CH_3 \ (XLV)}{\overset{|}{}}$$

$$\xrightarrow{H^+}$$

(XLVI)

$$\xrightarrow{OH^-}$$

(XLVII)

The reaction of N^1,N^2-diarylbiguanides with acetone led to identical products under acidic or basic conditions.

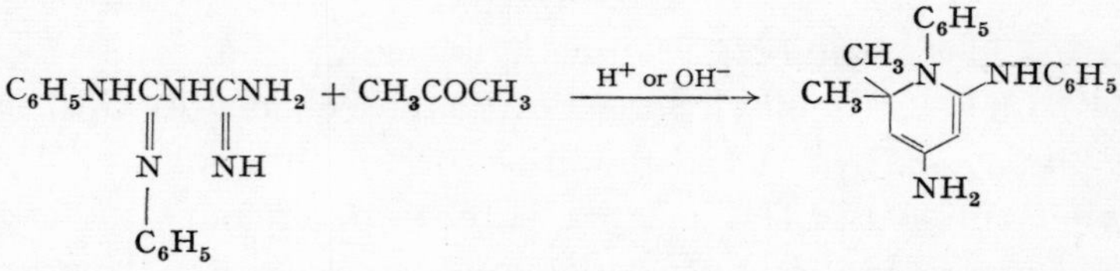

$$C_6H_5NHCNHCNH_2 + CH_3COCH_3 \xrightarrow{H^+ \ or \ OH^-}$$
$$\underset{N}{\overset{\|}{}} \quad \underset{NH}{\overset{\|}{}}$$
$$\underset{C_6H_5}{\overset{|}{}}$$

Many years earlier Cramer[109] had heated N^1,N^2-diarylbiguanides with formic acid and acetic anhydride, and obtained somewhat related compounds. These may be regarded as disubstituted diamino-s-triazines or as dihydroiminoamino-s-triazines.

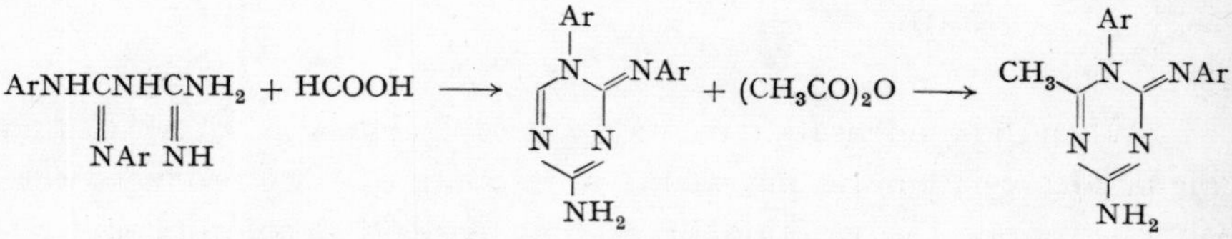

$$ArNHCNHCNH_2 + HCOOH \longrightarrow$$
$$\underset{NAr}{\overset{\|}{}} \quad \underset{NH}{\overset{\|}{}}$$

$$+ (CH_3CO)_2O \longrightarrow$$

The above results with N^1,N^2 disubstituted biguanides, along with the previous identification of the inactive compounds as s-triazine derivatives, constituted good evidence that the postulated structure for the active isomer was correct. However, the most conclusive piece of evidence was provided by X-ray crystallographic studies.[110]

Birtwell[111] had speculated about the structure of the active metabolite, but had been unsuccessful in attempts to synthesize it by reaction of 1-*p*-chlorophenyl-2-methylmercapto-4-amino-6,6-dimethyl-1,6-dihydro-s-triazine (**XLVIII**) with ammonia. Similar results were reported by Loo.[112]

(XLVIII)

The biological activity of the 1-aryl-2,4-diamino-6,6-dialkyl-1,6-dihydro-s-triazines was discovered independently by Modest[113] and co-workers at about the same time as the above work. They showed that this type of structure possessed anti-vitamin and anti-malarial activity, while the isomeric 2-arylamino compounds were without activity. The generality of the reaction of arylbiguanides with ketones or aldehydes in the presence of acid to yield the 1-arylamino-2,4-diamino-6-alkyl-1,6-dihydro-s-triazines was demonstrated, as well as the direct preparation by reaction of aromatic amines with cyano-

guanidine and a ketone or aldehyde. Also the ease of isomerization of the products to the 2-arylamino compounds was shown. Loo[112] has proposed a mechanism for the rearrangement which involves a base-catalyzed ring cleavage, followed by migration of the aryl group and reformation of the s-triazine ring. The driving force for the rearrangement is postulated as the achievement of coplanarity of the s-triazine ring with the phenyl group.

TABLE IV-5. 2,4-Diamino Dihydro-s-Triazines

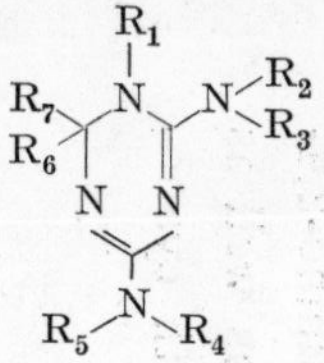

Structure (with substituent positions):

R_1, R_2, R_3 on one amino group; R_4, R_5 on the other amino group; ring carbon bearing R_6, R_7; three ring N atoms.

R_1	R_2	R_3	R_4	R_5	R_6	R_7	M.p., °C, crystn. solvent	Ref.
H	C_6H_5	H	H	H	CH_3	CH_3	184–5 (H_2O)	7
H	$pClC_6H_4$	H	H	H	CH_3	CH_3	130–1, 135	1, 3, 4, 6, 7
H	$C_2H_5OOCC_6H_4$	H	H	H	CH_3	CH_3	130–3	5
H	C_6H_5—C_6H_4	H	H	H	CH_3	CH_3	181–2 (pet. ether)	2
H	$pClC_6H_4$	H	H	H	H	C_3H_7 (iso)	118–20 (methanol)	7
H	$pClC_6H_4$	CH_3	H	H	CH_3	C_2H_5	140–2 (methanol)	7
H	C_6H_5	CH_3	H	H	CH_3	CH_3	239–40 (picrate)	7
H	$pClC_6H_4$	H	CH_3	H	CH_3	CH_3	196–7 (HCl salt)	7
H	$pClC_6H_4$	H	$pClC_6H_4$	CH_3	CH_3	CH_3	265 (HCl salt)	7
CH_3	$pClC_6H_4$	H	H	H	CH_3	CH_3	223–4/aq. methanol	7
CH_3	CH_3	H	H	H	CH_3	CH_3	184–5 (picrate)	7
C_6H_5	H	H	H	H	CH_3	CH_3	138–9/ether-pet. ether	7
C_6H_5	H	H	H	H	H	C_6H_5	232–3 (HCl salt)	7
C_6H_5	C_6H_5	H	H	H	CH_3	CH_3	236–8 (picrate)	7
$mClC_6H_4$	H	H	H	H	H	CH_3	194 (HCl salt)	8
$pClC_6H_4$	H	H	H	H	H	CH_3	174	8
$3,4 Cl_2C_6H_3$	H	H	H	H	H	CH_3	221–2 (HCl salt)	8
$mClC_6H_4$	H	H	H	H	H	C_2H_5	236–7 (HCl salt)	8
$pClC_6H_4$	H	H	H	H	H	C_2H_5	244–5 (HCl salt)	7
$3,4 Cl_2C_6H_3$	H	H	H	H	H	C_2H_5	233–4 (HCl salt)	8
$pClC_6H_4$	H	H	H	H	H	$C_3H_7(n)$	144–6	7
$pClC_6H_4$	H	H	H	H	H	$C_3H_7(iso)$	144–6	8

R_1	R_2	R_3	R_4	R_5	R_6	M.p.	Ref.
$3,4\,Cl_2C_6H_3$	H	H	H	H	C_3H_7, (iso)	237–8 (HCl salt)	8
$pClC_6H_4$	H	H	H	H	C_6H_5	241 (HCl salt)	8
$pClC_6H_4$	H	H	H	H	$C_6H_4N(CH_3)_2$	217 (HCl salt)	8
$mClC_6H_4$	H	H	H	CH_3	CH_3	191 (HCl salt)	8
$pClC_6H_4$	H	H	H	CH_3	CH_3	143–4, 146	6, 7, 8
$mBrC_6H_4$	H	H	H	CH_3	CH_3	217–8 (HCl salt)	8
$pBrC_6H_4$	H	H	H	CH_3	CH_3	141–2	8
mIC_6H_4	H	H	H	CH_3	CH_3	214–5 (HCl salt)	8
pIC_6H_4	H	H	H	CH_3	CH_3	201 (HCl salt)	8
$pCH_3C_6H_4$	H	H	H	CH_3	CH_3	197–8 (HCl salt)	8
$pCH_3OC_6H_4$	H	H	H	CH_3	CH_3	200–1 (HCl salt)	8
$pC_2H_5OC_6H_4$	H	H	H	CH_3	CH_3	212–3 (HCl salt)	8
$pNO_2C_6H_4$	H	H	H	CH_3	CH_3	204–6 (HCl salt)	8
$pC_2H_5SO_2C_6H_4$	H	H	H	CH_3	CH_3	251–2 (HCl salt)	8
$pC_2H_5OOCC_6H_4$	H	H	H	CH_3	CH_3	189–9 (HCl salt)	5
$3,4\,Cl_2C_6H_3$	H	H	H	CH_3	CH_3	140	8
$3,5\,Cl_2C_6H_3$	H	H	H	CH_3	CH_3	186–7 (HCl salt)	8
$3,4\,Br_2C_6H_3$	H	H	H	CH_3	CH_3	195–6 (HCl salt)	8
$3\,Br, 4\,Cl, C_6H_3$	H	H	H	CH_3	CH_3	197 (HCl salt)	8
$3\,Cl, 4\,I, C_6H_3$	H	H	H	CH_3	CH_3	205 (HCl salt)	8
$3\,CH_3\cdot 4\,Cl, C_6H_3$	H	H	H	CH_3	CH_3	210–11 (HCl salt)	8
$3,4\,(CH_3)_2C_6H_3$	H	H	H	CH_3	CH_3	198–200 (HCl salt)	8
$3,4,5\,Cl_3C_6H_2$	H	H	H	CH_3	CH_3	204 (HCl salt)	8
$mClC_6H_4$	H	H	H	C_2H_5	C_2H_5	180–1 (HCl salt)	7
$pClC_6H_4$	H	H	H	C_2H_5	C_2H_5	139–40	8
$3,4\,Cl_2C_6H_3$	H	H	H	C_2H_5	C_2H_5	210–11 (HCl salt)	8
$pClC_6H_4$	H	H	H	$-CH_2-CH_2-CH_2-$ / $-CH_2-CH_2-$ (piperidino)		221–2 (HCl salt)	8
$pClC_6H_4$	CH_3	H	H	CH_3	CH_3	179–81 (picrate)	7
$pClC_6H_4$	$pClC_6H_4$	H	H	CH_3	CH_3	196–7/aq. methanol	7
$pClC_6H_4$	H	CH_3	CH_3	CH_3	CH_3	172–3 (HCl salt)	8
$pClC_6H_4$	H	H	CH_3	CH_3	CH_3	120	7

1. S. Birtwell, F. Curd, J. Hendry and F. Rose, *J. Chem. Soc.*, **1948**, 1645.
2. L. Bauer, J. Cymerman and W. Sheldon, *J. Chem. Soc.*, **1951**, 2342.
3. N. Crounse, *J. Org. Chem.*, **16**, 492 (1951).
4. B. Chase, J. Thurston and J. Walker, *J. Chem. Soc.*, **1951**, 3439.
5. C. Modest, G. Foley, M. Pechet and S. Farber, *J. Am. Chem. Soc.*, **74**, 855 (1950).
6. W. Basu and A. Sen, *J. Sci. Ind. Res. (India)*, **11B**, 312 (1952).
7. H. Carrington, A. Crowther and G. Stacey, *J. Chem. Soc.*, **1954**, 1017.
8. A. Crowther, British Patent 709,906 (1954).

References

1. O. Diels, *Ber.*, **32**, 691 (1899).
2. J. English and J. Paden, U.S. Patent 2,334,162 (1944); cf. C. Grundmann, L. Schwennicke and E. Beyer, *Ber.*, **87**, 19 (1954).
3. R. Hirt, H. Nidecker and R. Berchtold, *Helv. Chim. Acta*, **33**, 1365 (1950).
4. A. Burger and E. Hornbaker, *J. Am. Chem. Soc.*, **75**, 4579 (1953).
5. C. Grundmann, L. Schwennicke and E. Beyer, *Ber.*, **87**, 19 (1954).
6. A. Weddige, *J. prakt. Chem.*, (2), **33**, 76 (1886).
7. C. Broche, *J. prakt. Chem.*, (2), **50**, 97 (1894).
8. J. Ephraim, *Ber.*, **26**, 2226 (1893).
9. N. Tscherven-Iwanoff, *J. prakt. Chem.*, (2), **46**, 142 (1892).
10. C. Grundmann and G. Weisse, *Ber.*, **84**, 684 (1951).
11. M. Nencki, *Ber.*, **7**, 775 (1874).
12. M. Nencki, *Ber.*, **9**, 232 (1876).
13. O. Diels, *Ber.*, **32**, 1219 (1899).
14. M. Nencki, *Ber.*, **7**, 1584 (1874).
15. W. Weith, *Ber.*, **9**, 458 (1876).
16. A. Claus, *Ber.*, **9**, 722 (1876).
17. E. Bamberger and W. Dieckman, *Ber.*, **25**, 534 (1892).
18. M. Nencki, *Ber.*, **9**, 228 (1876).
19. E. Bandrowski, *Ber.*, **9**, 240 (1876).
20. C. Haaf, *J. prakt. Chem.*, (2), **43**, 75 (1891).
21. J. Simons and W. Weaver, U.S. Patent 2,408,694 (1946).
22. W. Traube and K. Gorniak, *Angew. Chem.*, **42**, 379 (1929).
23. C. Korndorfer, *Arch. Pharm.*, **241**, 449 (1903).
24. C. Grundmann and E. Beyer, *Ber.*, **83**, 452 (1950).
25. G. Austerweil, British Patent 639,218 (1950).
26. E. Bamberger and L. Sieberger, *Ber.*, **25**, 525 (1892).
27. K. Rackmann, *Ann.*, **376**, 163 (1910).
28. R. Andreasch, *Monatsh.*, **48**, 145 (1927).
29. J. Thurston and D. Kaiser, U.S. Patent 2,309,680 (1943).
30. J. Thurston and D. Nagy, U.S. Patent 2,333,452 (1943).
31. D. Nagy, U.S. Patent 2,309,661 (1943).
32. W. Oldham, U.S. Patent 2,320,882 (1943).
33. E. Wagner, *J. Org. Chem.*, **5**, 133 (1940).
34. W. Oldham, U.S. Patent 2,309,663 (1943).
35. J. Thurston, U.S. Patent 2,309,679 (1943).
36. W. Oldham, U.S. Patent 2,344,784 (1944).
37. A. Grun, U.S. Patent 2,437,691 (1948).
38. A. Grun, U.S. Patent 2,447,175–177 (1948).

39. J. Thurston, U.S. Patent 2,305,118 (1943).
40. J. Thurston, U.S. Patent 2.394,526 (1946).
41. J. Thurston, U.S. Patent 2,423,353 (1947).
42. J. Thurston, U.S. Patent 2,425,287 (1947).
43. J. Thurston, U.S. Patent 2,427,315 (1947).
44. M. Bradley, U.S. Patent 2,309,624 (1943).
45. J. Thurston, U.S. Patent 2,461, 943 (1949).
46. C. Overberger and S. Shapiro, *J. Am. Chem. Soc.*, **76**, 1061 (1954).
47. A. Ostrogovich, *Rend. Acca. Lincei*, (5), **20**, 249 (1911).
48. A. Ostrogovich and G. Gheorghui, *Gazz. chim. ital.*, **60**, 648 (1930).
49. A. Ostrogovich and G. Gheorghui, *Gazz. chim. ital.*, **62**, 317 (1932).
50. W. Zerweck and W. Brunner, U.S. Patent 2,302,162 (1942).
51. W. Brunner and E. Bertsch, *Monatsh.* **79**, 106 (1948).
52. W. Gresham, U.S. Patent 2,491,658 (1949); British Patent 583,720 (1946).
53. J. Simons, U.S. Patent 2,510,761 (1950); Canadian Patent 455,200 (1949).
54. J. Simons, U.S. Patent 2,532,519 (1950).
55. J. Simons, U.S. Patent 2,684,366 (1954).
56. J. Castle, U.S. Patent 2,548,772 (1951).
57. British Patent 685,840 (1950).
58. V. Wystrach and J. Erickson, *J. Am. Chem. Soc.*, **75**, 6345 (1953).
59. British Patent 642,409 (1950).
60. D. Kaiser, U.S. Patent 2,606,904 (1952).
61. J. Simons and M. Saxton, *Organic Synthesis*, **Vol. 33**, p. 13, John Wiley and Sons, New York, 1953.
62. A. Ostrogovich, *Rend. Acca. Lincei*, (5), **20**, 182 (1911).
63. S. Birtwell, *J. Chem. Soc.*, **1952**, 1279.
64. P. Adams, U.S. Patent 2,397,396 (1946).
65. J. Bindler, U.S. Patent 2,451,432 (1948).
66. S. Birtwell, *J. Chem. Soc.*, **1949**, 2561.
67. J. Mackay, U.S. Patent 2,527,314 (1950).
68. D. Kaiser and J. Roemer, U.S. Patent 2,630,433 (1953).
69. A. Weddige, *J. prakt. Chem.*, (2), **28**, 188 (1883).
70. H. Bestian, et al., *Ann.*, **566**, 210 (1950).
71. A. Joyce and W. Munro, U.S. Patent 2.691,018 (1954).
72. Swiss Patent 252,530, 261,811–820 (1948).
73. J. Mackay and J. Paden, U.S. Patent 2,459,710 (1949).
74. A. Ostrogovich, *Rend. Acca. Lincei*, (6), **11**, 843 (1930).
75. A. Ostrogovich, *Bull. soc. sci. Bucharest*, **14**, 49 (1905).
76. V. Hunnicki, *Anzeiger akad. wiss. Krakau*, **1907**, 16, through *Chem. Zentr.*, 1907, II, 706.
77. G. Widmer and W. Fisch, U.S. Patent 2,197,357 (1940).
78. G. Wismer and W. Fisch, U.S. Patent 2,448,338 (1948).
79. W. Zerweck, K. Keller and H. Salkowski, Ger. Patent 870,110.
80. W. Zerweck and H. Salkowski, Ger. Patent 877,761.
81. H. Wohnsiedler and W. Thomas, U.S. Patent 2,356,718 (1944).
82. K. Keller and O. Hansen, U.S. Patent 2,603,624.
83. L. Bock and Houk, U.S. Patent 2,210,831 (1940).
84. F. Spencer, U.S. Patent 2,579,980 (1951).
85. J. Thurston, U.S. Patent 2,385,766 (1946).
86. J. Thurston, U.S. Patent 2,474,194 (1949).
87. G. Austerweil, *Chem. and Ind.*, **17**, 372 (1952).
88. Swiss Patent 243,738 (1948).

89. Swiss Patent 249,374 (1948).
90. Swiss Patent 244,769 (1948) through *Chemical Abstracts*, **43**, 7727.
91. Ericks, U.S. Patent 2,381,121 (1945).
92. Millson and Mooradian, U.S. Patent 2,638,404 (1953).
93. W. Niederhauser, U.S. Patent 2,577,477 (1951).
94. C. Overberger and S. Shapiro, *J. Am. Chem. Soc.*, **76**, 93 (1954).
95. J. Thurston, U.S. Patent 2,447,440 (1948).
96. J. Thurston and D. Kaiser, U.S. Patent 2,493,703 (1949).
97. New Product Bulletin, Collective Volume III, American Cyanamid Company, New York, 1954.
98. J. Dudley, *J. Am. Chem. Soc.*, **73**, 3007 (1951).
99. F. Nachod and E. Steck, *J. Am. Chem. Soc.*, **70**, 2818 (1948).
100. S. Freire, *Arquiv. biol. (San Paulo)*, **31**, 141 (1947); through *Chemical Abstracts*, **42**, 4672 (1948).
101. A. Turchetti, *Reforma med.*, **64**, 405 (1950); through *Chemical Abstracts*, **44**, 10165 (1950).
102. A. Kattus, E. Newman and J. Franklin, *Bull. John Hopkins Hosp.*, **89**, 1 (1951); through *Chemical Abstracts*, **45**, 10401 (1951).
103. W. Lipschitz and E. Stokey, *J. Pharmacol.*, **92**, 131 (1948); through *Chemical Abstracts*, **42**, 3482 (1948).
104. O. Clauder and G. Bulscu, *Magyar Kem. Polyoirat*, **57**, 68 (1951).
105. N. Crounse, *J. Org. Chem.*, **16**, 492 (1951).
106. S. Birtwell, F. Curd, J. Henry and F. Rose, *J. Chem. Soc.*, **1948**, 1645.
107. H. Carrington, A. Crowther, O. Davey, A. Levi and F. Rose, *Nature*, **168**, 1080 (1951).
108. H. Carrington, A. Crowther and G. Stacey, *J. Chem. Soc.*, **1954**, 1017.
109. W. Cramer, *Ber.*, **34**, 2594 (1901).
110. M. Bailey, *Acta Cryst.*, **7**, 366 (1954).
111. S. Birtwell, *J. Chem. Soc.*, **1952**, 1279.
112. T. Loo, *J. Am. Chem. Soc.* **76**, 5096 (1954).
113. E. Modest, G. Foley, M. Pechet and S. Faber, *J. Am. Chem. Soc.*, **74**, 855 (1952).

CHAPTER V

Ammelide, Ammeline and
Related Compounds

I. Ammelide

Ammelide (2-amino-4,6-dihydroxy-s-triazine) (I) was first prepared in 1834 and was the subject of considerable controversy during the following several decades. Liebig originally prepared[1] it by heating

(I)

melam or ammeline with concentrated sulfuric acid followed by precipitation of a crystalline mass with alcoholic ammonia. An empirical formula $C_6H_9N_9O_3$ was determined and the name "melanurensaure" or "cyamelursaure" was proposed for the new compound. Shortly thereafter, Knapp[2] obtained a similar compound by treating melam with nitric acid. A few years later Gerhardt[3] showed that hydrolysis of melamine with concentrated acids or bases yielded successively compounds which he called ammeline, ammelide and cyanuric acid.

Meanwhile, Wohler and Liebig[4] heated dry urea and obtained an amphoteric compound which was formulated as $C_6N_4H_4O_4$. Laurent and Gerhardt[5] immediately countered with the contention that Liebig's product from urea was actually ammelide, $C_3H_4N_4O_2$. There followed a series of polemical articles[6,7,8] and the issue not being resolved until about 40 years later. Subsequent work on the preparation of ammelide from melam and urea[9,10,11,12,13,14] indicated that Gerhardt and Laurent had been correct, and that Liebig had actually had a mixture of ammeline and ammelide.

Striegler[14] prepared ammelide in the following manner. Crude melam was first obtained by heating ammonium thiocyanate until no volatile products were evolved. The residue was mixed with concentrated sulfuric acid. When the initial reaction had subsided, the mixture was poured into cold water, whereupon ammelide sulfate precipitated. The free base was isolated after addition of ammonia. The yield by this procedure was forty grams from four hundred grams of ammonium thiocyanate. Klason[12,13] heated pure melem with either concentrated potassium hydroxide or concentrated sulfuric acid to obtain ammelide and ammonia as products.

Several alternate routes to ammelide were used by Klason to conclusively prove its structure. He showed that a product similar to that derived from melam, and melem was obtained by heating ammeline (II) with sulfuric acid at 160°. Oxidation of thioammelide (III)

with potassium permanganate yielded the same compound. Likewise, certain ethers of ammelide and thioammelide, derivable from cyanuric chloride, yielded ammelide upon hydrolysis.

The isolation of ammelide among the products obtained by the pyrolysis of urea has been reported by many workers. Wohler and Liebig, as well as Laurent and Gerhardt were probably the first to observe its formation from this source. Many years later Drechsel[10] isolated ammelide among other products, and speculated that the

$$3\,NH_2CONH_2 \longrightarrow 2\,HCNO + CNNH_2 + 2\,NH_3 + H_2O$$

mechanism involved formation of cyanic acid and cyanamide, which reacted to form ammelide.

Bouchardat[15] and Hantzsch and Stuer[16] obtained ammelide in addition to urea and other products, by the reaction of phosgene with ammonia in the vapor phase. Sundwich[17] reported the isolation of ammelide as a by-product in the preparation of xanthen by heating urea with oxalic acid in glycerine at 200°.

Werner[18] studied the decomposition of urea on heating above 150° and was able to obtain yields of ammelide as high as 18% (on the basis of urea decomposed). Other products included ammonium cyanate, biuret, and cyanic acid. When he heated biuret at 195–205°, he obtained ammelide in addition to cyanuric acid, ammonia and cyanic acid. The formation of ammelide was believed to be due to the reaction of biuret with cyanic acid. The possible reaction of cyanuric acid with ammonia was considered, but when cyanuric acid and ammonia were heated at 160–180°, no ammelide was formed.

$$NH_2CONHCONH_2 + HCNO \longrightarrow \underset{OH}{\underset{\displaystyle N\quad N}{H_2N\quad N\quad OH}} + H_2O$$

Das-Gupta[19] has disputed Werner's theory. He contended that ammelide is not formed in appreciable yields below 195°, which is the decomposition temperature of biuret. Therefore, he believed that the formation of ammelide is preceded by the breakdown of biuret. He postulated the formation of dicyanic acid from biuret followed by reaction with urea to form triuret which would cyclize with loss of water to yield ammelide. Credence for this theory was afforded by Werner

$$NH_2CONCO \longleftarrow NH_2CONHCONH_2 \longrightarrow NH_2CONH_2 + HCNO$$
$$+$$
$$NH_2CONH_2$$
$$\downarrow$$
$$NH_2CONHCONHCONH_2 \longrightarrow \underset{OH}{\underset{\displaystyle N\quad N}{H_2N\quad N\quad OH}} + H_2O$$

and Gray[20] who prepared triuret by treating urea with thionyl chloride. When triuret was heated at 175–232°, decomposition set in and ammelide was isolated in the residue.

The preparation of ammelide (and ammeline) by controlled pyrolysis of urea at 225–350° C has been studied.[21] With moderate pressures and ammonia to carbon dioxide ratios of less than four, optimal ammelide-ammeline yields were obtained. At high pressures and high ammonia concentrations, melamine is formed; whereas at atmospheric pressure and in the absence of ammonia, cyanuric acid is produced.

A more obscure preparation of ammelide from urea appears in the work of Poensgen,[22] Hallwachs,[23] and Schmidt,[24] who isolated ammelide from the reaction of urea and cyanogen iodide at 130–140°.

Bamberger[25] obtained a low yield of ammelide by heating cyanoguanidine with water at 160–170° for several hours. Other workers[26] have reported the preparation of ammelide from cyanamide. The conditions were such that melamine may have been formed initially, followed by hydrolysis to ammelide.

Ammelide was also isolated in the products of electrolysis of aqueous ammonia solutions at carbon electrodes,[27] and of benzene-ammonia-ammonium carbonate mixtures at platinum electrodes.[28]

Paden and MacLean[29] obtained good yields of ammelide by heating cyanamide or cyanoguanidine in the presence of water and carbon dioxide at 150° under moderate pressures.

The preparation of ammelide by the hydrolysis of 2-amino-4,6-dichloro-s-triazine was reported by Diels[30] in 1899, and now that cyanuric chloride is commercially available this is probably one of the more convenient preparations of ammelide. The hydrolysis is easily accomplished in the presence of acids, or bases.

$$H_2N \quad N \quad Cl \qquad \xrightarrow{H_2O} \qquad H_2N \quad N \quad OH$$

Ammelide can be obtained as minute prisms on recrystallization from hot water in which it is only slightly soluble. The compound does not possess a definite melting point; it decomposes without fusing when heated above 300°. It is insoluble in cold water and in most common organic solvents. Ammelide dissolves readily in aqueous alkali hydroxide solutions and aqueous ammonia. It is only slightly soluble in cold dilute sulfuric acid, but very soluble in warm acid. It dissolves easily in nitric, hydrochloric, and hot acetic acid.

When solutions of ammelide in aqueous bases or acids are boiled for long periods, hydrolysis to cyanuric acid occurs.

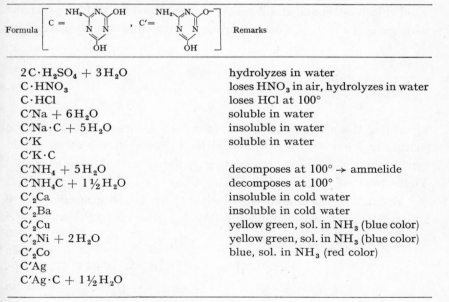

Striegler,[14] who studied the preparation of salts of ammelide, was able to isolate salts with mineral acids as well as many metallic salts. The salts prepared by Striegler are listed in table V-1. It should be noted that the alkali metals formed complex salts containing two molecules of ammelide.

The chemical reactions of ammelide were also studied by Striegler. He found it resistant to reaction with chlorine, bromine and hydrogen iodide. He was unable to prepare ethers by reacting the silver salt with ethyl bromide or ethyl iodide. Likewise, he was not successful

TABLE V-1. Ammelide Salts

Formula	Remarks
$2\,C \cdot H_2SO_4 + 3\,H_2O$	hydrolyzes in water
$C \cdot HNO_3$	loses HNO_3 in air, hydrolyzes in water
$C \cdot HCl$	loses HCl at 100°
$C'Na + 6\,H_2O$	soluble in water
$C'Na \cdot C + 5\,H_2O$	insoluble in water
$C'K$	soluble in water
$C'K \cdot C$	
$C'NH_4 + 5\,H_2O$	decomposes at 100° → ammelide
$C'NH_4C + 1\frac{1}{2}\,H_2O$	decomposes at 100°
C'_2Ca	insoluble in cold water
C'_2Ba	insoluble in cold water
C'_2Cu	yellow green, sol. in NH_3 (blue color)
$C'_2Ni + 2\,H_2O$	yellow green, sol. in NH_3 (blue color)
C'_2Co	blue, sol. in NH_3 (red color)
$C'Ag$	
$C'Ag \cdot C + 1\frac{1}{2}\,H_2O$	

in carrying out a reaction between ammelide and acetic anhydride or acetyl chloride. Reaction with phosphorus pentachloride yielded cyanuric chloride, and oxidation with potassium permanganate gave cyanuric acid.

II. Ammelide Ethers

Ethers of ammelide were first prepared in 1870 by Hofmann and Olshausen.[31,32] They allowed trimethyl and triethyl cyanurates to react with ammonia at room temperature and obtained 2-amino-4,6-dimethoxy-s-triazine (IV) and 2-amino-4,6-diethoxy-s-triazine, re-

spectively. They also reported the monoamino compounds as by-products in the preparation of the cyanurates by reaction of cyanuric chloride with sodium alkoxides.

More recently, Dudley and co-workers prepared a series of ammelide, and N^2-substituted ammelide ethers by reaction of 2-amino-4,6-dichloro-s-triazine and 2-substituted amino-4,6-dichloro-s-triazines with various alcohols. The preparations were conveniently carried out

by adding the aminodichloro-s-triazine to a solution or suspension of sodium hydroxide in the desired alcohol. Reaction was at 30–40° for thirty minutes, followed by a heating period of several hours at 60–75°. Yields were good, as shown in Table V-2.

Ammelide ethers were also prepared by a transetherification reaction.[34] Thus, when 2-amino-4,6-dimethoxy-s-triazine (V) was heated

TABLE V-2.   2-Amino-4,6-Dialkoxy-s-triazines

$$R_3O\underset{N\quad N}{\overset{N}{\bigvee}}N(R_1R_2)$$
$$R_3O$$

R_1	R_2	R_3	M.p. (°C)	% Yield (from dichloro-s-triazine)
H	H	CH_3	219	94
H	H	C_2H_5	97–8	78
H	H	C_3H_7	92–3	71
H	H	C_3H_7 (iso)	96	48
H	H	C_4H_9	101	69
H	H	$CH_2{=}CHCH_2$	60–1	91
H	H	$CH_2{=}C(CH_3)CH_2$	88–9	80
H	H	C_6H_5	181–2	85
C_4H_9	H	CH_3	65–65.5	92
C_6H_{11}	H	CH_3	127–9	80
C_6H_5	H	CH_3	133–4	96
C_6H_{11}	CH_3	CH_3	61–2	85
C_6H_5	CH_3	CH_3	51–2	94
C_2H_5	C_2H_5	CH_3	33–4	86
C_6H_5	$HOCH_2CH_2$	CH_3	143–5	56
—CH_2CH_2—		C_2H_5	163–6	66
C_6H_5	H	C_2H_5	106–7	92
$C_6H_4SO_3H$	H	C_2H_5	255–260	75
$C_{12}H_{25}$	H	$CH_2{=}CHCH_2$	49–51	82
$C_6H_3Cl_2(3,5)$	H	$CH_2{=}CHCH_2$	89.5–90	84
$HOCH_2CH_2$	$HOCH_2CH_2$	$CH_2{=}CHCH_2$	109–112	14

with butanol in the presence of sodium butoxide, methanol was formed and 2-amino-4,6-dibutoxy-s-triazine (VI) was produced in good yield. When polyhydric alcohols were used in this reaction, resinous products were obtained.

The interaction of ammelide ethers with amines was studied as a possible route to substituted melamines.[35] In the case of the aryloxy s-triazines, this reaction proceeds well to yield the melamines. When alkoxy groups are present, the reaction is more complicated. A side

reaction results in alkylation of the amine with formation of a hydroxy-
s-triazine. When 2,4-dimethoxy-6-methylanilino-s-triazine (VII) was

heated with methylaniline, a 37% yield of 2,4-dihydroxy-6-methyl-
anilino-s-triazine (VIII) was obtained with concurrent formation of
dimethylaniline. The scope of this alkylation reaction has not been
extensively explored.

The amination of aryloxy-s-triazines proceeds best with strong
amines. A weak amine such as N-phenylethanolamine requires a reaction temperature of 250°. When 2-amino-4,6-bis-phenoxy-s-triazine
(IX) was heated at 260–280°, self-condensation occurred with the formation of polymers. A similar polycondensation occurred with 2,4-di-
amino-6-phenoxy-s-triazine.

When 2-amino-4,6-dialkoxy-s-triazines were heated, various rearrangements occurred.[36] As is true of the trialkyl cyanurates (see
Chapter I), migration of alkyl groups to the ring nitrogens occurred
in many cases. This was true only if the amino groups contained at

least one hydrogen atom. Thus, 2-methylanilino-4,6-dimethoxy-*s*-triazine (X) was recovered unchanged after heating at 185–205° C.

$$CH_3O \overset{CH_3}{\underset{\displaystyle \underset{OCH_3}{N \;\; N}}{\overset{\displaystyle N \;\; NC_6H_5}{}}} \xrightarrow{\text{185–205°C}} \quad \text{No reaction}$$

(X)

When 2-butylamino-4,6-dimethoxy-*s*-triazine (XI) was heated at 170–180°, a 70% yield of a product believed to be 1,5-dimethyl-2-butyl-amino-4,6-dioxo-1,4,5,6-tetrahydro-*s*-triazine (XII) was obtained. The structure was shown by hydrolysis with strong sulfuric acid to dimethyl isocyanurate (XIII).

$$CH_3O \underset{OCH_3}{\overset{N \;\; NHC_4H_9}{N \;\; N}} \xrightarrow[\text{160–180°C}]{\varDelta} \quad O \overset{CH_3}{\underset{O}{\overset{N \;\; NHC_4H_9}{H_3C^N \;\; N}}} \xrightarrow{H_2SO_4} \quad O \overset{CH_3}{\underset{O}{\overset{N \;\; O}{H_3C^N \;\; NH}}}$$

(XI)   (XII)   (XIII)

In other cases, the results of heating dialkoxyamino-*s*-triazines were considerably more complicated. For example, 2-anilino-4,6-dimethoxy-*s*-triazine (XIV) gave varying results depending upon reaction conditions. At 160°, two isomeric compounds were obtained, XV and XVI. The latter, the partially rearranged product, could be converted

$$CH_3O \underset{OCH_3}{\overset{N \;\; NHC_6H_5}{N \;\; N}} \xrightarrow{\text{160°C}} \quad O \overset{CH_3}{\underset{O}{\overset{N \;\; NHC_6H_5}{H_3C^N \;\; N}}} + \quad O \overset{CH_3}{\underset{OCH_3}{\overset{N \;\; NHC_6H_5}{N \;\; N}}}$$

(XIV)   (XV)   (XVI)

↑   *Δ*, 160°C

to the former by further heating. High yields of XVI were obtainable by heating XIV at 110° for prolonged periods. When acids were present, a third product, a hydroxy-*s*-triazine (XVII) was obtained. This was believed to have arisen as a result of an intermolecular alkylation reaction of the type discussed earlier. A similar alkylation is believed to have occurred when XVI was heated at 160° in a hydrocarbon solvent.

A dealkylated product XVIII, isomeric with XVII, was obtained. When methylcarbitol was used as a solvent, an 83% yield of XVIII was

$$CH_3O\underset{N\quad N}{\overset{N\quad NHC_6H_5}{\bigvee}}OCH_3 \quad\xrightarrow{160°C,\ H^+}\quad CH_3O\underset{N\quad N}{\overset{N\quad NHC_6H_5}{\bigvee}}OH \quad+\quad CH_3O\underset{N\quad N}{\overset{N\quad \overset{CH_3}{NC_6H_5}}{\bigvee}}OCH_3$$

(XVII)   (Not isolated)

obtained from XVI. In this case, it was postulated that alkylation of the alcohol occurred.

$$2\ O\underset{N\quad N}{\overset{\overset{CH_3}{N}\quad NHC_6H_5}{\bigvee}}OCH_3 \ (XVI) \longrightarrow O\underset{N\quad N}{\overset{\overset{CH_3}{N}\quad NHC_6H_5}{\bigvee}}OH\ (XVIII) \quad+\quad O\underset{N\quad N}{\overset{\overset{CH_3}{N}\quad \overset{CH_3}{NC_6H_5}}{\bigvee}}OCH_3$$

An interesting intramolecular reaction of some β-acetoxyethylamino dialkoxy-s-triazines was discovered by Schaefer and co-workers. While attempting to prepare vinylamino-s-triazines by pyrolysis of β-acetoxyethylamino-s-triazines, they found that the desired reaction occurred only when an alkoxy-s-triazine group was present in the same molecule. Thus, 2,4,6-tris(N-β-acetoxyethylanilino)-s-triazine (XIX)

$$\underset{(XIX)}{C_6H_5N\underset{N\quad N}{\overset{CH_3COOCH_2CH_2\qquad CH_2CH_2OOCCH_3}{\overset{|\qquad\qquad\qquad |}{\bigvee}}}NC_6H_5}\ \ \underset{C_6H_5}{\overset{NCH_2CH_2OOCCH_3}{}}$$

was stable and no acetic acid was evolved at 350°. When 2-(N-β-acetoxyethylanilino)-4,6-dimethoxy-s-triazine (XX) was pyrolyzed, the pro-

$$RO\underset{N\quad N}{\overset{\overset{CH_2CH_2OOCCH_3}{|}}{\overset{N\quad NC_6H_5}{\bigvee}}}OR \quad\xrightarrow{\Delta}\quad RO\underset{N\quad N}{\overset{\overset{CH=CH_2}{|}}{\overset{N\quad NC_6H_5}{\bigvee}}}OH \quad+\ CH_3COOR$$

(XX), R=CH$_3$ (XXII), R=CH$_3$
(XXI), R=C$_2$H$_5$ (XXIII), R=C$_2$H$_5$

duct was the hydroxy-s-triazine (XXII); methylacetate was also formed. Similar results were obtained when the corresponding diethoxy derivative (XXI) was heated.

III. Aminodichloro-s-Triazines

The preparation of aminodichloro s-triazines has been accomplished almost exclusively by the reaction of cyanuric chloride with ammonia or an amine. This reaction is generally applicable and has been used

with a variety of amines. Replacement of two chlorines is avoided by carrying out the reaction at low temperatures (0° C or below); disubstitution occurs at higher temperatures (30–50° C).

The earliest preparation of a 2-amino-4,6-dichloro-s-triazine was reported by Fries[38] in 1886. He treated cyanuric chloride with two moles of α-naphthylamine in ether solution and obtained 2-α-naphthyl-

amino-4,6-dichloro-s-triazine (XXIV). The reaction of ammonia and aliphatic amines was studied several years later by Diels[30] who reported a 90% yield of 2-amino-4,6-dichloro-s-triazine when cyanuric chloride in ether was treated with gaseous ammonia at 0° C. Methyl and ethyl amines afforded monoaminodichloro-s-triazines in good yields by reaction at —20° C.

A more detailed study of these reactions was made many years later by Pearlman and Banks[39] and Thurston and co-workers.[40] The former workers used acetone solution at —40° C for reactions with anhydrous ammonia and at —10 to —30° C with amines. The products were isolated by precipitation in ice.

TABLE V-3.   2-Amino-4,6-Dichloro-*s*-Triazines

$$Cl-\underset{N\,\diagdown N}{\overset{N\,\diagup N-R_1}{\bigcirc}}-\underset{Cl}{}$$

R_1	R_2	M.p. (°C) recrystallization solvent	Yield	Ref.
H	H	> 400°	90	1, 2
		235–6°/dioxane	95	3
H	CH_3	161°	85	1
H	C_2H_5	107°		1
H	CH_2CN	178–80°		4
H	C_4H_9	51–2°/benzene	92	3
H	$C_{12}H_{25}$	65°/hexane	100	3
H	C_6H_{11}	oil	88	3
H	C_6H_5	133–5°, 138°/benzene	99	3, 11
H	C_6H_4Cl (*p*)	185–6°		7
H	$C_6H_4OCH_3$ (*p*)	168–70°		7
H	$C_6H_4SO_3Na$	water	100	3
H	$C_6H_3NH_2,CH_3$ (3,4)	—		6
H	NHC_6H_5	—		6
H	$C_{10}H_7$ (α)	149° (dec.)		5
H	$C_{10}H_7$ (β)	154°		6
H	$C_6H_4AsO_3H_2$			8
H	C_6H_4HgOH			9
H	$C_6H_4Hg \cdot OCOCH_3$			9
H	$C_6H_4SbO_3H_2$			9, 10
H	$C_6H_4PO_3H_2$			9
H	$C_6H_4SeO_3H_2$			9
CH_3	CH_3	122.5–123.5°/pet. ether	38	2
C_2H_5	C_2H_5	78–9°/benzene	91	3
C_4H_9	CH_2CN	80–1°/naphtha	73	3, 4
C_6H_{11}	CH_2CN	145–6°/methanol	66	3, 4
CH_2CH_2CN	CH_2CH_2CN	212–15°/naphtha	93	3, 4
CH_3	C_6H_5	131–2°/benzene	92	3
CH_2CN	C_6H_5	152–4°	—	4
C_6H_5	C_6H_5	172–4°/ethanol	85	3

1. O. Diels, *Ber.*, **32**, 691 (1899).
2. W. Pearlman and C. Banks, *J. Am. Chem. Soc.*, **70**, 3726 (1948).
3. J. Thurston, J. Dudley, D. Kaiser, I. Hechenbleickner, F. Schaefer and D. Holm-Hansen, *J. Am. Chem. Soc.*, **73**, 2981 (1951).
4. I. Hechenbleickner, U. S. Patent 2,476,546 (1949).
5. H. Fries, *Ber.*, **19**, 242 (1886).
6. H. Fries, *Ber.*, **19**, 2055 (1886).
7. F. Curd, J. Landquist and F. Rose, *J. Chem. Soc.*, 1947, 154.
8. E. Friedheim, U. S. Patent 2,334,321 (1943).
9. E. Friedheim, U. S. Patent 2,415,555 (1947).
10. E. Friedheim, U. S. Patent 2,418,115 (1947).
11. H. Fierz-David and M. Matter, *J. Soc. Dyers Colourists*, **53**, 424 (1937).

Thurston and co-workers found that a slurry of cyanuric chloride in dilute aqueous dioxane reacted with two moles of ammonia at 5–8° C to give excellent yields of 2-amino-4,6-dichloro-s-triazine. For the preparation of the substituted amino derivatives, a slurry of cyanuric chloride in water was treated at 0—5° with two moles of amine, or one mole of amine and 1 mole of sodium hydroxide, carbonate or bicarbonate. The products, isolated by filtration after reaction periods of one half to one hour, were obtained in excellent yields.

The aminodichloro-s-triazines which have been reported are listed in Table V-3.

2-Amino-4,6-dichloro-s-triazine is a moderately high melting solid (235–6° C). It is slightly soluble in alcohol, ether, chloroform and acetone, and nearly insoluble in water. On heating with water, it is fairly rapidly converted to ammelide. This transformation also occurs slowly on storage in the presence of moist air. The reaction with alcohols and phenols to form ammelide ethers has been discussed earlier. Reaction of 2-amino-4,6-dichloro-s-triazine with sodium hydrosulfide yields dithioammelide (2-amino-4,6-dimercapto-s-triazine) (XXV). The reaction with ammonia and amines will be discussed in a later section of this chapter.

IV. Ammeline

Ammeline (2-hydroxy-4,6-diamino-s-triazine) was first prepared by Liebig[41] in the early 1830's with less uncertainty than his work on ammelide. This first synthesis was by heating melam with potassium hydroxide. After removal of melamine, ammeline was obtained on acidification with acetic acid. Liebig showed the relationship of ammeline to other s-triazines by its reaction with water to form cyanuric acid. Knapp[42] was able to obtain ammelide as an intermediate in the hydrolysis of ammeline to cyanuric acid. The synthesis from melam was confirmed later by Klason.[13]

Many of the subsequent syntheses of ammeline employed cyano-guanidine as a starting material. Smolka and Friedreich[43] heated cyano-guanidine with urea at 180°, and observed the formation of ammeline accompanied by vigorous evolution of ammonia. They believed that the reaction involved conversion of urea to cyanic acid and ammonia, followed by reaction of cyanoguanidine with cyanic acid. They proposed the acyclic structure XXVI for ammeline.

$$NH_2CONH_2 \longrightarrow NH_3 + HOCN$$

$$HOCN + \underset{\underset{NH}{\|}}{C}NNHCNH_2 \longrightarrow \underset{\underset{NH}{\|}\ \underset{O}{\|}}{C}NNHCNHCNH_2$$

(XXVI)

The above workers[44] and Bamberger,[45] independently, showed that ammeline was the product obtained by heating cyanoguanidine with urethane at 180–190°C. Bamberger also prepared ammeline in good

$$\underset{\underset{NH}{\|}}{C}NNHCNH_2 + NH_2COOC_2H_5 \longrightarrow \left[\underset{\underset{NH}{\|}\ \underset{O}{\|}}{C}NNHCNHCNH_2 \right] + C_2H_5OH$$

yield by heating a dry mixture of cyanoguanidine and potassium cyanate at 200–205° C for twenty minutes. The product was obtained by dissolving the reaction mixture in caustic solution, filtering, and precipitating the ammeline by addition of acetic acid.

Stolle and Krauch[46] heated a mixture of cyanoguanidine and concentrated ammonia for three hours at 120° and obtained a mixture of melamine (35% yield) and ammeline (20% yield). They postulated that hydrolysis of cyanoguanidine to guanidine and cyanic acid occurred, followed by reaction of cyanic acid with cyanoguanidine to give ammeline.

Davis[47] obtained ammeline in fairly good yield by fusing cyano-guanidine with ammonium nitrate. Ostrogovich and Gheorghiu[48] observed a mixture of ammeline and melamine as the products, when cyanoguanidine was heated.

Other syntheses of ammeline have been based on biguanide. Parallel to their work with cyanoguanidine, Smolka and Friedrich[42] obtained ammeline by heating biguanide sulfate with urea at 160°, and

$$NH_2CNHCNH_2 \cdot H_2SO_4 + NH_2CNH_2 \xrightarrow[160°C]{\Delta} \underset{NH_2}{\underset{|}{\overset{H_2N \quad N \quad OH}{\underset{N \quad N}{\bigtriangleup}}}} + (NH_4)_2SO_4$$

with urethane at 180°. Rackmann[50] prepared ammeline by heating biguanide with ethyl carbonate.

$$NH_2CNHCNH_2 + (C_2H_5O)_2CO \longrightarrow \underset{NH_2}{\overset{H_2N \quad N \quad OH}{\bigtriangleup}} + 2 C_2H_5OH$$

Klason[12] isolated ammeline in the complex mixture obtained by heating ammonium thiocyanate at 260°. He also prepared ammeline by hydrolysis of 2,4-diamino-6-chloro-s-triazine and on treatment of 2,4-diamino-6-mercapto-s-triazine with potassium permanganate.[13] Wed-

$$\underset{NH_2}{\overset{H_2N \quad N \quad Cl}{\bigtriangleup}} + NaOH \longrightarrow \underset{NH_2}{\overset{H_2N \quad N \quad OH}{\bigtriangleup}} + NaCl$$

dige[51] obtained ammeline by heating 2,4,6-tris(trichloromethyl)-s-triazine with aqueous ammonia, and similarly from 2,4-diamino-6-trichloromethyl-s-triazine.

$$\underset{CCl_3}{\overset{Cl_3C \quad N \quad CCl_3}{\bigtriangleup}} + 2 NH_4OH \longrightarrow \underset{NH_2}{\overset{H_2N \quad N \quad OH}{\bigtriangleup}} + 3 CHCl_3$$

$$\underset{NH_2}{\overset{H_2N \quad N \quad CCl_3}{\bigtriangleup}} + NH_4OH \longrightarrow \underset{NH_2}{\overset{H_2N \quad N \quad OH}{\bigtriangleup}} + CHCl_3$$

An unusual preparation of ammeline is that of Rathke[52] who reported its preparation by heating 2,4-diamino-6-mercapto-s-triazine with ethyl bromide in the presence of ethanol.

Ammeline is usually obtained as a white microcrystalline powder. It does not possess a definite melting point; on heating it decomposes into a complex mixture of ammonia, H_2O, melon, HCN, etc. It is very sparingly soluble in cold and hot water, and is insoluble in most common organic solvents. Solutions in strong acids and bases are easily obtained, but on heating or long standing, hydrolysis to ammelide occurs. Ammeline dissolves in warm aqueous sodium carbonate and on cooling is reprecipitated. This is a convenient way of separating it from ammelide.

Ammeline forms easily hydrolyzable salts with acids and bases, and double salts have been prepared with silver nitrate, and platinum chloride. A yellow picrate melting at 266° has been reported.[48]

A solution of ammeline in concentrated sulfuric acid yields ammelide and ammonium sulfate.[41] When treated with hot nitric acid, ammeline is converted finally to cyanuric acid, with ammelide as an intermediate.[42] Smolka and Friedreich[44] were unable to acetylate or benzoylate ammeline.

The chlorination of ammeline in aqueous slurry has been reported to yield a water soluble product believed to be a dichloroammeline.[53] This is possibly an N-chloro derivative as shown in the equation. The

product, having "active" chlorine is reported useful as a bleaching or sterilizing agent.

The reaction of ethylene oxide with ammeline under basic conditions yields a polyoxyethylene derivative useful as a wetting agent.[54]

V. Ammeline Ethers

The first preparations of ammeline ethers date back to the work of Hofmann[31,32] in the 1870's just as was the case for the ammelide ethers. By allowing 2-amino-4,6-diethoxy-s-triazine to stand in the presence of concentrated ammonia for long periods, he obtained 2,4-

diamino-6-ethoxy-s-triazine. Otto[55] treated 2,4-diamino-6-chloro-s-triazine with the sodium salts of phenol and o-cresol and obtained the corresponding aryl ammeline ethers. This latter route, reaction of an

appropriate diaminochloro-s-triazine with an alcohol or alcoholate, has been used by later workers.

Banks and coworkers,[56,57,58] in the course of a study of anti-histamine agents, prepared an extensive series of ammeline ethers and N^2-, N^4-substituted ammeline ethers. They treated a diaminochloro-s-triazine with the sodium alcoholate in alcohol or xylene solution at reflux. The reaction with alcohols in the presence of potassium carbonate gave poorer yields. Dudley and his colleagues,[33] however, obtained good yields of ammeline ethers by heating a diaminochloro-s-triazine with sodium hydroxide dissolved or suspended in an alcohol.

The reaction of 2-alkoxy-4,6-dichloro-s-triazines with ethylenimine to prepare 2-alkoxy-4,6-ethylenimino-s-triazines has been reported.[59,60]

A list of ammeline ethers is given in Table V-4.

TABLE V-4. Ammeline Ethers

$$R_5O\text{—}C \overset{\displaystyle N \quad N\text{—}N(R_1R_2)}{\underset{\displaystyle N \quad N(R_3R_4)}{}}$$

R_1	R_2	R_3	R_4	R_5	M.p. °C	Yield %	Ref.
H	H	H	H	CH_3	229–30	81	3
H	H	H	H	C_2H_5	238	93	6
H	H	H	H		190–200	—	1
H	H	H	H		182	72	3
H	H	H	H	nC_3H_7	182–3	88	3, 6
H	H	H	H	$isoC_3H_7$	172	78	3, 6
H	H	H	H	nC_4H_9	174–5	75	3, 6
H	H	H	H	$isoC_4H_9$	186	93	3
H	H	H	H	$secC_4H_9$	173–4	50	3
H	H	H	H	nC_5H_{11}	147	28	3
H	H	H	H	$isoC_5H_{11}$	181–3	30	5
H	H	H	H	$CH_3CH_2CH(CH_3)CH_2$	170–2	30	5
H	H	H	H	C_6H_{13}	152	58	3
H	H	H	H	C_7H_{15}	139	63	3
H	H	H	H	C_8H_{17}	122–4	46	3
H	H	H	H	C_9H_{19}	115	41	3
H	H	H	H	$C_{10}H_{21}$	121–3	29	3
H	H	H	H	$CH_2{=}CHCH_2$	181–2	82	3, 6
H	H	H	H	$C_2H_5OCH_2CH_2$	155–6	33	3
H	H	H	H	$C_6H_5OCH_2CH_2$	184–5	77	3
H	H	H	H	$CH_2{<}^{CH_2CH_2}_{CH_2CH_2}{>}CH$	209	53	3
H	H	H	H	$C_6H_5CH_2$	187	65	3
H	H	H	H	$(CH_3)_2NCH_2CH_2$	122	37	3
H	H	H	H	$(C_2H_5)_2N(CH_2)_3$	147	38	3

					M.p. (°C)	Yield (%)	Ref.
H	H	H	H	C_6H_5	245	—	2
H	H	H	H	p-$CH_3C_6H_4$	225	—	2
H	H	H	H	o-$NO_2C_6H_4$	249–50	64	8
H	H	H	H	p-$NO_2C_6H_4$	250	94	8
H	H	H	H	o-$NH_2C_6H_4$	220–2	83	8
H	H	H	H	p-$NH_2C_6H_4$	250	92	8
H	H	H	H	p-$HO_3AsC_6H_4$	250	55	8
H	H	H	H	p-$As(SCH_2COOH)_2C_6H_4$	226–8	56	8
H	H	H	H	$2',4'$-$NO_2,HO_3AsC_6H_3$	—	13	8
H	H	H	CH_3	CH_3	155–6	66	4
H	H	H	CH_3	C_2H_5	170–1	79	5
H	H	H	CH_3	n-C_3H_7	175–7	68	5
H	H	H	CH_3	C_4H_9	173–5	88	4
H	H	H	CH_3	C_6H_{13}	166–8	75	5
H	H	H	CH_3	$CH_2{(CH_2CH_2)_2}CH$ (cyclohexyl ring)	232–4	64	5
H	H	H	CH_3	CH_3	211–3	64	5
H	H	H	C_2H_5	C_6H_5	168–70	24	4
H	H	H	C_2H_5	CH_3	116–18	86	4
H	H	H	C_2H_5	C_4H_9	211–13	90	8
H	H	H	C_2H_5	p-$NO_2C_6H_4$	204–6	77	8
H	H	H	C_2H_5	p-$NH_2C_6H_4$		25	8
H	H	H	C_2H_5	p-$HO_3AsC_6H_4$	148–50	81	4
H	H	H	C_3H_7	CH_3	116–18	85	4
H	H	H	C_3H_7	C_4H_9	125–7	89	4
H	H	H	C_4H_9	CH_3	104.5–6	78	6
H	H	H	C_4H_9	$CH_2{=}CHCH_2$	103–4	72	4
H	H	H	C_5H_{11}	CH_3	104–8	86	4
H	H	H	C_5H_{11}	C_2H_5	103–5	55	5
H	H	H	C_5H_{11}	C_3H_7	92–5	46	5
H	H	H	C_5H_{11}	C_4H_9	107–9	81	4

(Table continued)

TABLE V-4 (continued)

R_1	R_2	R_3	R_4	R_5	M.p. °C.	Yield %	Ref.
H	H	H	C_6H_{13}	CH_3	104–6	92	4
H	H	H	C_6H_{13}	C_4H_9	119–21	99	4
H	H	H	$CH_2{=}CHCH_2$	CH_3	148–50	89	4
H	H	H	$CH_2{=}CHCH_2$	C_4H_9	87–9	75	4
H	H	H	$CH_2{=}C(CH_3)CH_2$	CH_3	129–31	88	4
H	H	H	$CH_2{=}C(CH_3)CH_2$	C_4H_9	106–8	79	4
H	H	H	$CH_2\langle\substack{CH_2CH_2\\CH_2CH_2}\rangle CH$	CH_3	170–2	99	4
H	H	H	$CH_2\langle\substack{CH_2CH_2\\CH_2CH_2}\rangle CH$	C_4H_9	141–3	96	4
H	H	H	$CH_3CHOHCH_2$	C_2H_5	140–2	83	3
H	H	H	$CH_3CHOHCH_2$	C_4H_9	131	87	3
H	H	H	$CH_2\langle\substack{CH_2CH_2\\CH_2CH_2}\rangle NCH_2CH_2CH_2$	C_2H_5	152–3	86	4
H	H	CH_3	CH_3	CH_3	169–71	81	4
H	H	CH_3	CH_3	C_2H_5	156–8	88	5
H	H	CH_3	CH_3	C_4H_9	103–4	88	4
H	H	C_2H_5	C_2H_5	CH_3	113–5	73	4
H	H	C_2H_5	C_2H_5	C_4H_9	73–5	51	4
H	H	$CH_2{=}CHCH_2$	$CH_2{=}CHCH_2$	CH_3	87–9	83	4
H	H	$CH_2{=}CHCH_2$	$CH_2{=}CHCH_2$	C_4H_9	b.p.172–5/1 mm.	65	4
H	H	$CH_2{=}C(CH_3)CH_2$	$CH_2{=}C(CH_3)CH_2$	CH_3	101–3	90	4
H	H	$CH_2{=}C(CH_3)CH_2$	$CH_2{=}C(CH_3)CH_2$	CH_3	60–2	87	4
		CH_2	CH_2				

R1	R1'	R2	R2'	R3	R3'	m.p. (°C)	Yield (%)	Ref.
$-CH_2-CH_2-CH_2-$ (bridge, CH_2)				C_4H_9	H	115–7	87	4
$-CH_2-O-CH_2-$ (bridge, CH_2)				CH_3	H	182–4	80	4
H	H	$HOCH_2CH_2$	C_2H_5	C_4H_9	H	108–10	43	4
H	H	$HOCH_2CH_2$	C_2H_5	CH_3	H	162–4	87	4
H	H	$HOCH_2CH_2$	C_6H_5	C_4H_9	H	123–5	64	4
H	H	$HOCH_2CH_2$	C_6H_5	CH_3	H	224–6	91	4
H	H	$HOCH_2CH_2$	C_6H_5	C_2H_5	H	194–6 (dec.)	83	5
H	H	CH_3	H	C_4H_9	H	157–9	61	4
H	H	CH_3	H	CH_3	H	184–6	76	4
H	H	CH_3	H	C_2H_5	H	171–3	61	5
H	H	C_2H_5	H	C_4H_9	H	103–4	60	4
H	H	C_2H_5	H	CH_3	H	81–3	46	4
H	H	C_2H_5	H	C_2H_5	H	116–18	44	5
H	H	C_2H_5	H	C_3H_7	H	82–4	88	5
H	H	C_2H_5	H	C_4H_9	H	50–2	85	4
H	H	C_2H_5	H	$p\text{-}NO_2C_6H_4$	H	210–11	76	8
H	H	C_2H_5	H	$p\text{-}NH_2C_6H_4$	H	226–8	77	8
H	H	C_2H_5	H	$p\text{-}HO_3AsC_6H_4$	H		9	8
H	H	C_2H_5	H	$p\text{-}As(SCH_2COOH)_2C_6H_4$	H	70–3	45	8
H	H	$CH_2{=}CHCH_2$	H	CH_3	H	84–6	88	4
H	H	$CH_2{=}CHCH_2$	H	C_4H_9	H	b.p. 185–90/1 mm.	51	4
H	H	$CH_2{=}C(CH_3)CH_2$	H	CH_3	H	112–14	93	4
H	H	$CH_2{=}C(CH_3)CH_2$	H	C_4H_9	H	58–60	70	4

(Table continued)

TABLE V-4 (continued)

R_1	R_2	R_3	R_4	R_5	M.p. °C.	Yield %	Ref.
H	$CH_3CHOHCH_2$	H	$CH_3CHOHCH_2$	C_2H_5	119–20	49	3
H	C_6H_5	H	C_6H_5	CH_3	165–6	100	6
H	C_6H_5	H	C_6H_5	C_3H_7	148–9	93	6
H	CH_3	CH_3	CH_3	CH_3	187–8	80	4
H	CH_3	CH_3	CH_3	C_2H_5	173–5	80	5
H	CH_3	CH_3	CH_3	C_4H_9	129–31	87	4
H	CH_3	CH_3	CH_3	$CH_2{\Big\langle}{{CH_2CH_2}\atop{CH_2CH_2}}{\Big\rangle}CH$	154	75	5
H	C_2H_5	C_2H_5	C_2H_5	C_2H_5	107–9	99	4
H	C_2H_5	C_2H_5	C_2H_5	C_4H_9	80–82	96	4
$CH_2{-}$	$CH_2{-}$	$CH_2{-}$	$CH_2{-}$	CH_3	120–120.5	44	9, 10
CH_3	CH_3	CH_3	CH_3	CH_3	90–2	73	4
$CH_2{-}$	$CH_2{-}$	$CH_2{-}$	$CH_2{-}$	C_2H_5	75.5–76.5	50.3	9
CH_3	CH_3	CH_3	CH_3	C_4H_9	b.p. 155–7/4 mm.	69	4
C_2H_5	C_2H_5	C_2H_5	C_2H_5	CH_3	b.p. 146–9/1 mm.	65	4
C_2H_5	C_2H_5	C_2H_5	C_2H_5	C_4H_9	b.p. 164–5/4 mm.	84	4
$CH_2{=}CHCH_2$	$CH_2{=}CHCH_2$	$CH_2{=}CHCH_2$	$CH_2{=}CHCH_2$	CH_3	b.p. 150–3/1 mm.	93	4
$CH_2{=}CHCH_2$	$CH_2{=}CHCH_2$	$CH_2{=}CHCH_2$	$CH_2{=}CHCH_2$	C_4H_9	b.p. 157–60/1 mm.	93	4
$\overset{CH_3}{CH_2{=}CCH_2}$	$\overset{CH_3}{CH_2{=}CCH_2}$	$\overset{CH_3}{CH_2{=}CCH_2}$	$\overset{CH_3}{CH_2{=}CCH_2}$	CH_3	b.p. 151–4/1.5 mm.	71	4
$\overset{CH_3}{CH_2{=}CCH_2}$	$\overset{CH_3}{CH_2{=}CCH_2}$	$\overset{CH_3}{CH_2{=}CCH_2}$	$\overset{CH_3}{CH_2{=}CCH_2}$	C_4H_9	b.p. 164–7/1 mm.	82	4

			b.p. 182–5/2 mm.	71	4
		CH_3	153–5	78	4
		C_4H_9	117–19	66	4
		C_6H_5	104–5	50	9
		$C_6H_4CH_2$	127.5–129.5	53.6	9
		$p\text{-}NO_2C_6H_4$	227–9	77	8
		$p\text{-}NH_2C_6H_4$	227–9	quant	8
$HOCH_2CH_2$	C_6H_5	CH_3	115–125		6

1. A. Hofmann, *Ber.*, 19, 2072 (1886).
2. R. Otto, *Ber.*, 20, 2236 (1887).
3. J. Controulis and C. Banks, *J. Am. Chem. Soc.*, 67, 1946 (1945).
4. W. Pearlman and C. Banks, *J. Am. Chem. Soc.*, 71, 1128 (1949).
5. W. Pearlman, J. Mitulski and C. Banks, *J. Am. Chem. Soc.*, 71, 3248 (1949).

6. F. Schaefer, J. Dudley and J. Thurston, *J. Am. Chem. Soc.*, 71, 3004 (1951).
7. H. Mosher and F. Whitmore, *J. Am. Chem. Soc.*, 67, 662 (1945).
8. I. Witt and C. Hamilton, *J. Am. Chem. Soc.*, 67, 1078 (1945).
9. G. Braz, *Zhur. Obshchei Khim.*, 25, 1413 (1955).
10. F. Schaefer, J. Geoghegan and D. Kaiser, *J. Am. Chem. Soc.*, 77, 5518 (1955).

The chemistry of the ammeline ethers has not been extensively explored. Thurston and co-workers[35] showed that their reactions with amines were subject to the same limitations as was the case of the ammelide ethers. For example, when 2,4-dianilino-6-methoxy-s-triazine (XXVII) was heated with benzylamine, the product was 2,4-dianilino-6-hydroxy-s-triazine, and not the substituted melamine. Presumably the phenoxy derivative would have yielded the melamine.

The acetylation of 2,4-bis(N-β-hydroxyethylanilino)-6-methoxy-s-triazine (XXVIII) afforded good yields of the hydroxy-s-triazine (XXX), apparently by way of the monoacetate (XXIX), which underwent the intramolecular elimination reaction discussed under ammelide ethers.

VI. Diaminochloro-s-Triazines

2,4-Diamino-6-chloro-s-triazine was probably first prepared by Liebig[61] in 1834. He believed that the compound he obtained by heating cyanuric chloride with aqueous ammonia was a chloro-cyanamide. Laurent and Gerhardt[5] attacked Liebig's proposed structure, and it was not until the late 1800's that the work of Hofmann[62] and Lemoult[63] cleared up the controversy and proved the s-triazine structure.

A systematic study of the reactions of amines with cyanuric chloride was undertaken only recently.[39, 40] The reaction of cyanuric chloride with ammonia and amines at temperatures in the range of 25 to 70° C leads to the formation of the diaminochloro-s-triazines in good yield. Melamines in general are formed only at temperatures above 100° C. As discussed earlier, the chlorines on the s-triazine ring become progressively less reactive with increased substitution of the ring. In preparing unsymmettrically substituted diaminochloro-s-triazines, it is best to use the least reactive amine first. The reactions are preferably

R_1NH_2 weaker than R_2NH_2

carried out in aqueous suspensions. With some very reactive amines, the temperatures mentioned above do not apply. For example, dimethylamine replaces all three chlorine atoms at 25°. With morpholine and piperidine, temperatures higher than 25–30° must be avoided to prevent further reaction. Either an excess of amine or an inorganic base may be used to fix the hydrogen chloride formed.

A tabulation of well-characterized diaminochloro-s-triazines is found in Table V-5.

The principal use of the diaminochloro-s-triazines has been in the further reaction with alcohols to form diaminoalkoxy-s-triazines, and

with amines to form substituted melamines. In a few instances, hydrolysis to N^2-, N^4-substituted ammelines (XXXI) has been reported.[30, 64, 65]

(XXXI)

TABLE V-5. Diaminochloro-s-Triazines

$$
\begin{array}{c}
Cl\diagdown\underset{N}{\overset{N}{|}}\diagup NR_1R_2 \\
NR_3R_4
\end{array}
$$

R₁	R₂	R₃	R₄	M.p. °C.	Yield %	Ref.
H	H	H	H	Infusible	100	1, 5
H	H	H	CH_3	244–6	76	4
H	H	H	C_2H_5	177–9	85	4
H	H	H	C_3H_7	169–171	76	4
H	H	H	C_4H_9	142–4, 148–50	85	4, 5
H	H	H	C_5H_{11}	148–50	84	4
H	H	H	C_6H_{13}	149–51	75	4
H	H	H	$CH\!\!\diagup^{CH_2CH_2}_{CH_2CH_2}\!\!\diagdown CH$	185–7	67	4
H	H	H	$CH_2\!=\!CHCH_2$	168–70	—	4
H	H	H	$CH_2\!=\!C(CH_3)CH_2$	168–70	79	4
H	H	H	$CNCH_2$	260 dec.	—	9
H	H	H	$HOCH_2CH_2$	187–9	76	4
H	H	H	$CH_3CHOHCH_2$	192–4	41	4
H	H	H	$\diagup^{CH_2CH_2}_{CH_2CH_2}\!\!\diagdown NCH_2CH_2CH_2$	178–9	75	7
H	H	H	C_6H_5	213–4	99	5
H	H	CH_3	CH_3	220–22	95	4
H	H	C_2H_5	C_2H_5	123–5	66	4
H	H	C_4H_9	C_4H_9	119–20	100	5
H	H	$CH_2\!=\!CHCH_2$	$CH_2\!=\!CHCH_2$	78–80	63	4
H	H	$CH_2\!=\!\underset{CH_2}{\overset{CH_3}{C}}CH_2$	$CH_2\!=\!\overset{CH_3}{C}CH_2$	114–16	79	4

R_1	R_2	R_3	m.p. (°C)	Yield (%)	Ref.
H		$-CH_2CH_2-O-CH_2CH_2-$ (bridge)	189–91	35	4
H	$HOCH_2CH_2$	C_2H_5	136–8	75	4
H	$HOCH_2CH_2$	C_6H_5	188–9	72	4
H	H	CH_3	241	—	3
H	H	C_2H_5	>335	96	4
H	H	$C_{18}H_{37}$	—	—	3
H	H	$CH_2=CHCH_2$ (/ CH_3)	228–9	82	4,5
H	H	$CH_2=CCH_2$	136–7	100	5
H	H	$CH_2\!\!\begin{smallmatrix}CH_2CH_2\\[2pt]CH_2CH_2\end{smallmatrix}\!\!CH$	203–5	85	4
H	H	$HOOCCH_2$	209–11	91	4
H	H	$CNCH_2$	228–9	—	5
H	H	$HOCH_2CH_2$	230–5	61	6
H	H	$CH_3CHOHCH_2$	275–280	76	5
H	H	$HOCH_2CH_2CH_2$	192–4, 205–6	93	6.5
H	H	$O(CH_2CH_2)_2NCH_2CH_2CH_2$	195–8	40–50	6
H	H	$O(CH_2CH_2)_2NCH_2CH_2CH_2$	210–12	100	5
H	$O(CH_2CH_2)_2NCH_2CH_2CH_2$	$O(CH_2CH_2)_2NCH_2CH_2CH_2$	154–5	48	10
H	$(C_2H_5)_2NCH_2CH_2CH_2$	C_6H_5	50–1	—	11
H	$isoC_3H_7$	$p\text{-}ClC_6H_4$	164–6	—	11
H	$(C_2H_5)_2NCH_2CH_2$	$p\text{-}ClC_6H_4$	174–5	—	11
H	$[(C_2H_5)_2NCH_2]_2CH$	$p\text{-}ClC_6H_4$	156	100	11
H	$(C_2H_5)_2NCH_2CH_2CH_2$	$p\text{-}CH_3OC_6H_4$	120–21 (HCl)	—	11
H	C_6H_5	C_6H_5	199–201	—	5, 8
H	$p\text{-}ClC_6H_4$	$p\text{-}ClC_6H_4$	223	—	11
H	$p\text{-}CH_3OC_6H_4$	$p\text{-}CH_3OC_6H_4$	197–9	—	11
H	$2,4\text{-}NH_2, CH_3C_6H_3$	$2,4\text{-}NH_2, CH_3C_6H_3$	172	—	12

(Table continued)

TABLE V-5 (*continued*)

R₁	R₂	R₃	R₄	M.p., °C	Yield %	Ref.
H	α-$C_{10}H_7$	H	α-$C_{10}H_7$	215		13
H	β-$C_{16}H_7$	H	β-$C_{16}H_7$	178		12
H	CH_3	CH_3	CH_3	207–9	75	4
H	C_2H_5	C_2H_5	C_2H_5	100–2	70	4
H	$CH_2{=}C(CH_3)CH_2$	$CH_2{=}C(CH_3)CH_2$	$CH_2{=}C(CH_3)CH_2$	72	70	4
H	$CH_2{=}CCH_2$	CH_3	$CH_2{=}CCH_2$	87	79	4
CH_3	CH_3	CH_3	CH_3	66–8	41	4
C_2H_5	C_2H_5	C_2H_5	C_2H_5	b.p. 154–5/4 mm.	87	4,5
$CH_2{-}$	CH_2	$CH_2{-}CH_2$	CH_2	117–19	75	4
$CH_2{-}CH_2$	CH_2	CH_2	CH_2	172–4, 175–6	87	4,14
$CH_2{-}O$	CH_2	$CH_2{-}O$	CH_2	b.p. 147–50/1 mm.	81	4
$CH_2{=}CHCH_2(CH_3)$	$CH_2{=}CHCH_2(CH_3)$	$CH_2{=}CHCH_2(CH_3)$	$CH_2{=}CHCH_2(CH_3)$	b.p. 175/2 mm.	79	4
$CH_2{=}CCH_2$	$CH_2{=}CCH_2$	$CH_2{=}CCH_2$	$CH_2{=}CCH_2$	163–5	90	5
$CNCH_2CH_2$	$CNCH_2CH_2$	$CNCH_2CH_2$	$CNCH_2CH_2$	147–8	79	5
$HOCH_2CH_2$	$HOCH_2CH_2$	$HOCH_2CH_2$	$HOCH_2CH_2$	75–6	—	9
C_4H_9	$CNCH_2CH_2$	C_4H_9	$CNCH_2CH_2$			

1. J. Liebig, *Ann.*, 10, 43 (1834).
2. A. Hofmann, *Ber.*, 18, 2765 (1885).
3. A. Hofmann, *Ber.*, 18, 2755 (1885).
4. W. Pearlman and C. Banks, *J. Am. Chem. Soc.*, 70, 3726 (1948).
5. J. Thurston, J. Dudley, D. Kaiser, I. Hechenbleikner, F. Schaefer and D. Holm-Hansen, *J. Am. Chem. Soc.*, 73, 2981 (1951).
6. C. Banks, O. Cavalit... (cut off)
7. H. Mosher and F. Whitmore, *J. Am. Chem. Soc.*, 67, 662 (1945).
8. A. Laurent, *Compt. rend.*, 22, 695 (1846).
9. I. Heckenbleikner, U. S. Patent 2,476,547 (1949).
10. B. Harrom, *J. Am. Chem. Soc.*, 76, 3032 (1954).
11. F. Curd, J. Landquist and E. Rose, *J. Chem. Soc.*, 1947, 154.
12. H. Fries, *Ber.*, 19, 2055 (1886).
13. H. Fries, *Ber.*, 19, 242 (1886).

VII. Dithioammelide

Dithioammelide (2-amino-4,6-dimercapto-*s*-triazine) has been a relatively neglected member of the *s*-triazine series. Its first preparation was probably by Ponomarew [66] who heated "pseudothiocyanogen" with alkali sulfides. Jamieson[67] reported a similar compound by the same route. He noted that on heating the product with hydrochloric or sulfuric acid, it liberated hydrogen sulfide and yielded cyanuric acid.

Diels[30] obtained dithioammelide by heating 2-amino-4,6-dichloro-*s*-triazine with potassium hydrosulfide. A similar route has been used for the preparation of N²-substituted thioammelides.[68]

Kaiser[69] prepared dithioammelide from cyanoguanidine and carbon disulfide via the intermediate *ω*-cyanoguanidinodithiocarbonic acid, (potassium salt) (XXXII) or 2-thio-4,6-diamino-1,3,5-thiadiazine (XXXIII). The latter compound is convenient to handle, and on treatment with base at 50–100° is smoothly converted to dithioammelide.

Other than the hydrolysis to cyanuric acid and the mention of metal salts,[67] the chemistry of dithioammelide has been neglected. Jamieson noted that is was insoluble in water, and soluble in ammonia. On heating at 140–150°, his preparation decomposed with liberation of hydrogen sulfide.

The preparation of ethers from dithioammelide is mentioned, without supporting data, in several of the patents describing thioammeline ethers. Another route to dithioammelide ethers is the reaction of ammonia or amines with triesters of thiocyanuric acid.

$$CH_3S \underset{N \quad N}{\overset{N}{\bigg\langle}} SCH_3 \quad + R_1R_2NH \longrightarrow \quad CH_3S \underset{N \quad N}{\overset{N}{\bigg\langle}} NR_1R_2$$

(with SCH_3 below each ring)

A tabulation of the individual compounds of this category is found in Table V-6.

TABLE V-6. Dithioammelides and Ethers

$$R_3S \underset{N \quad N}{\overset{N}{\bigg\langle}} NR_1R_2$$

(with SR_3 below the ring)

R_1	R_2	R_3	M.p. °C.	Ref.
H	C_6H_5	H	248	3
H	$C_{10}H_7$	H	260–2	3
H	H	CH_3	200	1
H	H	C_2H_5	112	2
H	H	C_5H_{11}	82	2
H	CH_3	CH_3	174–5	1
H	C_2H_5	CH_3	114	1
H	C_5H_{11}	CH_3	96	1

1. A. Hofmann, Ber., 18, 2755 (1885).
2. P. Klason, J. prakt. Chim., (2), 33, 290 (1886).
3. French Patent 697,599 (1930).

VIII. Thioammeline

In 1885, Rathke[70,71] heated cyanoguanidine with ammonium thiocyanate in the presence of hydrochloric acid and obtained a water insoluble compound to which he ascribed the structure 2,4-diamino-6-mercapto-s-triazine (thioammeline). An alternate, but poorer, preparation was by reaction of cyanoguanidine with carbon disulfide. The same compound in less pure form was probably prepared a few years earlier by Ponomarew[66] by heating "pseudocyanogen" with ammonia. Thioammeline has also been prepared by heating cyanamide with ammonium thiocyanate.[72]

$$NH_2CNHCN + NH_4SCN \xrightarrow{\ HCl\ } \underset{NH_2}{\overset{HS\diagup N\diagdown NH_2}{\underset{N\diagdown\diagup N}{\big|\big|}}} + NH_4Cl$$
$$\overset{\|}{NH}$$

Klason obtained thioammeline by treating 2,4-diamino-6-chloro-s-triazine with potassium hydrosulfide.

$$\underset{NH_2}{\overset{Cl\diagup N\diagdown NH_2}{N\diagdown\diagup N}} + KSH \longrightarrow \underset{NH_2}{\overset{HS\diagup N\diagdown NH_2}{N\diagdown\diagup N}} + KCl$$

Thioammeline is a high melting solid, soluble to the extent of about 0.3 % in boiling water. It is soluble in ammonia, sodium hydroxide and mineral acid solutions. Several salts with acids such as sulfuric, hydrochloric, nitric, and oxalic have been prepared. It forms a double salt with silver nitrate and a complex salt with platinum chloride and hydrogen chloride. It is reported to be stable to hot barium hydroxide solutions, while on treatment with strong hydrochloric acid at 130°, it is converted to cyanuric acid. Oxidation with potassium permanganate is reported[13] to give ammeline. However, Rathke[73] showed that on treatment with bromine, thioammeline is converted rapidly to 2,2'-

$$\underset{NH_2}{\overset{H_2N\diagup N\diagdown SH}{N\diagdown\diagup N}} + Br_2 \longrightarrow \underset{NH_2}{\overset{H_2N\diagup N\diagdown S—S\diagup N\diagdown NH_2}{N\diagdown\diagup N\qquad N\diagdown\diagup N}}\underset{NH_2}{} + 2\,HBr$$

(XXXIV)

dithiobis(4,6-diamino-s-triazine) (XXXIV). Similar results were obtained using nitrous acid. Thioammeline can be regenerated by reduction of the bis-s-triazine with zinc and sodium hydroxide.

$$\underset{NH_2}{\overset{H_2N\diagup N\diagdown S—S\diagup N\diagdown NH_2}{N\diagdown\diagup N\qquad N\diagdown\diagup N}}\underset{NH_2}{} \xrightarrow{\ Zn,\ NaOH\ } 2\ \underset{NH_2}{\overset{H_2N\diagup N\diagdown SH}{N\diagdown\diagup N}}$$

Rathke heated the silver salt of thioammeline with ethyl bromide and obtained a compound which he believed to be 2,4-diamino-6-ethylthio-s-triazine (XXXV). The formation of thioethers from thio-

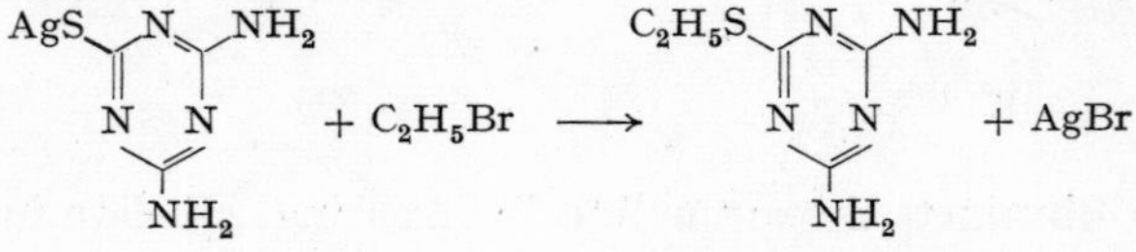

AgS—C(=N)—NH₂ ring + C₂H₅Br ⟶ C₂H₅S—C(=N)—NH₂ ring + AgBr

(XXXV)

ammeline has been studied extensively in the patent literature (see Section IX below). In most cases, later workers have used a sodium hydroxide solution of thioammeline which was treated with the appropriate halo-compound.

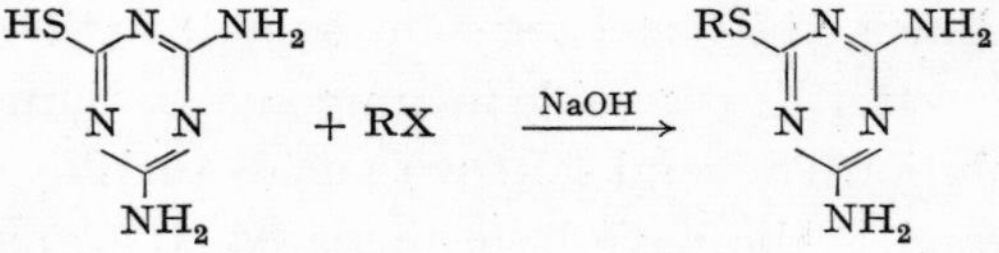

HS-triazine-NH₂,NH₂ + RX —NaOH→ RS-triazine-NH₂,NH₂

Rathke studied the reaction of thioammeline with ethylene dibromide. He obtained a compound which he formulated as the bicyclic derivative (XXXVI). On chlorination, this was believed to have

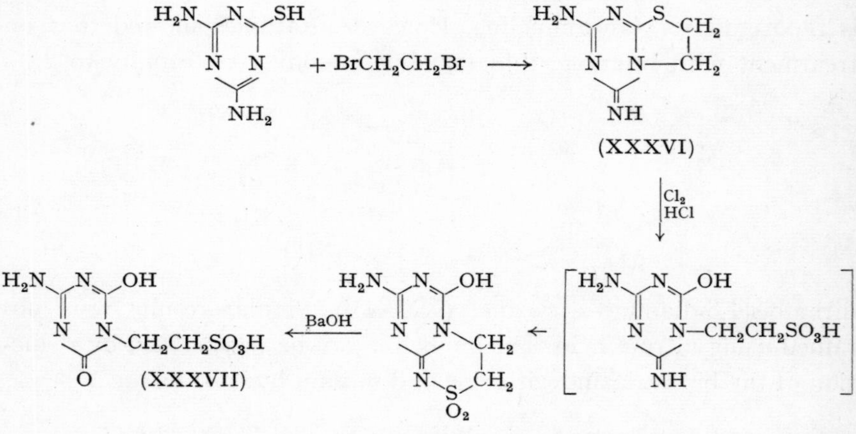

H₂N-triazine-SH,NH₂ + BrCH₂CH₂Br ⟶ (XXXVI bicyclic, S–CH₂, N–CH₂, NH)

(XXXVI)

↓ Cl₂ / HCl

[H₂N-triazine-OH, N–CH₂CH₂SO₃H, NH]

← H₂N-triazine-OH bicyclic with N–CH₂, N–S(O₂)–CH₂

—BaOH→ H₂N-triazine-OH, N–CH₂CH₂SO₃H, with O (XXXVII)

been converted, by the reactions outlined, to 2-(2'-amino-4-hydroxy-6-oxo-5,6-dihydro-s-triazin-5-yl) ethylsulfonic acid (XXXVII) which he called "tauroammelide." The same compound was obtained by another route. Nitric acid oxidation of "ethylenethioammeline" yielded a dimeric compound which Rathke called "taurodiammeline" (XXXVIII). Hydrolysis with barium hydroxide yielded "tauro-ammelide."

(XXXVIII)

IX. Thioammeline ethers

Several syntheses have been used for the preparation of ethers of thioammeline. The earliest was the reaction of a triester of thiocyanuric acid with ammonia or amines.[13,64] These reactions do not proceed readily, requiring elevated temperatures and prolonged heating periods to replace two alkylthio groups.

A more generally useful synthesis is the reaction of thioammeline with a halo compound. This reaction has been reported extensively in the patent literature, especially in the work of D'Alelio and Bruson.

Aromatic halides, except for those with activated halogen atoms, (e.g. 2,4-dinitro chlorobenzene) do not react.[74]

The use of dihalo compound leads to 2,2'-(alkylenedithio)-bis-4,6-diamino-s-triazines. This is illustrated in the reaction of dichloro-diethyl ether with thioammeline.[75]

For the preparation of certain aryl ethers, Friedheim[76,77] treated a sodium carbonate solution of thioammeline with a diazonium compound. This reaction was especially useful in preparing various arsenic, antimony, and mercury derivatives for pharmaceutical testing.

$$M = \begin{array}{l} AsO_3H_2 \\ SbO_3H_2 \\ HgX \\ SeO_3H_2 \end{array}$$

The reaction of 2,4-diamino-6-chloro-s-triazine with sodium p-nitrothiophenoxide has been reported.[74,78]

A list of ethers of thioammeline is given in Table V-7. In many cases, patents have listed many other derivatives of similar structure without physical properties or preparative details. The prototype of these compounds has been indicated by asterisk (*).

TABLE V-7. Thioammeline Ethers

$$\text{(triazine ring)}\quad NR_3R_4$$

R₁	R₂	R₃	R₄	R₅	M.p. °C	Yield	Ref.
H	H	H	H	CH_3	268	—	1, 4
H	H	H	H	C_2H_5	165, 173–4	—	2, 4
H	H	H	H	$n\text{-}C_4H_9$	147–8		4
H	H	H	H	$sec\text{-}C_4H_9$	184–5		4
H	H	H	H	$isoC_4H_9$	177–9		4
H	H	H	H	C_5H_{11}	178		2
H	H	H	H	$CH_2\!\left\langle{}^{CH_2CH_2}_{CH_2CH_2}\right\rangle\!CH$	239–40		4
H	H	H	H	$CH_2{=}CHCH_2$	152	70	5
H	H	H	H	$CH_2{=}C(CH_3)CH_2$	130–1	—	5
H	H	H	H	$C_6H_5CH_2$	166–7		4
H	H	H	H	$2,4\text{-}(NO_2)_2C_6H_3$	243		4
H	H	H	H	$HOCH_2CH_2$	185–6		6
H	H	H	H	$HOCH_2CH_2CH_2$	173–5		6
H	H	H	H	$CH_3CHOHCH_2$	179–80		6
H	H	H	H	$CH_3\underset{\underset{CH_3}{\mid}}{C}OHCH_2$	195–6		6
H	H	H	H	$HOCH_2CH_2OCH_2CH_2$	184–5		6
H	H	H	H	$CH_3\underset{\underset{O}{\|}}{C}CH_2$	172		7
H	H	H	H	$CH_3CH_2\underset{\underset{O}{\|}}{C}CH_2$	180		7
*H	H	H	H	$HOOCCH_2$	—		8
*H	H	H	H	$CH_3OOCCHClCH_2$	—		9
*H	H	H	H	NH_2COCH_2	—	—	10

(Table continued)

TABLE V-7 (continued)

R₁	R₂	R₃	R₄	R₅	M.p. °C	Yield	Ref.
*H	H	H	H	CNCH₂	—		11
H	H	H	H	NH₂CONHCOCH₂	220-40° (dec.)		12
*H	H	H	H	ClCH₂CONHCH₂CH₂NHCOCH₂	—		20
*H	H	H	H	CH₃CH₂OCH₂CH₂	148-9	—	13
H	H	H	H	CH₂=CHOCH₂CH₂	127-8		13
H	H	H	H	C₄H₉OCH₂CH₂OCH₂CH₂	80		13
H	H	H	H	C₆H₁₁OCH₂CH₂			13
H	H	H	H	C₆H₅OCH₂CH₂	177		13
H	H	H	H	o-CH₃C₆H₄OCH₂CH₂	183		13
H	H	H	H	C₆H₅OCH₂CH₂OCH₂CH₂	76-7		13
H	H	H	H	β-C₁₀H₇OCH₂CH₂OCH₂CH₂	148-9		13
H	H	H	H	[benzothiazolyl] C—SCH₂CH₂OCH₂CH₂	137-8		13
H	H	H	H	2,4-C₆H₅, Cl, C₆H₃OCH₂CH₂OCH₂CH₂	147		13
*H	H	H	H	C₆H₅COCH₂			14
*H	H	H	H	p-HOC₆H₄NHCOCH₂	—		14
*H	H	H	H	p-C₂H₅OOCC₆H₄NHCOCH₂	112-13		15
*H	H	H	H	RNHSO₂C₆H₄			16
*H	H	H	H	RNHSO₂C₆H₄NHCOCH₂			17
H	H	H	H	NH₂C₆H₄		—	18.
H	H	H	H	p-H₂O₃SbC₆H₄		—	18
H	H	H	H	p-H₂O₃PC₆H₄		—	18
H	H	H	H	p-CH₃COOHgC₆H₄		—	18
H	H	H	H	m-H₂SeO₃C₆H₄		—	18
H	H	H	H	p-H₂O₃AsC₆H₄		—	19
H	H	H	H	m-H₂O₃AsC₆H₄		—	19
H	CH₃	H	CH₃	CH₃	144		1
H	C₂H₅	H	C₂H₅	CH₃	83-4	—	1

TABLE V-7a. Alkylene-bis-(Thio-
diamino-s-triazines)

$$H_2N \overset{N}{\underset{N}{\diagup}} \overset{N}{\diagdown} \!\!- S \overset{R}{\diagdown} S \!\!- \overset{N}{\underset{N}{\diagdown}} \overset{N}{\diagup} NH_2$$

$$\overset{|}{NH_2} \qquad \overset{|}{NH_2}$$

R	M.p. °C.	Yield	Ref.
—CH$_2$CH$_2$—	264		4
CHCN	—		21
CH$_2$CHCN	—		21
CH$_2$CHCOOR	—		22
CH$_2$CH$_2$OCH$_2$CH$_2$	250–3	80	23
CH$_2$CH$_2$OCH$_2$CH$_2$OCH$_2$CH$_2$	250	85	23
CH$_2$CONHCH$_2$CH$_2$HNCOCH$_3$	230	—	24

1. A. Hofmann, *Ber.*, **18**, 2755 (1885).
2. P. Klason, *J. prakt. Chem.*, (2), **33**, 290 (1886).
3. B. Rathke, *Ber.*, **20**, 1059 (1887).
4. W. Terweck and I. Goffeye, U. S. Patent 2,267,068 (1941).
5. H. Bruson, U. S. Patent 2,258,130 (1941).
6. H. Bruson, U. S. Patent 2,237,584 (1941).
7. H. Bruson, U. S. Patent 2,277,267 (1942).
8. G. D'Alelio, U. S. Patent 2,312,699 (1943).
9. G. D'Alelio, U. S. Patent 2,335,045 (1943).
10. G. D'Alelio and J. Underwood, U. S. Patent 2,295,562 (1942).
11. G. D'Alelio and J. Underwood, U. S. Patent 2,295,561 (1942).
12. G. D'Alelio, U. S. Patent 2,324,286 (1942).
13. H. Bruson, U. S. Patent 2,227,215 (1940).
14. G. D'Alelio and J. Underwood, U. S. Patent 2,355,423 (1944).
15. G. D'Alelio, U. S. Patent 2,315,939 (1943).
16. G. D'Alelio, U. S. Patent 2,312,698 (1943).
17. G. D'Alelio, U. S. Patent 2,312,692 (1943).
18. E. Friedheim, U. S. Patent 2,391,452 (1945).
19. E. Friedheim, U. S. Patent 2,415,556 (1947).
20. G. D'Alelio, U. S. Patent 2,324,826 (1943).
21. G. D'Alelio and J. Underwood, U. S. Patent 2,324,285 (1943).
22. G. D'Alelio and J. Underwood, U. S. Patent 2,328,963 (1943).
23. H. Bruson, U. S. Patent 2,202,828 (1940).
24. G. D'Alelio, U. S. Patent 2,312,694 (1943).

X. Related Compounds

Rathke[79] investigated the reaction of diphenyl guanidine with phenylisothiocyanate. When the primary product, N^1, N^3, N^4-triphenyl-guanylthiourea (XXXIX) was heated to 150°, in addition to N^{1}N^2 diphenylthiourea and tetraphenyl melamine, he obtained a compound which he formulated as (XL), triphenylthioammeline. The same com-

pound was obtained by reaction of phenylcyanamide with phenyl isothiocyanate, and by heating tetraphenyl melamine with phenylisothio-

$$C_6H_5NHCNHC_6H_5 + C_6H_5NCS \longrightarrow C_6H_5NHCNHCNHC_6H_5$$
$$\underset{NH}{\|} \qquad\qquad\qquad \underset{S}{\|} \;\; \underset{NC_6H_5}{\|}$$

(XXXIX)

$\downarrow$

(XLI) ← KOH — (XL)

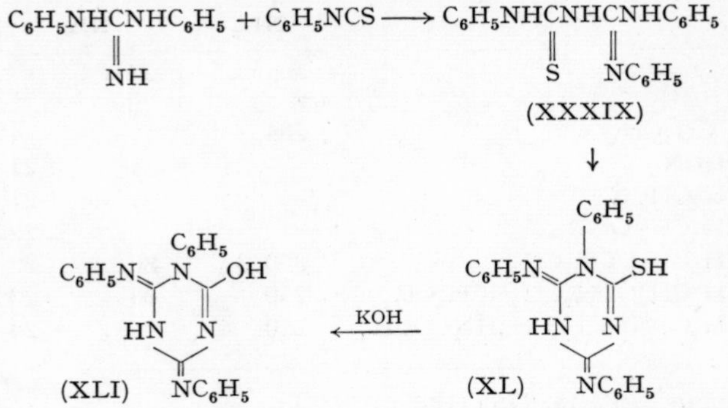

cyanate. When the thio compound was heated with aqueous potassium
hydroxide a hydroxy compound, triphenyl ammeline, (XLI) was
obtained.

Crowther and co-workers[80] encountered a similar compound as a
by-product in the preparation of N^1-p-chlorophenyl-N^4-n-butylguanyl-
thiourea by reaction of butylguanidine with p-chlorophenylisothiocya-
nate. They believed that two moles of the isothiocyanate condensed
with one mole of the guanidine to give a bis(thiocarbonyl) guanidine
(XLII), which cyclized with loss of hydrogen sulfide. As formulated,

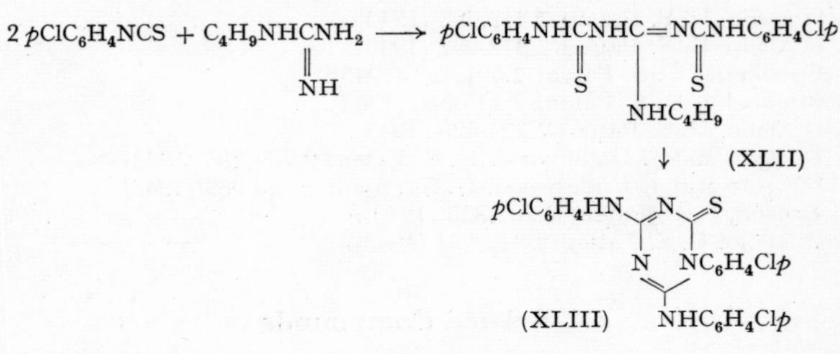

$$2\,pClC_6H_4NCS + C_4H_9NHCNH_2 \longrightarrow pClC_6H_4NHCNHC=NCNHC_6H_4Clp$$
$$\underset{NH}{\|} \qquad\qquad \underset{S}{\|} \;\; | \;\; \underset{S}{\|}$$
$$NHC_4H_9$$

$\downarrow$ (XLII)

(XLIII)

the product (XLIII) is tautomeric with the type proposed by Rathke.
The reaction of methylguanidine with phenyl isothiocyanate gave the
homologous methyl derivative.

Pellizzari[81] obtained a bicyclic product, which may be considered
a substituted thioammeline, by reaction of $N,^1N^2$-o-phenylene $N,^1$-N^3-

dicyanoguanidine with hydrogen sulfide. The product was formulated as (XLIV) or (XLV). Alkaline hydrolysis yielded the corresponding oxygen analog (=NH replaced by =O).

(XLIV)   (XLV)

References

1. J. Liebig, *Ann.*, **10**, 30 (1834).
2. F. Knapp, *Ann.*, **21**, 243 (1837).
3. M. Gerhardt, *Compt. rend.*, **18**, 160 (1844).
4. F. Wohler and J. Liebig, *Ann.*, **54**, 371 (1845).
5. A. Laurent and M. Gerhardt, *Compt. rend.*, **22**, 453 (1846).
6. J. Liebig, *Ann.*, **57**, 114 (1846).
7. J. Liebig, *Ann.*, **58**, 253 (1846).
8. J. Liebig, *Ann.*, **95**, 269 (1855).
9. J. Jager, *Ber.*, **9**, 1554 (1876).
10. E. Drechsel, *J. prakt. Chem.*, (2), **11**, 289 (1875).
11. S. Gabriel, *Ber.*, **8**, 1165 (1875).
12. P. Klason, *J. prakt. Chem.*, (2), **33**, 285 (1886).
13. P. Klason, *J. prakt. Chem.*, (2) **33**, 290 (1886).
14. M. Striegler, *J. prakt. Chem.*, (2) **33**, 161 (1886).
15. G. Bouchardat, *Ann.*, **154**, 354 (1870).
16. A. Hantzsch and B. Stuer, *Ber.*, **38**, 1042, 2326 (1905).
17. E. Sundwich, *Z. physik. Chem.*, **76**, 486 (1912).
18. E. Werner, *J. Chem. Soc.*, **103**, 2275 (1913).
19. J. Das-Gupta, *J. Ind. Chem. Soc.*, **11**, 207 (1934).
20. A. Werner and J. Gray, *Sci. Proc. Roy. Dublin Soc.*, **24**, 111 (1946) through *Chemical Abstracts*, **41**, 710 (1947).
21. L. Bechman, U. S. Patent, 2,572,587 (1950).
22. T. Poensgen, *Ann.*, **128**, 340 (1863).
23. F. Hallwachs, *Ann.*, **153**, 293 (1870).
24. E. Schmidt, *J. prakt. Chem.*, (2), **5**, 361 (1872).
25. E. Bamberger, *Ber.*, **16**, 1074, 1073 (1883).
26. C. Ceck and B. Dehmel, *Ber.*, **11**, 249 (1873).
27. A. Millot, *Compt. rend.*, **103**, 153 (1886).
28. F. Fichter and R. Stocker, *Ber.*, **47**, 2014 (1914).
29. J. Paden and A. MacLean, U. S. Patent 2,476,452 (1949).
30. O. Diels, *Ber.*, **32**, 691 (1899).
31. A. Hofmann and O. Olshausen, *Ber.*, **3**, 269 (1870).
32. A. Hofmann, *Ber.*, **19**, 2072 (1886).
33. J. Dudley, J. Thurston, F. Schaefer, D. Holm-Hansen, C. Hull and P. Adams, *J. Am. Chem. Soc.*, **73**, 2986 (1951).
34. J. Dudley, J. Thurston, F. Schaefer, C. Hull, D. Holm-Hansen and P. Adams, *J. Am. Chem. Soc.*, **73**, 2999 (1951).

35. J. Thurston, F. Schaefer, J. Dudley and D. Holm-Hansen, *J. Am. Chem. Soc.*, **73**, 2992 1951).
36. F. Schaefer, J. Dudley and J. Thurston, *J. Am. Chem. Soc.*, **73**, 2996 (1951).
37. F. Schaefer, J. Dudley and J. Thurston, *J. Am. Chem. Soc.*, **73**, 3004 (1951).
38. H. Fries, *Ber.*, **19**, 242 (1886).
39. W. Pearlman and C. Banks, *J. Am. Chem. Soc.*, **70**, 3726 (1948).
40. J. Thurston, J. Dudley, D. Kaiser, I. Hechenbleickner, F. Schaefer and D. Holm-Hansen, *J. Am. Chem. Soc.*, **73**, 2981 (1951).
41. J. Liebig, *Ann.*, **10**, 16 (1834).
42. F. Knapp, *Ann.*, **21**, 255 (1837).
43. A. Smolka and A. Friedreich, *Monatsh.*, **9**, 701 (1888). cf. T. Davis and H. Underwood, *J. Am. Chem. Soc.*, **44**, 2595 (1922).
44. A. Smolka and A. Friedreich, *Monatsh.*, **11**, 42 (1890).
45. E. Bamberger, *Ber.*, **23**, 1856 (1890).
46. R. Stolle and K. Krauch, *Ber.*, **46**, 2337 (1913).
47. T. Davis, *J. Am. Chem. Soc.*, **43**, 2234 (1921).
48. A. Ostrogovich and G. Gheorghiu, *Gazz. chim. ital.*, **60**, 648 (1930).
49. A. Smolka and A. Friedrich, *Monatsh.*, **10**, 86 (1889).
50. K. Rackmann, *Ann.*, **376**, 163 (1910).
51. A. Weddige, *J. prakt. Chem.*, (2), **33**, 76 (1886).
52. B. Rathke, *Ber.*, **20**, 1062 (1887).
53. I. Muskat and A. Cherniak, U. S. Patent 2,184,886 (1940).
54. W. Ericks, U. S. Patent 2,413,755 (1947).
55. R. Otto, *Ber.*, **20**, 2236 (1887).
56. J. Controulis and C. Banks, *J. Am. Chem. Soc.*, **67**, 1946 (1945).
57. W. Pearlman and C. Banks, *J. Am. Chem. Soc.*, **71**, 1128 (1949).
58. W. Pearlman, J. Mitulski and C. Banks, *J. Am. Chem. Soc.*, **71**, 3248 (1949).
59. F. Schaefer, J. Geoghegan and D. Kaiser, *J. Am. Chem. Soc.*, **77**, 5918 (1955).
60. G. Braz, *Zhur. Obshchei Khim.*, **25**, 1413 (1955).
61. J. Liebig, *Ann.*, **10**, 43 (1834).
62. A. Hofmann, *Ber.*, **18**, 2765 (1885).
63. P. Lemoult, *Compt. rend.*, **125**, 822 (1897).
64. A. Hofmann, *Ber.*, **18**, 2755 (1885).
65. A. Laurent, *Compt. rend.*, **22**, 696 (1846).
66. Ponomarew, *J. Russ. Phys.-Chem. Soc.*, **8**, 217 (1876).
67. A. Jamieson, *Ann.*, **59**, 339 (1876).
68. French Patent 697,599 (1930).
69. D. Kaiser, U. S. Patent 2,375,733 (1945).
70. B. Rathke, *Ber.*, **18**, 3102 (1885).
71. B. Rathke, *Ber.*, **20**, 1059 (1887).
72. Belg. Patent 446,700 (1945) through *Chemical Abstracts*, **39**, 1083 (1945).
73. B. Rathke, *Ber.*, **23**, 1675 (1890).
74. L. Bambas, *J. Am. Chem. Soc.*, **67**, 669 (1945).
75. H. Bruson, U. S. Patent 2,202,828 (1940).
76. E. Friedheim, U. S. Patent 2,391,452 (1945).
77. E. Friedheim, U. S. Patent 2,415,556 (1947).
78. G. D'Alelio, U. S. Patent 2,312,692 (1943).
79. B. Rathke, *Ber.*, **20**, 1065 (1887).
80. A. Crowther, F. Curd, D. Richardson and F. Rose, *J. Chem. Soc.*, **1948**, 1636.
81. G. Pellizzari, *Gazz. chim. ital.*, **54**, 451 (1924).

CHAPTER VI

Melamine and Substituted Melamines

I. Introduction

Melamine was first prepared in 1834 by Liebig[1] by fusing potassium thiocyanate with twice its weight of ammonium chloride. The reaction product, called "melam" by Liebig, actually was mostly melamine thiocyanate, with free melamine, some ammeline and other by-products. The free compound could be obtained by caustic treatment[1,2] or hot water extraction[3] of the reaction product. Whereas Liebig had considered that the long caustic treatment he had given his product caused a degradation to melamine, actually melamine was present bound as its thiocyanate salt.[2]

The preparation of melamine by fusion of a variety of nitrogen containing compounds is described in the synthesis section of this chapter. It was not until a century after its discovery that commercial syntheses became feasible. Since 1940 melamine has become an increasingly important chemical commodity, principally because of its utility in preparing a variety of resinous materials.

II. Physical Properties

Melamine is a high melting, colorless solid which can be obtained as monoclinic crystals from water.[4] It sublimes at 300° C under reduced pressure, and melts with decomposition at 350° C. The density of the solid is 1.573.[5] The solubility of melamine in water is 0.5% at 25° C and 5% at 90° C.[6] Melamine is only sparingly soluble in alcohol and insoluble in most organic solvents. It exhibits some solubility in polyhydroxy compounds. Melamine is a weak base having a dissociation constant of 1.1×10^{-9}.[7]

The ultraviolet spectrum of melamine in neutral solution shows only low intensity absorption in the 2800–3400 Å region.[8] The crystallographic properties have been studied in detail.[4,5,9]

Thermodynamic data which have been reported[10,11] includes:

Heat of Combustion (Δ Hc)	—469.98 k. cal./mole
Heat of Sublimation (340° C)	29 ± 1 k. cal./mole
Molar Heat Capacity (Cp)	37.1 cal./deg./mole
Entropy (S)	35.6 cal./deg./mole
Entropy of Formation Δ S	—199.39 cal./deg./mole
Free Energy of Formation Δ F°	42.3 k. cal./mole

III. Synthesis of Melamine

1. Laboratory Preparation

Small scale preparations of melamine may be divided into two main categories, one comprising those methods which involve the intermediate formation of cyanamide or dicyandiamide, and the other involving the replacement of substituents on the s-triazine ring with ammonia.

A. Methods Involving Cyanamide Formation

(1) As mentioned in the Introduction, melamine can be prepared, albeit in poor yield, by fusion of thiocyanates. For example, ammonium thiocyanate heated[12] at 250° gives melam and melamine thiocyanate[2] which can be recrystallized from alcohol. Melamine formation has not been noted during studies[14] on the equilibrium of ammonium thiocyanate and guanidine thiocyanate (see below).

(2) Guanidine thiocyanate gives melamine in yields of about 50% when pyrolyzed[13] at temperatures above 170°.

(3) If guanidine carbonate is heated with dicyandiamide, (1) melamine is obtained in 71% yield.[13]

$$2\ NH_2\overset{\overset{\displaystyle NH}{\|}}{C}NHCN + H_2N\overset{\overset{\displaystyle NH}{\|}}{C}NH_2\cdot H_2CO_3 \xrightarrow{\Delta} 2 \underset{(I)\quad NH_2}{\underset{N\quad N}{H_2N\diagdown N\diagup NH_2}} + 2\ NH_3 + CO_2 + H_2O \quad (1)$$

(4) Probably the simplest and most convenient laboratory procedure is one employing dicyandiamide alone. If several hundred grams

of dicyandiamide are heated to fusion in a large beaker, a vigorous reaction sets in. The temperature rises to 350° and copious fumes of ammonia and sublimed melamine are evolved. When the mass has been cooled and is powdered, leaching with boiling water produces good yields of pure melamine.[15] Many modification of the dicyandiamide method are known. For example, sodium or potassium carbonate fused with powdered dicyandiamide at 185° gave[16,18] a 70% yield of melamine, 99% pure and melting at 354° when recrystallized from water. Other mild bases may also be used. Basic organic liquids in which both melamine and dicyandiamide are insoluble are said[17] to be effective catalysts. The addition of a compound such as urea, which generates ammonia on heating has, also been described.[17]

Dicyandiamide can be converted to melamine in yields of about 90% by heating in the presence of a diluent gas,[19,20] such as nitrogen or hydrogen, at around 200° under 50–100 atmospheres pressure. It can be heated with a liquid diluent such as ethanolamine[21] at 175° to give melamine of high purity, or diethanolamine[21] at 240°, in which case some melam is formed. Addition of zinc chloride appears to allow the reaction to proceed at slightly lower temperatures (100–160°). Diluents such as ethylene glycol[22] or lactamide[23] are generally used with zinc chloride. Other salts have been used to effect formation of the s-triazine ring of melamine from dicyandiamide. With ammonium chloride[24] and potassium thiocyanate,[25] it becomes difficult to draw a dividing line between catalyst and reactant, but both have been employed.

(5) Heating cyanamide accomplishes the same purpose as heating dicyandiamide, however only the latter is stable and commercially available. Melamine is formed[26,27,28,29] from cyanamide above its melting point, usually at temperatures around 150°. Again an exothermic reaction occurs accompanied by evolution of ammonia. In addition to melamine, dicyandiamide, melon and other condensation products of melamine are formed.

(6) Excellent yields of melamine can be obtained by heating guanidine or biguanide either alone[30,31] or, more generally, in the presence of small amounts of cyanamide or dicyandiamide, usually the latter.[32–36] Conditions and modifications are similar to those employed with dicyandiamide alone.

Guanidine carbonate when heated to 180–190°, gives a 35 %
yield[13] of melamine and also some melam (2); if, however, dicyandi-

$$3 \; H_2NCNH_2 \cdot H_2CO_3 \xrightarrow{180-190°} 2 \quad \text{(I)} \quad + 3 \; H_2O + 6 \; CO_2 + 6 \; NH_3 \quad (2)$$

amide is added and the heating conducted at 160°, the melamine yield
rises[13] to 71 % (1).

(7) Urea and thiourea may be thermally decomposed to give
melamine and related products. The reaction is not well adapted to
laboratory scale work, but is becoming (in the case of urea) increasingly
important commercially. Using thiourea, in addition to melamine,
varying amounts of melam, melem, melon and guanidine are produced,[13]
while the urea decomposition gives also its aqueous degradation products, ammeline, ammelide and cyanuric acid, more ammonia being
evolved at each stage.[41]

(8) A most reliable way to prepare melamine by the urea process
without the use of a closed system and an ammonia atmosphere,
albeit in small yield (10 %) is by the pyrolysis of urea and ammonium
sulfamate[37] at 315° for fifteen minutes.

(9) Cyanourea, an unstable and difficultly prepared compound, has
been said to produce melamine when heated in a closed vessel with
ammonia[38] with a trace of water present. At 350° the yield of melamine
at the end of two hours was 26 %, but at 400°, an 89 % yield of melamine
resulted after only fifteen minutes.

(10) Patents have been issued[39, 40] for the preparation of melamine
directly from hydrogen cyanide and ammonia at 350–400° and 4,500
lbs. pressure over Fuller's earth (3). Ammonia is admitted before the

$$6 \; HCN + 6 \; NH_3 \xrightarrow[400° \, > \, 500 \text{ lbs.}]{\text{Fuller's earth}} 2 \quad \text{(I)} \quad + 3 \; H_2 \quad (3)$$
$$\text{(excess)}$$

application of heat. The best yield is only 9 % and the process has not
found acceptance. It is evident that hydrogen must be a by-product of
the reaction (3).

B. Mechanism of Melamine Formation

While no conclusive proof exists for the mechanism of melamine formation from dicyandiamide and other starting materials discussed above, there appear to be at least three probable pathways.

(1) There is good evidence that cyanamide is formed from most of the above materials and that it is the active intermediate.[42, 43] It is known, moreover, that dicyandiamide does undergo depolymerization[44] to cyanamide on heating above its melting point of 209°.

(2) The second and most probable mechanism consists of dimerization of dicyandiamide (4), followed by cyclization and cleavage to melamine and cyanamide (5). The latter could either trimerize or add

$$
\begin{array}{c}
\text{NH} \qquad\qquad\text{HNH} \\
\| \qquad\qquad\quad | \\
\text{H}_2\text{NCNHCN} + \text{HN}{=}\text{C}{-}\text{NHCN} \longrightarrow \left[\begin{array}{c} \text{NH}\ \ \text{NH}\ \ \text{NH} \\ \|\quad\ \|\quad\ \| \\ \text{H}_2\text{NCNHCNHCNHCN} \end{array} \right]
\end{array} \qquad (4)
$$

$$
\longrightarrow \underset{\text{(known)}}{\text{H}_2\text{N}\!\!-\!\!\underset{\substack{\text{N}\quad\text{N}\\ \text{NH}_2}}{\overset{\text{NH}}{\|}\text{NHCNH}_2}} \longrightarrow \underset{(I)}{\text{H}_2\text{N}\!\!-\!\!\underset{\substack{\text{N}\quad\text{N}\\ \text{NH}_2}}{\ \text{NH}_2}} + \text{H}_2\text{NCN} \qquad (5)
$$

to dicyanamide, giving more melamine in either case. Free energy changes are favorable for the condensation of cyanamide and dicyandiamide (6, 7) to form melamine (I)

$$
2\,\text{NH}_2\text{CN} \longrightarrow \text{HN}{-}\overset{\text{NH}}{\overset{\|}{\text{C}}}{-}\text{NHCN} \qquad (6)
$$

$$
\text{H}_2\text{N}{-}\overset{\text{NH}}{\overset{\|}{\text{C}}}{-}\text{NHCN} + \text{H}_2\text{NCN} \longrightarrow (I) \qquad (7)
$$

(3) When dicyandiamide was heated[45] in butanol or isobutanol, a 1–3% yield of cyanomelamine was obtained along with 70–90% yields of melamine. This indicates a possible pathway. Cyanomelamine could be formed by the condensation of two equivalents of dicyandiamide and thus could give rise to melamine (8). A 75% yield of melamine was obtained[45] by heating cyanomelamine and ammonia in a solvent.

The formation of melamine may be an explanation of the formation of cyanamide concurrent with or alternative to depolymerization of dicyandiamide.

$$
\begin{array}{c}
\text{CN} \\
| \\
\text{HN} \\
| \\
\text{H}_2\text{NC} \\
\| \\
\text{HN}
\end{array}
+
\begin{array}{c}
\text{HN} \\
\| \\
\text{C—NHCN} \\
| \\
\text{H}_2\text{N}
\end{array}
\longrightarrow
\left[\text{structures}\right]
+ \text{NH}_3 \text{ or } [\ldots]
$$

(8)

$$
\text{H}_2\text{N—(ring)—NH}_2 + \text{H}_2\text{NCN}
$$

Guanidine requires special mention. It has already been noted that heating guanidine, usually as its carbonic acid salt, produced melamine.[46] The reaction may be regarded in two ways. (A) Guanidine is thermally reversibly decomposed to cyanamide and ammonia (9),

$$
\begin{array}{c}
\text{NH} \\
\| \\
\text{H}_2\text{N—C—NH}_2
\end{array}
\overset{\Delta}{\rightleftharpoons} \text{NH}_3 + \text{H}_2\text{NCN}
$$

$$
\updownarrow
$$

$$
\text{HN=C=NH}
$$

(9)

and the former can condense to dicyandiamide and thence to melamine.[47] Guanidine itself can be formed from dicyandiamide[48] by heating the latter with aqueous ammonia at 150°. The reaction probably involves the intermediate formation of guanylurea. There furthermore exist favorable free energy[49] relationships for the transformations

$$
\begin{array}{c}
\text{NH} \\
\| \\
\text{NH}_2\text{C—NHCN(s)}
\end{array}
+ 2\,\text{NH}_3\,(\text{liq.}) \longrightarrow
\begin{array}{c}
\text{NH} \\
\| \\
2\,\text{NH}_2\text{C—NH}_2(\text{s})
\end{array}
\Delta\,\text{F} = -38,400 \text{ Kcal.}
$$

(10)

$$
\begin{array}{c}
\text{NH} \\
\| \\
\text{NH}_2\text{C—NH}_2(\text{s})
\end{array}
+
\begin{array}{c}
\text{NH} \\
\| \\
\text{NH}_2\text{C—NHCN(s)}
\end{array}
\longrightarrow \text{C}_3\text{N}_6\text{H}_6(\text{s}) + \text{NH}_3(\text{liq.})\ \Delta\,\text{F} = -6,300 \text{ Kcal.}
$$

(I)

(11)

(10 and 11). (B) A mechanism[46] that is less likely than 10 and 11 consists in direct condensation of guanidine with itself to give melamine (12).

$$\underset{\text{H}}{\underset{\|}{\text{H}_2\text{NC}-\text{N}}}\text{H} + \text{H}_2\text{N}-\underset{\underset{\|}{\text{NH}}}{\text{CNH}_2} \longrightarrow \begin{array}{c} \text{HN}=\text{C}-\text{N}\text{H} \quad \text{NH}_2 \\ | \\ \text{NH} \\ | \\ \text{HN}=\text{C}-\text{NH}_2 \quad \text{H}\text{NH} \end{array} + \begin{array}{c} \text{C}=\text{NH} \\ | \\ \end{array} \longrightarrow \begin{array}{c} \text{HN} \underset{\text{HN} \quad \text{NH}}{\overset{\text{N}}{\text{NH}}} \\ \underset{\text{NH}}{\bigvee} \end{array} \quad (12)$$

$$\begin{array}{c} \text{H}_2\text{N} \overset{\text{N}}{\underset{\text{N} \quad \text{N}}{\bigwedge}} \text{NH}_2 \\ (\text{I}) \quad \underset{\text{NH}_2}{} \end{array}$$

C. Preparation of Melamine by Methods Utilizing the Existing s-Triazine Nucleus

In this sub-section, compounds already possessing the s-triazine ring are treated to replace 2,4,6-substituents with amino groups, in contradistinction to the methods described in Section A. above, wherein the s-triazine ring is synthetically formed.

(1) From cyanuric acid derivatives. (a) *Cyanuric chloride.* The action of ammonia on cyanuric chloride, as might be expected, results in excellent yields of melamine.[2,50] The reaction (13) is exothermic

$$\underset{\text{Cl}}{\underset{\text{N} \quad \text{N}}{\overset{\text{N}}{\text{Cl}}}}\text{Cl} + 6\,\text{NH}_3 \longrightarrow \underset{\text{NH}_2}{\underset{\text{N} \quad \text{N}}{\overset{\text{N}}{\text{H}_2\text{N}}}}\text{NH}_2 + 3\,\text{NH}_4\text{Cl} + 172\,\text{Kcal.} \quad (13)$$

and requires six equivalents of ammonia and a temperature[51] of 100°. At 50–60°, only two chlorine atoms are replaced giving 2,4-diamino-6-chloro-s-triazine, while at 0° one is replaced and the product is 2-amino-4,6-dichloro-s-triazine.

(b) *Cyanuric acid esters.* Alkyl esters of cyanuric acid can undergo cleavage to produce melamine. For example, triethyl cyanurate gives melamine[52] when heated in a closed tube at 170–180° with aqueous ammonia; some ammeline is also obtained.

(c) *Thiocyanuric acid esters.* Like the alkyl cyanurates, thiocyanuric acid esters are cleaved[53] with aqueous ammonia at 180° after several hours heating and give melamine.

(d) *Ammeline, Ammelide, Cyanuric Acid.* Heating any one of these substances at 350–400° in an autoclave for fifteen minutes with anhydrous ammonia produces melamine in good yields.[54, 55] The process may become important from a commercial standpoint because the hydroxy-*s*-triazines, particularly cyanuric acid, can readily be made in good yields from urea.

(e) *Thioammeline, Dithioammelide, Thiocyanuric acid.* Melamine is obtained from the sulfur analogs of ammeline, ammelide and cyanuric acid by heating at 350° for two hours with ammonia.[56]

(2) From melamine condensation compounds. Melamine preparation, especially on the laboratory scale, is usually accompanied by the formation of melam, melem and melon, products formed by splitting out of one or more equivalents of ammonia. The lowest member of the series, melam (II) may be readily reconverted to

melamine by heating it at 150° with 30% aqueous ammonia.[57, 58] A Ciba patent[59] reports that while only a 10% yield of melamine can be obtained by heating melam with aqueous ammonia, the yield can be raised to 67% by using anhydrous ammonia at 300° and 50 atmospheres pressure for sixteen hours. A reaction residue amounting to 28% is also obtained, about 10% of which is melamine that is not easy to recover. Since it is difficult to remove melamine quantitatively from melam, apparent yields may be high owing to melamine present originally. While this is no disadvantage in commercial operation, for accurate yield determination in the laboratory, the use of pure melam is required. Ammeline is a by-product, but it can be removed by virtue of its insolubility in hot water. The amount can be reduced by using a two fold molar excess of anhydrous ammonia,[60] and can be entirely eliminated and a quantitative yield of melamine obtained by heating the anhydrous reaction mixture for two hours at 400° and 3000 lbs. pressure.[61] Such conditions also enable the use of melem and melon, ordinarily exceedingly difficult sources for melamine preparation.

D. Miscellaneous Melamine Preparations

Melamine has been prepared by several reactions of minor importance synthetically, but of some theoretical interest. Both general synthetic categories discussed above are exemplified in this section as well.

(1) Reduction of tribenzylisomelamine with hydrogen over palladium oxide produces melamine in 94% yield[62] (14).

$$
\begin{array}{c}
\text{tribenzylisomelamine} \xrightarrow[\text{PdO EtOH}]{\text{H}_2} \text{melamine (I)} + C_6H_5CH_3
\end{array}
\quad (14)
$$

(2) The adduct formed from alphatic ketones and dicyandiamide produces melamine upon treatment (15) with alkali.[64]

$$(H_2NCN)_4(CH_3)_2CO \cdot 2\,HCl + 3\,NaOH \xrightarrow{25°}$$

$$(I) + NaHNCN + 3\,H_2O + 2\,NaCl + CH_3COCH_3 \quad (15)$$

(3) Titanium chloride has been used[65] as a reducing agent for a number of substances among which is RDX, 2,4,6-trinitrohexahydro-s-triazine. Melamine is produced in this case (16).

$$
\text{RDX} + 12\,Ti_2Cl_3 \longrightarrow \text{melamine (I)}
\quad (16)
$$

(4) A five minute treatment of dicyandiamide, prepared from aqueous calcium cyanamide at 85° with sodium hydroxide at 200°, yields very pure melamine.[66]

(5) Melamine is said to be produced when perthiocyanic acid[a] is heated at 150–160° with liquid ammonia.[67] The free base is released from the thiocyanate salt upon treatment with caustic soda.

[a] Perthiocyanic acid $\left(HS\text{-}C\underset{N}{\overset{N\text{---}S}{\diagdown}}C\text{-}SH \right)$ is isomeric with and prepared from isoperthiocyanic acid $\left(S=C\underset{N}{\overset{S\text{---}S}{\diagdown}}C=NH \right)$. Only its salts are stable; the free acid rearranges back to isoperthiocyanic acid.

2. Commercial Preparation

Two practical fundamental commercial processes are available for the synthesis of melamine. One starts with dicyandiamide and the other uses urea.

A. The Dicyandiamide Process

The dicyandiamide process is used almost exclusively at the present time.

The steps involved consist of first preparing calcium carbide from coke and limestone in an electric arc furnace. The calcium carbide is converted to calcium cyanamide by passing nitrogen gas over the hot carbide. Acid treatment liberates cyanamide which is dimerized at a pH of 10, with heat, to dicyandiamide. Dicyandiamide is commonly converted to melamine by heating in a methanol-liquid ammonia solution[69] in an autoclave, carefully following a prescribed temperature-pressure-time control template until the reaction is complete. The pressure reactors are installed in concrete shelters outside the main working area of the plant and are operated by remote control.[70] The resulting melamine is filtered and given a caustic wash to remove hydroxy-s-triazines while the liquid ammonia and methanol filtrate are returned to underground storage tanks. Yields range from 85–90% melamine based on the dicyandiamide charged. Pressures of 1600–2000 lbs. develop. Ammonia serves to depress the condensation reaction of melamine with itself which gives deamination products, such as melam, melem and melon, while anhydrous methanol functions to prevent local overheating during the strongly exothermic reaction. The melamine so produced may be washed with tartaric acid or mannitol to remove iron and amidines before it is collected on filter plates. Melamine of 99.0% purity can be obtained from dicyandiamide and liquid ammonia at 135–150° after 20–25 minutes at pressures of 1400–3000 lbs.[71] Yields are almost quantitative, and in order to avoid having a hard cake of melamine, the reaction is carried to only 20–25% completion; the reaction mixture is cooled, the precipitated melamine filtered, and the mother liquor recycled.

Many variations of the commercial melamine process are reported in the patent literature; however, most commercial methods make use of pressures of 10–100 atmospheres and temperatures of 100–400° in either a batch or a continuous process.[68,72,73] One of the chief European sources of melamine is the process[63] of the Suddeutche Kalistickstoff-Werke where dicyandiamide is electrically ignited in the presence of ammonia and nitrogen. Pressures of 150 atms. develop during the reaction which ranges in temperature from 200–300° and requires under five hours.

Cyanamide is also claimed as a starting material in most proces patents[74,75] but its use offers more disadvantages than simplifications in spite of the facts that apparently a synthesis step is saved and liquid ammonia dissolves six parts of cyanamide against only one part of dicyandiamide.[76]

In processes based on liquid ammonia alone as a solvent, use of the minimum[77] amount, or, even better, less than enough ammonia[79,80] to dissolve the dicyandiamide, but not less than 0.3 part by weight[81] of ammonia per part of dicyandiamide, seems to offer an appreciable advantage. Other modifications, many of which result in yield improvements, are: the use of a fairly full reactor;[78,82] agitation[83,84] of the reaction mixture; addition of the ammonia below 100°; distilling the ammonia off at high temperatures and finishing the reaction below 200 atmospheres;[85] and the use of 5–8% of an alkaline material stronger than ammonia[86] such as caustic potash, together with a high boiling organic solvent. The latter modification results in yields of only 80% and some ammeline forms. In early work, the use of aqueous ammonia is described.[86] However, it was found that only 35% yields of melamine were produced together with 20% of ammeline and also lesser amounts of urea and guanidine when dicyandiamide was heated with concentrated aqueous ammonia for three hours at 120°. More recent work[88] indicates an improvement in yield to 60% when the reaction mixture is heated at 135° for twelve hours. The use of a diluent[88] such as methanol, ethanol, benzene or nitrobenzene under 3 to 30 atmospheres pressure raises the yields to 83%, while melamine yields of 98% are said to be obtainable from pure dicyandiamide and aqueous ammonia held for six hours at a temperature of 160° under 200 atmospheres pressure.

McClellan has reviewed[15] the literature on dicyandiamide processes and his conclusions, which follow, offer an excellent summary of melamine synthesis at this writing.

(1) The pyrolysis of anhydrous cyanamide or guanidine salts alone and dicyandiamide in the open or in the presence of solvents does not give high yields of melamine. (2) Heating dicyandiamide and guanidine together either dry or in the presence of free ammonia improves the yield or hastens the reaction or does both. (3) Heating dicyandiamide under pressure in the presence of free ammonia gives high yields of melamine. (4) Heating cyanamide and dicyandiamide in equimolar proportions in an autoclave with ammonia neither speeds up the reaction nor raises the yields normally obtained with dicyandiamide and ammonia. (5) When dicyandiamide is heated under pressure with free ammonia, the presence of cyanamide, guanidine and biguanide can be shown. There are indications that a reaction of dicyandiamide and ammonia occurs to give melamine, but it has not been conclusively established. Grubb[70] has studied melamine synthesis from ammonia and dicyandiamide in the vapor phase in fixed and in fluid beds. While yields in the latter case were poor, fixed bed yields exceeding 90% were reported at pressures of 300–400 psig., which are lower than present commercial processes employ.

There is a critical temperature above which conversion of dicyandiamide to melamine proceeds spontaneously. The critical temperature may be decreased from 209° at one atmosphere to 145° with 450 psig. pressure. Below these temperatures, conversion proceeds slowly.

B. The Urea Process

The urea process is not yet in commercial use, but the favorable economic picture it presents suggests that it is the process of the future and will gradually meet with wide industrial acceptance. Urea is heated in an autoclave at 200–300 atmospheres pressure with anhydrous ammonia at temperatures of 350–500° giving yields of about 90% of melamine.[89, 90, 91] At a temperature of 350°, the reaction requires

$$6NH_2CONH_2 \xrightarrow[\Delta]{NH_3} (I) + 3CO_2 + 6NH_3$$

six hours; at 400°, one half an hour, while at 500°, it is essentially complete within ten minutes. The presence of ammonia, some of which is produced during the thermal decomposition of urea, serves to prevent the usually extensive deammonation decomposition of melamine heated above its melting point (354°). Ammonium hydrogen phosphate is said[92] to catalyze the reaction.

Some indication of the course of the reaction is provided by the fact that such probable intermediates as biuret or guanylurea can be substituted for urea. Thus, for biuret the reaction can be written

$$3\,NH_2CONHCONH_2 \longrightarrow (I) + 3\,CO_2 + 3\,NH_3$$

and for guanylurea:

$$\underset{\substack{\| \\ NH}}{2\,NHC}\!\!-\!\!\underset{\substack{\| \\ O}}{NHCNH_2} \longrightarrow (I) + CO_2 + NH_3$$

Ammonium cyanate may also be used in place of urea, but it is, of course, easily convertible to urea anyway. Modifications of the process include the use of superheated ammonia to help bring the reaction mixture to temperature[93] and the passing of molten urea and ammonia countercurrently through a column of inert materials[94] such as glass beads, Rachig rings or saddles. The latter method serves to raise yields slightly by retaining intermediate hydroxy-s-triazines long enough to effect their ammonation. A possible mechanism may be the normal formation of cyanuric acid when urea is heated, followed by ammonation to melamine.

The melamine may be conveniently collected by introducing urea into a pressure vessel with ammonia present under such conditions that the melamine produced remains in the vapor phase[95] and is discharged as a fine powder. Or else molten melamine may be discharged as a spray from under pressure into a container with an ammonia atmosphere[96], this results in its vaporization and later condensation as a solid without repassing through the undesirable liquid base.

A process for the manufacture of melamine from urea has been described[97] which utilizes 2–10% of one of the following ammonium salts: chloride, bromide, sulfate or acetate. Ammonia, temperatures of 280–310° and pressure are used but yields are only 40%.

IV. Reactions of Melamine

Melamine undergoes a great many reactions in which the —NH$_2$ groups function chemically as amido rather than amino groups. Under drastic conditions, the highly stable s-triazine ring of melamine may be cleaved leading to guanidines, cyanamides, cyanates, and other products of degradation. It has been demonstrated that melamine can tauto- merize and undergo reaction at the ring nitrogen atoms giving as products substituted isomelamines. The isomelamines are the subject of a later section. This section includes the reactions of melamine which lead to definite chemical compounds. Resinous or polymeric substances are mentioned only briefly.

Reports in the literature to the effect that melamine does not enter into certain reactions should include a statement of the particular solvent and reaction conditions used. This obvious statement is empha- sized in the case of melamine because of its very low solubility in inert solvents. It is this insolubility which may be the cause of apparent lack of reactivity. Melamine is quite soluble in such solvents as hot ethylene glycol, ethanolamine, and triethanolamine; however these and other "solvents" for melamine will undergo many of the same reactions intended for melamine. A really good inert solvent remains to be discovered.

1. Salt Formation

A. Salts and Complexes with Inorganic Compounds

Melamine forms salts with a large number of acids. Many of these have been reported. Table VI-1 contains a list of those acid salts and inorganic complexes the existence of which has been demonstrated. Table VI-3 lists melamine salts of organic acids. Melamine functions as a monoacidic base in most cases, although some salts involving more than one equivalent of acid are known. It may also be considered acidic in that it forms silver salts and potassium salts (see Table VI-1). For example, hydrochlorides with one, two, and three equivalents of HCl are known.[98] The dihydrochloride forms slowly on standing with concentrated hydrochloric acid. The trihydrochloride is less readily made, but on several days' standing with hydrogen chloride, melamine absorbs three equivalents of HCl in definite stages. Tetrachloroaurates involving one and two amino groups are known.[99] A number of phos- phates are known (see Table VI-1) in addition to the normal phosphate. Normal melamine phosphate can be pyrolyzed to the insoluble heat

TABLE VI-1.   Inorganic Salts of Melamine

Salt	Formula M = melamine	Physical Properties	Reference
bis-Tetrachloro-aurate dihydrate	$M \cdot (HAuCl_4)_2 \cdot 2 H_2O$	M.p. 290–1° (dec.) yellow	16
bis-Tetrachloro-aurate tetrahydrate	$M \cdot (HAuCl_4)_2 \cdot 4 H_2O$	M.p. 271–272° (dec.) yellow	16
Borofluorate	—	—	17
Chromate	$2 M \cdot H_2CrO_4$	Long, orange-yellow needles	17, 22
Dihydrochloride	$M \cdot 2 HCl$	—	19
Disilver nitrate	$M \cdot 2 AgNO_3$	—	4, 9
Fluorosilicate	—	—	17
Hexachloroplatinate	$M \cdot 2 HClPtCl_4$	Needles. Changes to dihydrate on crystallizing from H_2O	7
Hexachloroplatinate dihydrate	$(M \cdot HCl)_2 PtCl_2 \cdot 2 H_2O$	Prisms (—2 H_2O at 100°)	7
Hydrochloride	$M \cdot HCl$	Crystallized from ethyl alc.	6
Hydrochloride hemihydrate	$M \cdot HCl \cdot \frac{1}{2} H_2O$	—	8
Hydroidide	$M \cdot HI$	Crystallized from ethyl alc.	6
Metaphosphate	$M \cdot HPO_3$	—	11, 13
Metavanadate	—	—	17
Monoborate	—	—	17
Nitrate	$M \cdot HNO_3$	—	2, 5, 8, 10
ortho-Phosphate	$3 M \cdot 2 H_3PO_4 \cdot H_2O$	(Dec.) 360°. Feather-like tufts of crystals	22
Perchlorate	$M \cdot HClO_4 \cdot H_2O$	Sublimes. Tufts of needles	22
Phosphate	$M_2 \cdot H_3PO_4$	—	15
Phosphate	$M_3(H_3PO_4)_2 \cdot 2 H_2O$	—	2, 10, 12
Polyphosphate	—	—	17
Potassium amide	$M \cdot KNH_2$	—	18
Pyrophosphate	$M_2 \cdot H_4P_2O_7$	Sparsely soluble H_2O; high thermal resistance	11, 12, 20
Silicon oxyamide	—		3
Silver nitrate	$M \cdot AgNO_3$	—	7, 9
Silver salt	$M \cdot Ag_2 (—2 H)$	—	9
Sulfamate	—	—	17
Sulfate	$M_2 \cdot H_2SO_4 \cdot H_2O$	—	10
Sulfate	$M \cdot H_2SO_4 \cdot H_2O$	—	17
Sulfate dihydrate	$M_2 \cdot H_2SO_4 \cdot 2 H_2O$	—	14

(Table continued)

TABLE VI-1 *(continued)*

Salt	Formula M = melamine	Physical Properties	Reference
Sulfate hemihydrate	$M_2 \cdot H_2SO_4 \cdot \frac{1}{2} H_2O$	—	8
Sulfite	$M \cdot HSO_3$	—	21
Setrachloroaurate	$M \cdot HAuCl_4$	M.p. 265–6°, yellow or orange-ochre	16
Thiocyanate	$M \cdot HSCN$	Crystallized from ethyl alc.	1
Trihydrochloride	$M \cdot 3HCl$	—	19
Tripotassium	$M \cdot K_3 (—3H)$	—	18

1. A. Claus, *Ber.*, **9**, 1915 (1876).
2. J. Liebig, *Ann.*, **10**, 17 (1834).
3. H. Walter, U. S. 2,514,268 (1950) to Monsanto Chemical Co.
4. J. Ponomareff, *Ber.*, **18**, 3267 (1885).
5. R. Andreasch, *Monatsh.*, **48**, 145 (1927), through, *Chem. Abstracts*, **22**, 226 (1928).
6. A. Claus, *Ann.*, **179**, 120 (1875).
7. A. Hofmann, *Ber.*, **18**, 2755 (1885).
8. S. Byk, *J. prakt. Chem.*, **20**, 345 (1879).
9. J. Wisclicenus and C. Zimmerman, *Ber.*, **7**, 289 (1874).
10. W. Scholl, R. Davis, B. Brown and F. Reid, *Ind. Eng. Chem.*, **29**, 202 (1937).
11. S. Vol'fkovich, E. Zusser and R. Remen, *Bull. acad. sci. U.S.S.R. Classe sci. chim.*, 1946, 571, through, *Chem. Abstracts*, **42**, 7781 (1948).
12. S. Vol'fkovich, E. Zusser and R. Remen, *U.S.S.R.*, **67**, 616 (1946), through, *Chem. Abtsracts*, **43**, 3473 (1949).
13. S. Vol'fkovich, E. Zusser and R. Remen, *U.S.S.R.*, **66**, 230 (1946), through, *Chem. Abstracts*, **41**, 2677 (1947).
14. J. Jager, *Ber.*, **9**, 1556 (1876).
15. W. Lipschitz and E. Stokey, *J. Pharmacol.*, **83**, 235 (1945), through, *Chem. Abstracts*, **39**, 4395 (1945).
16. A. Ostrogovitch, *Gazz. chim. ital.*, **65**, 566 (1934), through, *Chem. Abstracts*, **30**, 465 (1936).
17. Melamine bulletin – American Cyanamid Co.
18. E. Franklin, *J. Am. Chem. Soc.*, **44**, 486 (1922).
19. C. Barnett, *J. Phys. Chem.*, **34**, 1497 (1936).
20. F. Pollak and J. Fassel, U. S. 2,464,342 (1949).
21. H. Williams, *Cyanogen Compounds*, 2d. Ed., Edward Arnold & Co., London, 1948, p. 29.
22. K. Rehnelt, *Monatsh.*, **84**, 257 (1953).

stable pyrophosphate by heating at 250–270° (Ref. 11, Table VI-1), and the metaphosphate can be made by treating aqueous melamine with metaphosphoric acid or with an aqueous mixture containing 67.5% phosphorous pentoxide and about 40% salts, mainly sodium metaphosphate (Ref. 12, 13, Table VI-1). A polyphosphate is also known, (Ref. 17, Table VI-1). Most of the inorganic melamine salts are hydrated and, in some cases, several hydrates of the same salt exist or, more precisely, have been reported. A dihydrate and a tetrahydrate of the bis-tetrachloroaurate are listed in Table VI-1 (Ref. 16).

Mineral acid salts of melamine possess the same order of water solubility as melamine. The solubility of melamine and its mineral acid salts at 20° is as follows:[6, 100]

TABLE VI-2.   Solubility of Melamine Salts of Mineral Acids in Water

Salt	Solubility in H_2O, g./100 g. H_2O at 20°
Melamine	0.50 (25°)
Melamine sulfate	0.19
Melamine phosphate	0.43
Melamine nitrate	0.68

Other inorganic acid salts are even more sparingly soluble in water. Water solutions of melamine salts are acidic, indicating extensive hydrolysis.

Several salts other than the acid salts merit special mention. Melamine and aqueous silver nitrate, in the cold, form a white precipitate of the silver nitrate complex.[101] Heating with concentrated silver nitrate solution converts this complex to one containing two molecules of silver nitrate, $C_3N_6H_6 \cdot 2\,AgNO_3$, while further treatment of the latter with aqueous ammonia produces a white amorphous powder, said to be the disilver salt, $C_3H_6H_4Ag_2$. It should be useful for the preparation of dialkyl melamines. In a liquid ammonia solution of potassium amide, melamine forms a tripotassium salt, but if excess potassium amide is not present, only the addition compound $C_3N_6H_6 \cdot KNH_2$ forms.[102] As might be expected, these salts are vigorously decomposed by water. Copper sulfate solutions cause the slow precipitation from aqueous melamine solutions of a blue complex salt.[47]

Melamine salts of organic acids, such as the acetate, lactate, chloroacetate, α-hydroxyisobutyrate, and probably a number of untested ones are appreciably soluble in water. Many of the salts in Table VI-3 have been listed as insoluble, however, without accompanying data. In aqueous solutions, the salts hydrolyze giving solutions of about pH 4. Few melamine salts have definite melting points; most decompose on heating.

TABLE VI-3. Melamine Salts of Organic Acids
(M = melamine, A = acid)

Salt	Molecular ratio	Physical properties	Ref.
Acetate	M·A		1, 2
Triacetate	M·3A		2
Formate	M·A		1, 2
Triformate	M·3A		2
Oxalate	M·A		1, 2, 6, 8
Hemioxalate	M·½A		2
Dioxalate	M·2A		2
Aconitate	M·A		3
Adipate	M·A·H₂O		3
Benzoate	M·A		3
Bornyldinitrophenolate	M·A		4
Caproate	M·A·5H₂O		3
Chloroacetate	M·A		3
Citrate	M·A		3
Dinitro-*p-tert*-amyl-phenolate	M·A	Deep red, M.p. 175° (dec.)	4
Dinitro-*p-tert*-butyl-phenolate	M·A	Light red, M.p. 250° (dec.)	4
Dinitro-*o*-cresolate	M·A	Bright yellow, M.p. 240° (dec.)	4
Dinitro-*o*-cyclohexyl-phenolate	M·A	Yellow, M.p. 100°	4
Dinitrophenolate	M·A	Light yellow, (dec.) with heat	4
Cyanurate[a]	M·A		3, 5, 9
Dicaproate	M·2A		3
Dipropionate	M·2A		3
Fumarate	M·A·H₂O		3
Glutamate hydrochloride	M·2A·H₂O		3
α-Hydroxyisobutyrate	M·A½H₂O		3
Lactate	M·A·H₂O		3
Maleate	M·A		3
Phthalate	M·A		3
Pyruvate	M·A·H₂O		3
Salicylate	M·A		3
Sebacate	M·A·H₂O		3
Styphnate	M·A		3
Succinate	M·A·H₂O		3
Tartrate	M·A		3
Picrate[a]	M·A	Insol. water, darkens 240°; black at 300°	10
		Light yellow gel until heated, M.p. 316–7°	2
		Pale yellow threads, (dec.) 268°	11

(Table continued)

TABLE VI-3 (*continued*)

Salt[a]	Molecular ratio	Physical properties	Ref.
Panceau 2 G color acid	$C_{16}H_{12}N_2S_2O_7$		7
Chromotrope 2 R color acid	$C_{16}H_{12}N_2S_2O_8$		7
Orange II color acid	$C_{16}H_{12}N_2SO_4$		7
Orange IV color acid	$C_{18}H_{15}N_3SO_3$		7
Chloroacetate	$M \cdot A \cdot H_2O$		3
Penicillinate	$M \cdot$ Pencillin		12
Penicillinate G	$M \cdot$ Penicillin G		12
Monochloroacetate	$M \cdot CH_2ClCOOH$	Long, silky needles	13
Dichloroacetate	$M \cdot CHCl_2COOH \cdot H_2O$	Needles in double fans	13
β-Naphtholsulfonate	$M \cdot C_{10}H_8O_3S$	Long, six-sided plates	13
a-Naphtholsulfonate	$M \cdot C_{10}H_8O_3S \cdot H_2O$	(Dec.) 320°, short six-sided plates	13
β-Anilosulfonate	$M \cdot C_6H_7O_3NS \cdot H_2O$	Short, eight-sided plates	13
p-Toluenesulfonate	$M \cdot C_7H_8O_3S \cdot H_2O$	(Dec.) long needles; may also form as plates	13
p-Thymolsulfonate	$M \cdot C_{10}H_{14}O_4S \cdot 2 H_2O$	Needles or needles developing hexagonal plates	13
[p-Methyl-o,o'-dicarboxyphenoxy-(1)] acetic acid	$M \cdot C_{11}H_{10}O_7 \cdot H_2O$	(Dec.) 260°, needles	13
o-Bromthymol-p-sulfonate	$M \cdot C_{10}H_{13}O_4BrS \cdot H_2O$	(Dec.) 300°, groups of obliquely out needles	13

[a] The great insolubility of melamine cyanurate offers a better analytical method for determination of melamine than the picrate salt method formerly used.

1. J. Liebig, *Ann.*, **10**, 17 (1834).
2. A. Ostrogovitch, *Gazz. chim. ital.*, **65**, 566 (1934), through, *Chem. Abstracts*, **30**, 465 (1936).
3. Melamine Bulletin, American Cyanamid Co.
4. V. Migrdichian, U. S. 2,385,719 (1945) to American Cyanamid Co.
5. Brit. 583,504 (1946) to DuPont.
6. W. Lipschitz and E. Stokey, *J. Pharmacol.*, **83**, 235 (1945), through *Chem. Abstracts*, **39**, 4395 (1945).
7. L. Radlberger, *Monatsh.*, **29**, 937 (1908), through, *Chem. Abstracts*, **3**, 905 (1909).
8. W. Lipschitz and Z. Hadidian, *J. Pharmacol.*, **81**, 84 (1944), through, *Chem. Abstracts*, **38**, 4033 (1944).
9. J. Liebig, *Ann.*, **26**, 187 (1839).
10. H. Krall, *J. Chem. Soc.*, **103**, 1385 (1913).
11. E. Werner, *J. Chem. Soc.*, **107**, 721 (1915).
12. L. Cheney, U. S. 2,577,698 (1951) to Bristol Labs., Inc.
13. K. Rehnelt, *Monatsh.*, **84**, 257 (1953).

2. Ring Fission

The s-triazine nucleus of melamine is highly resistant to cleavage; however, several degradative methods are available.

A. Fusion of melamine (I) with potassium carbonate or mixtures of sodium and potassium carbonate in an aluminum pot[103] at 375–400° results in destruction of the melamine and formation of alkali cyanates (1). Similar results are obtained if, in place of the carbonates, potassium hydroxide is employed[104] at a temperature of 250°.

$$\text{(I)} \qquad + \ K_2CO_3 \ \xrightarrow[\text{Al}]{375\text{--}400°} \ KCNO \qquad (1)$$

B. Alkali amides such as sodamide, when used in conjunction with carbon at 760–850°, convert melamine to alkali cyanides; while at 350° the corresponding cyanamide salts are formed.[105]

C. If melamine is heated to around its melting point with ammonium salts such as the thiocyanate, chloride, sulfate, nitrate etc., the respective guanidine salt is said[106] to be produced in good yield.

In the case of melamine, these degradative reactions are seldom, if ever, of importance in the laboratory or commercially but, as will be discussed later, they are sometimes useful for structural identification of substituted melamines.

3. Hydrolysis

Amino groups on an s-triazine ring are attacked by alkalis and acids under rigorous conditions. Boiling dilute nitric acid hydrolyzes the amino groups of melamine in a stepwise manner[107] producing successively, ammeline, ammelide and cyanuric acid (2). Hydrochloric

$$\xrightarrow{\text{dil. HNO}_2} \qquad \longrightarrow \qquad \longrightarrow \qquad (2)$$

| Melamine | Ammeline | Ammelide | Cyanuric acid |

acid may also be used,[1] but if concentrated nitric or sulfuric acids are used at a temperature of 150°, the main product of the hydrolysis is ammelide.[108] Aqueous sodium hydroxide at 80–100° causes slow hydrolysis of melamine to ammeline and ammelide; but the hydrolysis may be inhibited by carrying out the reaction under a slight pressure of ammonia.

4. Pyrolysis

Melamine melts at 354° C. If it is heated above this point (3) in the absence of ammonia to inhibit the reaction, deammonation occurs and the products melam (III), melem (IV) and melon result. Melam can also be produced by a variety of other methods such as the thermal decomposition[109] of ammonium thiocyanate. In melamine deammonation, melam is formed first by the loss of an equivalent of ammonia from two molecules of melamine. Melem is usually found together with melam and is possibly the end product of a rearrangement of (III).

Melem, $C_6H_6N_{10}$ Melam, $C_6H_9N_{11}$

Heating the reaction mixture at 600° causes further loss of ammonia with the formation of melon, a compound, or rather substance, which can survive red heat. Redemann and Lucas, have suggested[110] that melam has the tetraaminodicyanurylimide structure (III), the secondary amine of melamine. Like melamine, (III) is a feeble base. The proposed structure (III) is supported by the behavior of melam at elevated temperatures with 30% aqueous ammonia, whereby melamine and ammeline are obtained. Melem (IV) probably is the triamide of cyameluric acid (See Chapter VIII) and bears the same relationship to melamine that cyanuric acid bears to cyameluric acid. Structure (IV) accounts for the formation of large quantities of ammelide upon hydrolysis and also for the fact that melem is more resistant than melam to hydrolysis. Melem is stated[110] to be an even weaker base than melam inasmuch as it is derived from a stronger acid; however melamine, melam and melem all have the same order of basicity. Melon, melam, and melem are discussed more fully in Chapter VIII, Section III, 3.E. All three of these deammonation products are formed reversibly; that is, the addition of ammonia at suitable pressures and temperatures regenerates melamine. This is the basis for a patent for a potential commercial process (see Section III, 2).

5. Nitration

Melamine can be nitrated with a mixture of nitric and acetic acids. While nitromelamine and dinitromelamine have been reported,[111] the usual course of the reaction with fuming nitric and acetic anhydride at 5° is hydrolytic nitration (4) in which a 50% yield of dinitroammeline (V) is obtained.[120] The latter (V) behaves as a dibasic acid;[111] it yields

$$\underset{(I)}{H_2N\underset{N\diagdown N}{\overset{N}{\diagup\diagdown}}NH_2}\ \ +\ 3\ HNO_3\ \xrightarrow[Ac_2O]{5°}\ \underset{(V)}{HO\underset{N\diagdown N}{\overset{N}{\diagup\diagdown}}NHNO_2}\ +\ NH_4NO_3\ +\ H_2O\quad(4)$$

a disodium salt,[113] $C_3HN_7O_5Na_2 \cdot H_2O$, as colorless needles upon recrystallization from 30–40% ethanol, and a potassium salt,[113] $C_3HN_7O_5 \cdot K_2 \cdot H_2O$, crystallizing as pale yellow iridescent blades from water. Dinitroammeline explodes violently when heated.

6. Halogenation

Halogenation of melamine can be accomplished readily under a variety of conditions and leads to products containing from one to six active halogen atoms of a structure which may be either dihaloamino $-NX_2$, or haloimino-haloamino, $-NHX \longleftrightarrow = NX$, or even a mixture of both structures. The limiting structures are represented by (VI and VII).

$$\underset{(VI)}{X_2N\underset{N\diagdown N}{\overset{N}{\diagup\diagdown}}NX_2}\ \ \text{and}\ \ \underset{(VII)}{XN\underset{XN\ \ NX}{\overset{\overset{X}{N}}{=}}NX}$$

It is customary to express the degree of halogenation of the products prepared from melamine in terms of the per cent active halogen. This figure represents an average for a product that very often contains mixtures of difficultly separable melamines containing one or more halogen atoms. It is twice the actual halogen content of the molecule since each halogen is equivalent to one oxygen molecule for purposes of oxidation in the reaction $X^+ + 2e \longrightarrow X^-$. During the chlorination of melamine in aqueous solution, the following reactions are said to take place[114] where Mel–NH_2 = melamine and M = an alkali metal:

$$Cl_2 + H_2O \rightleftarrows HOCl + HCl \tag{5}$$

$$Mel\text{—}NH_2 + HOCl \rightleftarrows Mel\text{—}NHCl + H_2O \tag{6}$$

$$Mel\text{—}NHCl + HCl \rightleftarrows Mel\text{—}NH_2 + Cl_2 \tag{7}$$

$$Mel\text{—}NHCl + MOH \rightleftarrows Mel\text{—}N{\underset{Cl}{\overset{M}{<}}} + H_2O \tag{8}$$

In aqueous media, incompletely halogenated products result no matter whether strong bases are present or not.[114,115,116] Hydrochloric acid is liberated in equation (5) and reacts with a portion of the melamine, forming a hydrochloride resistant to halogenation. If excess hydrochloric acid is present, as might be the case in an attempt to obtain more complete halogenation, reaction (7) proceeds destroying the halogenated product. The presence of a strong base to neutralize the by-product acid results in the preferential formation of salts of the type represented by equation (8). Thus treating an aqueous melamine solution with chlorine gas at 0–10° for four hours[115] or at 25° for two hours[114] gives a white solid containing about 73% of theory active chlorine (dichloromelamine), which is stable in water for many months and soluble in alkaline solutions, triacetin, acetonylacetone and ethyl acetate. Even with sodium carbonate or calcium hydroxide present, the product, in this case yellow orange, contains only 88.5% active chlorine. Similar results are obtained with bromine or iodine.[116] More extensive halogen uptake can be attained by running the reaction in weakly acidic buffered solutions using hypohalogen acids.[117] Hydrochloric acid, which forms by the reaction

$$Cl_2 + H_2O \longrightarrow HOCl + HCl$$

and decreases halogenation by forming salts with melamine, is absorbed by an acetic acid buffer system. For chlorination, sodium hypochlorite with excess acetic acid, or sodium acetate and chlorine are used while for bromination or iodination, propionic or chloracetic acids are used since neither is readily oxidized by bromine or iodine. Hexahalomelamines can be produced in nearly quantitative yields by this method. Good yields of hexabromo and hexachloromelamines can also be obtained by conducting the reaction in carbon tetrachloride[116, 118] in the presence of powdered sodium carbonate, using molecular halogens at a temperature of 10°. Some of the typical halogenated melamines that have been prepared and their percentage of active halogen are listed in Table VI-4.

TABLE VI-4.   Halogenated Melamines

Halogenated melamine	% Active halogen	Reference
Chloromelamine	44.2	1
Dichloromelamine	72.8	1, 2, 3
Trichloromelamine	93	1, 2, 3
Hexachloromelamine	128	1, 5
Dibromomelamine	112	2
Hexabromomelamine	160	1, 4
Diiodomelamine	128	2
Hexaiodomelamine	173	1

1. W. Arsem, U. S. 2,472,361 (1949).
2. I. Muscat and A. Chenicek, U. S. 2,184,883 (1939) to Pittsburgh Plate Glass Co.
3. I. Muscat and A. Chenicek, U. S. 2,184,886 (1939) to Pittsburgh Plate Glass Co.
4. I. Muscat and A. Chenicek, U. S. 2,184,888 (1939) to Pittsburgh Plate Glass Co.
5. I. Chenicek, U. S. 2,299,069 (1942) to Pittsburgh Plate Glass Co.

All of the halogens in these compounds are active and all are equivalent. Mixtures of more highly halogenated products with either melamine or less highly halogenated melamines will undergo halogen exchange to give intermediate equilibrium mixtures. For example, equimolar quantities of hexachloromelamine and melamine in acetic acid solution at 50° for thirty minutes results in complete conversion (9) of both reactants to trichloromelamine (Ref. 1, Table VI-4).

Mixtures of two or more halogenated melamines often can be separated[119] by virtue of their differing solubilities. Dichloromelamine is insoluble in acetone and carbon tetrachloride. Trichloromelamine is also insoluble in carbon tetrachloride but is acetone soluble, while hexachloromelamine is soluble in both these solvents as well as in benzene, ethanol and ethylene dichloride but not in water.[117]

Hexachloromelamine reacts with the olefinic bonds of such unsaturated compounds as styrene, hexene, cyclohexene, acrylic esters, and methacrylic esters. Trichloromelamine can chlorinate acetone in a standing solution[119] of the two. Although monochloroacetone is reported as the product (10), it would appear easier to chlorinate than

$$\text{ClHN}\underset{N\ \ N}{\overset{N}{\diagup\diagdown}}\text{NHCl} + \text{CH}_3\text{COCH}_3 \xrightarrow{\text{stand}} \text{H}_2\text{N}\underset{N\ \ N}{\overset{N}{\diagup\diagdown}}\text{NHCl} + \text{ClCH}_2\text{COCH}_3 \quad (10)$$
$$\overset{|}{\text{NHCl}} \qquad\qquad\qquad \overset{|}{\text{NHCl}}$$

acetone. Dichloroacetone would be still easier to chlorinate and the expected product from this reaction should be trichloroacetone. Dibromomelamine yields a mixture[115] of melamine, ammeline and ammelide when hydrolyzed. An explosion has been reported on using tribromomelamine as a brominating agent.

7. Acylation

Acylation of melamine with one to three acyl groups can be carried out with acid anhydrides. Acid halides, commonly used for acylations in the laboratory, do not acylate the —NH₂ (amido) groups of melamine. Most acid anhydrides can be made to react as desired to give the triacyl derivatives. Acetic anhydride is an exception and triacetylmelamine is formed only with the greatest difficulty. Diacetylmelamine is readily prepared upon warming melamine and acetic anhydride but only small amounts of the triacetyl derivative are obtained.[99] The difficulty of introducing the third acetyl group may be due[113] to either the low solubility of diacetylmelamine and to its precipitation from the reaction mixture or to the occurrence of a tautomeric change prior to acetylation, or both. Neither explanation is adequate in view of the fact that melamine is acylated by other acid anhydrides, going through intermediates of lesser solubility and similar electronic character. High

TABLE VI-5. Acylated Melamines
(Prepared using respective acid anhydrides)

Acyl groups	Reaction time	Conditions Temp., °C.	Yield %	Melting point[a], °C.	Salts; solubility	References
Acetyl, mono	10 hrs. in xylene	140	—	325	S. sol. hot H_2O	4
Acetyl, di	2 min.	120	—	305–306	Dark yellow picrate, M.p. 209–210° (dec.). Light yellow tetrachloro-aurate, no M.p. (dec.). With $Ag(NH_3)_2{}^+$ forms salt $C_3H_2N_6Ag_2(OAc)_2$	3, 5, 6
Acetyl, tri	5 hrs.	120	99	Dec. 310	Forms monohydrate	3, 5, 6, 7
Valeryl, tri	30 min.	170–175	94	228–9		1, 2
Isovaleryl, tri	15 min.	165–170	85	216–218		1, 2
Caproyl, tri	15 min.	175	91	220		1, 2
Enanthyl, tri	5 min.	160	90	210		1, 2
Caprylyl, tri	15 min.	175	94	209		1, 2
Pelargonyl, tri	5 min.	185	88	194–5		1, 2
Lauryl, tri	15 min.	190–195	99	178–179		1, 2
Oleyl, tri	30 min.	195–200	99	138–140		1, 2
Stearyl, tri	30 min.	200	93	159–161		1, 2
Propionyl, tri	15 min.	158	94	282		1, 2
Butyryl, tri	30 min.	160	98	258		1, 2
Formyl, mono[b]	—	160–165	80	Cryst. from ethyl alc. water or 20% acetic acid	Insol. acetic acid	3
γ-Carboxypropionyl, mono	10 hrs. in o-di-chlorobenzene	140	—	262–263 Cryst. from water	S. sol. cyclohexanone, dimethylcyan-amide, dimethyl formamide, butyrolacetone; Sol. H_2O Insol. ethanol, benzene, butanol, ...	4

Acyl groups	Reaction time	Temp, °C.	Yield %	Melting point^a, °C.	Salts; solubility	References
Benzoyl, mono	10 hrs. in xylene	140	—	—	Solubility same as above	4
o-Carboxybenzoyl, mono	10 hrs. in xylene	140	—	250–252 Cryst. from water	Solubility same as above	4
Benzoyl, tri	4 hrs.	130–135	100	201–203	Needles or prisms from ethyl acetate or acetone. Sol. cold NaOH. Salt with $2C_6H_5OH$, M.p. 192.5–193.5. Dark yellow picrate, M.p. 228–229°. Alcoholate with $3C_3H_7OH$, (dec.) 85–90°. Forms salt: $C_3H_4N_6Ag_2(COC_6H_5)_2 \cdot 2H_2O$	2, 3
p-Nitrobenzenesulfonyl, mono	—	60–70	—	—	Sol. NaOH	8,9
p-Aminobenzenesulfonyl, mono	—	—	—	290–295 Cryst. from water	Sol. H_2O	8, 9
Tall oil, tri	30 min.	200–210	60	Completely molten at 197°	Light tan, waxy solid	10

^{a} Recrystallized from acetic acid unless otherwise stated.
^{b} Prepared from melamine and formamide.

1. W. Emerson and T. Patrick, U. S. 2,507,700 (1950) to Monsanto Chemical Co.
2. W. Emerson and T. Patrick, J. Am. Chem. Soc., 70, 343 (1948).
3. A. Ostrogovitch, Gazz. chim. ital., 65, 566 (1934), through, Chem. Abstracts, 30, 465 (1936).
4. German Patent Applic. 7432 (1943), P. B. 61187, frames 680–682, Bib., 8, 342.
5. J. Cason, J. Am. Chem. Soc., 69, 495 (1947).
6. J. Cason, P. B. 52316, Bib., 5, 287.
7. E. Atkinson, J. Am. Chem. Soc., 73, 4443 (1951).
8. R. Roblin and P. Winnek, U. S. 2,407,177 (1946) to American Cyanamid Co.
9. G. Anderson, et al., J. Am. Chem. Soc., 64, 2902 (1942).
10. P. Hamm, U. S. 2,577,418 (1951) to Monsato Chemical Co.

conversions and almost quantitative yields of triacetylmelamine have been obtained, however, by the addition[113] of sodium acetate to the acetylation reaction mixture and recyclization of acetic anhydride.

A number of acyl derivatives have been prepared and are listed in Table VI-5.

Acyl melamines are soluble in cold alkali and can be reprecipitated with carbon dioxide. Most are high melting compounds. The higher alkyl triacyl melamines are prepared by heating melamine with excess acid anhydride at 160–200° with stirring. These are waxy substances, insoluble in water and most organic solvents, resistant to hydrolysis, and recrystallizable from acetic acid. All known acyl melamines are stable to boiling water (Ref. 2, Table VI-5), but are readily hydrolyzed by strong acids or weak bases (Ref. 3, Table VI-5), such as alcoholic ammonia.

The diacetyl and tribenzoyl derivatives of melamine are deserving of some further comment. The latter, because of its three benzoyl groups, is much less basic than the diacetyl compound. Both formed picrates in toluene solution but boiling was required in the case of tribenzoylmelamine. Diacetylmelamine (VI) and tribenzoylmelamine are both soluble in alkali and are precipitated with carbon dioxide. Both form hydrated silver salts[99] with ammoniacal silver nitrate. The tribenzoyl compound crystallizes with two equivalents of propanol[99] upon evaporation of its propanol solution. These are lost at 85–90°. Tribenzoylmelamine also forms a complex salt with phenol at 130°. Diacetylmelamine (VIII) can also be made[99] from melamine and thioacetic acid (11).

$$\text{H}_2\text{N}\overset{\text{N}}{\underset{\text{N}\ \ \text{N}}{\diagup\diagdown}}\text{NH}_2 \underset{\text{NH}_2}{} + 2\,\text{CH}_3\text{COSH} \xrightarrow{\Delta} \text{H}_2\text{N}\overset{\text{N}}{\underset{\text{N}\ \ \text{N}}{\diagup\diagdown}}\text{NHCOCH}_3 \underset{\text{(VIII)}\ \ \text{NHCOCH}_3}{} + \text{H}_2\text{S} \quad (11)$$

Triacetylmelamine can be nitrated at room temperature (12). With fuming nitric acid, the product is 2-nitro-4,6-diacetylmelamine.[120] The

$$\text{AcHN}\overset{\text{N}}{\underset{\text{N}\ \ \text{N}}{\diagup\diagdown}}\text{NHAc} \underset{\text{NHAc}}{} \xrightarrow[20-25°]{\text{fuming HNO}_3} \text{AcHN}\overset{\text{N}}{\underset{\text{N}\ \ \text{N}}{\diagup\diagdown}}\text{NHNO}_2 \underset{\text{NHAc}}{} + \text{H}_2\text{O} \quad (12)$$

use of acetic anhydride with nitric acid at the same temperature results[120] in the formation of nitroammelide (IX). Compound (IX) is soluble in bicarbonate and decomposes at 300°. Cason[112,113] obtained the trisodium and tripotassium salts of (IX), each a trihydrate. The free acid is usually isolated as a monohydrate. Hydrolysis[121] with dilute sulfuric acid produces cyanuric acid (13).

$$\text{(13)}$$

8. Active Halides

Melamine can be readily acylated by acid anhydrides, but it is ordinarily inert to acid halides[121] for a reason that is not apparent. Neither acetyl chloride nor benzoyl chloride reacts with melamine.[99] Certain very active acid chlorides do react with melamine, however. An example is furnished by the reaction of one equivalent of p-nitrobenzenesulfonyl chloride with melamine in the presence of pyridine.[122,123] The resulting sulfonamide is soluble in alkali and can be reprecipitated with dilute acetic acid. It can be reduced (14) with iron dust and acetic

$$\text{(14)}$$

M.p. 290–295°

acid to the corresponding p-amino derivative which is slightly soluble in water (0.728% at 37°) and melts at 290–295°. Other compounds containing moderately active halogen atoms, benzyl chloride for example, do not react with melamine, probably owing to the fact that many of them decompose under reaction conditions faster than they react. The presence of groups which activate halogen does enable

melamine to react with a limited number of compounds. For example,
(I) reacts with an equivalent of 3-nitro-4-chlorostilbonic acid[124] or
p-chloroarsonic acid[125] giving the corresponding mono-aryl-substituted
melamine (15).

$$(15)$$

9. Aldehydes

Melamine reacts rapidly with aldehydes. By far the largest share
of information available concerns the commercially important reaction
with formaldehyde which ultimately results in resin formation.

Reaction with formaldehyde first gives rise to methylol derivatives.
The reaction to prepare methylolmelamines is conducted by dissolving
melamine in a calculated amount of formaldehyde[124, 127] at a pH of 8.0,
heating rapidly to 70–80° for a few minutes, and cooling to crystallize
the products which are then washed with alcohol and dried in air or
in an oven at 60°. The di-, tri-, tetra-, penta- and hexamethylol-
melamines have been isolated with a fair degree of purity, usually as
monohydrates, but the monomethylol compound has not, as yet. These
derivatives are difficult to purify because of their instability towards
heat and low solubility in most solvents. The stability is in general a
direct function of the number of methylol groups on the compound,
consequently it is less difficult to purify the higher substituted methylol
melamines,[126, 127] and hexamethylolmelamine is the most stable and
least prone to undergo resinification. It can be obtained by heating
melamine for 10 minutes at 95° with eight equivalents[128, 129] of 32 %
aqueous formaldehyde and then cooling, or by stirring an aqueous
melamine formaldehyde solution 3–4 hours at room temperature in the
presence of a trace of nitric acid.[130, 131] At 150°, the colorless needles of
hexamethylolmelamine melt to a clear liquid which is soon converted
to an insoluble glass. The trimethylol compound[72, 130, 131] can be obtained

from melamine and three equivalents of neutral or slightly alkaline formaldehyde in the cold after 15 hours. In contrast to hexamethylolmelamine, it is extremely reactive, must be purified rapidly and at low temperatures, and has no definite melting point. It is said to crystallize also as a dihydrate.

The solubility of the methylolmelamines reaches a maximum for tetramethylolmelamine and decreases[126] with more or fewer methylol groups.

TABLE VI-6.   Solubility of Methylolmelamines

	g./100 g. H_2O		
Di	2.05	Penta	2.85
Tri	4.75	Hexa	1.40
Tetra	5.00		

The rate of reaction of melamine with aqueous formaldehyde is a function of pH, temperature, ratio of reactants, length of reaction time, and isolation procedure.[126,127,130,131] Formation of the methylol compounds is slowest[42] at a pH of 7.0, while with acid or base present, it is much more rapid. The methylol compounds are most stable[130,131] at pH 8–9; resinification proceeds readily in neutral and strongly basic solutions, and even more rapidly in acid solutions.

Okano and Ogata[132] have studied the rates of condensation of melamine and formaldehyde in aqueous media in the pH range of 3–10.6 at temperatures of 35°, 40°, and 70° following the course of the reaction by means of iodine and sulfite methods. Methylolmelamine consumes iodine as does formaldehyde and the latter can be determined by the sulfite method. There seem to be three probable mechanisms for the formation of methylolmelamine corresponding to the pH of the reaction media. If MH represents melamine, with the H portion an amino hydrogen, then in alkaline solution, the reaction is that of the conjugate base of melamine with formaldehyde-attack of the —NH$^-$ anion of melamine on the carbonyl of formaldehyde (16, 16A, 17).

$$MH + OH^- \rightleftarrows M^- + H_2O \text{ fast} \tag{16}$$

$$M^- + HCHO \rightleftarrows MCH_2O^- \text{ slow} \tag{16A}$$

$$MCH_2O + H_2O \rightleftarrows MCH_2OH + OH^- \text{ fast} \tag{17}$$

In acid media, melamine reacts with the conjugate acid of form-aldehyde-attack of the conjugate acid of formaldehyde on the amino nitrogen of melamine (18, 19).

$$HCHO + H_3O^+ \rightleftarrows \overset{+}{C}H_2OH + H_2O \text{ fast} \tag{18}$$

$$MH + \overset{+}{C}H_2OH \rightleftarrows MCH_2OH + H^+ \text{ slow} \tag{19}$$

In neutral solutions, reaction (20) takes place:

$$MH + CH_2O \rightleftarrows MCH_2OH \text{ slow} \tag{20}$$

As the reaction proceeds beyond the methylol stages, the first manifestation of resinification is failure to obtain crystallization on cooling although the hydrophilic solution still may be diluted with water or ethanol. As resinification proceeds, ethanol will cause separation of the polymer. On further condensation, the resin becomes hydrophobic and precipitates on cooling, or even when hot it may separate into two layers. Still further reaction produces a rubbery phase and finally the very hard, insoluble end product. Heat also causes these transformations,[132] which may be due to the formation of ether linkages (21) and/or methylene bridges (22).[130, 131, 132]

and/or

Methylene bridge formation between melamine molecules probably[132] proceeds by way of a rate-determining attack of the conjugate acid of methylolmelamine (in its dehydrated form) on free melamine (23, 24).

$$MCH_2OH + H_3O^+ \rightleftarrows MCH_2^+ + 2 H_2O \text{ fast} \tag{23}$$

$$MCH_2^+ + MH \rightleftarrows MCH_2M + H^+ \text{ slow} \tag{24}$$

The methylol compounds of melamine probably possess structures similar to those postulated for melamine itself—either the triamino, trimino or mixed amino-imino structures—where there are sufficient hydrogens available on the amino groups for existence of the latter two types. They are characteristically complex alcohols and, unlike ordinary polyhydric alcohols, do not discolor at high temperatures. They will react with certain polybasic and/or polyfunctional acids to form complex resinous esters.[72] Etherification with low molecular weight alcohols occurs in the presence of an acidic catalyst. The hexamethylolmethyl ether is obtained (25) at room temperature in two

$$(HOCH_2)_2N \text{---} N(CH_2OH)_2 + 6\,CH_3OH \xrightarrow[20° \, 10 \, min.]{trace \, HNO_3} (H_3COCH_2)_2N \text{---} N(CH_2OCH_3)_2 + 3\,H_2O$$

$$N(CH_2OH)_2 \qquad\qquad N(CH_2OCH_3)_2$$

Needles, M.p. 55°/H_2O (25)

minutes.[130,131] Compared to the free alcohol it is a very stable compound, possesses a definite melting point and is completely distillable at 180° at 0.02–0.03 mm. At aspirator pressure it can be distilled at temperatures a little over 220°, and undergoes some resinification. It is soluble in all common organic solvents. In water the maximum solubility (15 %) is obtained at a temperature of 40°. De-etherification is readily accomplished in the presence of acid or slowly in neutral solution. The hexaethyl ether is known and is less soluble in water than the hexamethyl ether but more so in petroleum ether. It is more difficult to purify.

All other ethers are obtained as viscous liquids or glass-like solids which are complex mixtures of monomeric materials containing small quantities of low molecular weight condensation products.[127] These ethers have not been isolated in a pure state because of their instability under the acidic conditions of their formation and/or because of the presence of condensed products arising from competing side reactions.[126] Etherification is usually carried out to modify the solubility of the methylol compounds. Reaction media consist of such solvents as alcohols and xylenes. The resulting syrups are water soluble and stable. They have good solubility in organic solvents and can be converted by heat or catalysts, or both, to infusible resinous products. Etherification is carried out on a commercial scale, using methanol and butanol but can also be carried out with other low molecular weight primary and secondary alcohols and probably with some of the higher molecular weight primary alcohols. Dry hydrogen chloride or sulfuric acid act as condensation agents at temperatures of 0–25° and gives[134] mono-, di- and triethers in yields of about 65 %.

Melamine and formaldehyde will react with amines in aqueous solution. The products are alkylaminomethyl-s-triazines. Melamine, formaldehyde and dimethylamine in a water solution at 65° for one hour[135] yield 2,4,6-tri(dimethylaminomethyl) s-triazine (26).

$$\text{H}_2\text{N} \begin{array}{c} \text{N} \\ \text{NH}_2 \\ \text{N} \quad \text{N} \\ \text{NH}_2 \end{array} + 3\,\text{CH}_2\text{O} + 3\,(\text{CH}_3)_2\text{NH} \xrightarrow[\text{H}_2\text{O}]{\text{1 hr. 60–70°}} (\text{CH}_3)_2\text{NCH}_2\text{NH} \begin{array}{c} \text{N} \\ \text{NHCH}_2\text{N}(\text{CH}_3)_2 \\ \text{N} \quad \text{N} \\ \text{NHCH}_2\text{N}(\text{CH}_3)_2 \end{array} \quad (26)$$

Melamine reacts with a number of other aldehydes which are listed in Table VI-7 together with the alcohols used to etherify the products.

TABLE VI-7. Aldehydes and Alcohols Reacting with Melamine

Aldehyde (plus)	Alcohol	References
Acetaldehyde		1
Butyraldehyde		2
Buten-2-al		2
Chloral hydrate		3
Cyclohexane carboxaldehyde		4
Benzaldehyde		1
Formaldehyde	Ethanol	1
Formaldehyde	Benzyl alcohol	1
Formaldehyde	Methanol	1
Formaldehyde	Ethyl-2-hexanol	1
Formaldehyde	Allyl alcohol	1
Formaldehyde	Cetyl alcohol	1
Formaldehyde	Lauryl alcohol	1
Formaldehyde	Oleic alcohol	1
Formaldehyde	Stearic alcohol	1
Formaldehyde	Glycerol	1
Cinnamaldehyde	—	4
Terephthalic aldehyde	—	4
Furfural	—	4

1. G. Widmer and W. Fisch, U. S. 2,197,357 (1940) to Ciba.
2. W. Talbot, U. S. 2,260,239 (1941) to Monsanto Chemical Co.
3. E. Atkinson and A. Bump, *J. Am. Chem. Soc.*, **72**, 629 (1950).
4. Brit. 468,746 (1937) to Ciba.

The products of most of these reactions are resinous materials which have not found wide application in industry.

Only chloral hydrate of the compounds listed in Table VI-7 gives a definite compound (27). Yields of 90% of 2,4(trichloromethylmethylol)

$$H_2N \underset{N \quad N}{\overset{N}{\bigcirc}} NH_2 \ + 2\ Cl_3CCHO \cdot H_2O\ aq. \xrightarrow{70-80°} H_2N \underset{N \quad N}{\overset{N}{\bigcirc}} NHCHOHCCl_3 \tag{27}$$

6-amino-1,3,5-triazine are obtained.[136] The compound does not melt but evolves chloral on heating. It is stable to cold dilute sodium hydroxide and boiling formaldehyde, but is hydrolyzed by warm dilute caustic soda.

10. Amides and Esters

The addition of formamide to melamine at temperatures of 160–165° serves to introduce one formyl group on an amino nitrogen.[99] The product, 2-formylamino-4,6-diamino-s-triazine, is obtained in 80% yields (28). It is easily hydrolyzed and is insoluble in all common solvents

$$H_2N \underset{N \quad N}{\overset{N}{\bigcirc}} NH_2 \ + HCONH_2 \xrightarrow{160-165°} NH_3 \uparrow + \ H_2N \underset{N \quad N}{\overset{N}{\bigcirc}} NHCHO \tag{28}$$

except possibly acids. By further treatment with formic acid, it may be converted to a triformate. The same compound is also produced from melamine and ethyl formate; however, temperatures of 230–235° must be used,[99] and the yields are only 10–15%.

Neither acetamide nor benzamide reacts with melamine even under drastic conditions.[99]

A number of amino esters have been heated with melamine (see section 12 below) but the result is a product in which only the amino groups of both molecules are involved.[137]

11. Alkylation

Attempts to alkylate melamine with alkyl sulfates such as methyl (4 hours at 100°) and ethyl (16 hours at 120°) sulfates, either with or without[138] inert solvents, have produced the corresponding monoalkyl-

*iso*melamines, isolated as the alkyl sulfate salts. The reaction (29) probably proceeds by isomerization of melamine to a species involving at least one imino group and it is this group that is alkylated. Less likely, but possible, is alkylation of normal melamine followed by migratory rearrangement of the alkyl group. While evidence as to the

$$(29)$$

true mechanism of the reaction is lacking, rearrangement of the normal melamine to the iso is considered unlikely. Otherwise, any mono-substituted melamine ought to be capable of rearrangement; this is not so.[139] It should be noted that while *normal cyanurates* rearrange to *isocyanurates*, the *isomelamines* can be rearranged[139] to the *normal* indicating that the normal is the more stable form for alkyl and also for aryl substituted melamines.

Monoalkyl*iso*melamines are strong bases compared to melamine. The isomelamines are discussed in Section VIII.

12. Amines

The reaction with amines is another form of alkylation. Amines or amine hydrochlorides react with melamine, usually in the temperature range of 150–200°, either with or without a suitable solvent, and give substituted melamines as products (30). Depending on the amine in question and on whether it is used in sufficient excess, either one, two or three equivalents may react splitting out one, two or three

$$(30)$$

Amine	time, hours	temperature, °C	Solvent	substituted	Physical properties	Ref.
Hydrazine	5	150	—	3	M.p. 287°. Sol. hot H_2O, but insol. cold dil. acid	1
Methylamine (hydrochloride)	6	190–195	—	2	M.p. 260–262° (dec.)	2, 3
Methylamine (hydrochloride)	6	190–195	—	3	M.p. 130°	2, 3
Dimethylamine (hydrochloride)	—	180	—	1	M.p. 307–308°	2, 3
Dimethylamine (hydrochloride)	—	180	—	2	M.p. 222°	2, 3
Octadecylamine	4	200–210	—	2	M.p. 72–75. Cryst. ethyl alc.	2, 3
Aniline (hydrochloride)	5	180–190	—	3	M.p. 225°. Cryst. n-butanol	2, 3
Tetraethylenepentamine (hydrochloride)	24	220	—	—	—	4
Phenylhydrazine	16	160	—	1	White, flaky crystals; cryst. from H_2O. Sublimes > 290°	5
o-, m-, and p-Aminophenols	18	180–190	Diethylene glycol	1, 2, or 3 as desired	Sol. hot water	6
o-, m-, and p-Aminocresols	18	180–190	Diethylene glycol	1, 2, or 3 as desired	Sol. hot water	6
o-, m-, and p-Carbomethoxyanilines	17	180–200	—	1, 2, or 3 as desired	M.p. 250°. Cryst. H_2O	7
m- and p-Carbethoxyanilines	—	—	—	2	—	7
o-, m-, and p-Aminophenylbenzoates	—	—	—	1	—	7
Sulfanilamide	6	160	Ethylene glycol	1	M.p. 250°. Cryst from H_2O	8

[a] In addition to the list above, the following amines have also been reported to react with melamine to give similar products (Ref. 8 below) whose physical properties have not been indicated: Hydroxybromoanilines, hydroxychloroanilines, hydroxynaphthylamines, hydroxytoluidines, hydroxylidines, and hydroxyxenylamines.

1. R. Stolle and K. Kranch, *Ber.*, **46**, 2337 (1913).
2. Brit. 496,690 (1938) to I.G. Farbenind.
3. W. Zerweck and K. Keller, U. S. 2,228,161 (1941) to I.G. Farbenind.
4. J. Dudley, U. S. 2,467,523 (1949) to American Cyanamid Co.

5. Brit. 596,286 (1948) to Brit. Thomson-Houston Co. Ltd.
6. G. D'Alelio, U. S. 2,393,755 (1946) to General Electric Co.
7. G. D'Alelio and J. Underwood, U. S. 2,328,961 (1943) to General Electric Co.
8. G. D'Alelio, U. S. 2,312,698 (1943) to General Electric Co.

equivalents of ammonia as a byproduct. Table VI-8 lists amines which have been utilized in this condensation reaction (32).

Often several different compounds are formed in the same reaction even when a strict stoichiometric reactant ratio is used. For example, equimolar quantities of melamine and octadecylamine hydrochloride produce[140] mixtures of mono- and dioctadecylmelamine (31). In the

$$2 \; H_2N{-}\overset{N}{\underset{N \; N}{\bigodot}}{-}NH_2 \;\; (NH_2) + 2\,C_{18}H_{37}NH_2 \cdot HCl \xrightarrow{\text{4 hrs. 200–218}} H_2N{-}\overset{N}{\underset{N \; N}{\bigodot}}{-}NH_2 \;(NHC_{18}H_{37}) + H_2N{-}\overset{N}{\underset{N \; N}{\bigodot}}{-}NHC_{18}H_{37} \;(NHC_{18}H_{37}) + 2\,NH_3 \quad (31)$$

few instances in which they have been used, low molecular weight secondary amines react[140] with equal facility at least for the introduction of the first alkyl group (32). Hydrazine reacts readily with

$$(I) + 2/3\,(CH_3)NH \cdot HCl \xrightarrow{180°} H_2N{-}\overset{N}{\underset{N \; N}{\bigodot}}{-}N(CH_3)_2 \;(NH_2) + H_2N{-}\overset{N}{\underset{N \; N}{\bigodot}}{-}N(CH_3)_2 \;(N(CH_3)_2) \quad (32)$$

trace

melamine (33) at relatively mild temperatures substituting at all three amino groups.[87] 2,4,6-Triaminomelamine or 2,4,6-trihydrazino-s-triazine is not soluble in dilute acids, but can be dissolved by hot water. The compound reduces Tollen's reagent. It behaves like an aromatic hydrazine in a number of ways; with benzaldehyde, a tribenzylidine

$$(I) + 3\,NH_2NH_2 \xrightarrow{\text{5 hrs. 150°}} 3\,NH_3 + H_2NNH{-}\overset{N}{\underset{N \; N}{\bigodot}}{-}NHNH_2 \;(NHNH_2) \xrightarrow{3\,C_6H_5CHO}$$

$$C_6H_5CH{=}NN{\overset{H}{{-}}}\overset{N}{\underset{N \; N}{\bigodot}}{-}NHN{=}CHC_6H_5 \;(NHN{=}CHC_6H_5) + 3\,H_2O \quad (33)$$

derivative is obtained (33). Melamine and aniline hydrochloride react to give triphenylmelamine, m.p. 225°, but if, instead, melamine hydrochloride is treated with aniline, the product is reported to be mostly triphenylisomelamine,[140] m.p. 185°, together with traces of di- and triphenylmelamines. The *iso* compound is soluble in ether while the normal compound is not. This work is viewed with some skepticism.

One would expect the same distribution of hydrogen chloride between the two bases, regardless of how it was introduced, and therefore the same product.

13. Cyanates and Isocyanates

Melamine reacts with isocyanates and isothiocyanates. Only one amino group reacts readily and the products are 2-ureido-4,6-diamino-s-triazines or their sulfur analogs.[141] The preparation of mono-, di-, and

$$H_2N \underset{N \quad N}{\overset{N}{\diagdown}} Cl + NaNHCONHR \longrightarrow H_2N \underset{N \quad N}{\overset{N}{\diagdown}} NHCONHR + NaCl$$

$$\underset{NH_2}{\qquad\qquad\qquad\qquad\qquad\qquad\qquad NH_2} \tag{34}$$

triureidomelamines is an extension (34) of this reaction and is accomplished by treating halo-s-triazines or haloamino-s-triazines with sodium salts of ureas.[141] These compounds are listed and discussed further in Section VI, "Substituted Melamines."

14. Miscellaneous Reactions

Melamine has been said[109] to cause hydrolysis of ethyl bromide or ethyl iodide when heated with water and either halide for eight hours. Ethanol is the product and the melamine can be isolated as the hydrogen halide salt. With benzyl chloride and melamine in Cellosolve, the products are benzyl Cellosolve and melamine hydrochloride.

Melamine undergoes reaction with such substances[142] as cellulose, sugars, glycols, hydroxy containing compounds etc., usually with formaldehyde present as well. It is likely that methylolmelamines form, and these substances react rather than melamine. The products are resinous materials with one reported[143a] exception. Glucose and two moles of melamine are said[142a] to react (35) in dilute alcohol solution to give a

$$2 \; H_2N \underset{N \quad N}{\overset{N}{\diagdown}} NH_2 + \begin{array}{c} HO \\ | \\ HC \longrightarrow \\ | \\ (CHOH)_3 \\ | \\ HC \longrightarrow \\ | \\ CH_2OH \end{array} \xrightarrow[\text{33\% alcohol}]{\text{5 hrs. 95°}} H_2N \underset{N \quad N}{\overset{N}{\diagdown}} NH-CH-NH \underset{N \quad N}{\overset{N}{\diagdown}} NH_2 + H_2O$$

$$\underset{NH_2}{\qquad} \qquad \underset{CH_2OH}{\overset{(CHOH)_4}{|}} \qquad \underset{NH_2}{\qquad} \tag{35}$$

M.p. 281°/Ethyl alc.–H_2O

product which, on recrystallization from an alcohol-water mixture, melts at 281°, does not reduce Fehling's solution, and turns brown in ultraviolet light. According to Radlburger,[142a] the structure is probably one in which the aldehyde function in the glucose molecule reacts to give a methylol derivative which can then lose a molecule of water in combining with a second molecule of melamine. While reaction (37) is possible and has remained unchallenged in the literature for many years, it is of highly doubtful authenticity. Many attempts[49] to prepare glucosylidenedimelamine by the original and modified methods have met with a complete lack of success.

V. Structure

The structure of melamine has been a subject of controversy for many years. Many of the early workers in the field believed it had the triamino structure (I) or else did not assign a definite structure to the

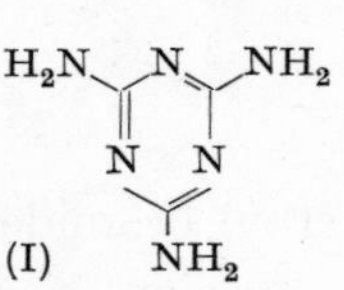

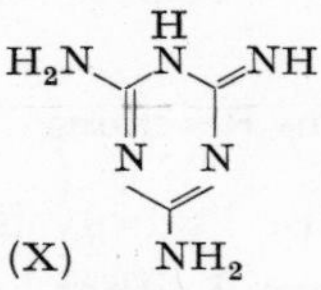

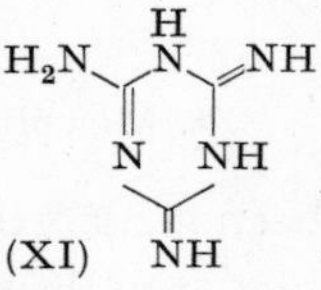

molecule. In 1901, Hartley and co-workers studied the ultraviolet absorption spectra of cyanuric acid, melamine and some substituted melamines.[143] The failure of these compounds to show specific absorption bands was cited as evidence against aromatic structures such as (I).

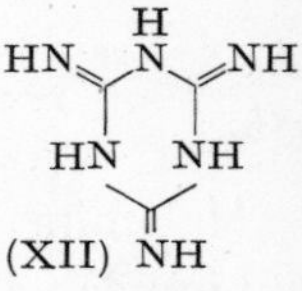

Barnett[97] proposed an imine structure, (XIII), to account for the fact that melamine adds three moles of hydrogen chloride slowly. He also

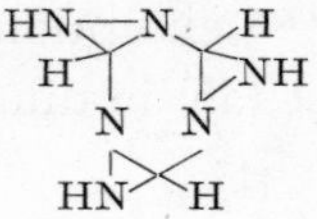

(XIII)

believed the above structure explained anomalies in Van Slyke nitrogen determinations on the free base and on the trihydrochloride. Ostrogovitch[98] preferred to consider the monoamino structure (XI) as an explanation of the ease of reaction with one equivalent of acid.

Detailed X-ray diffraction studies of melamine crystals[4,5] have shown that it exists as a coplanar molecule having three conjugated double bonds analogous to those in benzene.

The infrared spectrum is compatible with such a structure, and more recent ultraviolet studies of melamine solutions and gaseous melamine lend added weight to the symmetrical "amino" structure.[7,8,144] The weak band at 2950 Å was attributed to a singlet-triplet transition analogous to that of the 3400 Å absorption band of benzene. The strong absorption bands observed in the s-triazines in the 2200–2500 Å region were believed to correspond to the 2600 Å bands of benzene. Similarities of the melamine spectrum to that of cyanuric chloride, which can exist only in the aromatic form, were also cited.

Measurements of the dissociation constant of melamine, and the isomeric monoethyl melamines further substantiate the aromatic struc-

Ethylmelamine
$K_b = 1.7 \times 10^{-9}$

Ethylisomelamine
$K_b = 3.5 \times 10^{-4}$

ture for melamine.[145] Ethylisomelamine is a stronger base by a factor of 10^5 than normal ethylmelamine. Thus melamine, whose dissociation constant is 1×10^{-9}, must exist in the weakly basic normal form rather than as one of the isomeric iso structures.

VI. Substituted "Normal" Melamines

"Normal" melamines are distinguished from the isomelamines by the location of the substituent groups. The "normal" compounds have substitution on the amino groups of melamine (XIV) while the iso compounds have ring substitution (XV). These forms are sometimes

(XIV) "normal"

(XV) "iso"

called "exo" and "eso" respectively. Of course, as is true of other s-triazines, tautomeric structures may be written. The principal distinguishing characteristics of the two structures is the greater basicity of the isomelamines, and the fact that on hydrolysis they are converted to isocyanurates and ammonia, while the normal melamines yield cyanuric acid and an amine.

$$\text{RHN}-\underset{\underset{\text{NHR}}{\overset{\text{N}}{\vert}}}{\overset{\text{N}}{\underset{\text{N}}{\vert}}}-\text{NHR} \xrightarrow[\varDelta]{\text{H}_2\text{O HCl}} \text{HO}-\underset{\underset{\text{OH}}{\vert}}{\overset{\text{N}}{\vert}}-\text{OH} + 3\text{ RNH}_2$$

$$\text{HN}-\underset{\underset{\text{NH}}{\overset{\text{R}}{\vert}}}{\overset{\text{R}}{\underset{}{\vert}}}-\text{NH} \xrightarrow[\varDelta]{\text{H}_2\text{O HCl}} \text{O}-\underset{\underset{\text{O}}{\vert}}{\overset{\text{R}}{\vert}}-\text{O} + 3\text{ NH}_3$$

The first synthesis of a substituted melamine was carried out by Weith in 1874.[146] He was attempting to prepare tetraphenylguanidine by reaction of cyanogen chloride with diphenylamine. Instead he obtained a product which was a trimer of diphenylcyanamide, probably N^2,N^4,N^6-hexaphenylmelamine (XVI). Ciamician and Dennstedt[147] obtained similar results using pyrrole instead of diphenylamine.

$$3\ (\text{C}_6\text{H}_5)_2\text{NH} + 3\ \text{CNCl} \longrightarrow 3\ (\text{C}_6\text{H}_5)_2\text{NCN} \longrightarrow (\text{C}_6\text{H}_5)_2\text{N}-\underset{\underset{\text{N}(\text{C}_6\text{H}_5)_2}{\vert}}{\overset{\text{N}}{\vert}}-\text{N}(\text{C}_6\text{H}_5)_2$$

$$\text{(XVI)}$$

In 1885 Hofmann[53] prepared N^2,N^4,N^6-trimethylmelamine by reaction of trimethylthiocyanurate with methylamine, and by treating cyanuric chloride with methylamine. These preparations served to relate the substituted melamines to the other members of the s-triazine family.

Since this early work a considerable number of substituted melamines have been prepared, many of them during the 1940's. Several synthetic methods were developed which allowed the preparation of a wide variety of compounds.

1. Preparative Methods

A. From Chloro-s-Triazines

The most widely applicable and most convenient synthetic method for substituted melamines is that based on the reaction of cyanuric chloride (or cyanuric bromide) or a chloroamino-s-triazine with ammonia or an amine. This approach, which was first used by Hofmann in 1885,[53] allows the preparation of mono-, di-, and trisubstituted melamines, symmetrically or asymmetrically substituted. The various permutations are illustrated in simplified form in the equations below.

Indeed, in 1899 Diels[148] prepared N²-methyl-N⁴-ethylmelamine by three of the routes available from cyanuric chloride and showed that the three products were identical.

The most detailed description of this route to substituted melamines is found in the work of Banks[149] and Kaiser[150] and their colleagues. Both of these groups preferred to use a water suspension of cyanuric chloride or the aminochloro-s-triazine. It was desirable to have an acceptor for the hydrogen chloride liberated. This was either an excess of amine, or an inorganic base. Since, in most cases the aryl melamines are stronger bases than the arylamine, no acid acceptor was needed in their preparations. The melamines were usually formed at temperatures of 80–100° C., but with increasing bulkiness of substituent groups, temperatures above 100° C and long reaction times were required for melamine formation. The most strongly basic amine should be used in the final step in the preparation of unsymmetrically substituted melamines. In general, good to excellent yields of melamines can be obtained by this route.

In a few cases the melamine is formed directly at low temperatures. Thus Wystrach, Kaiser and Schaefer[151] obtained N^2,N^4,N^6-tris-(ethyleneimino)-s-triazine (XVII) by the reaction of ethyleneimine with cyanuric chloride at 5° C.

(XVII)

When diamines and triamines are used, bis and trismelamines result.[150,152] Hydrazine and phenylhydrazine have been employed

successfully to give 2,4,6-tris(hydrazino)-s-triazine (triaminomelamine) and 2,4,6-tris(phenylhydrazino)-s-triazine.[153] In these cases cyanuric bromide was used.

In a few examples alkali metal salts of amino compounds were treated with cyanuric chloride to give the substituted melamine. This was the case with urea[140] and substituted cyanamides.[154]

With cyanuric chloride commercially available, this synthesis is the preferred route to substituted melamines.

$$\text{(triazine with } H_2N, N, Cl; \; N N; \; NH_2) + NaHNCONH_2 \longrightarrow \text{(triazine with } H_2N, N, NHCONH_2; \; N N; \; NH_2)$$

$$\text{(triazine with } Cl, N, Cl; \; N N; \; Cl) + 3\,C_6H_5NCN \;(K) \longrightarrow \text{(triazine with } C_6H_5N(CN), N, NNC_6H_5(CN); \; N N; \; NC_6H_5, CN)$$

B. Reaction of Cyanoguanidine with Substituted Cyanamides

Kaiser[155] prepared a series of N^2-substituted melamines by the reaction of disubstituted cyanamides with cyanoguanidine. This synthesis may be regarded as analogous to the preparation of 2,4-

$$R_2NCN + H_2NCNHCN\ (\|\,NH) \longrightarrow \text{(triazine with } H_2N, N, NR_2; \; N N; \; NH_2)$$

diamino-s-triazines from nitriles and cyanoguanidine. The reaction was carried out in the presence of a basic catalyst at 90–110° C. When a substituted cyanoguanidine was used, an N^2,N^4-disubstituted melamine resulted. In most cases mono-substituted cyanamides (perhaps because

$$R_2NCN + R'HNCNHCN\ (\|\,NH) \longrightarrow \text{(triazine with } H_2N, N, NR_2; \; N N; \; NHR')$$

of their ease of polymerization) do not yield substituted melamines. However, Kaiser was able to prepare N^2-isopropylmelamine by the reaction of isopropylcyanamide with cyanoguanidine. Bortnick[156] prepared a series of N^2-substituted melamines using tertiary alkyl cyanamides

$$(R_2-\overset{\overset{\displaystyle R_1}{|}}{\underset{\underset{\displaystyle R_3}{|}}{C}}-NHCN).$$

Zerweck and Bruner[157] carried out the reaction of substituted cyanamides with cyanoguanidine, in the absence of a catalyst at 200–205° C.

A special application was in the preparation of 2,4-diamino-6-
cyanamino-s-triazine from sodium dicyanimide.[158]

$$NaN(CN)_2 + H_2NCNHCN \xrightarrow{\quad\quad}$$

(with structural formulas)

A similar reaction probably occurred in the work of Gupta and
Guha.[159] They heated p-chlorophenylbiguanide with p-chlorophenylcya-
namide and obtained N^2,N^4-bis(p-chlorophenyl)melamine. It is possible
that under their reaction conditions some p-chlorophenylcyanoguanidine

$$ClC_6H_4NHCNHCNH_2 + ClC_6H_4NHCN \xrightarrow{\quad\quad} \quad + NH_3$$

(with structural formulas)

was formed. An alternate course would have been through intermediate
formation of a triguanide which cyclized with loss of ammonia.

An interesting variation was described by de Benneville.[160] Using
the reaction of N-cyanoaminonitriles with two moles of cyanoguanidine they obtained bis(amino-s-triazines) which may be regarded
as both substituted melamines and substituted 2,4-diamino-s-triazines.

(with structural formulas)

$$R_1-N-C-CN + 2H_2NCNHCN \xrightarrow{\quad\quad}$$

C. From s-Triazines other than Chloro-s-Triazines

Substituted melamines may be prepared by replacement of groups
other than chlorine atoms on the s-triazine ring.

Hofmann[53] showed at an early date that alkylthio groups on
cyanuric thioesters could be replaced by ammonia or amines. He

(with structural formulas)

$$+ 3R_1R_2NH \xrightarrow{\quad\quad} \quad + 3CH_3SH$$

(XVIII)

prepared trimethyl, triethyl, and tripyridyl melamines by long heating of trimethylthiocyanurate (XVIII) with the amine. Similarly, D'Alelio and Pyle[161] heated thioammeline (XIX) with amines and obtained substituted melamines.

Thurston and his colleagues[162] studied the preparation of substituted melamines by reaction of alkoxy-s-triazines with amines. They found that in the case of the alkoxy derivatives a competing reaction occurred leading to the hydroxy-s-triazines (see Chapter 5). The aryloxy-s-triazines reacted smoothly with amines and this reaction was used for the preparation of certain substituted melamines which were difficult to isolate by the cyanuric chloride route.

Mackay and Paden[163] showed that the hydroxyl groups of ammeline, ammelide, and cyanuric acid could be replaced with amines to yield mono-, di- and trisubstituted melamines. The reactions were carried out under pressure at 350° C.

The displacement of ammonia from melamine by reaction with an amino compound was first carried out by Stolle and Krauch.[86] They heated melamine with hydrazine at 150° C. for five hours and obtained N^2,N^4,N^6-triaminomelamine. Zerweck and Keller[139] were able to prepare mono-, di- and trisubstituted melamines by heating varying ratios of amine hydrochlorides with melamine. This reaction has been described in the patent literature as a route to a variety of arylsubstituted melamines.[136,164,165] It is interesting to note that when Zerweck and

$$H_2N\text{-}(triazine)\text{-}NH_2 + 2\,CH_3NH_2 \cdot HCl \longrightarrow H_2N\text{-}(triazine)\text{-}NHCH_3 + 2\,NH_4Cl$$

Keller heated melamine hydrochloride with aniline the product was N^1,N^3,N^5-triphenylisomelamine, whereas when they used melamine and aniline hydrochloride they obtained the normal melamine. This work has not been confirmed by other investigators.

$$H_2N\text{-}(triazine)\text{-}NH_2 + 3\,C_6H_5NH_2 \cdot HCl \longrightarrow C_6H_5HN\text{-}(triazine)\text{-}NHC_6H_5$$

$$H_2N\text{-}(triazine)\text{-}NH_2 \cdot HCl + 3\,C_6H_5NH_2 \longrightarrow (isomelamine\ structure)$$

The use of the reaction between an aromatic compound containing an activated halogen atom and melamine to produce a substituted melamine has been disclosed.[123]

$$H_2N\text{-}(triazine)\text{-}NH_2 + Cl\text{-}C_6H_3(NO_2)\text{-}SbO_3H_2 \longrightarrow H_2N\text{-}(triazine)\text{-}NH\text{-}C_6H_3(NO_2)\text{-}SbO_3H_2 + HCl$$

An interesting class of substituted melamine are the guanyl-melamines prepared by Kaiser and Redmon.[166] They treated N^2-cyanomelamine with a series of amines to obtain the substituted guanyl-melamines (XX).

$$H_2N\text{-}(triazine)\text{-}NHCN + RNH_2 \longrightarrow H_2N\text{-}(triazine)\text{-}NHC(=NH)NHR \quad (XX)$$

The preparation of other melamine derivatives, such as the acylated derivatives and aldehyde condensation products, by direct reaction of melamine is discussed under melamine reactions (see section IV).

D. Cyanoguanidine plus Amines

The reaction of amines with cyanoguanidine at temperatures of 120–250° C can lead in some instances to substituted melamines.[167] Usually a mixture of melamine and mono-, di- and trisubstituted derivatives is obtained. It is possible that this synthesis proceeds via the intermediate formation of melamine.

E. Dicyanoguanidine plus Amines

Nagy[168, 169] showed that when 1,3-dicyanoguanidine was heated with an amine under strongly acidic conditions (pH < 1), good yields of N^2-substituted melamines were obtained. The reaction was applied to primary

$$R_2NH + CNNHC{=}NHCN \longrightarrow$$
$$\underset{NH_2}{|}$$

and secondary aromatic amines and secondary aliphatic amines.[171] At neutral pH's, primary amines yield the isomelamines[170] (see Section VIII).

F. Polymerization of Substituted Cyanamides

Just as melamine may be regarded as the cyclic trimer of cyanamide, a symmetrically trisubstituted melamine is a trimer of a substituted cyanamide. The trimerization of monosubstituted cyanamides is usually considered to yield isomelamines (see Section VIII), while disubstituted cyanamides yield normal melamines. In many cases rigorous structure proof for the reaction products has not been offered. Weith[146] heated the reaction mixture of cyanogen chloride with diphenylamine and, instead of the desired tetraphenylguanidine, obtained a trimer of diphenylcyanamide, probably N^2,N^4,N^6, hexaphenyl-

$$3\ (C_6H_5)_2NH + 3\ CNCl \longrightarrow$$

melamine. The same compound was obtained when N^1,N^3-tetraphenyl-guanidine was heated with hydrochloric acid at 280–300° C.

$$(C_6H_5)_2NCN(C_6H_5)_2 \xrightarrow[280-300°C]{HCl} (C_6H_5)_2NH \cdot HCl +$$
$$\underset{NH}{|}$$

Nadelung and Kern[172] heated the sodium salt of dicyanimide and obtained the trisodium salt of N^2,N^4,N^6-tricyanomelamine (XXI).

$$3 \, NaN(CN)_2 \longrightarrow$$

During a study of the reaction of aryl substituted ureas with aryl-sulfonyl chlorides, Kurtzer[173] observed that in addition to the expected arylsulfonylarylcyanamides, the reaction products contained variable amounts of s-triazines. The s-triazines were formed only from ortho-

$$ArNHCONH_2 + Ar'SO_2Cl \longrightarrow Ar'SO_2NCN + HCl + H_2O$$
$$\qquad\qquad\qquad\qquad\qquad\qquad Ar$$

substituted ureas. He postulated that an intermediate unstable isourea was obtained which spontaneously decomposed to a substituted cyanamide and a sulfonic acid. The ortho aryl-substituted cyanamides polymerized before they could react with the excess sulfonyl chloride.

The substituted melamines which were found had the normal melamine structure.

G. Isomerization of Isomelamines

Thurston[138] showed that N^1-substituted isomelamines could be isomerized to the N^2-substituted normal melamines when heated in solution at 100° C. in the presence of a basic catalyst. This interconversion of iso and normal melamine has utility in cases where the isomelamine is easily synthesized from dicyanoguanidine and an amine. It also may help explain the results obtained by Kurtzer (see above).

$$\underset{\text{HN}}{\text{HN}}\overset{\overset{\text{R}}{\underset{\text{HN}}{\text{N}}}}{\underset{\text{NH}}{\text{NH}}} \quad \xrightarrow[100°C]{OCH_3^-} \quad H_2N\underset{\text{N N}}{\overset{\text{N}}{\underset{\text{NH}_2}{\text{NHR}}}}$$

H. Miscellaneous Syntheses

Mackay and Paden,[174] who heated melam with butylamine and aniline, reported obtaining mixtures of the mono- and disubstituted melamines. The same workers obtained substituted melamines as the products of reaction of urea with amines at 350–500° C. Melamine may have been an intermediate in these reactions.

Hantzsch and Bauer[175] heated urea to 130–200° C and in addition to cyanuric acid obtained a compound which they believed to be 2,4,6-tris(ureido)-s-triazine (XXII). They prepared the same compound by reaction of cyanuric bromide with urea.

$$H_2NCONH_2 \quad \xrightarrow{\Delta} \quad H_2NCOHN\underset{\text{N N}}{\overset{\text{N}}{\underset{\text{NHCONH}_2}{\text{NHCONH}_2}}}$$

$$(XXII) \quad NHCONH_2$$

MacLean[176] studied, in some detail, the reaction of cyanoguanidine with anhydrous inorganic acids. He found that it was possible to obtain varying amounts of mono-, di- and tri-guanyl melamines de-

$$2\,H_2NCNHCN \underset{\text{NH}}{\overset{\|}{}} \quad \xrightarrow{HX} \quad H_2N\underset{\text{N N}}{\overset{\text{N}}{\underset{\text{NH}_2}{}}}\underset{\text{NH}}{\overset{\text{NHCNH}_2}{\overset{\|}{}}}$$

pending upon reaction conditions. Under the most favorable conditions use of a pyridine-nitrobenzene solvent mixture, 85–90% yields of monoguanylmelamine could be obtained. The same compound was also prepared by reaction of N²-cyanomelamine with ammonium formate.[177]

A listing of substituted melamines which have been reasonably well characterized is found in Table VI-9.

TABLE VI-9. A. N²-Substituted Melamines

$$H_2N \begin{array}{c} N \\ N \end{array} N\begin{array}{c} R_1 \\ R_2 \end{array}$$

with NH_2 substituent on ring

R_1	R_2	M.p. °C.	Preparative method[a]	Yield %
H	C_2H_5	171–2	A	96
H	iso C_3H_7	216–8	C	—
H	C_4H_9	167–9	A	90
		160–2	D	
			H	
		180–5	I	
			J	
H	iso C_4H_9	160–6	I	
H	tert C_4H_9	156–8	C	82
H	$(CH_3)_3CCH_2C(CH_3)_2$	160–2	C	68
H	$C_{12}H_{25}$	110	D	100
H	$C_8H_{17}(C_2H_5)_2$	—	C	—
H	$CH_2\begin{array}{c} CH_2-CH_2 \\ CH_2-CH_2 \end{array}C\begin{array}{c} \\ CH_3 \end{array}$	—	C	72
H	CN	infusible	C	87
H	$CONH_2$	> 280	A, F	
H	$NH_2C \atop \parallel \atop NH$	258–60 (picrate)	F	32
		240–1	M	
H	$C_4H_9NHC \atop \parallel \atop NH$	217–8	F	50
H	$C_{12}H_{25}NHC \atop \parallel \atop NH$	paste	F	—
H	$CH_2\begin{array}{c} CH_2-CH_2 \\ CH_2-CH_2 \end{array}CHNHC \atop \parallel \atop NH$	217–9	F	—
H	$C_6H_5NHC \atop \parallel \atop NH$	249–50/methoxyethanol	F	91
H	$4'ClC_6H_4NHC \atop \parallel \atop NH$	260–1	F	—
H	$3'CF_3C_6H_4NHC \atop \parallel \atop NH$	253–4	F	61
H	$C_6H_5CH_2NHC \atop \parallel \atop NH$	228–30	F	—

(Table conti

BLE VI-9 (*continued*)

R_2	M.p. °C.	Preparative method[a]	Yield %	Ref.
$4'NH_3SO_2C_6H_4NHC$ $\parallel$ NH	272 (dec.)	F	52	10
$2,5Cl_2C_6H_3NHC$ $\parallel$ NH	270	F	54	10
CH_3 $\mid$ C_6H_5NC $\parallel$ NH	305 (dec.) HCl salt)	F	85	10
$HOCH_2CH_2$	223–5	D	90	3
$(C_2H_5)_2NCH_2CH_2CH_2$	132	A	71	11
$(C_2H_5)_2NCH_2CH_2CH_2CH_2$	241	A	74	11
$CH_2\langle{CH_2-CH_2 \atop CH_2-CH_2}\rangle NCH_2CH_2CH_2$	152.5–3.5	A	83	11
$O\langle{CH_2-CH_2 \atop CH_2-CH_2}\rangle NCH_2CH_2CH_2$	163–4	A	65	11
$H_2N(CH_2)_6$	154	A	78	11
C_6H_5	284, 204	A	82	1, 12, 13, 14
		B	62–75	61
		D	95	3
		G		2, 5
		H		4
		J		6
$2'CH_3C_6H_4$	211–2/ethanol-H_2O	A	81	12
$3'CH_3C_6H_4$	229–30	A	82	12
$4'CH_3C_6H_4$	265–6	A	80	12
$2',4'(CH_3)_2C_6H_3$	239–41	A	92	12
$2',5'(CH_3)_2C_6H_3$	237–39	A	89	12
$2'C_6H_5C_6H_4$	191–3	A	98	1
$2'ClC_6H_4$	205–8	A	81	12
$3'ClC_6H_4$	173–5	A	98	12
$4'ClC_6H_4$	245–9	A	82	12
$2'HOC_6H_4$	257–9	A	87	12
$3'HOC_6H_4$	241–2	A	76	12
$4'HOC_6H_4$	282–3	A	88	12
		E	—	15
$2'C_2H_5OC_6H_4$	203–5	A	76	12
$3'C_2H_5OC_6H_4$	211–12	A	82	12
$2'NO_2C_6H_4$	300	A	—	12
$3'NO_2C_6H_4$	144–5	A	99	12

(*Table continued*)

TABLE VI-9 (*continued*)

R_1	R_2	M.p. °C.	Preparative method[a]	Yield %	Ref.
H	$4'NO_2C_6H_4$	318	A, D	—	3, 1
H	$4'NH_2C_6H_4$	232–5	B	61.5	61
H	$2'HOOCC_6H_4$	—	A	42	12
H	$3'HOOCC_6H_4$	304–6	A	42	12
H	$4'HOOCC_6H_4$	300	A	68	12
H	$2'CH_3OOCC_6H_4$	>250	E	—	40
H	$4'CH_3OOCC_6H_4$	—	A	98	12
H	$4'NH_2SO_2C_6H_4$	253	E	—	16
H	$4'OAsC_6H_4$	300–350 (dec.)		48	17
H	$4'H_2O_3AsC_6H_4$	300–350 (dec.)	A	57	1, 1
					1
			D	74	3
H	$3'Cl_2SbC_6H_4$		A	—	21
H	$3'OSbC_6H_4$		A	—	21
H	$4'H_2O_3SbC_6H_4$	250 (dec.)	A	40	21,
H	$4'(HOCH_2CH_2S)_2SbC_6H_4$	—	A	—	21,
H	$4'(4''NH_2C_6H_4SO_2)C_6H_4$	240–5	A	—	65
H	$2',4'Cl_2C_6H_3$	255–7	A	86	12
H	$2',5'Cl_2C_6H_3$	228–30	A	84	12
		223–5	B	—	3
H	$3',5'Cl_2C_6H_3$	210–11	4	98	12
H	$3'-H_2O_3As, 4'-OHC_6H_3$	300–350 (dec.)	A	58	17
H	$2'-OH, 4'H_2O_3AsC_6H_3$	300–350 (dec.)	A	49	17
H	$2'OH, 5'Cl_2AsC_6H_3$	300–350 (dec.)	F		19,
H	$2'OH, 5'OAsC_6H_3$	300–350 (dec.)	F		25
H	$2'OH, 5'Cl_2SbC_6H_3$	—	A		21,
H	$2'OH, 5'H_2O_3SbC_6H_3$	—	A		24
H	$\alpha C_{10}H_7$	223	A	—	66
H	$\beta C_{10}H_7$	>300	A	75	12
H	(structure: quinoline with CH₃, OCH₃ substituents)	180 (dec.) (HCl salt)	A		26
H	(structure: 4-amino quinoline with CH₃, CH₃ substituents)	267	A	—	29
H	C_6H_5NH	290 sublimes	E		27
H	$4'HOC_6H_4SO_2$	>360	F		28
CH_3	CH_3	307–8 (214)	C	81	2,
		307–8	E	—	31
			I	—	5

(*Table c*

LE VI-9 (*continued*)

R₂	M.p. °C.	Preparative method[a]	Yield %	Ref.
————CH₂	220 (dec.)	A	34	55b.
C₂H₅	168–70	A	93	1
	—	B	—	62
	177–8	C	74	2
	254	C	75	63
C₄H₉	134–5	B	—	62
		G	—	32
=CHCH₂ CH₂=CHCH₂	144–5	C	75	2
CH₂ ————CH₂	295–7	A	75	33
CH₂ —CH₂———CH₂	{ 216–7,222–3	A	22, 75	12, 33
	210	C	84	30
CH₂ —O———CH₂	{ 236–40, 256–2	A	48, 79	12, 33
	251–2	C	93	2
CH₂ —N———CH₂	263–71	A	—	33
C₆H₅	{ 257–9	A	97	12
		B		62
	248–50 (240–2)	C	78, 98	2, 30, 63
C₆H₅	215–7	A	94	12
CH₂ C₆H₅	311–4	A	99	12
CH₂ C₆H₅CH₂	222–3, 217–8	C	73, 85	2, 30
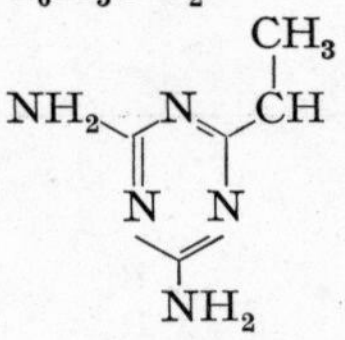 *structure (triazine with CH₃, CH, NH₂)*	320	C	44	34
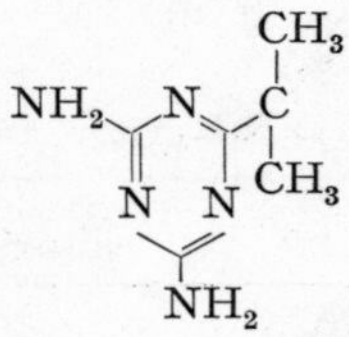 *structure (triazine with CH₃, C, CH₃, NH₂)*	430–35	C	70	34
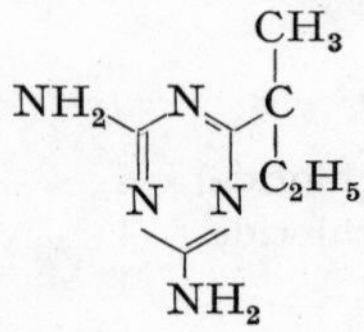 *structure (triazine with CH₃, C, C₂H₅, NH₂)*	>290	C	56	34

(Table continued)

TABLE VI-9 (*continued*)

R_1	R_2	M.p. °C.	Preparative method[a]	Yield %
CH_3	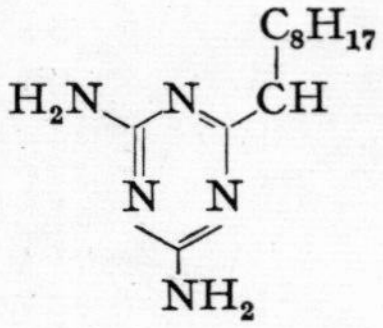	256–8	C	55
C_4H_9	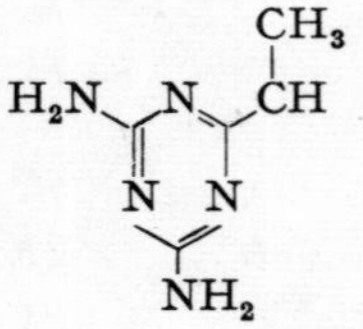	210–11	C	48
C_4H_9	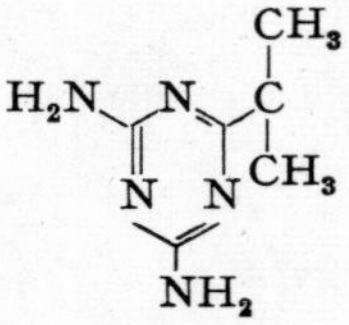	271–2	C	48
C_8H_{17}	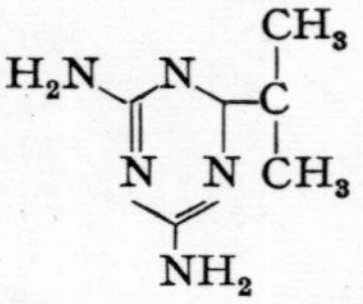	243–6	C	37

B. N^2,N^4-Disubstituted Melamines – Like Substitution

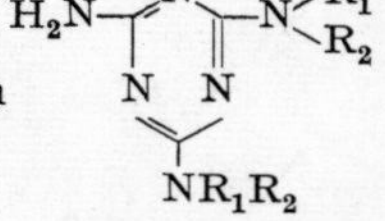

R_1	R_2	M.p. °C.	Preparative method[a]	Yield %
H	CH_3	—	A	—
		260–2 (dec.)	E	
H	C_2H_5	156–8	A	91
H	n-C_4H_9	245–7 (Hydrochloride)	I	—
H	isoC_4H_9	230–5 (Hydrochloride)	I	—
H	$C_{17}H_{35}$	72–5	E	—

(*Table co*

LE VI-9B (*continued*)

R_2	M.p. °C.	Preparative method[a]	Yield %	Ref.
$CNCH_2$	220	A	80	1
H_2NC ‖ NH	297–8 (picrate)	M	—	67
$HOCH_2CH_2$	160–1	A	86	1
		K	—	37
$HOCH_2CH_2CH_2$	110–112	A	—	1
$CH_2\langle \overset{CH_2-CH_2}{CH_2-CH_2} \rangle NCH_2CH_2CH_2$	78–80	A	47	11
C_6H_5	216–18, 219-20	A	75–80, 96	1, 13
$4'ClC_6H_4$	276–9, 284–5, (Hydrochloride)	A, C		38, 39
$4'CH_3OC_6H_4$	202–3	A		38
$4'C_2H_5OC_6H_4$	269–70 (Hydrochloride)	A	87	1
$2CH_3OOCC_6H_4$	—	E	—	40
$4NH_2SO_2C_6H_4$	—	A	—	16
[structure: 4-amino-6-methylquinoline]	235 (dec.)	A	—	41
[structure: 4-amino-2,6-dimethylquinoline]	245	A	—	29
[structure: 4-amino-2,3-dimethyl-6-methylquinoline]	220 (dec.)	A	—	41
[structure: 4-amino-2-methyl-6-methyl-7-methoxyquinoline]	>305	A	—	29
CH_3	222	E	trace	31
	220–22	I	—	5
——CH_2	231 (dec.)	A	65	70
C_2H_5	71–2	A	97	1
I$_2CH_2$ $HOCH_2CH_2$	128–9	A	100	1
—O——$\overset{CH_2}{\underset{|}{CH_2}}$	170	A	100	1
C_6H_5	166–7	A	98	1
I$_2CH_2$ C_6H_5	158–9	A	10	12

C. N^2,N^4-Disubstituted Melamines – Unlike Substitution

Structure:

$$H_2N\text{—}\underset{\displaystyle NR_3R_4}{\underset{|}{\text{triazine}}}\begin{matrix}\nearrow R_1\\ N\\ \searrow R_2\end{matrix}$$

R_1	R_2	R_3	R_4	M.p. °C.	Preparative method[a]	Yield %	Ref.
H	CH_3	H	C_2H_5	176	A	75	42
H	CH_3	H	C_6H_5	84–6	A	48	12
H	CH_3	H	$4'H_2O_3AsC_6H_4$	>300	A	64	17
H	C_2H_5	H	C_6H_5	153–5	A	49	12
H	iso C_3H_7	H	$4'ClC_6H_4$	166	A	—	26, 38
H	$CH_2=C(CH_3)CH_2$	H	$4'CH_3C_6H_4$	137–9	A	60	12
H	$CH_2=C(CH_3)CH_2$	H	$4'ClC_6H_4$	237–9 (Hydrochloride)	A	64	12
H	$HOCH_2CH_2$	H	C_6H_5	156–8	A	76	12
H	$HOCH_2CH_2$	H	$3'ClC_6H_4$	147–50	A	43	12
H	$HOCH_2CH_2$	H	$4'ClC_6H_4$	173–74	A	40	12
H	$CH_3CHOHCH_2$	H	C_6H_5	138–40	A	—	12
H	$(C_2H_5)_2NCH_2CH_2$	H	C_6H_5	128–9	A	—	38
H	$(C_2H_5)_2NCH_2CH_2$	H	$4'ClC_6H_4$	136–7	A	—	38
H	$[(C_2H_5)_2NCH_2]_2CH$	H	$4'ClC_6H_4$	132	A	—	38
H	$C_{12}H_{25}$	CH_3	CH_3	95–6	C	50	2
CH_3	CH_3	H	$2'ClC_6H_4$	133–5	A	50	12
CH_3	CH_3	H	$4'ClC_6H_4$	173–5	A	—	12
C_2H_5	C_2H_5	H	methoxyquinolinyl ($4'CH_3C_6H_4$, OCH_3)	191	A	—	26
$CH_2=CHCH_2$	$CH_2=CHCH_2$	H	$4'CH_3C_6H_4$	119–21	A	60	12
$CH_2=C(CH_3)CH_2$	$CH_2=C(CH_3)CH_2$	H	$2'ClC_6H_4$	78–81	A	44	12
$CH_2=C(CH_3)CH_2$	$CH_2=C(CH_3)CH_2$	H	$4'ClC_6H_4$	154–7	A	—	12
$CH_2{-}O{-}CH_2$ (bridge)		H	C_6H_5	224–5	C	84	2
H	NH_2	H	$4'H_2O_3AsC_6H_4$	—	A	—	43

N^2,N^4,N^6-Trisubstituted Melamines – Like Substituents

R_2	M.p. °C.	Preparative method[a]	Yield %	Ref.
CH_3	115	A		14, 35
		K		35
C_2H_5	73–4	A	91	1, 14, 35
		K		35
CN		C		44, 45
H_2NCO	>300	A		46, 47
H_2NC $\parallel$ NH	303–4 (picrate)	M		67
$HOCH_2CH_2$	100–1	A	100	1
		K	63	37
$CH_3CHOHCH_2$	113–4	A	87	1
NH_2	>300	A		47, 48
	287	E		36
C_6H_5NH		A	89	47, 49
C_6H_5	227–8, 232–4	A	85–95	1, 13, 14, 31, 35, 50
		K		35
$4'CH_3C_6H_4$	283	A		14
$2'ClC_6H_4$	165–6	A		47, 51
		L	25	51
$3'4'Cl_2C_6H_3$	261	A		47
$2'BrC_6H_4$	188–9	A	87	51
		L	62	51
$3'NO_2C_6H_4$		A		47
$2'CH_3OOCC_6H_4$	160	L		52
$2'C_2H_5OOCC_6H_4$	190	L		52
$4'NH_2C_6H_4$		A		47
$4'NH_2SO_2C_6H_4$		A		16
$4'(4''NH_2C_6H_4)C_6H_4$		A		47
$3'NH_2, 4'CH_3C_6H_3$		A		49
$\alpha C_{10}H_7$	225	A		47, 49
$\beta C_{10}H_7$	209	A		49
[benzothiazolyl] $C-SCH_2$	225–7 dec.	F		53
CH_3	171–2	A	37	1, 35
C_2H_5	46–7	A	93	1, 35
——CH_2	150d.	A	85–95	54, 55
H——CH_2	104–5	A	33, 73	68, 69
—CH_2—CH_2	256–9	A	90	69

(*Table continued*)

TABLE VI-9D (*continued*)

R_1	R_2	M.p. °C.	Preparative method[a]	Yield %
CH_2 | CH_2———CH_2 CH_2	CH_2 | CH_2	186–190	A	95
CH || CH———CH	CH || CH	210	L	
CH_2 | CH_2—CH_2—CH_2	CH_2 | CH_2	219–221	{ A { K	93
CH_2 | CH_2———O———CH_2	CH_2 | CH_2	284–9 dec.	A	92
$HOCH_2CH_2$	$HOCH_2CH_2$	169–70	A	65
CH_3	CN	241 215–268	A F	
$CNCH_2$	$CH_2\Big\langle{CH_2-CH_2\atop CH_2-CH_2}\Big\rangle CH$	165–7	A	82
$CNCH_2$	$C_{12}H_{25}$	46–8	A	67
CH_3OOCCH_2	$CH_2\Big\langle{CH_2-CH_2\atop CH_2-CH_2}\Big\rangle CH$	136–7	A	91
CH_3	C_6H_5	115	A	
CN	C_6H_5	210	A	
CN	$2'CH_3C_6H_4$	203	A	
CN	$2'CH_3OC_6H_4$	110	A	
CN	$4'C_2H_5OC_6H_4$	151	A	
CN	$2',4'(CH_3)_2C_6H_3$	193	A	
CN	$C_6H_5CH_2$	158	A	
CN	$aC_{10}H_7$	271	A	
$HOCH_2CH_2$	C_6H_5	163–4	K	43
C_6H_5	C_6H_5	292	L	
$C_6H_5CH_2$	C_6H_5	120	A	

E. N^2,N^4,N^6-Trisubstituted Melamines – Unlike substituents

$$R_3R_4N-\underset{\underset{NR_1R_2}{\displaystyle N\;\;N}}{\overset{N}{\bigtriangleup}}-N\!<^{R_1}_{R_2}$$

R_1	R_2	R_3	R_4	M.p. °C.	Preparative method[a]	Yield %
H	CH_3	H	$2'5'Cl_2C_6H_3$	153–5	A	76
H	C_2H_5	H	C_6H_5	178–80 (hydro- chloride)	A	70

(*Table con*

LE VI-9E (*continued*)

R_2	R_3	R_4	M.p. °C.	Preparative method[a]	Yield %	Ref.
C_2H_5	H	$3'ClC_6H_4$	165–7 (hydro-chloride)	A	94	12
$HOCH_2CH_2$	H	C_6H_5	134–5	A	94	1, 12
$HOOCCH_2$	H	C_6H_5	—	A	—	12
$CH_3CHOHCH_2$	H	C_6H_5	150–2 (hydro-chloride)	A	—	12
$CH_2=CHCH_2$	H	$2'ClC_6H_4$	56–9	A	—	1
$CH_2=CHCH_2$	H	$4'ClC_6H_4$	103–6	A	66	1
C_6H_5	$CNCH_2CH_2$	$CNCH_2CH_2$	181–3	A	84	1
CH_3	H	$2'ClC_6H_4$	114–7	A	43	12
C_2H_5	H	C_2H_5	B.p. 120–0.4 mm.	A	95	1
C_2H_5	H	C_6H_5	87–9	A	90	12
C_2H_5	H	$4'ClC_6H_4$	134–5	A	76	12
CH_3	$CH_2\text{————}CH_2$		55–57	A	>12	70
$-CH_2$	H	CH_3	128.5–131	A	38	70
$-CH_2$	H	$ClCH_2CH_2$	87–8	A	46	70
$-CH_2$	CH_3	CH_3	67–9	A	73	70
$-CH_2$	C_2H_5	C_2H_5	66.5–68	A	44	70
C_6H_5	CN	$4'C_2H_5OC_6H_4$	98–104	A	—	57
$4'C_2H_5OC_6H_4$	CN	C_6H_5	115–20	A	—	57

-Substituted Melamines

	R_2	R_3	R_4	M.p. °C.	Preparative method[a]	Yield	Ref.
H$_2$	H	H	H	314–16	A	—	1, 59
10	H	H	H	183–95	A	—	59
H$_2$	$CH_2\langle{}^{CH_2CH_2}_{CHCH_2}\rangle CH_2$	H	H	335–40	A	—	1, 59
H$_2$	C_6H_5	H	H	350–4	A	—	59
H$_2$	CH_2CH_2	H	H	398–400	A	48	33
	NHCONH	H	H	—	F	—	60
H$_2$C$_6$H$_4$	H	H	H	322–6	A	—	59

a Preparative Methods

A   From cyanuric chloride or a chloroamino-s-triazine.
B   Dicyanoguanidine plus an amine.
C   Reaction of cyanoguanidine with a substituted cyanamid.
D   Isomerization of an isomelamine.
E   Reaction of melamine with an amine.
F   Other reactions of melamine.
G   Melam with an amine.
H   Reaction of a hydroxyamino-s-triazine with an amine.
I   Reaction of cyanoguanidine with an amine.
J   Reaction of urea with an amine.
K   Reaction of an alkoxy- or alkylthio-s-triazine with an amine.
L   Trimerization of a substituted cyanamide.
M   From reaction of cyanoguanidine with an amine.

1. D. Kaiser, J. Thurston, J. Dudley, F. Schaefer, I. Hechenbleikner and D. Holm-Hansen, *J. Am. Chem. Soc.*, **73**, 2985 (1951).
2. D. Kaiser, U. S. 2,567,847 (1951).
3. J. Thurston, U. S. 2,482,076 (1949).
4. J. Mackay and J. Paden, U. S. 2,566,226 (1951).
5. K. Keller and E. Korten, U. S. 2,222,350 (1941).
6. J. Mackay and J. Paden, U. S. 2,566,225 (1951).
7. M. Bortnick, U. S. 2,628,234 (1953).
8. D. Kaiser and B. Redmon, U. S. 2,510,981 (1950).
9. G. D'Alelio, U. S. 2,394,042 (1946).
10. D. Kaiser and B. Redmon, U. S. 2,537,834 (1951).
11. H. Mosher and F. Whitmore, *J. Am. Chem. Soc.*, **67**, 662 (1945).
12. D. Walker, Y. L'Italien, W. Pearlman and C. Banks, *J. Am. Pharm. Assoc.*, **39**, 383 (1950).
13. Schultz, P. B. 70309 frames 8256–8266; *Bib.*, **6**, 199.
14. P. Klason, *J. prakt. Chem.*, (2), **33**, 290 (1886).
15. G. D'Alelio, U. S. 2,393,755 (1946).
16. G. D'Alelio, U. S. 2,312,698 (1943).
17. E. Fiedheim, *J. Am. Chem. Soc.*, **66**, 1775 (1944).
18. E. Friedheim, Swiss 209,035 (1940).
19. E. Friedheim, U. S. 2,295,574 (1942).
20. E. Friedheim, U. S. 2,334,321 (1943).
21. E. Friedheim, Brit. 598,075 (1948).
22. E. Friedheim, U. S. 2,463,861 (1949).
23. E. Friedheim, Brit. 585,678 (1947).
24. E. Friedheim, U. S. 2,430,462 (1947).
25. E. Friedheim, U. S. 2,400,547 (1946).
26. W. Cuthbertson and J. Moffat, *J. Chem. Soc.*, **1948**, 561.
27. Brit. 596,286 (1948).
28. M. Hultquist, R. Germann, J. Webb, W. Wright, B. Roth, J. Smith, and Y. Subbarow, *J. Am. Chem. Soc.*, **73**, 2558 (1951).
29. Brit. 414,105 (1934), Ger. 606,497 (1936).
30. W. Zerweck and W. Brunner, Ger. 889,593 (1953).
31. W. Zerweck and K. Keller, U. S. 2,228,161 (1941).
32. J. Mackay and J. Paden, U. S. 2,606,497 (1951).

33. W. Detweiler and E. Amstutz, *J. Am. Chem. Soc.*, **74**, 1483 (1952).
34. P. de Benneville, U. S. 2,675,383 (1954).
35. A. Hofmann, *Ber.*, **18**, 2755 (1885).
36. R. Stolle and K. Krauch, *Ber.*, **46**, 2337 (1913).
37. J. Thurston, F. Schaefer, J. Dudley and D. Holm-Hansen, *J. Am. Chem. Soc.*, **73**, 2992 (1951).
38. F. Curd, J. Landquist and F. Rose, *J. Chem. Soc.*, **1947**, 154.
39. P. Gupta and P. Guha, *Current Science (India)*, **18**, 294 (1949).
40. G. D'Alelio, and J. Underwood, U. S. 2,328,961 (1943).
41. H. Jensch, *Ann.*, **568**, (1950).
42. O. Diels, *Ber.*, **32**, 691 (1899).
43. E. Friedheim, U. S. 2,390,529 (1945).
44. W. Burdick, *J. Am. Chem. Soc.*, **47**, 1485 (1925).
45. W. Madelung and E. Kern, *Ann.*, **427**, 26 (1922).
46. A. Hantzsch and H. Bauer, *Ber.*, **38**, 1010 (1905).
47. V. Meyer and Fr. Näbe, *J. prakt. Chem.*, (2), **82**, 532 (1909).
48. H. Finger, *J. prakt. Chem.*, (2), **75**, 103 (1902).
49. H. Fries, *Ber.*, **19**, 2055 (1886).
50. Fr. 828,532 (1938); *Chem. Abstracts*, **33**, 175 (1939).
51. F. Kurtzer, *J. Chem. Soc.*, **1949**, 3033.
52. R. McKee, *J. prakt. Chem.*, (2), **84**, 825 (1911).
53. R. Seymour, U. S. 2,455,528 (1948).
54. H. Bestian, *et al.*, *Ann.*, **566**, 210 (1950).
55. a. V. Wystrach and D. Kaiser, U. S. 2,520,619 (1950).
    b. V. Wystrach, D. Kaiser and F. Schaefer, *J. Am. Chem. Soc.*, **77**, 5915 (1955).
56. G. Ciamician and M. Dennstedt, *Ber.*, **16**, 64 (1883).
57. J. Biechler, *Compt. rend.*, **203**, 568 (1936).
58. A. Perrot and R. Perrot, *Bull. Soc. Chim. France*, **7**, 743 (1940).
59. J. Dudley, U. S. 2,544,071 (1951).
60. G. D'Alelio and J. Underwood, U. S. 2,328,958 (1943).
61. D. Nagy, U. S. 2,392,607 (1946).
62. D. Nagy, U. S. 2,392,608 (1946).
63. W. Zerweck and W. Bruner, *Ger.* 898,591 (1953).
64. W. Weith, *Ber.*, **7**, 848 (1874).
65. R. Vogel and M. Kopac, *Proc. Soc. Exptl. Biol. Med.*, **77**, 859 (1951).
66. H. Fries, *Ber.*, **19**, 242 (1886).
67. A. MacLean, U. S. 2,537,840 (1951).
68. G. Braz, *Zhur. Obshchei Khim.*, **25**, 1413 (1955).
69. F. Schaefer, *J. Am. Chem. Soc.*, **77**, 5928 (1955).
70. F. Schaefer, J. Geoghegan and D. Kaiser, *J. Am. Chem. Soc.*, **77**, 5918 (1955).

2. Physical and Chemical Properties

No systematic study of the chemical and physical properties of the substituted melamines has been made. Substitution of the amino hydrogen atoms in melamine by aliphatic groups in general lowers the melting point and increases the solubility of the derivative in organic solvents as compared with melamine. The above effects are true to a lesser extent in the aromatic derivatives. The following table illustrates the melting point effect in the ethyl melamines.

A. Melting Points of Ethylmelamines

N^2-monoethyl	171–2° C	N^2-diethyl	168–170° C
N^2,N^4-diethyl	156–8° C	N^2,N^4-tetraethyl	17–72° C
N^2,N^4,N^6-triethyl	73–74° C	N^2,N^4,N^6-hexaethyl	46–7° C
N^2,N^4,N^6-pentaethyl	liquid		

Substitution on the amino nitrogens of melamine tends to increase the base strength of the derivative over that of melamine.[145] The dissociation constants of the ethylmelamines illustrates this.

B. Dissociation Constants (K_b) of Melamines

Melamine	1×10^{-9}
N^2-Ethylmelamine	1.7×10^{-9}
N^2,N^4-Diethylmelamine	3.4×10^{-9}
N^2-Diethylmelamine	4.2×10^{-9}
N^2,N^4,N^6-Triethylmelamine	6.9×10^{-9}
N^2,N^4-Tetraethylmelamine	1.9×10^{-8}

In the case of hydroxyalkyl substitution, the effect is moderated. The one aromatic derivative for which a measurement is available, monophenylmelamine, is less basic than melamine ($K_b = 4.5 \times 10^{-10}$).

The substituted melamines form water-soluble salts with inorganic acids. Platinum chloride-hydrogen chloride double salts have been reported for some of the simpler derivatives.[2, 53] In many cases picrates can be prepared.[178]

The chemical reactions of substituted melamines containing free —NH₂ groups may be expected to be similar to those of melamine. Condensations with formaldehyde and other aldehydes have been mentioned in the patent literature without details as to structures and products.

Friedheim[179,189,196] has described the reduction of p-arsenophenyl melamine, the corresponding antimony compounds, and certain of their derivatives to compounds in which the metal atom has a valence of three.

$$H_2N-N=NHC_6H_4AsO_3H_2 \xrightarrow[\text{or } SO_2, Na]{SnCl_2} H_2N-N=NHC_6H_4AsCl_2 \xrightarrow{H_2O} H_2N-N=NHC_6H_4AsO$$

$$H_2N-N-NHC_6H_4As=AsC_6H_4HN-N-N-NH_2$$

Substituted melamines containing hydroxy and amino-substituted aromatic groups have been coupled with diazonium compounds to yield dyestuffs (see Chapter 1).

VII. Applications of Melamine and Derivatives

Applications of melamine or its derivatives extend into nearly every industrial field. As noted in the Preface, however, the scope of this book is limited to the coverage of melamine and its monomeric reaction products. The section dealing with melamine-formaldehyde condensates is therefore a limited one, and these products are not included in the other sections. For a more complete coverage of the subject the reader is referred to references.[180-185]

1. Medical: Chemotherapy

Friedheim has shown that various arsenic- and antimony-containing substituted melamines, especially *p*-arsenophenylmelamine (XXIII), are effective chemotherapeutic agents against trypanosomes and

$$H_2N-N=NHC_6H_4AsO_3H \quad (XXIII)$$

$$H_2N-N=NHC_6H_4AsO \quad (XXIV)$$

spirochetes.[186,187,188,189,190] The disodium salt of this compound is called "Melarsen." It has shown definite activity against tryparsamide-resistant sleeping sickness.[191] Melarsen oxide (XXIV) has been found active against trypanosomes,[191-197] malaria,[198] yaws and tropical ulcer,[199] and human filariasis.[200]

The chemotherapeutic utility of N^2,N^4,N^6-triethylenemelamine (XVII) has been the subject of considerable study.[201-206] It has been shown to inhibit the growth of certain types of tumors and has been used with some benefit in leukemia.[207, 208]

Although melamine itself showed no activity, the methylol-melamines are reported to have a striking effect on the Walker tumor in mice.[209] The trimethylol compound was not only the most active of the melamines tested, but it also was the least toxic.

Melamine resembles such compounds as adenine, 2,4-diamino-s-triazine, urea and certain xanthine derivatives in that it contains nitrogen-carbon-nitrogen linkages and is also a potent diuretic.[210] However, the safety of this application has not as yet been determined.

2. Commercial

A. Dyeing

Triphenylmelamine is among those organic bases which have been suggested[211] for use with complex, acidic, organic dyestuffs or their complex inorganic salts. The base in this case precipitates the dye in the form of a salt from aqueous or alcoholic solution. The resulting pigments may be applied with lacquers in an organic solvent.

It has been claimed[212] that the addition of alkyl- or alkaryl-melamines to the spinning bath used in the processing of cellulosic fibers increases the dye affinity of the fiber almost to that of wool. The melamine derivatives are soluble in the solutions used.

The fact that many colors fade when exposed to the small amounts of acidic gases present in the atmosphere presents a serious problem. Melamine and certain of its derivatives, for example, monoalkyl- and monoacetylmelamines, may be adsorbed on such fibers as cellulose acetate to reduce greatly this gas fading.[213] Melamine, being essentially non-toxic, non-irritating, and resistant to dry cleaning solvents, is particularly useful for this kind of application.

B. Explosives

Melamine has been suggested[214] as one component of a stable, easily handled explosive mixture, the other components of which are ammonium perchlorate or ammonium nitrate and carbon. When melamine is added to nitrocellulose or mixtures of nitroglycerin and nitrocellulose, the product is said[215] to be a gelatinous explosive characterized by a low combustion temperature and increased effectiveness.

C. Flameproofing Agent

An aqueous suspension of melamine pyrophosphate may be padded into cellulose textiles giving them excellent flame resistance.[216] This salt is effective for the same purpose when added to plasticized cellulose acetate films, a number of commercial resins, and even paraffins.[49] Silicon oxyamides of melamine have been treated with formaldehyde,[217] to produce resinous products capable of fire-proofing paper.

D. Graphic Arts

The photolysis of zinc sulfide and cadmium sulfide phosphors by the action of short-wave ultraviolet light and moisture is said[218] to be prevented by the use of an intimate mixture of the sulfides with melamine.

Trimethylolmelamine has been claimed[219] as an effective agent for imparting blue-black tones to photographic images when added to the emulsion bath. The addition of N^2,N^4,N^6-triisopropylmelamine or its tributyl analog to a photographic developer is reported to increase the density of direct positive images.[220]

E. Ion Exchange Resins

The reaction of melamine with tetraethylenepentamine in the presence of hydrochloric acid leads to the formation of resins which are recommended[178] for use in ion exchange.

F. Leather

Melamine-formaldehyde mixtures[221] or resins are important to the leather industry, particularly as tanning agents for light-colored products.

G. Linoleum

Melamine acts[222] as an accelerator for curing siccative compositions used to prepare linoleum floor-covering. A typical recipe contains a small amount of melamine with lithopone, whiting, wood flour and a binder. The melamine also lends increased alkali resistance to the linoleums.

H. Oxidizing Agent

The N-halogenated melamines have been suggested[223] as oxidizing agents to be used in applications similar to those requiring calcium or sodium hypochlorite.

I. Pest Control

Chlorinated melamines may[224] be dissolved in dry cleaning solvents such as carbon tetrachloride, and may be impregnated during the cleaning operation into the fabric, making it moth repellent.

J. Petroleum

Melamine has been used not only as an oil preservative,[225] but also as an additive to oilwell brines[226] to reduce their corrosive action. It is probable that the melamine reacts with the various sulfur compounds rendering them essentially inert to steel and iron pipes and fittings.

K. Resin Modification

Melamine has been claimed as a basic curing assistant in the preparation of thermosetting[227] resins and adhesive resins.[228]

The addition of about 5 % melamine, during the preparation of oil modified alkyd resins of the glycerol-phthalic anhydride type, has been recommended.[229] It is said to prevent premature gelation of the mass and to allow the use of high temperatures during the reaction.

L. Rubber

Melamine is classified[230] as a mild accelerator for the vulcanization of rubber but N,N',N"-tris(methylenemercaptobenzothiazyl)-melamine, prepared by the reaction of melamine with formaldehyde and mercaptobenzothiazole in alcohol, is said to be an excellent accelerator.[231]

During the milling process and before vulcanization, rubber often becomes heated to temperatures around 200° F. It is difficult at such temperatures to prevent the accelerator in the mix from initiating vulcanization. It has been claimed[232] that the addition of mono- or dichloromelamine minimizes this so-called scorching. The melamine derivatives inhibit vulcanization below about 230° F but have essentially no effect on the process at 275° F. It is possible that the chlorine atoms, available from the chloromelamine, break any chain reactions which start below certain temperatures.

M. Stabilizing Agent

Melamine and methylolmelamine, in amounts of from 1 to 10%, stabilize[233] aqueous formaldehyde solutions containing as high as 35–44% of formaldehyde.

N. Steel

It has been suggested[234] as early as 1905 that melamine was a good source of nitrogen for the case-hardening of iron and steel in the presence or absence of alkali. Melamine and its pyrolysis products, such as melam, are used now[235] to activate salt-baths employed in this case-hardening process.

O. Sterilizing Agent

Chloromelamine may be used[236] in conjunction with phenolic resins or carbon-base filter materials for the sterilization and purification of water. Chlorine itself is said to have a deleterious effect on these filters.

The chloromelamines also may be[223, 224] impregnated into bandages to keep the latter sterile and antiseptic. The bleaching and disinfecting properties of halogenated melamines have been described.[237]

P. Surface Active Agents

It is claimed[238] that polymerized fatty acids react with melamine to give polyamides which find use as antifoaming agents in steam generation. Alkylaminomethylenemelamines prepared from melamine, formaldehyde and aliphatic amines are said[134] to be good surface active agents.

Q. Textiles

The use of the triacylmelamines to increase the water-repellency of certain fabric finishes has been proposed.[239] The impregnation of cellulosic fibers with alkylaminomethylenemelamines results in animalization, making the cloth more susceptible[134, 240] to acid dyestuffs. These products also impart softening and water-repellency to the fiber.

Melamine pyrophosphate applied to textiles[241] imparts flame-resistance, mildew-resistance and water repellency to the cloth.

During World War II, N^2,N^4,N^6-triethylenemelamine, under the name Persistol HO 1/163, was used in Germany as an effective cross-linking agent for wool and a hydrophobizing agent for regenerated cellulose.[242]

R. Wood Products

When wood pulp is impregnated with solutions of melamine followed by thermal treatment in a press or mold, the products are said[243] to have good water and heat resistance.

S. Melamine-Formaldehyde Condensation Products

Among the most useful products which are made by the reaction of melamine with formaldehyde are aminoplastics. These condensation products are thermosetting, translucent, infusible, odorless, tasteless, and easily pigmented. They may be molded or cast into a wide variety of plastics.[180, 184] The methylolmelamines also may be impregnated into sheets of glass cloth and polymerized thereon for the preparation of thermally and chemically resistant laminates of great hardness.

In the paper industry, melamine-formaldehyde polymers with a wide range of molecular weights and modified by various means give tremendously increased wet strength[244, 245] to paper for bags, maps, toweling, food wrappers etc.

Methylolmelamines, modified with aliphatic alcohols for organic solubility, find extensive use in industrial baking finishes.[180, 246] Some of the principal fields of applications are in the finishing of refrigerators, washing machines, automobiles, tin cans, Venetian blinds, wall tile, kitchen utensils, hospital equipment and toys.

Condensation products of melamine with formaldehyde in conjunction with alcohols, amines, acids and various fillers are important as adhesives and binders in plywood manufacture, general woodworking, paper products, asbestos, and in plaster of Paris. They are used for joining fabric to rubber in tires and overshoes, and in general where strong and chemically resistant adhesion is required.

The resins appear in dyeing and printing applications such as the binding of pigments and color lakes, ion exchange resins, pickling inhibitors, flotation agents, drilling muds, germicides, abrasives and surface active agents. Their use in the electric industries is extensive. The outstanding heat resistance and arc resistance of the products make them desirable for battery separators, insulating covers, commutator segments, wire coverings, and other uses within the latter category.

VIII. Isomelamines

In 1869 Hofmann[247, 248] heated ethylthiourea with mercuric oxide and obtained a product which he thought to be N^2,N^4,N^6-triethyl-melamine. He believed the reaction involved the intermediate formation of ethylcyanamide which then trimerized. In subsequent work[249, 250] he showed that in fact the product was the isomelamine (XXV), which

$$3\ C_2H_5NHCNH_2 \overset{\text{S}}{\underset{}{\|}} \xrightarrow{\text{HgO}} \text{(XXV)} + 3\ H_2S$$

had properties differing from the triethylmelamine obtained by reaction of cyanuric chloride or trimethylthiocyanurate with ethylamine. Hydrolysis with hydrochloric acid yielded triethylisocyanurate with loss of ammonia. He concluded that the normal melamines could be

$$\xrightarrow{H_2O} + NH_3$$

regarded as derivatives of cyanamide (H_2NCN) while the "iso" compounds were derivatives of carbodiimide ($HN{=}C{=}NH$).

Hofmann prepared triphenylisomelamine (M.p. 185°) by heating phenylcyanamide at water bath temperature. Hydrolysis of this com-

$$3\ C_6H_5NHCN \longrightarrow \longrightarrow$$

pound, stepwise, yielded triphenylisocyanurate. Normal triphenyl-melamine, prepared by reaction of aniline with cyanuric chloride, melted at 228°, and yielded cyanuric acid and aniline upon hydrolysis.

$$3\ C_6H_5NH_2 + \longrightarrow \xrightarrow[150°]{3\ HCl} + 3\ C_6H_5NH_2\cdot HCl$$

When Hofmann heated phenylthiourea with mercuric oxide, he obtained a third, isomeric triphenylmelamine (M.p. 217°). Hydrolysis with concentrated hydrochloric acid yielded a compound melting at 261° with formation of one mole of aniline and two moles of ammonia. Further degradative hydrolysis at 280° gave two moles of aniline. On the basis of these experiments, formula (XXVI) was assigned to this asymmetrical triphenylmelamine.

A fourth isomeric triphenylmelamine was prepared by Rathke.[251] Triphenylthioammeline (XXVII) (See Chapter V) was treated with alcoholic ammonia. The resulting triphenylmelamine (M.p. 221°) was hydrolysed to a monophenylisocyanuric acid (XXIX). On this basis

structure (XXVIII) with one phenyl group directly attached to the ring was assigned. Rathke also reported that when the asymmetrical triphenylisomelamine was heated in the presence of ammonia, it isomerized to N^2,N^4,N^6-triphenylmelamine.

No detailed, systematic study of the preparation and properties of the isomelamines has appeared. The trimerization of substituted cyanamides has been reported several times. In some cases the isomelamine structure has been assigned the products,[173, 252, 253, 254, 255] while in other instances the normal melamine structures have been used.[147, 256] Trimerization has usually been accomplished by heating or allowing the cyanamide to stand for a prolonged period. Kurtzer[173] studied the reaction of aryl sulfonyl chlorides with substituted ureas. In the case of ortho-substituted arylureas he obtained normal melamines as products. He believed that these arose from intermediate formation of substituted cyanamides. However, when he prepared the substituted cyanamides and heated them, he found the main product was the isomelamine, with small quantities of the normal melamines formed also.

The trimerization of substituted cyanamides is the only method which has been reported for symmetrically trisubstituted isomelamines.

Traube[257] reported a mixed trimerization of ethylcyanamide and cyanamide. The product was believed to be a diethylmelamine, but the structure was not proven. Similarly, the reaction of phenylcyanamide with cyanamide gave a diphenylmelamine of unknown structure.[258]

$$2\ C_2H_5NHCN + H_2NCN \longrightarrow \quad \begin{array}{c} C_2H_5 \\ H_2N\diagdown\ N\diagup NH \\ \| \quad \| \\ N \quad NC_2H_5 \\ \diagdown\diagup \\ NH \end{array} \quad ?$$

The monosubstituted isomelamines were unknown until the work of Kaiser and Nagy. They showed that the reaction of N^1,N^3-dicyano-guanidine with primary aliphatic and aromatic amines under mildy acid or neutral conditions gave good yields of isomelamines.[170] The

$$\begin{array}{c} CNNHCNHCN + RNH_2 \\ \| \\ NH \end{array} \quad \xrightarrow{\ HX\ } \quad \begin{array}{c} R \\ H_2N\diagdown\ N\diagup NH \\ \| \quad \| \\ N \quad N \\ \diagdown\diagup \\ NH_2 \end{array}$$

reaction was carried out at temperatures of 90–130°, and the products isolated as the hydrochlorides of free bases.

Nagy also obtained methyl and ethylisomelamine by the reaction of melamine with methyl and ethyl sulfate.[259]

$$\begin{array}{c} H_2N\diagdown\ N\diagup NH_2 \\ \| \quad \| \\ N \quad N \\ \diagdown\diagup \\ NH_2 \end{array} \quad \xrightarrow{(C_2H_5)_2SO_4} \quad \begin{array}{c} C_2H_5 \\ H_2N\diagdown\ N\diagup NH \\ \| \quad \| \\ N \quad N \\ \diagdown\diagup \\ NH_2 \end{array}$$

In 1909 Busch and co-workers[260] heated diphenylcarbodiimide (XXX) in the presence of anhydrous hydrogen chloride. The product

$$3\ C_6H_5N{=}C{=}NC_6H_5 \quad \xrightarrow{\ HCl\ } \quad \begin{array}{c} C_6H_5 \\ C_6H_5N\diagdown\ N\diagup NC_6H_5 \\ \| \quad \| \\ C_6H_5N \quad NC_6H_5 \\ \diagdown\diagup \\ NC_6H_5 \end{array}$$

$$\text{(XXX)} \qquad\qquad \text{(XXXI)}\ NC_6H_5$$

TABLE VI-10.   Isomelamines

R$_1$	R$_2$	R$_3$	M.p. °C.	Yield	Ref.
CH$_3$	H	H	259–260 (monohydrate)		1
C$_2$H$_5$	H	H	312° (Hydrochloride)	61.5	1, 2
C$_4$H$_9$	H	H	230–1	77	2
C$_{12}$H$_{25}$	H	H	225	52	2
HOCH$_2$CH$_2$	H	H	271–2 (hydrochloride)	54.5	2
C$_6$H$_5$	H	H	232	"quant"	2
o-CH$_3$C$_6$H$_4$	H	H	255	53	2
o-BrC$_6$H$_4$	H	H	250	60	2
o-HOC$_6$H$_4$	H	H	255	69	2
p-C$_2$H$_5$OC$_6$H$_4$	H	H	265	87.5	2
m-NO$_2$C$_6$H$_4$	H	H	241	56.5	2
p-NO$_2$C$_6$H$_4$	H	H	262	45	2
p-NH$_2$C$_6$H$_4$	H	H	265	—	2
p-HSO$_3$C$_6$H$_4$	H	H	infusible	86.5	2
p-NH$_2$SO$_2$C$_6$H$_4$	H	H	272–3	88	2, 3
p-H$_2$O$_3$ASC$_6$H$_4$	H	H	320°	76.5	2
2,'5'Cl$_2$C$_6$H$_3$	H	H	240	50	2
o-CH$_3$, p-isoC$_3$H$_7$C$_6$H$_3$	H	H	—	60	2
a-C$_{10}$H$_7$	H	H	260	60	2
CH$_3$	CH$_3$	CH$_3$	179	25	4, 5
C$_2$H$_5$	C$_2$H$_5$	C$_2$H$_5$	92	—	5
C$_6$H$_5$	C$_6$H$_5$	C$_6$H$_5$	185	—	6
p-CH$_3$C$_6$H$_4$	p-CH$_3$C$_6$H$_4$	p-CH$_3$C$_6$H$_4$	256, 183	—	7, 8
p-ClC$_6$H$_4$	p-ClC$_6$H$_4$	p-ClC$_6$H$_4$	280	—	7
p-CH$_3$OC$_6$H$_4$	p-CH$_3$OC$_6$H$_4$	p-CH$_3$OC$_6$H$_4$	218	—	9
C$_6$H$_5$CH$_2$	C$_6$H$_5$CH$_2$	C$_6$H$_5$CH$_2$	129–30	—	10,

1. D. Nagy, U. S. 2,485,983 (1949).
2. D. Kaiser and D. Nagy, U. S. 2,481,758 (1949).
3. D. Nagy and D. Kaiser, U. S. 2,498,217 (1950).
4. W. Traube, F. Kegel and H. Schultz, *Z. Angew. Chem.*, **39**, 1465 (1926).
5. A. Hofmann, *Ber.*, **18**, 2781 (1885).
6. F. Arndt, *Ann.*, **384**, 350 (1911).
7. B. Singh, K. Krall and R. Sahasrabudhey, *J. Indian Chem. Soc.*, **23**, 373 (1946).
8. G. Heller and W. Bauer, *J. prakt. Chem.*, (2), **65**, 365 (1902).
9. H. King and I. Tonkin, *J. Chem. Soc.*, **1946**, 1063.
10. L. Birkofer, *Ber.*, **75B**, 429 (1942).
11. J. Strakosch, *Ber.*, **5**, 695 (1872).

was believed to be N^1,N^2,N^3N^4,N^5,N^6-hexaphenylisomelamine (XXXI).
In related work, Rivier and Langer[261] allowed diphenylcarbodiimide to
react with N-methylaniline at room temperature. A 70% yield of a
product formulated as (XXXII) was obtained.

$$3 C_6H_5N=C=NC_6H_5 + C_6H_5NHCH_3 \longrightarrow$$

$$\begin{array}{c} C_6H_5 \\ C_6H_5N \diagdown N \diagdown NHC_6H_5 \\ {-}NC_6H_5 \\ C_6H_5N \quad NC_6H_5 \quad CH_3 \\ \\ (XXXII) \quad NC_6H_5 \end{array}$$

Hofmann[262] heated N^1,N^3-diphenylguanidine to 170° and obtained
a product which he believed to be a tetraphenylisomelamine. The same
compound was apparently obtained by Weith and Ebert[263] by passing
cyanogen chloride into boiling aniline. The structure of this product has
not been established.

A listing of isomelamines is found in table VI-10.

References

1. J. Liebig, *Ann.*, **10**, 17 (1834).
2. P. Klason, *J. prakt. Chem.*, (2), **33**, 290 (1886).
3. J. Volhard, *J. prakt. Chem.*, (2), **9**, 29 (1874).
4. E. Hughes, *J. Am. Chem. Soc.*, **63**, 1737 (1940).
5. I. Knaggs, K. Lonsdale, R. Wood and G. Williams, *Proc. Roy. Soc. London,* A **177**, 140 (1940).
6. R. Chapman, P. Averell and R. Harris, *Ind. Eng. Chem.*, **35**, 137 (1943).
7. J. Dixon, N. Woodberry and G. Costa, *J. Am. Chem. Soc.*, **69**, 599 (1947).
8. G. Costa, R. Hirt and D. Salley, *J. Chem. Phys.*, **18**, 434 (1950).
9. T. Rochow, R. Stafford, D. Davis and R. Gilbert, *Ind. Eng. Chem.*, **32**, 1187 (1940).
10. D. Salley and J. Gray, *J. Am. Chem. Soc.*, **70**, 2650 (1948).
11. C. Stephenson and D. Berets, *J. Am. Chem. Soc.*, **74**, 882 (1952).
12. A. Claus, *Ber.*, **9**, 1915 (1876).
13. A. Smolka and A. Friedrich, *Monatsh.*, **10**, 86 (1889).
14. H. Krall, *J. Chem. Soc.*, **103**, 1385 (1913).
15. P. McClellan, *Ind. Eng. Chem.*, **32**, 1181 (1940).
16. D. Jayne and H. Day, U. S. 2,341,180 (1944) to American Cyanamid Co.
17. Fr. 991,211 (1951) to Produits Chimiques de Ribecourt.
18. D. Jayne and H. Day, Brit. 536,743 (1944) to American Cyanamid Co.
19. R. Köhler, U. S. 2,301,053 (1943) to Proctor & Gamble.
20. Brit. 525,185 (1940) to Henkel & Cie, through, *Chem. Abstracts*, **35**, 6604 (1941).
21. D. Jayne, U. S. 2,180,295 (1939) to American Cyanamid Co.
22. G. Foster, U. S. 2,206,603 (1940).
23. J. Thurston, U. S. 2,223,333 (1941) to American Cyanamid Co.
24. Brit. 533,426 (1941) to Brit. Ind. Plastics Ind., through *Chem. Abstracts*, **36**, 1050 (1942).

25. D. Jayne and D. May, U. S. 2,377,499 (1949) to American Cyanamid Co.
26. S. Cloez and Cannizzaro, *Compt. rend.*, **32**, 62 (1851).
27. S. Cloez and Cannizzaro, *Ann.*, **78**, 229 (1851).
28. E. Drechsel, *J. prakt. Chem.*, (2), **11**, 302 (1874).
29. E. Drechsel, *J. prakt. Chem.*, (2), **13**, 330 (1876).
30. Swiss 205,525 (1939) to Ciba, through, *Chem. Abstracts*, **35**, 2534 (1941).
31. H. Krall, *J. Chem. Soc.*, **107**, 1397 (1915).
32. A. Brookes, U. S. 2,287,597 (1943) to American Cyanamid Co.
33. W. Fisch, Ger. 715,761 (1941) to Ciba, through, *Chem. Abstracts*, **38**, 2052 (1944).
34. Swiss 209,503 (1940) to Ciba, through, *Chem. Abstracts*, **35**, 4397 (1941).
35. Brit. 527,697 (1940) to Ciba, through, *Chem. Abstracts*, **35**, 7424 (1941).
36. Fr. 849,752 (1939) to Ciba.
37. J. Mackay, U. S. 2,566,228 (1951) to American Cyanamid Co.
38. J. Paden and J. Mackay, U. S. 2,396,193 (1946) to American Cyanamid Co.
39. L. Lane, U. S. 2,577,201 (1951) to American Cyanamid Co.
40. L. Lane, U. S. 2,615,018 (1952) to American Cyanamid Co.
41. E. Drechsel, *J. prakt. Chem.*, (2), **12**, 289 (1875).
42. E. Werner, *J. Chem. Soc.*, **107**, 721 (1915).
43. F. Chastellain, *Helv. Chim. Acta*, **18**, 1287 (1935).
44. E. Werner and J. Bell, *J. Chem. Soc.*, **117**, 1133 (1920).
45. P. B. 76483.
46. M. Nencki, *J. prakt. Chem.*, (2), **17**, 235 (1878).
47. T. Davis and H. Underwood, *J. Am. Chem. Soc.*, **44**, 2595 (1922).
48. T. Davis, *J. Am. Chem. Soc.*, **43**, 2230 (1921).
49. American Cyanamid Co., unpublished results.
50. P. Lemoult, *Compt. rend.*, **125**, 824 (1897).
51. P. Lemoult, *Ann. chim. phys.*, **16**, 338 (1849).
52. J. Ponomarew, *Ber.*, **18**, 3267 (1885).
53. A. Hofmann, *Ber.*, **18**, 2755 (1885).
54. J. Mackay and J. Paden, U. S. 2,566,230 (1951) to American Cyanamid Co.
55. Brit. 598,175 (1948) to American Cyanamid Co.
56. J. Mackay and J. Paden, U. S. 2,537,936 (1951) to American Cyanamid Co.
57. J. Volhard, *J. prakt. Chem.*, (2), **9**, 29 (1874).
58. B. Rathke, *Ber.*, **23**, 1675 (1890).
59. Swiss 202,245 (1949) to Ciba.
60. Brit. 523,448 (1940) to Ciba, through, *Chem. Abstracts*, **35**, 6271 (1941).
61. J. Mackay and J. Paden, U. S. 2,475,709 (1949) to American Cyanamid Co.
62. L. Birkofer, *Ber.*, **75B**, 429 (1942).
63. F. Kaess and E. Vogel, *Chem.-Ing.-Tech.*, **26**, 380 (1954).
64. A. MacLean, U. S. 2,402,061 (1946) to American Cyanamid Co.
65. H. Rathsburg, *Ber.*, **54**, 3183 (1921).
66. Y. Aiya, *J. Soc. Chem. Ind. Japan*, **50**, 131 (1947), through, *Chem. Abstracts*, **45**, 630 (1951).
67. J. Ponomarew, *Ber.*, **7**, 1792 (1874).
68. A. Wintringham and V. King, U. S. 2,324,450 (1944) to American Cyanamid Co.
69. Fr. 817,895 (1937) to I.G. Farbenind., through, *Chem. Abstracts*, **32**, 2149 (1938).
70. H. Grubb, *Synthesis of Melamine*, Thesis, June 1951, Georgia Tech.
71. W. Caldwell, R. Swain and J. Paden, U. S. 2,375,731 (1945) to American Cyanamid Co.
72. T. Hodgins, *et al.*, *Ind. Eng. Chem.*, **33**, 769 (1941).

73. Belg. 451,171 (1943) to Soc. belge de l'azote & des produits chimique du Marly, through *Chem. Abstracts*, **42**, 229 (1948).
74. Swiss 189,406 (1937) to Ciba through *Chem. Abstracts*, **31**, 6678 (1937).
75. Brit. 524,349 (1940) to I.G. Farbenind. through *Chem. Abstracts*, **35**, 6272 (1941).
76. Swiss 205,527 (1939) to Ciba, through *Chem. Abstracts*, **35**, 2534 (1941).
77. Swiss 199,784 (1938) to Ciba.
78. Swiss 200,244 (1938), through *Chem. Abstracts*, **33**, 3400 (1939).
79. Fr. 841,022 (1939) to Ciba, through *Chem. Abstracts*, **34**, 1688 (1940).
80. G. Widmer, U. S. 2,265,215 (1941) to Ciba.
81. G. Widmer, Ger. 734,014 (1943) to Ciba, through *Chem. Abstracts*, **38**, 982 (1944).
82. G. Widmer, W. Fisch and J. Jakl, U. S. 2,161,940 (1939).
83. Brit. 557,164 (1943) American Cyanamid to Brit. Ind. Plastics Ltd., through *Chem. Abstracts*, **39**, 2416 (1945).
84. Brit. 557,662 (1943) to Brit. Ind. Plastics Ltd., through *Chem. Abstracts*, **39**, 3702 (1946).
85. Fr. 843,440 (1939) to Ciba, through *Chem. Abstracts*, **34**, 6658 (1940).
86. J. Grim, U. S. 2,206,005 (1940) to American Cyanamid Co.
87. R. Stolle and K. Krach, *Ber.*, **46**, 2337 (1913).
88. G. Widmer, W. Fisch and J. Jakl, U. S. 2,191,361 (1940) to Ciba.
89. J. Paden and J. Mackay, U. S. 2,566,231 (1951) to American Cyanamid Co.
90. Brit. 598,175 (1948) to American Cyanamid Co.
91. Brit. 583,504 (1946) to E. I. du Pont & Co.
92. R. Vingee, U. S. 2,550,659 (1951) to Allied Chem & Dye.
93. J. Paden and J. Mackay, U. S. 2,566,227 (1951) to American Cyanamid Co.
94. J. Mackay, U. S. 2,566,224 (1951) to American Cyanamid Co.
95. J. Mackay, U. S. 2,566,223 (1951) to American Cyanamid Co.
96. J. Mackay, U. S. 2,566,229 (1951) to American Cyanamid Co.
97. Brit. 644,374 (1950) to Monsanto Chemical Company.
98. C. Barnett, *J. Phys. Chem.*, **34**, 1497 (1930).
99. A. Ostrogovitch, *Gazz. Ital.*, **65**, 566 (1934), through *Chem. Abstracts*, **30**, 465 (1936).
100. W. Scholl, R. Davis, B. Brown and F. Reid, *Ind. Eng. Chem.*, **29**, 202 (1937).
101. J. Wisclicenus and C. Zimmerman, *Ber.*, **7**, 289 (1874).
102. E. Franklin, *J. Am. Chem. Soc.*, **44**, 486 (1922).
103. L. Lento and D. Jayne, U. S. 2,546,551 (1951) to American Cyanamid Co.
104. H. Williams, *Cyanogen Compounds*, 2d ed., Arnold & Co., London, 1948, p. 30.
105. E. Ashcraft, Brit. 16,765 (1910), through *Chem. Abstracts*, **6**, 1261 (1912).
106. German 222,522 (1908) to Sprengstoffwerke, *Frdl.*, **10**, 105.
107. F. Knapp, *Ann.*, **21**, 239 (1837).
108. J. Jager, *Ber.*, **9**, 1556 (1876).
109. A. Claus, *Ann.*, **179**, 112 (1875).
110. C. Redemann and H. Lucas, *J. Am. Chem. Soc.*, **62**, 842 (1942).
111. Schultz, *P. B.* 70309 frames 8256–8266, *Bib.*, **6**, 199.
112. J. Cason, *J. Am. Chem. Soc.*, **69**, 495 (1947).
113. J. Cason, P. B. 52316; *Bib.*, **5**, 287.
114. I. Muscat and A. Chenicek, U. S. 2,184,883 (1939) to Pittsburgh Plate Glass Co.
115. I. Muscat and A. Chenicek, U. S. 2,184,886 (1939) to Pittsburgh Plate Glass Co.
116. I. Muscat and A. Chenicek, U. S. 2,184,888 (1939) to Pittsburgh Plate Glass Co.
117. W. Arsem, U. S. 2,472,361 (1949).
118. A. Chenicek, U. S. 2,299,069 (1942) to Pittsburgh Plate Glass.
119. D. Luce, P. B. 70429, Frame 8567, April 1943, *Bib.*, **9**, 213.
120. E. Atkinson, *J. Am. Chem. Soc.*, **73**, 4443 (1951).

121. P. Hamm, U. S. 2,577,418 (1951) to Monsanto Chemical Co.
122. R. Roblin and P. Winnek, U. S. 2,407,177 (1946) to American Cyanamid Co.
123. G. Anderson, *et al.*, *J. Am. Chem. Soc.*, **64**, 2902 (1942).
124. E. Friedheim, U. S. 2,430,462 (1947).
125. E. Friedheim, U. S. 2,334,321 (1943).
126. J. Thurston, Gibson Island Conference, July 1941.
127. J. Dudley and E. Lynn, *Symposium on Fibrous Proteins, Soc. Dyers & Colorists*, **1948**, p. 215.
128. G. Widmer and W. Fisch, U. S. 2,387,547 (1945).
129. Swiss 197,486 (1935) to Ciba.
130. A. Gams, G. Widmer and W. Fisch, *Brit. Plastics*, **14**, 508 (1943).
131. A. Gams, G. Widmer and W. Fisch, *Helv. Chim. Acta*, **24E**, 302 (1941).
132. M. Okano and Y. Ogata, *J. Am. Chem. Soc.*, **74**, 5728 (1952).
133. M. Norris and J. Bacon, *Official Digest, Fed. Paint and Varnish*, **285**, 785 (1948).
134. F. McGrew, U. S. 2,454,078 (1948) to Du Pont.
135. L. Bock and A. Houk, U. S. 2,210,831 (1940) to Resinous Products and Chemicals Co.
136. E. Atkinson and A. Bump, *J. Am. Chem. Soc.*, **72**, 629 (1950).
137. G. D'Alelio and J. Underwood, U. S. 2,328,961 (1943) to General Electric Co.
138. D. Nagy, U. S. 2,485,983 (1949) to American Cyanamid Co.
139. J. Thurston, U. S. 2,482,076 (1949) to American Cyanamid Co.
140. W. Zerweck and K. Keller, U. S. 2,228,161 (1941) to I.G. Farbenind.
141. G. D'Alelio, U. S. 2,394,042 (1946) to General Electric Co.
142. G. Widmer and W. Fisch, U. S. 2,197,357 (1940) to Ciba.
142a. L. Radlberger, *Oesterr. Ung. Z. Zuckerind.*, **42**, 236 (1914), through *Chem. Abstracts*, **8**, 680 (1914).
143. W. Hartley, J. Dobbie and A. Landers, *J. Chem. Soc.*, **79**, 848 (1901).
144. I. Klotz and T. Askounis, *J. Am. Chem. Soc.*, **69**, 801 (1947).
145. J. Dudley, *J. Am. Chem. Soc.*, **73**, 3007 (1951).
146. W. Weith, *Ber.*, **7**, 848 (1874).
147. G. Cimmician and M. Dennstedt, *Ber.*, **16**, 64 (1883).
148. O. Diels, *Ber.*, **22**, 691 (1899).
149. D. Walker, Y. L'Italien, W. Pearlman, and C. Banks, *J. Am. Pharm. Assoc.*, **39**, 383 (1950).
150. D. Kaiser, J. Thurston, J. Dudley, F. Schaefer, I. Hechenbleikner and D. Holm-Hansen, *J. Am. Chem. Soc.*, **73**, 2985 (1951).
151. V. Wystrach, D. Kaiser and F. Schaefer, *J. Am. Chem. Soc.*, **77**, 5915 (1955).
152. J. Dudley, U. S. 2,544,071 (1951).
153. V. Meyer and Fr. Nabe, *J. prakt. Chem.*, (2), **82**, 532 (1909).
154. J. Blechler, *Compt. Rend.*, **203**, 568 (1936).
155. D. Kaiser, U. S. 2,567,847 (1951).
156. M. Bortnick, U. S. 2,628,234 (1953).
157. W. Zerweck and W. Bruner, Ger. 898,591 (1953).
158. D. Kaiser and B. Redmon, U. S. 2,510,981 (1950).
159. P. Gupta and P. Guha, *Current Sci.* (*India*), **18**, 294 (1949).
160. P. de Benneville, U. S. 2,675,383 (1954).
161. G. D'Alelio, and J. Pyle, U. S. 2,361,823 (1944).
162. J. Thurston, F. Schaefer, J. Dudley and D. Holm-Hansen, *J. Am. Chem. Soc.*, **73**, 2992 (1951).
163. J. Mackay and J. Paden, U. S. 2,566,226 (1951).
164. G. D'Alelio, U. S. 2,312,698 (1943).
165. G. D'Alelio, U. S., 2,393,755 (1946).

166. D. Kaiser and B. Redmon, U. S. 2,537,834 (1951).
167. K. Keller and E. Korten, U. S. 2, 222,350 (1941).
168. D. Nagy, U. S. 2,392,607 (1946).
169. D. Nagy, U. S. 2,392,608 (1946).
170. D. Kaiser and D. Nagy, U. S. 2,481,758 (1949).
171. W. Detweiler and E. Amstutz, *J. Am. Chem. Soc.*, **74**, 1483 (1952).
172. W. Madelung and E. Kern, *Ann.*, **427**, 26 (1922).
173. F. Kurtzer, *J. Chem. Soc.*, **1949**, 3033.
174. J. Mackay and J. Paden, U. S. 2,537,937 (1951).
175. A. Hantzsch and H. Bauer, *Ber.*, **38**, 1010 (1905).
176. A. MacLean, U. S. 2,537,840 (1951).
177. D. Kaiser and B. Redmon, U. S. 2,537,834 (1951).
178. H. Mosher and F. Whitmore, *J. Am. Chem. Soc.*, **67**, 662 (1945).
179. E. Friedheim, U. S. 2,386,204 (1945).
180. J. Dudley, *Chem. Inds.* Feb. (1949).
181. Hodgins, Hovey, Hewett, Barrett, and Meeske, *Ind. Eng. Chem.*, **33**, 769 (1941).
182. Kohler, *Kunstoff-Technik.*, **11**, 1 (1941).
183. Niedercorn, *Shoe and Leather Reporter*, **231**, No. 3, 20 (1943).
184. Patterson, Detwiler, and Suen, Boston Meeting, *Am. Chem. Soc.*, 1951.
185. H. Payne, *Paint, Oil, and Chem. Rev.*, **109**, No. 6, 12 (1946).
186. E. Friedheim, *Rept. Proc. 3rd. Int'l. Congress Microbiology*, **1939**, 428.
187. E. Friedheim, U. S. Pat. 2,295,574 (1942).
188. E. Friedheim, U. S. 2,334,321 (1942).
189. E. Friedheim, U. S. 2,430,462 (1947).
190. E. Friedheim, H. Vogel and R. Berman, *J. Am. Chem. Soc.*, **69**, 560 (1947).
191. Williamson and Lourie, *Nature*, **161**, 103 (1948).
192. Rollo, Williamson, and Laurie, *Ann. Trop. Med. Parasitol.*, **43**, 194 (1949; *C.A.*, **44**, 6521 (1950).
193. Weinman, *Amer. Journ. Trop. Med.*, **26**, (Suppl. to No. 5), 95 (1946).
194. Weinman and Franz, *Amer. Journ. Trop. Med.*, **25**, 343 (1945).
195. C. Banks, *J. Am. Chem. Soc.*, **66**, 1771 (1944).
196. E. Friedheim, *J. Am. Chem. Soc.*, **66**, 1775 (1944).
197. Van Hoof, *Trans. Roy. Soc. Trop. Med. Hyg.*, **40**, 727 (1947).
198. Payne, Balthazar, and Bezerra, *South Med. Jour.*, **39**, 970 (1946).
199. Payne, Balthazar and Fernandez, *South. Med. Journ.*, **39**, 372 (1946).
200. Rose and Culbertson, *Jour. Parasitol.* **31**, (Suppl. to No. 6), 17 (1945).
201. M. Lewis and M. Crossley, *Arch. Biochem.*, **26**, 319 (1950).
202. J. Burchenal, *et al.*, *Arch. Biochem.*, **26**, 321 (1950).
203. F. Rose, J. Hendry, and A. Walpole, *Nature*, **165**, 993 (1950).
204. E. Patterson and J. Boland, *Brit. J. Cancer*, **5**, 28 (1951).
205. J. Burchenal, *et al.*, *Proc. Soc. Exptl. Biol. Med.*, **74**, 708 (1950).
206. S. Kraus *et al.*, *Proc. Soc. Exptl. Biol. Med.*, **76**, 489 (1951).
207. D. Karnofsky *et al.*, *Arch. Intern. Med.*, **87**, 477 (1951).
208. W. H. Bond *et al.*, *Arch. Intern. Med.*, **91**, 602 (1953).
209. Henry, Rose and Walpole, *Brit. J. of Pharm. and Chem.*, **6**, (2), 201 (1951).
210. Lipschitz and Hadidian, *J. Pharmacol.*, **81**, 84 (1944); *C.A.*, **38**, 4033 (1944).
211. Kranzlein, Hartmann, and Hardt, U. S. 1,800,300 (1931).
212. Fr. Pat. 843,781 (1939); *C.A.*, **34**, 7109 (1940).
213. McNally and Dickey, U. S. 2,176,506 (1939).
214. Manuelli and Bernardini, U. S. 1,409,963 (1922).
215. Ger. 201,215 (1908).
216. Brit. 638,434 (1950).

217. Walters, U. S. 2,514,268 (1950).
218. Gorev, Izvest. Akad. Nauk., *U.S.S.R.*, *Sev. Fiz.*, **13**, 257 (1949: through *C.A.*, **43**, 6921 (1949).
219. Baldsiefen, U. S. 2,364,017 (1944).
220. Stauffer, U. S. 2,497,917 (1950).
221. Windus, U. S. 2,470,450 (1949).
222. W. Durant, U. S. 2,305,215 (1942).
223. Arsem, U. S. 2,472,361 (1949).
224. Muskat and Chenicek, U. S. 2,275,593 (1942).
225. Fr. 636,332 (1927).
226. Moyer and Hersh, U. S. 2,496,354 (1950).
227. Pinkney, U. S. 2,495,282 (1950).
228. Swiss 251,647 (1948); *C.A.*, **44**, 376 (1950).
229. West, U. S. 2,276,243 (1942).
230. Bedford and Urnkelmann, Systematic Survey of Rubber Chemistry, *Chem. Const. Co.*, 1923.
231. Seymour, U. S. 2,455,528 (1948).
232. Wilson and Lang, U. S. 2,171,901 (1939).
233. R. Swain and P. Adams, U. S. 2,237,092 (1941).
234. Reininger, U. S. 801,339 (1905).
235. Holt, U. S. 2,049,806 (1936).
236. Klumb, Marks and Wilson, *J. Am. Water Works Assoc.*, **41**, 933 (1949).
237. H. Marks and F. Strandshov, U. S. 2,580,808 (1952).
238. Gunderson, U. S. 2,493,453 (1950).
239. Emerson and Patrick, U. S. 2,507,700 (1950).
240. *Silk and Rayon*, Feb. 1947, p. 248.
241. Pollack and Fassel, U. S. 2,464,342 (1949).
242. R. Pingee and M. Dahlen, "Textile Finishing Treatment," P. B. 1576, (Office of Technical Sales, Dept. of Commerce, Washington, D.C.).
243. Berlin and Kostryukova, Russ. Pat. 69,582 (1947).
244. Collins and Adrian, Wet Strength Paper, Boyce Publishing Co., New York, 1949.
245. C. Landes and C. Maxwell, *Paper Trade J.*, **121**, No. 6, 37 (1945).
246. W. Norris and J. Bacon, Official Digest, Federation of Paint and Varnish Production Clubs, October 1948, p. 1.
247. A. Hofmann, *Ber.*, **2**, 600 (1869).
248. A. Hofmann, *Ber.*, **3**, 264 (1870).
249. A. Hofmann, *Ber.*, **18**, 2781 (1885).
250. A. Hofmann, *Ber.*, **18**, 3217 (1885).
251. B. Rathke, *Ber.*, **21**, 867 (1888).
252. F. Arndt, *Ann.*, **384**, 350 (1911).
253. G. Heller and W. Bauer, *J. prakt. Chem.*, (2), **65**, 365 (1902).
254. L. Birkofer, *Ber.*, **75B**, 429 (1942).
255. H. King and J. Tonkin, *J. Chem. Soc.*, **1946**, 1063.
256. R. McKee, *J. Prakt. Chem.*, (2), **84**, 825 (1911).
257. W. Traube, F. Kegel and H. Schulz, *Z. Angew. Chem.*, **39**, 1465 (1926).
258. K. Sugino, *J. Chem. Soc. Japan*, **60**, 411 (1939).
259. D. Nagy, U. S. 2,485,983 (1949).
260. M. Busch, G. Blume and E. Pungs, *J. prakt. Chem.*, (2), **79**, 541 (1909).
261. H. Rivier and M. Langer, *Helv. Chem. Acta*, **26**, 1722 (1943).
262. A. Hofmann, *Ber.*, **7**, 1736 (1874).
263. W. Weith and R. Ebert, *Ber.*, **8**, 913 (1875).
263. W. Weith, and R. Ebert, *Ber.*, **8**, 913 (1875).

CHAPTER VII

Isocyanuric Acid and Derivatives

I. Isocyanuric Acid

1. Structure

Isocyanuric acid (I) is the triketo form of cyanuric acid (II). As such it is not distinguished as a solid physical entity separate from cyanuric acid, albeit the triketo form is probably the true solid state structure. In water solutions of cyanuric acid, the "iso" form predominates to the extent of twenty to one, while in acid solutions it probably is present in a still greater ratio. The enol or cyanuric acid form exists largely in basic media (for further discussion of this keto-enol tautomerism, see Chapter I).

Since isocyanuric acid is indistinguishable in physical properties from cyanuric acid, it is only by means of its derivatives, principally those involving substitution on the nitrogen atoms, that isocyanuric acid (or isocyanurates) may be characterized. Commonly the 1,3,5-trisubstituted-2,4,6-trioxohexahydro-s-triazines can be and are named as derivatives of isocyanuric acid as, for example, trimethyl isocyanurate. When derivatives become more complex, such a practice becomes overly cumbersome, and resort must be made to naming the compounds as derivatives of 2,4,6-trioxohexahydro-s-triazine.

2. Salts of Isocyanuric Acid

Few examples exist of salts of isocyanuric acid. Hantzsch[1] has reported that a mercury salt (IV) may be obtained by treating a solution of trisodium cyanurate (III) with mercurous chloride or with mercurous acetate at 100°. The dihydrate formed loses water at 140°. The struc-

ture written for the mercury salt is hypothetical only. The sole piece of evidence for the N—Hg type salt is that it is different from the known mercury salt of cyanuric acid. If the reaction is conducted at a temperature of 0°, the mercury salt of cyanuric acid results. At intermediate temperatures, it is claimed that mixtures are produced in which mercury replacement of hydrogen on nitrogen and on oxygen occurs in the same molecule. It is more likely that inseparable mixtures of mercury cyanurate and mercury isocyanurate are formed. For a discussion of these mixed salts, see page 73.

Close[2] has found that molecular complexes of monosubstituted biurets and monosubstituted isocyanurates are easily formed. A 1:1 molecular complex between isocyanuric acid (cyanuric acid) and biuret was prepared in 87% yield. These complexes are discussed further under Section III below.

II. 1,3,5-Trihalo-2,4,6-trioxohexahydro-s-Triazines

1. 1,3,5-Trichloro-2,4,6-trioxohexahydro-s-triazine

A. Historical

This compound, also called trichloroisocyanuric acid, was discovered by Chattaway and Wadmore[3] in 1902 and called trichloriminocyanuric acid by them. That is was different from cyanuric chloride was established by analysis by its discoverers, who further demonstrated that it contained the nitrogen-chlorine structure which is not possessed by cyanuric chloride. The name trichloroisocyanuric acid is commonly used, but the systematic nomenclature of 1,3,5-trichloro-2,4,6-trioxo-hexahydro-s-triazine is preferred.

B. Physical Properties

1,3,5-Trichloro-2,4,6-trioxohexahydro-s-triazine (V) possesses the characteristic odor of hypochlorous acid. It forms white crystalline prisms melting at 145°. Chloroform and water dissolve it slightly; ligroin not at all.

C. Synthesis

(1) Laboratory Methods. (a) *Potassium hypochlorite.* 1,3,5-Trichloro-2,4,6-trioxohexahydro-s-triazine may be prepared[3] in the laboratory by treating a solution of cyanuric acid (II) dissolved in the theoretical amount of 5% potassium hydroxide solution with a rapid current of chlorine at 0°. After washing the heavy white crystalline powder a few times with water and drying on a water bath, the pure substance is obtained in 90% yields.

K salt of II   (V) 90% yield

(b) *Sodium hypochlorite and ultraviolet light.* It has also been prepared by passing a chlorine stream activated by ultraviolet light[4] over a cooled flowing film of cyanuric acid in aqueous sodium hydroxide. Yields of 56% ware reported.

(2) Commercial. (a) The sodium hypochlorite-ultraviolet light method (b) above is the basis for a pilot plant process[5] suitable for the production of about 70 lbs. per week of 1,3,5-trichloro-2,4,6-trioxohexahydro-s-triazine.

(b) The compound has been prepared commercially from phosgene and ammonia[6] by treating the intermediate, cyanuric acid, with a 15% excess of sodium hydroxide and chlorine at 5°. Yields are said to be 85%.

D. Structure and Reactions

1,3,5-Trichloro-2,4,6-trioxohexahydro-*s*-triazine in every way demonstrates[2] reactions typical of the nitrogen-chlorine bond. When added to hydrochloric acid, chlorine is rapidly liberated with effervescence.[2] It liberates bromine from hydrobromic acid,[2] and iodine from hydriodic acid.[2] It oxidizes sulfites to sulfates[2] and sets sulfur free from hydrogen sulfide.[2] Cyanuric acid is formed in all cases. A violent reaction which may become explosive takes place with ammonia;[2] nitrogen is evolved and (II) is produced. When boiled with water or dilute acids or bases, hydrolysis occurs and cyanuric acid together with hypochlorite decomposition products result.

When 1,3,5-trichloro-2,4,6-trioxohexahydro-*s*-triazine was heated with cyclohexene[7] at 60° in carbon tetrachloride, 3-chlorocyclohexene was produced together with some cyanuric acid and resinous products.

E. Commercial Applications

1,3,5-Trichloro-2,4,6-trioxohexahydro-*s*-triazine is useful as a decontaminant,[4,5] behaving in much the same fashion as hypochlorite solutions. Commercially, it is known as Decontaminant 40.

2. 1,3,5-Tribromo-2,4,6-trioxohexahydro-*s*-triazine

In attempts[2] to prepare the tribromo compound, which is commonly called tribromoisocyanuric acid, by treatment of potassium cyanurate with bromine in a manner similar to that described above for chlorine, the reaction proceeds only partially, and an impure product is obtained.[2]

3. 1,3,5-Triiodo-2,4,6-trioxohexahydro-*s*-triazine

This compound (VI) was prepared in 1930 by trimerization of the corresponding monomer. 1,3,5-Triiodo-2,4,6-trioxohexahydro-*s*-triazine is a heavy orange-colored powder either insoluble or difficultly soluble in most organic solvents. It dissolves to some degree in acetone, dioxane, and alcohol, but these solvents cause[8] a gradual decomposition even at —80°. It is prepared by a method entirely different from that used for the trichloro analog. This consists of the cautious polymerization, with cooling, of iodine isocyanate, INCO, which is prepared by treatment[8] of an ethereal suspension of silver cyanate with iodine. The dimer, $(INCO)_2$, may also be further polymerized.

$$3\ INCO \longrightarrow$$

III. Esters of Isocyanuric Acid

The largest single group of isocyanuric acid derivatives are the esters. These may be regarded structurally as N-substituted cyclic amides; however, they have been designated as esters throughout the literature, and this nomenclature is retained throughout this volume. The corresponding derivatives of cyanuric acid, the 2,4,6-trialkoxy-s-triazines, are also called esters. The latter are sometimes called O-esters or normal esters in the literature and have been referred to as "esters" in a majority of papers published in the field.

Although quite a number of the isocyanuric esters are known, much of the chemical work has dealt with the lower members of the alkyl and aryl series, a situation already encountered with cyanuric acid esters (alkoxy-s-triazines).

Isocyanurates and cyanurates are distinguished, and their structures originally were determined, by means of their behavior upon alkaline hydrolysis. Hydrolysis of alkyl isocyanurates produces the alkylamine and carbon dioxide, while hydrolysis of the alkyl cyanurates gives cyanuric acid and the respective alcohol.

1. Alkyl Esters

A. Monoesters and Derivatives

(1) Monoesters. The monoalkyl isocyanurates have been only recently synthesized as a series with the exception of the lowest member, monomethyl isocyanuric acid or 1-methyl-2,4,6-trioxohexahydro-*s*-triazine (IX) which was prepared[9] in 1897 from both 1,7-dimethyl-3-nitrotriuret (VII) and 1,7-dimethyltriuret (VIII). The other compounds of the alkyl series were not known until the work of Close appeared in 1953.[10]

All of the known monoalkyl isocyanurates are high melting solids insoluble in water. They are weak acids and are alkali soluble.[10] The methyl derivatives may be recrystallized from hot water,[9] separating as leaflets containing one equivalent of water which is only lost at 100°. All other monoaryl isocyanurates have been recrystallized from ethanol.

Several procedures are available for synthesis of monoalkyl isocyanurates. The best general method consists in the condensation of a substituted biuret with ethyl carbonate by refluxing in alcoholic solution for one to twenty hours in the presence of sodium ethoxide.[10]

A second general method, one which gives much poorer yields,[10] is to heat a monoalkylurea with two equivalents of urea at 200–250° for two hours. It was only in the case of monomethyl isocyanurate where a 31% yield was achieved that this method was found practical.[10] The

alkyl isocyanurate can be separated from by-product cyanuric acid owing to its greater solubility in alkali. Several other methods have been described for the preparation of monomethyl isocyanurate (IX). It can be prepared by heating 1,7-dimethyl-3-nitrosotriuret (VII) (nitrosocarbonyldimethylurea in the older literature), or by treating

1,7-dimethyltriuret (VIII) (carbonyldimethylurea in the older literature) with 20% sodium hydroxide. Methylbiuret is obtained as a by-
product. The yield[1] from (VIII) is 85%. Compound (IX) has also been
obtained as a degradation product of theobromic acid (X), possibly
through the following intermediates.[11,12]

The monoalkyl isocyanurates are listed in Table VII-1 together
with their melting points and yields. All compounds were recrystallized
from ethanol and were prepared from ethyl carbonate and the respective
monoalkylbiuret unless otherwise indicated.

TABLE VII-1. Monoalkyl Isocyanurates

R	Melting Point, °C.	Yield, %	Ref.
CH_3	275–285[a]	85[c], 31[b]	1, 2
C_2H_5	230–231	82, 4[b]	1
$n\text{-}C_3H_7$	226–227	85	1
$n\text{-}C_4H_9$	239–240	2[b]	1
$sec\text{-}C_4H_9$	266–267	81, 2[b]	1
$iso\text{-}C_4H_9$	229–230	95	1
$n\text{-}C_5H_{11}$	232–233	95	1
$n\text{-}C_6H_{13}$	226–227	94	1

[a] Fischer reports a M.p. of 297°, ref. 2 below.
[b] By fusion of monoalkylurea and urea.
[c] By treating 1,7-dimethylbiuret with alkali, ref. 2 below.

1. W. Close, *J. Am. Chem. Soc.*, **75**, 3617 (1953).
2. E. Fischer and R. Frank, *Ber.*, **30**, 2612 (1897).

The reactions of the monoalkyl isocyanurates have not been extensively investigated. Fischer[9] found that treatment of methyl isocyanurate with alkali and methyl iodide yields trimethyl isocyanurate (XII). This suggests that alkylation of mono- and dialkyl isocyanurates

may be a general reaction. A reaction of monoalkyl isocyanurates which has been shown[3] to be general is formation of 1:1 molecular addition compounds with monosubstituted biurets. The complexes are made in excellent yield[3] by dissolving the starting components in a solvent, heating and then cooling, Leaflets or needles of the complex precipitate. Table VII-2 lists the molecular complexes of monoalkyl isocyanurates and monoalkylbiurets. The complex of cyanuric (isocyanuric) acid and biuret is included also for the sake of completeness.

TABLE VII-2.   Molecular Complexes of Monoalkyl Isocyanurates and Monoalkylbiurets

$\cdot RNHCONHCONH_2$

R	Solvent[a]	Melting Point, °C.	Yield, %
H	A	(Dec.)	87
CH_3	B	(Dec.)	64
C_2H_5	A	172–173	87
$n\text{-}C_3H_7$	A or C	173–175	85
$n\text{-}C_4H_9$	A or C	181–182	93
$iso\text{-}C_4H_9$	B	(Dec.)	85
$n\text{-}C_5H_{11}$	A	178–179	96
$iso\text{-}C_5H_{11}$	B or C	177–178	90
$n\text{-}C_6H_{13}$	B	180–181	94

[a] $A = H_2O$; $B = H_2O$ + acetone; $C = C_2H_5OH$.

As a class, the monoalkyl isocyanurates are mildly hypnotic. n-Propyl and n-hexyl isocyanurates possess anti-convulsant action[10] which is shared by other members of the series to a slight degree.

(2) Derivatives: N-Carboxymethyl Isocyanuric Acid and Ethyl Ester. An interesting methyl substitution derivative of monomethyl isocyanurate (IX) is obtained as one of the products of the hydrochloric acid hydrolysis (1) of N-(carbethoxymethyl) isomelamine[13] (XVIII). N-Carboxymethyl isocyanuric acid (XIX) is isolated as the

$$
\text{(XVIII)} \quad \xrightarrow[180°]{\text{HCl}} \quad \text{(XIX)} \quad + \quad \tag{1}
$$

monohydrate. It readily forms copper, barium, silver and potassium hydrated salts. Treatment (2) of the silver salt with ethyl iodide esterifies the carboxylic acid group giving N-carbethoxymethyl isocyanuric acid (XX) which forms needles melting at 208°.

$$
\text{CH}_2\text{COOAg} \quad + \quad \text{C}_2\text{H}_5\text{I} \quad \longrightarrow \quad \text{CH}_2\text{COOC}_2\text{H}_5 \quad + \quad \text{AgI} \quad \text{(XX)} \tag{2}
$$

B. Diesters

(1) Dimethyl Isocyanurate. Hofmann[14] isolated dimethyl isocyanurate (XIII) in 1881 from the reaction mixture obtained when a,ω-methylacetylurea was heated. It crystallizes in the form of colorless leaflets melting at 222°.

Two convenient methods for preparing the dimethyl ester (which may also be named 1,3-dimethyl-2,4,6-trioxohexahydro-s-triazine) are known as well as several procedures of minor importance. A 40–50% yield[15] may be obtained[15,16] by heating methylurea for five hours at 220–230° (3). The product is difficult to isolate due to the presence of

$$
\xrightarrow[5 \text{ hrs.}]{220-230°} \quad \text{HN} \quad \text{NCH}_3 + 2\,\text{NH}_3 + \text{CH}_3\text{NH}_2 \quad \text{(XIII)} \tag{3}
$$

traces of trimethyl isocyanurate (XII). The above summary of the mechanism is probably not representative of what actually takes place. It is more logical to presume first disproportionation (4) of the substituted urea, rather than straightforward elimination of methylamine.

$$2\,CH_3NHCONH_2 \xrightarrow{\;\varDelta\;} CH_3NHCONHCH_3 + NH_2CONH_2 \qquad (4)$$

Following this, the elimination of three equivalents of ammonia would give (XIII). A second method of preparation[17] is to heat dimethyl

(XIII)

cyanurate (XIV) above 170°, whereupon isomerization to (XIII) takes place (5). The transformation is effected even more readily than that of the trimethyl ester to the corresponding isocompound. Thus when

(XIV)   (XIII)   (5)

dimethyl cyanurate (XIV) is heated in an oil bath, it begins to soften at 165–170°. A few degrees above this temperature, the mass suddenly melts and comes to a vigorous boil with the evolution of cyanic acid (6). The temperature may rise to 320°. Dimethyl isocyanurate can also be obtained[15] in small amounts by the action of methyl iodide on silver cyanurate and also by treatment of trimethyl isocyanurate (XII) with vigorous oxidizing agents.

A crystalline silver salt may be precipitated from a solution of the ammonium salt by addition of silver nitrate. The silver salt crystallizes with one-half mole of water which is lost at 120°, and has the formula: $C_3N_3O_3(CH_3)_2Ag \cdot \tfrac{1}{2}H_2O$. A copper-ammonium salt, $Cu(C_5H_6O_3N_3)_2 \cdot 2\,NH_3$, red-violet crystals, is also known.[18] Dimethyl isocyanurate is a weak acid, soluble in ammonia. Strong heating causes decomposition, from the products of which cyanic acid can be identified. Alkaline fusion produces methylamine and carbon dioxide as the end-products.

(2) Diethyl Isocyanurate. Diethyl isocyanurate (XXV) was prepared[19] in 1859 by ethylation of cyanuric acid. It crystallizes from water in the form of hexagonal rhomboids which melt at 173°. Several convenient methods of preparation are available, all of which involve starting with compounds already containing the s-triazine ring. Possibly the simplest and most reliable is the heat induced isomerization[20] of normal diethyl cyanurate (XXVI). In the event that isomerization is incomplete, the remaining normal ester may be removed by virtue of

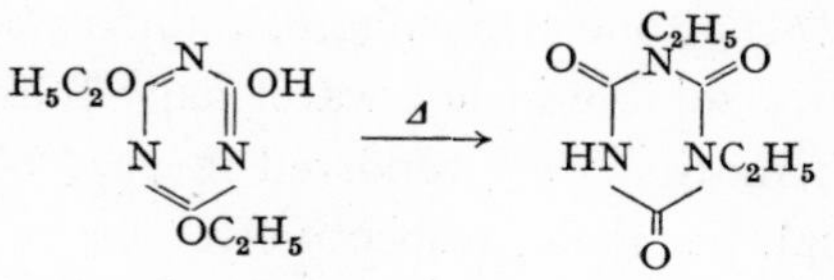

(XXVI)   (XXV)

its greater water solubility. A second method of preparation[21] consists in treating either the mono- or the di-potassium salts of cyanuric acid with ethyl iodide at a temperature of 150–180° (6). Diethyl isocyanurate

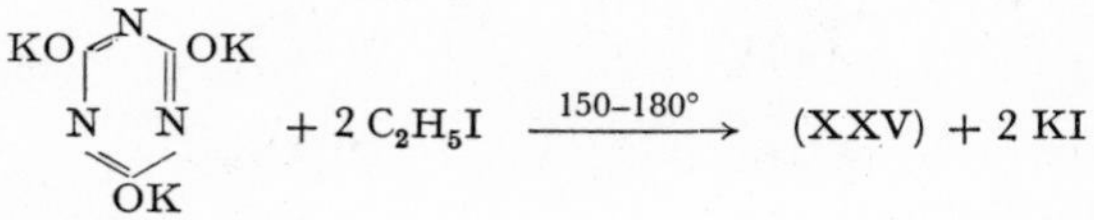

$+ 2 C_2H_5I \xrightarrow{150-180°} (XXV) + 2 KI$ (6)

may be obtained from cyanuric acid by heating with alcoholic potassium hydroxide and potassium ethyl sulfate.[19] However, triethyl isocyanurate is also obtained by this procedure and results in a product which is not easily purified.

Diethyl isocyanurate forms salts easily. Copper-ammonia, barium and silver salts are known. Fusion with potassium hydroxide produces

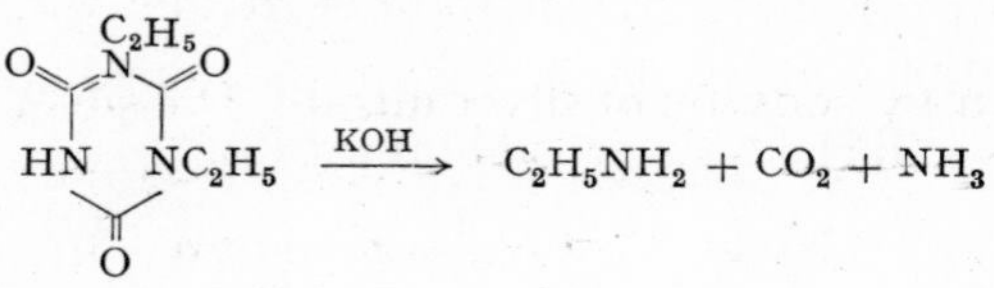

$\xrightarrow{KOH} C_2H_5NH_2 + CO_2 + NH_3$ (7)

(XXV)

ethylamine and carbon dioxide (7), products to be expected from the decomposition of so-called nitrogen esters.

C. Triesters and Derivatives

(1) Trimethyl Isocyanurate and Derivatives. (a) *Trimethyl Iso-cyanurate.* The chemistry of the *s*-triazines in general and the cyanurates and isocyanurates in particular was greatly elucidated by the contributions of A. W. Hofmann. In 1870,[23] he identified trimethyl isocyanurate (XII) and proved that it was produced by the heat induced isomerization of trimethyl cyanurate.

The trimethyl ester of isocyanuric acid has a melting point of 176°, a boiling point of 274° at one atmosphere, and may be crystallized from alcohol. It is slightly soluble in hot water as well as alcohol. Heats of combustion and formation were reported in very old work[22] as 269.3 Kcal. and 22.8 Kcal. per mole, respectively.

The simplest method by which trimethyl isocyanurate may be prepared is by heating or distillation of trimethyl cyanurate (XIII).[17, 23, 24] This is a general reaction of the "normal" cyanuric

(XIII)   (XII)

esters; heating converts them to the iso compounds. The isomerization reaction has not as yet been applied successfully to the amyl and phenyl triesters of cyanuric acid (II), however. In some cases it is possible to convert cyanurates to isocyanurates by heating with an alkyl halide in which the alkyl group is the same as that of the ester.[25] Thus heating trimethyl cyanurate with methyl iodide produces isomerization to (XII).

If mono- or dimethyl isocyanurate is treated with sodium hydroxide and methyl iodide, alkylation of the remaining nitrogens or nitrogen occurs and the triester is obtained (8).[26]

(IX)   (XIV)   (XII)   (8)

Trimethyl isocyanurate can be obtained directly from cyanuric acid by (1) treating silver cyanurate (which may react in the form of silver isocyanurate) with methyl iodide[21] (9), and (2) treating cyanuric

$$\text{AgO} \underset{\text{N}\quad\text{N}}{\overset{\text{N}}{\bigtriangleup}} \text{OAg} \quad \left(\text{or} \quad \underset{\text{AgN}\quad\text{NAg}}{\overset{\text{O}\quad\overset{\text{Ag}}{\text{N}}\quad\text{O}}{\bigtriangledown}} \right) + 3\,CH_3I \longrightarrow (XII) + 3\,AgI \qquad (9)$$

acid with diazomethane.[27] Here again the reaction (10) may be written as a reaction of isocyanuric acid.

$$\underset{\text{HN}\quad\text{NH}}{\overset{\text{O}\quad\overset{\text{H}}{\text{N}}\quad\text{O}}{\bigtriangledown}} \quad + 3\,CH_2N_2 \longrightarrow (XII) \qquad (10)$$

A violent decomposition (11) occurs when nitrosomethylurea is heated; the main product is trimethyl isocyanurate.[28] Methyl isocyanate is also obtained, indicating that this by-product was probably the active intermediate and that the formation occurred through methyl isocyanate rather than by a ring closure-elimination path from the starting material.

$$CH_3N(NO)C(=NH)OH \xrightarrow{\Delta} (XII) + N_2 + H_2O + CH_3N=C=O \qquad (11)$$

Further evidence to support this contention is the fact that methyl (and also ethyl) isocyanurates have been prepared from methyl and ethyl isocyanates,[29] respectively. They can be easily purified when prepared by this method (12).

$$3\,CH_3NCO \xrightarrow{\Delta} (XII) \qquad (12)$$

Trimethyl isocyanurate may be considered an ester with regard to its stability in alkaline solution. Ordinarily it is quite stable, but with $1N$ potassium hydroxide solution at only 40–45° for a few minutes, almost quantitative transformation (13) to trimethylbiuret

$$(XII) \xrightarrow[1\,N\ KOH]{40-45°} CH_3NHCON(CH_3)CONHCH_3 + CO_2 \qquad (13)$$
$$(XV)$$

(XV) occurs.[30] Treatment of (XII) with ammonia results at once in replacement (14) of one oxo group[23] giving 1,3,5-trimethyl-2,4-dioxo-6-

iminohexahydro-s-triazine (XVI). Compound (XVI) melts at 212° when recrystallized from hot water. It forms a 1:1 addition compound with silver nitrate.

$$(XII) \qquad\qquad (XVI)$$

Only one of the carbonyl groups of (XII) will react with Grignard reagents.[31] Attempts to force further Grignard addition resulted in ring cleavage and gave only decomposition products. The products of reaction with ethyl, propyl or phenylmagnesium halides are ring alkylated (arylated) carbinols. For example, trimethyl isocyanurate and ethylmagnesium bromide produce 1,3,5-trimethyl-2-ethyl-2-hydroxy-4,6-dioxohexahydro-s-triazine. The tertiary alcohol group can be readily replaced by treatment with bromine or iodine (15).

$$(XII) + C_2H_5MgBr \longrightarrow \qquad\qquad (15)$$

Trialkyl isocyanurates may be treated with dry hydrogen chloride at temperatures of 180–270° to give isocyanates.[49a] The reaction is best carried out by passing the reactants through heated tubes packed with inert carrier materials.

In order to complete the discussion of the methyl isocyanurates, references is made at this point to the discussion of mixed esters (alkyl groups on both N and O atoms in the same triazine ring) and the Principle of Symmetry [see Chap. I, IV, 1, A, (4)]. To that discussion should here be added the observation that the "mixed esters" reported by Hantzsch and Bauer[32] were found to rearrange upon heating to give the pure trimethyl isocyanurate (16).

$$\xrightarrow{\Delta} (XII) \qquad\qquad (16)$$

(b) *1,3,5-Tri-(chloromethyl)-2,4,6-trioxohexahydro-s-triazine.* (XXI) was isolated in 1885 by Hofmann.[33,34,35] It forms crystals from alcohol which melt at 184°. The compound is soluble in alcohol, chloroform; slightly soluble in benzene and ether; and insoluble in water.

This chlorinated ester is obtained by the action of phosphorous pentachloride[33,34,35] on trimethyl isocyanurate (17). If trimethyl

(XII)   (XXI)   (17)

cyanurate (XIII) is similarly treated, the products obtained are cyanuric chloride (XXII) and methyl chloride (18).

(XIII)   (XXII)   (18)

Treatment of 1,3,5-tri(chloromethyl)-2,4,6-trioxohexahydro-s-triazine (XXI) with boiling water hydrolyzes the compound to cyanuric acid and formaldehyde. This hydrolysis represents one of the few instances in which cyanuric acid is formed from an isocyanuric ester (19).

(II)   (19)

It is known that the halogen atoms on (XXI) are very active, although no semi-quantitative comparison with such derivatives as benzyl chloride, benzoyl chloride or benzal chloride exists.

(c) *Tri(azidomethyl) Isocyanurate.* The 1,3,5-triazido derivative of trimethyl isocyanurate was prepared in 1910.[36] It forms white crystals which melt with decomposition at 153°. It is soluble in pyridine, slightly soluble in acetone and chloroform, and insoluble in alcohol.

1,3,5-Triazidomethyl-2,4,5-trioxohexahydro-s-triazine (XXIII) was reported[36] as having been obtained only once in many repeated distillations of azidomethylisocyanate.[20] Although in this isolated instance the catalysis was obscure, bases such as potassium carbonate

$$3\ N_3CH_2N{=}C{=}O \xrightarrow{\text{distill.}} \begin{array}{c} CH_2N_3 \\ O{\diagdown}N{\diagup}O \\ | \qquad | \\ N_3CH_2N \qquad NCH_2N_3 \\ {\diagdown}C{\diagup} \\ \| \\ O \end{array} \qquad (20)$$

(XXIII)

generally catalyze the trimerization of isocyanates and in most cases alkyl isocyanates spontaneously polymerize or trimerize unless pure.

Alkali treatment of the triazido compound yields cyanuric and hydrazoic acids; this proves it to be an isocyanate trimer rather than a tetrazole derivative. This hydrolysis[21] is a second example [see Section

$$(XXIII) \xrightarrow[\Delta]{NaOH} \left[\begin{array}{c} CH_2OH \\ O{\diagdown}N{\diagup}O \\ | \qquad | \\ HOCH_2N \qquad NCH_2OH \\ {\diagdown}C{\diagup} \\ (XXIV)\ O \end{array} \right] \longrightarrow \begin{array}{c} NaO{\diagup}N{\diagdown}ONa \\ N \qquad N \\ {\diagdown}C{\diagup} \\ ONa \end{array} + 3\ NaN_3 + 3\ CH_2O \quad (21)$$

(II)

III, 1, C, (1), (b) above for the first] in which an isocyanurate, on hydrolysis, yields cyanuric acid instead of an amine and carbon dioxide. Both examples proceed by way of the same intermediate, 1,3,5-tri-methylolhexahydro-s-triazine (XXIV) and the reaction may be explained by assuming reverse addition of formaldehyde. The addition of formaldehyde to amines is known to be reversible.

(2) Triethyl Isocyanurate. From a preparative standpoint, triethyl isocyanurate (XXVII) is probably the best known of the alkyl isocyanurates. It was prepared by Wurtz[38] as early as 1848 and has been prepared since then by a variety of methods, but not until 1876 was evidence[39] for its structure presented. This triester forms rhombic crystals which, after recrystallization from alcohol, melt at 95° and boil at 276° at one atmosphere. The compound is volatile in steam, soluble in dilute acids, ether, and alcohol. Thermochemical values of 424.4 Kcal. and 31 Kcal. for the heats of combustion and formation, respectively, are reported in the older literature.[22] Triethyl isocyanurate may be prepared by methods listed below.

(1) Triethyl cyanurate (XXVII) undergoes heat induced iso-merization to triethyl isocyanurate.[17, 21, 40] The heating (22) requires a longer period of time than is necessary for the isomerization of tri-methyl cyanurate to trimethyl isocyanurate.

(22)

(XXVII)   (XXVIII)

(2) Heating the dipotassium salt of cyanuric acid with excess iodide[21] also gives (XXVIII). The yield could undoubtedly be improved by using the tripotassium salt instead. When in place of the dipotassium salt, the silver salt was used, a mixture of normal and iso esters resulted. This is difficult to explain. Silver salts generally give the iso or abnormal product, and silver salts of nitrogen compounds are generally considered to have silver bound to nitrogen. For example, silver cyanide and an alkyl halide give alkyl carbylamines while sodium cyanide in the same reaction gives aliphatic nitriles. Silver nitrite and alkyl halides give nitroalkanes while sodium nitrite and alkyl halides give alkyl nitrites. It may be that the silver salt of cyanuric acid exists in two forms similar to the silver salts of benzamide, $C_6H_5CONHAg$, orange, and $C_6H_5C(OAg)=NH$, colorless. In considering the salts of cyanuric acid and conversion of them to isocyanurates with alkyl halides, it is ob-served that relatively mild conditions are required to effect reaction when heavy metal salts of cyanuric acid are employed, but more vigorous conditions are needed for alkali metal salts. This is likely due to the heavy metal salts actually existing as salts of isocyanuric acid, (=N—Metal). As such, they would be readily converted to iso-cyanurates while the alkali metal salts might first give rise to cyanurates and these, under the rigorous reaction conditions, undergo isomeriza-tion to the corresponding isocyanurates.

(3) Triethyl isocyanurate may be obtained by hypochlorous acid hydrolysis of triethyl isoammeline (XXIX)[23] or of triethylisomelamine (XXX).[41]

(4) Ethyl chlorocarbonate and potassium cyanate give[42] triethyl

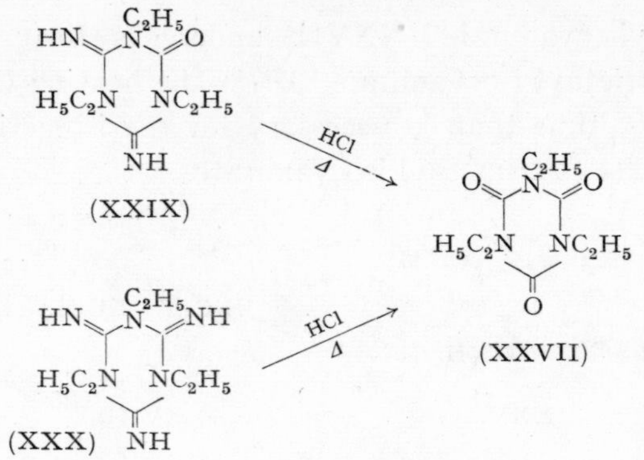

(XXIX)

(XXX)

(XXVII)

isocyanurate when heated together at 200°. The mechanism for this condensation, based on the formation of isocyanurates or carbamates from potassium cyanate and alkyl chlorides, is probably that shown in equation (23). A less likely alternative mechanism is one involving the

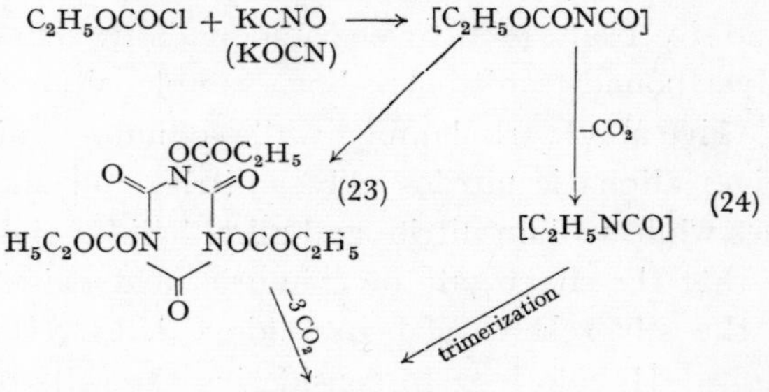

$$C_2H_5OCOCl + KCNO \longrightarrow [C_2H_5OCONCO]$$
$$(KOCN)$$

(23)

$-CO_2$

$[C_2H_5NCO]$ (24)

(XXVII)

formation of ethyl isocyanate, which could undergo trimerization and isomerization during the reaction (24).

(5) Triethyl isocyanurate has been prepared by several miscellaneous procedures which are not of great value synthetically. It is obtained by suitable treatment[39] of ethyl cyanamide, as a by-product in the preparation of ethyl isocyanate from potassium cyanate and potassium ethyl sulfate,[19, 43, 44, 45] and indirectly from ethylamine or ethyl isocyanate[46, 47, 48] and hydrochloric or hydrobromic acids.

The reactions in which triethyl isocyanurate will participate are similar to those described for trimethyl isocyanurate (XII). The principal known reactions (25) involve alkali. As is typical of the alkyl isocyanurates, fusion with potassium hydroxide gives ethylamine and carbon dioxide. Treatment with aqueous barium hydroxide gives[39] tri-ethylbiuret and carbon dioxide, in a manner similar to that of the methyl analog, while sodium methoxide gives the same compound but produces decomposition to ethylene, ethanol, ethylamine, and triethyl guanidine as well.

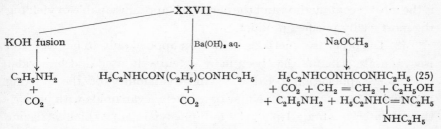

$$\text{XXVII}$$

KOH fusion   Ba(OH)$_2$ aq.   NaOCH$_3$

$C_2H_5NH_2$ $H_5C_2NHCON(C_2H_5)CONHC_2H_5$ $H_5C_2NHCONHCONHC_2H_5$ (25)
+   + $+ CO_2 + CH_2 = CH_2 + C_2H_5OH$
CO_2 CO_2 $+ C_2H_5NH_2 + H_5C_2NHC=NC_2H_5$
        $\underset{NHC_2H_5}{}$

2. Aryl and Arylalkyl Isocyanurates

A. Monoesters

The history of monoaryl isocyanurates is the history of mono-phenyl isocyanurate because most of the synthetic methods were developed in order to prepare the lowest member of the series. After monophenyl isocyanurate (XXXI) was first prepared in 1887 by Rathke,[49] other synthetic methods were gradually developed. The high melting monoaryl isocyanurates can now be synthesized by four principal methods illustrated below:

(1) Ring closure of ethyl-ω-arylallophanates (XLII) with dilute alkali[50] provides a simple means of entry to the series of monoaryl isocyanurates. The starting material is synthesized from the corresponding arylamine and carbonyl diurethane and must be recovered from a by-product, diarylbiuret. When ethyl-ω-arylbiuret carboxylate is added to a solution of dilute sodium hydroxide, ethanol comes off readily[50]

$$ArNH_2 + CO(NHCOOC_2H_5)_2 \longrightarrow \underset{\underset{H}{\underset{|}{H_5C_2OOCNCO}}}{ArNHCONH} + (ArNHCO)_2NH$$

(XLII)

dil. NaOH

$$O \underset{\underset{Y}{\underset{|}{\underset{O}{}}}}{\overset{\overset{Ar}{\overset{|}{N}}}{\underset{HN\quad NH}{\diagup\diagdown}}} O \quad + H_2O$$

(XLIII)

and can easily be detected. The free acid (or its sodium salt) then spontaneously loses an equivalent of water and the ring closes.

(2) The second method has been described above in (Section III, 1, A) for monoalkyl isocyanurates. It comprises the condensation of ethyl carbonate with monoarylbiurets in the presence of alkali.[10] This is the most recent method and the one which appears capable of yielding the most easily purified product.

(3) The other two methods have been applied only to monophenyl isocyanurate. The first has been more extensively used and has wider laboratory application because of the availability of the starting materials. The procedure is to first treat phenylcyanamide with phenyl-thiocyanate[51] to obtain 1-phenyl-4,6-di(phenylamino) 2-thion-s-triazine (XXXIII). The reaction intermediate is not isolated in a pure state but is further treated with hydrochloric acid at 160–170° giving monophenyl isocyanurate or 1-phenyl-2,4,6-trioxohexahydro-s-triazine (XXXI). The

compound may also be obtained by hydrochloric acid hydrolysis of the corresponding 2-imino analog[49] of the above intermediates.

(4) The final method involves hydrolysis of phenylisomelamine

(XXXV), and serves as one of the proofs for the structure of that compound.

The monoaryl isocyanurates are listed in Table VII-3 with their physical properties and methods of preparation.

TABLE VII-3. Monoaryl and Arylalkyl Isocyanurates

Ar	Methods of preparation[a]	M.p., °C.	Solvent	Remarks	Ref.
C_6H_5-	1[c], 2, 3, 4	310–311[b]	Water, ethyl alc.	Yield 89 % by 4	1, 2, 3, 4
$C_6H_5CH_2$-	4	244–245	Ethyl alc.	Yield 73 % by 4	4
$o\text{-}CH_3C_6H_4$-	3	> 300	Ethyl alc.		3
$\beta\text{-}C_{10}H_7$-	3	290–291	—	Insol. most organic solvents	3
$\alpha\text{-}C_{10}H_7$-	3	>290	—	Analysis lacking	3

[a] See Methods of Preparation above.
[b] Rathke[1, 2] reports 290–300°.
[c] From the allophanic acid salt.

1. B. Rathke, *Ber.*, **21**, 867 (1888).
2. B. Rathke, *Ber.*, **20**, 1070 (1887).
3. F. Davis, H. Greider and C. Kidwell, *J. Am. Chem. Soc.*, **41**, 1004 (1919).
4. W. Close, *J. Am. Chem. Soc.*, **75**, 3617 (1953).

The monoaryl isocyanurates are acidic compounds. The phenyl compound (XXXI) forms a silver salt from silver nitrate which is water insoluble but which dissolves in nitric acid and in ammonia. The *o*-tolyl derivative forms a silver salt also. The only compounds tested, monophenyl and monobenzyl isocyanurates, enter into salt formation with the corresponding monoarylbiuret in the same manner as all monoalkyl isocyanurates.[3] A 94% yield of the 2:1 addition compound of phenylbiuret and monophenyl isocyanurate was obtained[3] from water. The complex melts at 209–211°. An 84% yield of the 1:1 addition compound of benzylbiuret and monobenzyl isocyanurate are obtained[3] from acetone-water or alcohol. It melts at 185–186°.

Monobenzyl isocyanurate possesses some anti-convulsant action.[3]

B. Diester

Diphenyl isocyanurate (XXXVI) is the only diaryl isocyanurate reported in the literature. Diphenyl isocyanurate has been reported to melt at 275° when crystallized from water and at 261° when ethanol was used. It may be obtained by hydrochloric acid hydrolysis of 1,3-

diphenyl-2,4-diimino-6-aminophenyl-1,2,3,4-tetrahydro-*s*-triazine
(XXXVII).[49,52]

$$3\ \text{etc. structures} $$

C. Triesters

(1) Triphenyl Isocyanurate. Triphenyl isocyanurate (XXXVIII)
was discovered by Hofmann[23] in 1885 when he found that the substances
resulting from acid hydrolysis of triphenyl isomelamine and from
polymerization of phenyl isocyanate were identical.

The ester melts at 281° when recrystallized from glacial acetic
acid.[53] It may be prepared conveniently by the trimerization of phenyl
isocyanate either by means of heat alone[53] or heat and catalysts, the
best of which are bases. If a catalyst is used, both the nature and the

amount of catalyst govern the time of heating and the temperature
necessary for the trimerization to proceed to completion. For example,
one part of potassium acetate with three parts of phenyl isocyanate
produces complete trimerization at 100° in three hours,[54] while, if the
catalyst ratio is reduced to one part in ten parts of phenyl isocyanate,
a temperature of 180–200° is required. Sodium acetate can be substituted for potassium acetate and used in the one to three ratio but
at temperatures of 180°. If, however, the ratio of sodium acetate catalyst
is reduced to 1:100, a temperature of 200° for a twenty-four hour
period gives only a minor amount of reaction product. Sodium formate
and sodium carbonate behave much like sodium acetate, but sodium
sulfate and sodium phosphate are much slower acting. Pumice stone has
no effect whatever. Sodium ethoxide[55,56] is an excellent catalyst as are
other sodium alkoxides,[57] but suffer from the disadvantage that the
product may become contaminated with phenylurethan. Use of sodium
phenoxide[58,59] and *p*-bromo sodium phenoxide[58] leads to results comparable to those obtained with potassium acetate. Triethyl phosphite,[60]

$(C_2H_5)_3P$, and even acetone[61] have been found to catalyze the trimerization, so broad is the range of usable catalysts. A second useful method for preparing (XXXVIII), triphenyl isocyanurate, is by hydrochloric acid hydrolysis (26) of 1,3,5-triphenylisomelamine conducted at temperatures[23, 52] over 150°. The intermediate product of hydrolysis, 1,3,5-triphenyl-2,6-dioxo-4-iminohexahydro-s-triazine (XXXIX) may

$$\text{(XXXIX)} \xrightarrow[\text{150°}]{\text{HCl}} \text{(XXXVIII)} + NH_3 \tag{26}$$

also be used as a starting material and gives similar results. Small amounts of (XXXVIII) may also be obtained[58] by treating phenylcarbanilate with sodium in the presence of acetic acid. A considerable amount of s-diphenylurea is also produced.

If (XXXVIII) is heated to 300°, decomposition occurs and diphenylcarbodiimide is obtained (27).

$$\text{(XXXVIII)} \longrightarrow C_6H_5N{=}C{=}NC_6H_5 + CO_2 \tag{27}$$

(2) Tribenzyl Isocyanurate. In 1870 Canizzarro[62] isolated a product from the reaction mixture of cyanuric chloride and benzyl alcohol which proved to be tribenzyl isocyanurate (XL). This solid ester can be recrystallized from ethanol and is obtained as glittering needles which melt at 165° and boil at 320° at one atmosphere. Synthesis can be accomplished by any one of several routes.

(a) If benzyl chloride is treated with silver isocyanate, benzyl isocyanate is obtained. Carrying out the reaction under the influence of heat[63] or distilling[63, 64] the benzyl isocyanate also results in the formation of tribenzyl isocyanurate, but the yields are poor.

$$3C_6H_5CH_2Cl + 3AgN{=}C{=}O \rightarrow 3C_6H_5CH_2N{=}C{=}O \xrightarrow[\text{distill}]{\Delta\text{ or}} \text{(XL)}$$

(b) A second route, which gives low yields, but which also involves benzyl isocyanate as the active intermediate, is as follows: benzylamine and carbon oxysulfide react (28) to give benzylthiocarbamic acid,

$$C_6H_5CH_2NH_2 + COS \longrightarrow C_6H_5CH_2NHCOSH \tag{28}$$

which, for the most part, reacts[65] further with another molecule of benzylamine to give s-dibenzylurea. A small portion undergoes hydrogen sulfide elimination and gives benzylisocyanate which, under reaction conditions, trimerizes to tribenzyl isocyanurate (XL).

$$C_6H_5CH_2NHCOSH \xrightarrow{-H_2S} C_6H_5CH_2N{=}C{=}O \longrightarrow XL \qquad (29)$$

(c) In some cases, it is possible to convert cyanurates to isocyanurates by heating them with an alkyl halide.[66] For example, heating trimethyl cyanurate with methyl iodide gave trimethyl isocyanurate, and similarly heating tribenzyl cyanurate with benzyl bromide gives tribenzyl isocyanurate. It is not necessary for the alkyl halide to be the same as the group on the triazine oxygen. To illustrate this, the smooth and almost quantitative conversion of trimethyl cyanurate to tribenzyl isocyanurate may be effected with benzyl

bromide. The alkyl groups of the entering alkyl halide add to the ring nitrogen atoms forming bonds which are stronger than the oxygen-alkyl group bonds by the same token that alkyl amide nitrogen bonds are more resistant to hydrolysis than alkyl ester oxygen bonds. As a result the groups on the oxygen atoms are preferentially eliminated as alkyl halides.

(d) Hantzsch reported[66] that tribenzyl isocyanurate (XL) may be obtained by treating either silver isocyanate or trisilver cyanurate with benzyl iodide. The reaction (30) is said to be vigorous unless the reaction mixture is diluted with ether.

$$\begin{array}{c} 3\,AgNCO \\ or \\ C_3N_3O_3Ag_3 \end{array} + 3\,C_6H_5CH_2I \longrightarrow (XL) + 3\,AgI \qquad (30)$$

(e) A small amount of (XL) may be isolated from the reaction of cyanuric chloride[62] on benzyl alcohol (31), but the major product is

$$Cl\underset{N\quad N}{\overset{N}{\diagdown}}Cl \quad + \; C_6H_5CH_2OH \; \longrightarrow \; (XL) \; + \; \underset{(XLI)}{\overset{CH_2OCONH_2}{\bigcirc}} \tag{31}$$

benzylurethan, XLI. This method represents the first known preparation of tribenzyl isocyanurate.

Reactions of this ester have not been extensively examined but are probably similar to the reactions of other isocyanurates. One reaction that appears unusual is that tribenzyl isocyanurate forms a trihydrochloride[66] (M.p. 128°).

(3) Tritolyl Isocyanurates. Tri-p-tolyl isocyanurate has a melting point of 265°. Both the tri(p-tolyl) (XLIV) and the tri(o-tolyl) isocyanurates are prepared[67] in the same manner as the phenyl and the benzyl analogs, by trimerization of their respective isocyanates under

$$CH_3-\bigcirc-N\underset{CO}{\overset{CO}{\diagup}}N-\bigcirc-CH_3$$

p-tolyl uretidione

the influence of potassium acetate at a temperature of 100° (32). If, in place of potassium acetate, triethyl phosphine is used, the reaction proceeds only as far as the isocyanate dimer, the uretidione. Warming

$$\underset{CH_3}{\overset{N=C=O}{\bigcirc}} \xrightarrow[100°]{KOAc} \quad p\text{-}C_6H_4CH_3N\underset{\underset{O}{(XLIV)}}{\overset{\overset{p\text{-}C_6H_4CH_3}{O\diagdown_N\diagup O}}{}}N p\text{-}C_6H_4CH_3 \qquad \text{m.p. } 265° \tag{32}$$

$$\xrightarrow[\Delta]{P(C_2H_5)_3} \quad \underset{\text{m.p. } 185°}{\text{uretidione}} \xrightarrow[\Delta]{C_2H_5OH} \quad \underset{\underset{\text{m.p. } 111°}{NHCONHCONHCOOC_2H_5}}{\overset{CH_3}{\bigcirc}} \tag{33}$$

the uretidione with alcohol gives only the allophanate (33). No additional data have been published on the properties or chemistry of the tolyl esters of isocyanuric acid.

(4) Tri-*m*-nitrophenyl Isocyanurate. Tri-*m*-nitrophenyl iso-cyanurate (XLV), which forms yellow prisms from acetic acid (M.p. 260°), is obtained along with a great deal of *s*-di(*m*-nitrophenyl) urea[68] (XLVII) when isonitrosoaceto-*m*-nitroanilide (XLVI) is heated with benzoyl chloride in the presence of pyridine.

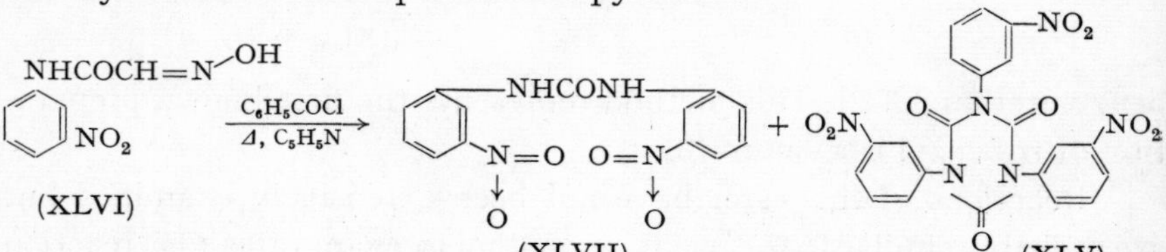

3. Alkyl-Aryl Isocyanurates

Isocyanuric acid derivatives containing both alkyl and aryl groups on the same ring, although both groups are *not* on nitrogen atoms, may be prepared by N-alkylation[69] of 2-phenyl-4,6-dihydroxy-2,3-dihydro-*s*-triazine (XLVIII). The compounds prepared in this manner are 1-methyl-4-phenyl-2,6-dioxohexahydro-*s*-triazine and 1-ethyl-4-phenyl-2,6-dioxohexahydro-*s*-triazine (XLIX). The methyl compound forms colorless prismatic needles, M.p. 238°, and the ethyl derivative melts at 250°, in both cases when crystallized from water. The starting compound, 2-phenyl-4,6-dihydroxy-2,3-dihydro-*s*-triazine, is best written in the iso form. It is prepared by condensing two molecules of urea with one of benzaldehyde and pyrolyzing the product. Alkylation is readily accomplished using ethyl or methyl iodide and methanolic

$$C_6H_5CHO + 2\,NH_2CONH_2 \rightarrow C_6H_5CH(NHCONH_2)_2 \xrightarrow{\Delta}$$

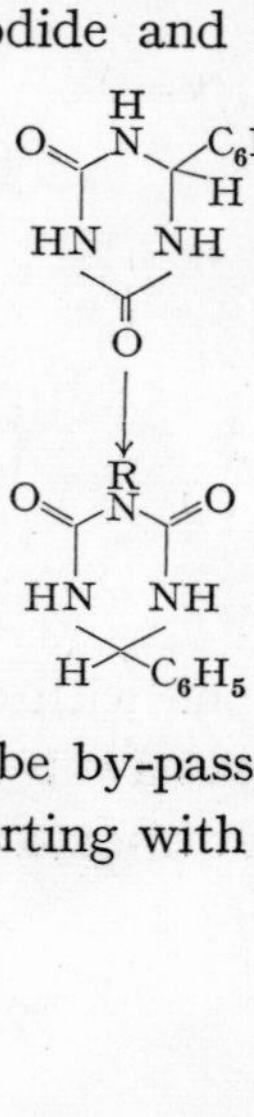

(XLVIII)

RI + KOH/CH$_3$OH

potassium hydroxide. The alkylation step may be by-passed and the 1-alkyl derivative obtained more directly by starting with the appropriate monoalkyl urea. The reaction (34) is illustrated for the methyl compound (L).

$$2\ CH_3NHCONH_2 + C_6H_5CHO \longrightarrow C_6H_5CH(NHCONHCH_3)_2$$

(34)

Yields by this method are relatively poor (30%), and substantial amounts of benzaldehyde, 2-phenyl-1,2-dihydro-2,4-dihydroxy-s-triazine etc., contaminate the product.

A bisymmetrical compound in the same structural category as the above esters is known.[70] It is 1,4-bis(2,3,4,5-tetrahydro-2,4-dioxo-5-phenyl-s-triazin-6-yl) butane (LI), white crystals which melt at 135° after recrystallization from alcohol. It is soluble in alcohol, dioxane and acids. Compound (LI) and other members of the series[70] may be obtained by dilute acid hydrolysis of a 1,4-bis(2,3,4,5-tetrahydro-4-oxo-2-imino-5-aryl-s-triazin-6-yl) butane (LII). The starting compounds are prepared by condensation of dicarboxylic acids or acid chlorides with

aryl biurets. Their chemistry is discussed elsewhere. The 1,4-bis(2,3,4,5-tetrahydro-2,4-dioxo-5-aryl-s-triazin-6-yl)-butanes are used to destroy microorganisms and are useful in the field of medicinals.

The following 2-aryl or alkyl-2-hydroxytrimethyl isocyanurates are known: 2-phenyl-2-hydroxytrimethyl isocyanurate, M.p. 174°, 2-ethyl-2-hydroxytrimethyl isocyanurate, M.p. 112–113°, and 2-n-propyl-2-hydroxytrimethyl isocyanurate.[31] These compounds are prepared by the action of Grignard reagents on trimethyl isocyanurate.

For example, 1,3,5-trimethyl-2-phenyl-2-hydroxy-4,6-dioxohexahydro-s-triazine (LIII) is obtained in 69% yield by the action of phenyl-magnesium bromide[31] on trimethyl isocyanurate (XII). For a discussion of the reaction, see [Section III, 1, C, (1), (a)]. The tertiary hydroxyl group in the resulting carbinols is readily displaced by bromine or iodine.

IV. Isothiocyanuric Acid

1. Esters of Isodithiocyanuric Acid

A. 1,5-Diphenyl-2,6-dithion-4-oxohexahydro-s-triazine (LIV)

This diester of isodithiocyanuric acid was isolated in 1930 during an investigation of an extension of the Michael reaction. It crystallizes from methyl alcohol in the form of beautiful yellow rectangular prisms melting at 248°. (LIV) is soluble in cold alkali from which it is precipitated by acids. Boiling with dilute alkali causes decomposition.

Urethane adds to the double bond of unsaturated esters.[71] It also reacts with such unsaturated compounds as isocyanates and thiocarbimides or isothiocyanates.[71] For example, phenyl isocyanate reacts readily with urethane and gives the sodium derivative of carbethoxyphenylurea (35).

$$C_6H_5N{=}C{=}O + NaNHCOOC_2H_5 \longrightarrow C_6H_5N(Na)CONHCOOC_2H_5 \xrightarrow{H^+}$$
$$C_6H_5NHCONHCOOC_2H_5 \tag{35}$$

Phenyl isothiocyanate also reacts with urethane in the presence of sodium to yield the sodium derivative of carbethoxyphenylthiourea. The reaction (36) does not stop at this point, however, and the substituted thiourea reacts with another molecule of mustard oil to form

$$C_6H_5N{:}C{:}S + NaNHCOOC_2H_5 \longrightarrow C_6H_5(Na)CSNHCOOC_2H_5 \xrightarrow{H^+}$$

$$C_6H_5NHCSNHCOOC_2H_5 \xrightarrow[Na]{C_6H_5N:C:O} \tag{36}$$

(LIV)

the s-triazine (LIV). The reaction is shown[72] to proceed in this fashion by the fact that an identical product was obtained by treating the intermediate, carbethoxyphenyl thiourea, with phenylisothiocyanate (37).

$$C_6H_5NHCSNHCOOC_2H_5 + C_6H_5N{=}C{=}O \xrightarrow{Na} \text{(LIV)} \tag{37}$$

An isomer of 1,5-diphenyl-2,6-thion-4-oxohexahydro-s-triazine (LIV) which might have been produced in the reaction and which possesses the same molecular formula is (LV). Structure (LV) is rejected for the reaction product because of the fact that from the thiomethyl

$$
\begin{array}{c}
S \\
\| \\
H_5C_6N \quad NH \\
C_6H_5N \diagdown S \diagup O \quad (LV)
\end{array}
$$

derivative of the compound in question, only one atom of sulfur can be removed as mercuric sulfide on treatment with red mercuric oxide in alcoholic solution. This shows that the second sulfur atom is not present in the molecule as a member of the ring, which would be the case if (LV) were the correct structure, but rather that it is present in the thioketonic form as in (LIV).

The monomethyl derivative (LVI) is obtained upon treating (LIV), dissolved in a minimum amount of caustic soda solution, with

$$
\underset{O \;(LIV)}{\overset{C_6H_5}{\underset{H_5C_6N \quad N}{S \diagdown N \diagup SH}}} \quad + \; CH_3I + NaOH \; \xrightarrow[\text{EtOH}]{\Delta} \; \underset{O \;(LVI)}{\overset{C_6H_5}{\underset{H_5C_6N \quad N}{S \diagdown N \diagup SCH_3}}} \quad + \; NaI + H_2O
$$

the requisite quantity of methyl iodide. The mixture is boiled for about fifteen minutes afte rwhich colored crystals separate, in the form of shining hexagonal prisms, melting at 220°. When an alcoholic solution of (LVI) was boiled with excess mercuric oxide, it turned black due to conversion of the oxide to mercuric sulfide. The alcoholic filtrate gives a white solid. On recrystallization from alcohol, shining colorless plates of 1,5-diphenyl-2-thiomethyl-4,6-dioxotetrahydro-s-triazine

$$
\underset{O \;(LVI)}{\overset{C_6H_5}{\underset{H_5C_6N \quad N}{S \diagdown N \diagup SCH_3}}} \quad \xrightarrow{\text{HgO red}} \quad \underset{O \;(LVII)}{\overset{C_6H_5}{\underset{H_5C_6N \quad N}{O \diagdown N \diagup SCH_3}}} \quad + \; HgS \qquad (37)
$$

(LVII), M.p. 195°, are obtained[71] (37). The benzoyl derivative (LVIII) of 1,5-diphenyl-2,6-thion-4-oxohexahydro-s-triazine is obtained by the Schotten-Baumann process. When crystallized from alcohol, the shining, colorless prisms melt at 158–159°. It is possible that the structure of the benzoyl derivative may not be correct as written (LVIII). The

benzoyl group may have migrated to, or have become directly attached
at the nitrogen atom, giving instead 1,5-diphenyl-3-benzoyl-4-oxo-

2,6-dithionhexahydro-s-triazine (LIX). A bromo derivative was obtained by dissolving (LIX) in glacial acetic acid and adding bromine
water. The precipitate was crystallized from alcohol. It was found to
shrink and soften at 140°, and melted at 200°.[71]

B. Other 1,5-Esters of 2,6-Dithion-4-oxohexahydro-s-triazine

A number of other esters of dithioisocyanuric acid have been prepared by the reaction of the corresponding isothiocyanate with
urethane. These derivatives are the o-tolyl, m-tolyl, 3,4-xylyl, and allyl-
esters. Their properties and those of their derivatives are included in
Table VII-4. Only in the case of allyl isocyanate is the reaction somewhat different. In this reaction the first product, the carbethoxy-
thiourea, had to be separated. It, in turn, was treated with another
equivalent of allyl isocyanate giving the diallyl-substituted s-triazine.
In the case of aromatic isothiocyanates, the s-triazines are formed
irrespective of the quantity of isothiocyanate used.

The second step of the urethane-isothiocyanate synthesis of 1,5-
diesters of isodithiocyanuric acid; that is, the addition of an isothiocyanate to the intermediate carbethoxyarylthiourea, gives a useful
method of preparing isomeric s-triazine compounds. This method

furnishes a series of isomeric *s*-triazines which are also listed in Table VII-4 together with their physical properties and known derivatives. For example, carbethoxyphenylthiourea (LX) and *o*-tolylisothiocyanate (LXI) give compound (LXIV) which is different from, but

TABLE VII-4. 1,5-Esters of 2,6-dithion-4-oxohexahydro-*s*-triazines and Derivatives[1,2]

$$S{\bigvee_{R_2N}^{R_1}}{\bigvee_{NH}^{S}}$$
$$O$$

R_1	R_2	M.p., °C./Solvent; Crystalline form	Derivatives (Derivative, M.p., °C./solvent)
C_6H_5-	C_6H_5	248/CH_3OH. Yellow, rectangular prisms	2-CH_3-, 220/C_2H_5OH 2-C_6H_5CO-, 158–159/ C_2H_5OH. Bromo, 200/C_2H_5OH 1,5-Diphenyl-2-methyl-thiol 4,6-dioxohexa-hydro-*s*-triazine[a]
o-$CH_3C_6H_4$-	*o*-$CH_3C_6H_4$-	280/CH_3OH. Yellow, rectangular prisms	
m-$CH_3C_6H_4$-	*m*-$CH_3C_6H_4$-	237/CH_3OH (shrinks at 226). Yellow, rectangular prisms	
3,4-$(CH_3)_2C_6H_3$-	(R_1 and R_2)	223–225/dil. C_2H_5OH	
$CH_2{=}CHCH_2$-	$CH_2{=}CHCH_2$-	133/C_2H_5OH	
o-$CH_3C_6H_5$-	C_6H_5	235–236/CH_3OH. Rectangular prisms	2-C_6H_5CO-, 155/C_2H_5OH
p-$CH_3C_6H_4$-	C_6H_5	251–252/CH_3OH	
C_6H_5-	*o*-$CH_3C_6H_4$-	244–245/CH_3OH	2-C_6H_5CO-, 205/C_2H_5OH. Shining prisms. Insoluble Hg and Pb salts result with $HgCl_2$ and $Pb(OAC)_2$, respectively
p-$CH_3C_6H_4$-	*o*-$CH_3C_6H_4$-	224/CH_3OH. Yellow rectangular prisms	
p-$CH_3C_6H_4$-	$CH_2{=}CHCH_2$-	145/C_2H_5OH	
o-$CH_3C_6H_4$-	$CH_2{=}CHCH_2$-	136–137/C_2H_5OH	

[a] This compound, M.p. 195° recrystallized from alcohol, was discussed in Section IV, 1 under reactions of 1,5-diphenyl-2,6-dithion-4-oxohexahydro-*s*-triazine and its derivative 1,5-diphenyl-2-methylthiol-6-thion-4-oxohexahydro-*s*-triazine. It represents the only known derivative of monothioisocyanuric acid.

1. T. Ghosh and P. Guha, *J. Indian Chem. Soc.*, **7**, 263 (1930).
2. R. Doran, *J. Chem. Soc.*, **69**, 326 (1896).

isomeric with (LXV) obtained from carbethoxy-*o*-tolythiourea (LXII) and phenyl isothiocyanate (LXIII). In a similar manner, carbethoxy-*p*-tolylthiourea can be condensed with phenyl, *o*-tolyl, and allyl isocyanates and carbethoxy-*o*-tolylthiourea with allyl isocyanate. Carbethoxyphenylurea $C_6H_5NHCONHCOOC_2H_5$, does not react further with isocyanates or isothiocyanates to yield *s*-triazine compounds as the corresponding thioureas always do.

2. Esters of Isotrithiocyanuric Acid

The only member of this series is 1,3,5-tri(1-carbomethoxyisobut-1-enyl)-*s*-triazine-2,4,5-trithion (LXVI), yellow crystals which melt at 206–208° after recrystallization from ethanol. This 1,3,5-trisubstituted derivative of 2,4,6-isotrithiocyanuric acid can be obtained by either of two methods.[73]

A. Refluxing sodium ethylacetoacetate and methyl-2-chloro-5,5-dimethylthiazoline-4-carboxylate (LXVII) in benzene for twenty hours or

B. Heating the thiazoline (LXVII) with sodium acetate and hydantoin at 100° for a day.

V. Other Isocyanuric Compounds

1. 1,3,5-Tricarbethoxyhexahydro-*s*-triazine (LXIX)

The polymerization of carbethoxy isocyanate (LXVIII) is reported in the literature[37] but without details (38).

2. Tetrahydro-1-phenyl-3,5-di-p-tolyl-2-oxo-s-triazine

This s-triazine (LXX) is not, strictly speaking, an isocyanurate, but rather a miscellaneous compound which is discussed in several places in this volume. It melts at 148° upon recrystallization from benzene and ligroin. It is weakly basic. Preparation[37] is carried out by treating p-toluidine with formaldehyde at 45° and then with phenyl isocyanate at 100° (39). Treatment with acid causes decomposition to phenyl-p-tolylurea, formaldehyde, and p-toluidine.

(39)

(LXX)

References

1. A. Hantzsch, *Ber.*, **35**, 2721 (1902).
2. F. Chattaway and J. Wadmore, *J. Chem. Soc.*, **81**, 200 (1902).
3. W. Close, *J. Am. Chem. Soc.*, **75**, 3619 (1953).
4. C. Hands, F. Whitt and J. Phillips, Brit. 634,801 (1950) through *Chem. Abstracts*, **44**, 7356 (1950).
5. C. Hands and F. Whitt, *J. Soc. Chem. Ind.*, **67**, 66 (1948).
6. R. Jenkins and E. Hardy, PB 27396, OSRD#6390, Dec. 31, 1945.
7. K. Ziegler, A. Spath, E. Schaal, W. Schumann and E. Winkelmann, *Ann.*, **551**, 80 (1942).
8. L. Birckenbach and M. Linhard, *Ber.*, **63B**, 2528 (1930).
9. E. Fischer and F. Frank, *Ber.*, **30**, 2612 (1897).
10. W. Close, *J. Am. Chem. Soc.*, **75**, 3617 (1953).
11. H. Blitz, *Ber.*, **67**, 1856 (1934).
12. H. Blitz, M. Heyn, H. Mundt and P. Damm, *Ber.*, **67B**, 1856 (1934).
13. R. Kruger, *J. prakt. Chem.*, (3), **42**, 473 (1890).
14. A. Hofmann, *Ber.*, **14**, 2728 (1881).
15. K. Slotta and R. Tschesche, *Ber.*, **60**, 301 (1927).
16. H. Schiff, *Ann.*, **291**, 367 (1896).
17. A. Hofmann, *Ber.*, **19**, 2063 (1886).
18. H. Ley and F. Werner, *Ber.*, **46**, 4048 (1913).
19. A. Habich and H. Limpricht, *Ann.*, **109**, 101 (1859).
20. A. Hofmann, *Ber.*, **19**, 2077 (1886).
21. J. Ponomarew, *Ber.*, **18**, 3261 (1885).
22. P. Lemoult, *Ann. chim. phys.*, (7), **16**, 338 (1849).
23. A. Hofmann, *Ber.*, **3**, 264 (1870).
23. A. Hofmann and O. Olshausen, *Ber.*, **3**, 269 (1870).
24. P. Klason, *J. prakt. Chem.*, (2), **33**, 129 (1886).
25. E. Bilmann and J. Bjerrum, *Ber.*, **50**, 503 (1917).

26. E. Fischer and F. Frank, *Ber.*, **30**, 2612 (1897).
27. F. Palazzo and G. Scelsi, *Gazz. Ital.*, **381**, 664 (1908).
28. E. Werner, *J. Chem. Soc.*, **115**, 1098 (1919).
29. W. Hartley, J. Dobbie and A. Lander, *J. Chem. Soc.*, **79**, 848 (1901).
30. E. Fischer, *Ber.*, **31**, 3773 (1898).
31. H. Sobotka and E. Block, *J. Am. Chem. Soc.*, **59**, 2606 (1937).
33. A. Hofmann, *Ber.*, **19**, 2087 (1886).
34. A. Hofmann, *Ber.*, **18**, 2796 (1885).
35. A. Hofmann, *Ber.*, **18**, 2800 (1885).
36. M. Forster and R. Müller, *J. Chem. Soc.*, **97**, 1064 (1910).
37. C. Ingold and H. Piggott, *J. Chem. Soc.*, **123**, 2745 (1923).
38. A. Wurtz, *Compt. rend.*, **26**, 368 (1848).
39. M. Mencki, *Ber.*, **9**, 1011 (1876).
40. E. Mulder, *Rec. trav. chim.*, **1**, 191 (1882).
41. A. Hofmann, *Ber.*, **18**, 2786 (1885).
42. A. Wurtz and Henniger, *Bull. soc. chim.*, (2), **44**, 26 (1885).
43. A. Wurtz, *Ann. chim. phys.*, (3), **42**, 57 (1854).
44. A. Hofmann, *Jahr. Fort. Chem.*, **1861**, 515.
45. Rammelsberg, *Jahr. Fort. Chem.*, **1857**, 273.
46. H. Gal, *Ann.*, **137**, 127 (1866).
47. H. Gal, *Compt. rend.*, **61**, 527 (1865).
48. A. Hofmann, *Compt. rend.*, **52**, 1290 (1861).
49. B. Rathke, *Ber.*, **20**, 1070 (1887).
49a. F. Schaefer and E. Drechsel, Can. 505,435 (1954) to American Cyanamid Co.
50. F. Dains, H. Greider and C. Kidwell, *J. Am. Chem. Soc.*, **41**, 1004 (1919).
51. B. Rathke, *Ber.*, **21**, 867 (1888).
52. A. Hofmann, *Ber.*, **18**, 3217 (1885).
53. J. Bailey and A. McPherson, *J. Am. Chem. Soc.*, **39**, 1338 (1917).
54. A. Hofmann, *Ber.*, **18**, 764 (1885).
55. N. Dieckmann and A. Kron, *Ber.*, **41**, 1261 (1908).
56. A. Michael, *Ber.*, **38**, 22 (1905).
57. J. Hoppe, *Dissert.*, Munich, 1902, p. 30.
58. G. Chelintsev and J. Smorgonskii, *J. Gen. Chem.*, **16**, 1485 (1946), through *Chem. Abstracts*, **41**, 5466 (1947).
59. A. Hantzsch and L. Mai, *Ber.*, **28**, 2466 (1895).
60. R. Stolle, *Ber.*, **41**, 1125 (1908).
61. J. Krasuskii and M. Movsum-Zade, *J. Gen. Chem.*, **6**, 1203 (1936), through *Chem. Abstracts*, **31**, 1377 (1937).
62. S. Canizzarro, *Ber.*, **3**, 517 (1870).
63. Kuhn and Riesenfeld, *Ber.*, **24**, 3815 (1891).
65. G. Hazelloch, *Ber.*, **83**, 258 (1950).
64. E. Letts, *Ber.*, **5**, 93 (1872).
65. E. Bilmann and J. Bjerrum, *Ber.*, **50**, 503 (1917).
66. A. Hantzsch and H. Bauer, *Ber.*, **38**, 1005 (1905).
67. W. Frenzel, *Ber.*, **21**, 411 (1888).
68. W. Borsche and A. Fritzsche, *Ber.*, **59B**, 272 (1926).
69. H. Schiff, *Ann.*, **291**, 367 (1896).
70. Swiss 233,870 (1947) to J. R. Geigy, A–G., through *Chem. Abstracts*, **43**, 1444 (1949).
71. T. Ghosh and P. Guha, *J. Indian Chem. Soc.*, **7**, 263 (1930).
72. R. Doran, *J. Chem. Soc.*, **69**, 326 (1896).
73. O. Diels and E. Jacoby, *Ber.*, **41**, 2392 (1908).

CHAPTER VIII

Condensed Ring *s*-Triazine Systems

Compounds in which *s*-triazine rings are fused with other atoms forming heterocyclic compounds containing two or more rings are discussed in this chapter. The material is organized on the basis of (1) the size of the condensed ring, (2) the number of hetero atoms, (3) their position, (4) the number of condensed rings, and (5) the nature of the hetero atoms if other than nitrogen. The organization under this system is usual with respect to Chemical Abstracts with the exception that endo compounds, excluding hexamethylenetetramine which is classified as three condensed triazine rings and treated separately (Chapter X), are presented first.

In a limited number of instances, the usual system of discussing the history, physical properties, preparation, etc., of each compound has of necessity not been followed because of the nature and paucity of literature available.

I. Endo Compounds

1. 1,4-Endomethylene-2-amino-6-imino-*s*-triazine (I)

This compound melts at 215°. A small amount is formed by the primary reaction of chloracetic ester at the central nitrogen atom of biguanide. The reaction is accompanied by splitting off of water and

$$\underset{H_2NCNHCNH_2}{\overset{NH\ NH}{\overset{\|\ \ \|}{}}} + ClCH_2COOC_2H_5 \rightarrow \underset{(I)}{\overset{HN\diagdown N\diagup NH_2}{\underset{N\diagdown\diagup N}{\overset{|CH_2|}{}}}} + \text{mostly } HCl\cdot\underset{H_2NCNHCNHCH_2COOH}{\overset{NH\ NH}{\overset{\|\ \ \|}{}}} \tag{1}$$

alcohol and formation of the triazine, however the chief product is biguanide-5-acetic acid hydrochloride. For comments on the structure offered[1] for (I), see Section I.2. immediately below.

423

Unlike biguanides and guanylureas containing an unsubstituted amino group, the triazine (I) forms no copper complex.

2. 1,4-Endomethylene-2-dimethylamino-6-imino-s-triazine (II)

If, in the method for the synthesis of 1,4-endomethylene-2-amino-6-imino-s-triazine (I), dimethylbiguanide is used in place of biguanide (2), approximately equal amounts of 1,4-endomethylene-2-dimethylamino-6-imino-s-triazine (II) and 1,1-dimethylbiguanide-5-acetic acid hydrochloride are formed.[1]

$$
\begin{array}{c}
NH \quad NH \\
\parallel \quad \parallel \\
(CH_3)_2NCNHCNH_2 + ClCH_2COOC_2H_5 \rightarrow
\end{array}
\quad
\begin{array}{c}
HN \quad N \quad N(CH_3)_2 \\
| \quad CH_2 \\
N \quad | \quad N \\
(II)
\end{array}
\quad + \quad
\begin{array}{c}
HCl \cdot NH \quad NH \\
\parallel \quad \parallel \\
(CH_3)_2N—C—NHC \\
| \\
NH \\
| \\
CH_2 \\
| \\
COOH
\end{array}
\quad (2)
$$

Compounds (I) and (II) were both isolated and analyzed as their hydrochlorides. (I) was analyzed for nitrogen only and (II) for all elements. In each case the analysis was well within experimental limits. Despite this, the authors cannot accept the postulated structures (I and II) both of which violate Bredt's Rule and are not substantiated by chemical proof. It still has not been proved possible to obtain compounds with double bonds at the bridgehead carbon. The structures offered by Slotta and Tschesche[1] are retained for classification purposes and only in the absence of more plausible structures.

3. 1,3,5-Triazatricyclo[3,3,1,1³,⁷] decane (IIa)

This polynuclear s-triazine is a homomorph of hexamethylene-tetramine (Chapter X) in which the central nitrogen atom is replaced by a carbon atom. Compound (IIa) has been numbered as indicated.[3a]

In the same manner as hexamethylenetetramine is named 1,3,5,7-tetrazatricyclo[3,3,1,1³·⁷]decane; compound (IIa) is named as a derivative of tricyclodecane: 1,3,5-triazatricyclo[3,3,1,1³·⁷]decane.[3a]

It is a white, hygroscopic, crystalline solid. In a sealed tube it sublimes at 185° and melts with decomposition at 260°. Needles are obtained by evaporating toluene solutions under vacuum. The substance easily sublimes and can be resublimed at 40–45° at 1.5 mm. It is soluble in water, methanol, ethanol, *n*-butanol and acetone; slightly soluble in toluene; and insoluble in petroleum ether, benzine fractions and ether. Aqueous solutions are neutral to phenolphthalein. Compound (IIa) may be prepared as illustrated below (2a) in 80% yield.

$$\begin{array}{c}
CH_2COOCH_3 \\
| \\
CHCH_2COOCH_3 \\
| \\
CH_2COOCH_3
\end{array}
\longrightarrow
\begin{array}{c}
CH_2NH_2 \\
| \\
CHCH_2NH_2 \\
| \\
CH_2NH_2
\end{array}
\xrightarrow[\text{paraformaldehyde}]{(CH_2O)_x}
\begin{array}{c}
(IIa) + H_2O \\
(80\%)
\end{array}
\qquad (2a)$$

4. 1-Methyl-3,5,7-triazatricyclo[3,3,1,1³·⁷]decane (III)

This compound is also analogous to hexamethylenetetramine. In this case the central nitrogen atom is replaced by an alkyl substituted carbon atom. It is numbered as indicated[2] and named in the same manner. Compound (III) melts at 175° when crystallized from ligroin,

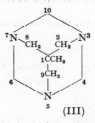

(III)

and is slightly soluble in water, alcohol, benzene, and acetone and insoluble in ether. 1-Methyl-3,5,7-triazatricyclo-[3,3,1,1,³·⁷]decane is prepared from propionaldehyde by the following total synthesis[3] (3).

With dry hydrogen chloride a hygroscopic dihydrochloride, m.p. 195° (dec.), is formed. The free base sublimes at 100° but is less volatile than hexamethylenetetramine. It does not decompose when heated with hydrochloric acid at 100°. Evaporation of such a solution pro-

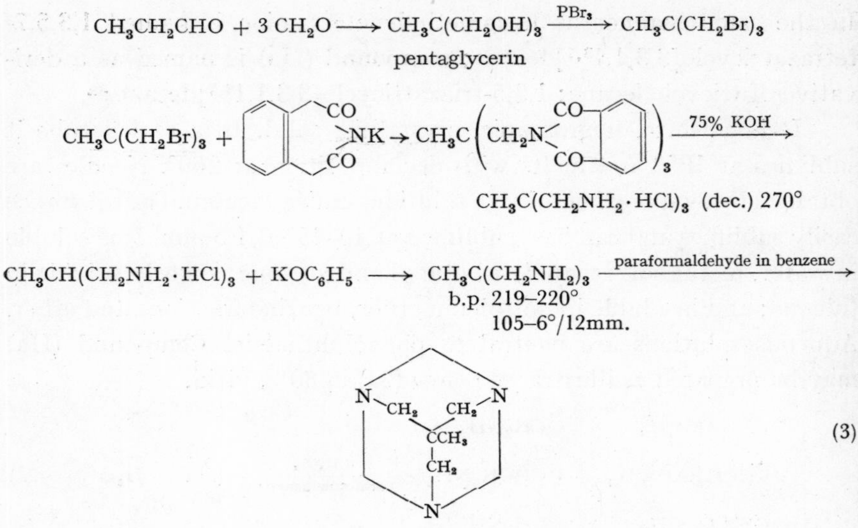

$$CH_3CH_2CHO + 3 CH_2O \longrightarrow CH_3C(CH_2OH)_3 \xrightarrow{PBr_3} CH_3C(CH_2Br)_3$$

pentaglycerin

$$CH_3C(CH_2NH_2 \cdot HCl)_3 \text{ (dec.) } 270°$$

$$CH_3CH(CH_2NH_2 \cdot HCl)_3 + KOC_6H_5 \longrightarrow CH_3C(CH_2NH_2)_3 \xrightarrow{\text{paraformaldehyde in benzene}}$$

b.p. 219–220°
105–6°/12mm.

(3)

(III)

duces a hygroscopic monohydrochloride, soluble in water, methanol and ethanol.

No *s*-triazines containing condensed rings of three or four members have been reported in the literature.

II. Condensed Five-Membered Ring Compounds

1. Compounds with One Imidazole Ring, RI 1554

In 1955, a study of the reactions of aziridinomelamines led[4a] to the synthesis of dihydroimidazo-*s*-triazines. The two compounds of this category are discussed first in this section; others appear in Section II, 3 and 4.

The largest group of compounds of this section are triazinobenzimidazole derivatives, all of which have common physical properties. They are very high melting crystalline solids. In many cases melting is accompanied by decomposition; in other cases the melting point is well over 300° and has not yet been accurately measured. The triazinobenzimidazoles are listed in Table VIII-1 with their most probable structural formulas, the common and Chemical Abstracts and Ring Index name, physical properties where known, salts and references.

Compounds of this group are named as derivatives of s-triazino[a]-benzimidazole. Numbering is as indicated (IV). Because there are fewer

(IV)

than two dozen compounds in this section and all but one are prepared by a common procedure, they are discussed as a group rather than individually.

A. Dihydroimidazo-s-triazines

(1) 5,7 - Diamino - 2,3 - dihydroimidazo[1,2 - a]s - triazine (IIIA). 5,7-Diamino-2,3-dihydroimidazo[1,2-a]s-triazine (IIIA) melts at 308–310°. It is a weak base (pKa = 10.7) with a basic dissociation constant of 5×10^{-4}, typical for an alphatic isomelamine. It has been prepared by two methods.[4a] 2,4-Diamino-6-aziridino-s-triazine may be refluxed in acetonitrile for 2–½ hours in the presence of triethylamine hydrochloride. The mechanism is discussed under Section II,3.

Compound (IIIA) was obtained in 50% yield as the hydro-

chloride, m.p. 360°. It can also be made (3A) from potassium cyano-dicyandiamide and β-chloroethylamine hydrochloride.

(2) 5(or 7)-Hydroxy-7(or 5)methoxy-2,3-dihydroimidazo[1,2-a]-s-triazine (IIIB). (IIIB) probably has the 5-hydroxy-7-methoxy structure although this has not been rigorously proved.[4a] It has been prepared[4a] by treating 2,4-dimethoxy-6-(β-chloroethylamino)-s-triazine with aqueous sodium hydroxide.

B. Preparation and Chemical Properties of
s-Triazino[a]benzimidazoles

(1) From 1-Cyano-2(3H)benzimidazolone phenylhydrazone. **(o-phenylene-α,β-dicyanoguanidines).** The triazinobenzimidazoles can be prepared from 1-cyano-2(3H)benzimidazolone phenylhydrazone (which will be designated by its common name, o-phenylene-α,β-dicyanoguanidine) or from substituted o-phenylene-α,β-dicyanoguanidines by cyclization. The o-phenylene-α,β-dicyanoguanidines have been prepared by treating[4,5] an o-phenylenediamine with cyanogen bromide

$$R \quad \overset{NH_2}{\underset{NH_2}{\bigcirc}} + 3\ BrCN \longrightarrow R \quad \bigcirc \overset{\overset{H}{N}}{\underset{\underset{CN}{N}}{}} C=NCN + 3\ HBr \qquad (4)$$

(4). The R group may be halogen, hydrogen, alkyl, carbalkoxy, alkoxy etc. The reaction may proceed through a substituted cyanamide as an intermediate (5).

$$\bigcirc \overset{NH_2}{\underset{NH_2}{}} + 2\ BrCN \longrightarrow \left(\bigcirc \overset{NHCN}{\underset{NHCN}{}} \right) + 2\ HBr \longrightarrow$$

$$\left[\bigcirc \overset{\overset{H}{N}}{\underset{\underset{CN}{N}}{}} C=NH \right] + BrCN \longrightarrow \bigcirc \overset{\overset{H}{N}}{\underset{\underset{CN}{N}}{}} C=NCN + HBr \qquad (5)$$

The procedure[5] can be reduced to one step by addition of sodium bicarbonate to neutralize the hydrobromic acid liberated.

Treatment of o-phenylene-α,β-dicyanoguanidine with water, ammonia, amines or hydrogen chloride causes cyclization and formation of the s-triazine ring. Cyclization with each of these reagents is discussed below.

(a) *With Water.* Addition of water without removal of the hydrobromic acid from the synthesis mixture of o-phenylene-α,β-dicyanoguanidine causes hydrolysis to give amido compounds. These cyclize[4] when gently heated[6] giving compounds which are derivatives of 1,2,3,4-

$$\bigcirc \overset{\overset{H}{N}}{\underset{\underset{CN}{N}}{}} C=NCN + 2\ H_2O \xrightarrow{H^+} \bigcirc \overset{\overset{H}{N}}{\underset{\underset{CONH_2}{N}}{}} C=NCONH_2 \xrightarrow{-NH_3} \bigcirc \overset{\overset{H}{N}}{\underset{N}{}} \overset{\overset{H}{N}}{\underset{NH}{}} {\underset{O}{}}^{O} \qquad (6)$$

$$(IVA)$$

tetrahydro-*s*-triazino[a]benzimidazole-2,4-dione (IVA), also known as phenylmelanuric acid (when written as the dihydroxy compound instead of the dione).

Benzene ring substituted derivatives of this group are useful[5] as stabilizers or as fog inhibitors for light sensitive silver halide emulsions. These tricyclic compounds function as monobasic acids. Strong acid or strong bases decompose them giving *o*-phenyleneguanidines, ammonia and carbon dioxide.

(b) *With HCl.*   *o*-Phenylene-α,β-dicyanoguanidine reacts with hydrogen chloride or hydrochloric acid to give 1,4-dihydro-2-chloro-4-imino-*s*-triazino[a]benzimidazole,[6,7] known by the trivial name *o*-phenyleneammelyl chloride (V). Further heating with hydrochloric

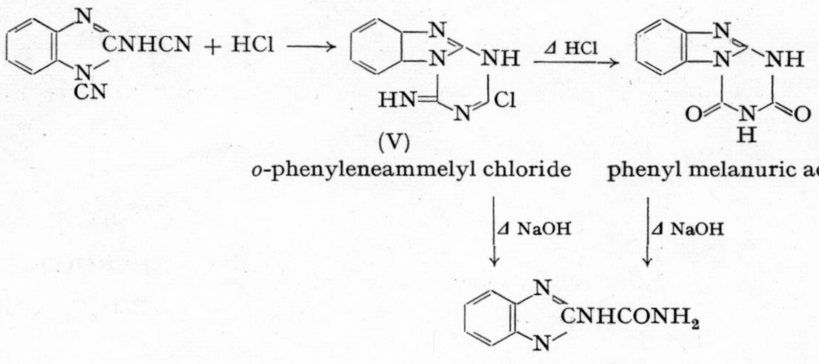

(V)
o-phenyleneammelyl chloride   phenyl melanuric acid   (IVA)

phenyleneguanyl urea

acid, removes the chlorine atom and imino substituents giving 1,2,3,4-tetrahydro-*s*-triazino[a]benzimidazo-2, 4-dione (IVA). Both 1,2,3,4-tetrahydro-*s*-triazino[a]benzimidazo-2,4-dione and 1,4-dihydro-2-chloro-4-imino-*s*-triazino[a]benzimidazole are degraded by hot alkali to 1-cyano-2-ureidobenzimidazole which, in keeping with other common names in the series is known as phenyleneguanyl urea. If, however, the chloro compound is treated with alkali, neutralized with acid and further treated with ammonia (7), the chlorine is replaced by an amino (or imino) group and 1,2,3,4-tetrahydro-*s*-triazino[a]benzimidazole-

(7)

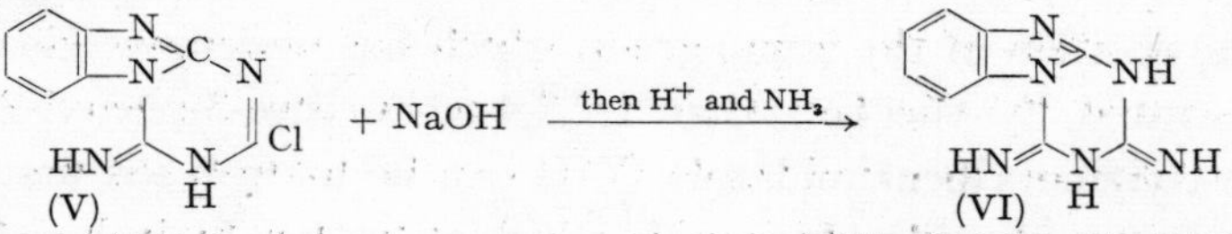

(V)   (VI)
phenyleneisomelamine

2,4-diimine, commonly known[6],[7] as phenyleneisomelamine (VI), results.

(c) *With Ammonia and Amino Compounds.* Ammonia, amines and hydrazine react[6],[7] with *o*-phenylene-α,β-dicyanoguanidine to give 3-substituted derivatives of 1,2,3,4-tetrahydro-*s*-triazino[a]benzimidazole-2,4-diimine (VA). Isomeric derivatives result from the reaction of the same amino compound with 1,4-dihydro-2-chloro-*s*-triazino[a]-benzimidazole-4-imine (V). Both isomers give the same phenylene-biguanide with hot alkali. The two pathways are illustrated for the

$$(8)$$

case in which aniline is the amine used (8). Both isomeric types can be readily hydrolyzed to the corresponding mono-oxo compounds with hot hydrochloric acid (9) and (10).

$$(9)$$

$$(10)$$

The position of the imino group which has undergone cleavage is demonstrated by the fact that 1,2,3,4-tetrahydro-3-phenyl-2-imino-4-oxo-*s*-triazino[a]benzimidazole (VII) can be hydrolyzed first to the corresponding phenylenebiguanide which is further hydrolyzed to the phenyleneguanylurea (11). Phenyleneguanylurea would have been obtained directly (12) if the oxo group on (VII) were in the 4-position and not the 2-position. Thus, isolation of the phenylenebiguanide proves the structure.

$$(12)$$

$$(11)$$

Hydrazine reacts with *o*-phenylene-α,β-dicyanoguanidine to give 1,2,3,4-tetrahydro-3-amino-*s*-triazino[a]benzimidazole-2,4-diimine (IX), a compound in which the hydrazine function is retained and which can, therefore, undergo condensation reactions with aldehydes[6,7] to give Schiffs' bases. The Schiffs' base is decomposed by ammonia regenerating the free base. Hot caustic attacks the triazine ring. The product is ω-amino-*o*-phenylenebiguanide.

(2) From *o*-Phenyleneguanidine. Another means of preparing 1,2,3,4-tetrahydro-*s*-triazino[a]benzimidazole-2,4-dione (IVA) is to treat *o*-phenyleneguanidine with biuret at 180° for one hour[4] (13).

$$(13)$$

(3) From *o*-Phenylene Isoammeline. The same compound (IVA) has also been made by hydrolysis of 1,2,3,4-tetrahydro-4-oxo-

s-triazino[a]benzimidazole-2-imine (VIII) with nitrous acid[6] or by oxidation of the hydrochloride salt of compound (VIII) with nitrous anhydride.[6]

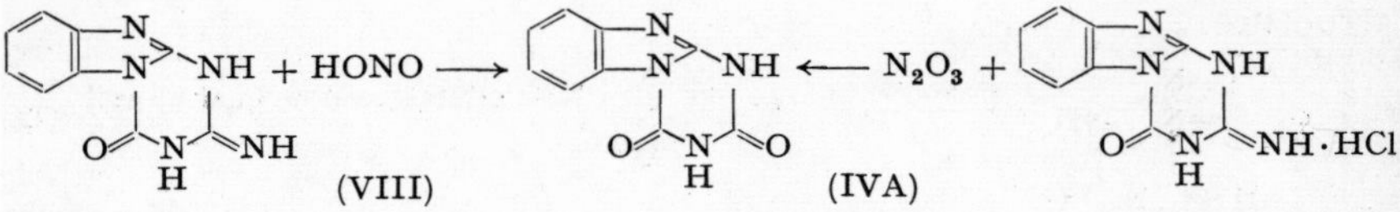

Compounds containing condensed *s*-triazinobenzimidazole rings, discussed above, *s*-triazinoimidazolidinedione rings, and *s*-triazino-benzimidazolidone rings (the last two discussed below) are listed in Table VIII-1.

2. Compounds with One Reduced Imidazole Ring

A. Two Condensed Rings. R.I. 741

Perhydro-1,6-dimethyl-2,4,5,7-tetraoxo-imidazo[1,5-a]*s*-triazino (XI) melts at 264° and can be crystallized from water.[4] It is a weak acid probably of the order of cyanuric acid.

Preparation of (XI) may be accomplished by cyclization of theobromic acid. This can be effected by the use of hydriodic acid containing a trace of phosphonium iodide.[8] The product is commonly called hydrotheobromic acid anhydride. It is numbered starting with the *s*-triazine ring (X).

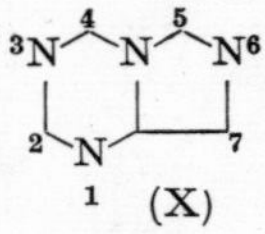

Alkali ruptures the five-membered ring giving hydrotheobromic acid while dichromate oxidation produces methylparabamic acid.[8]

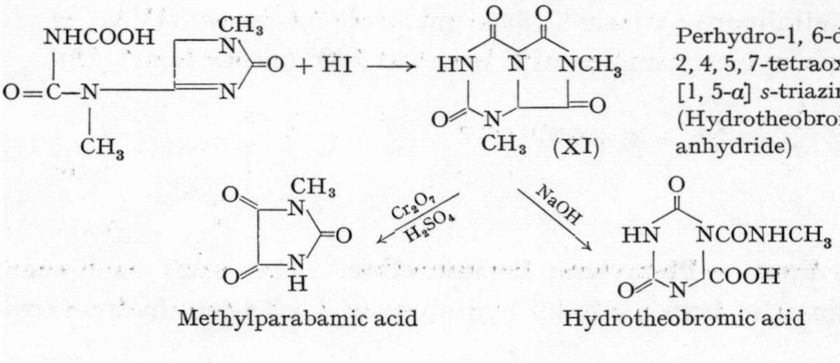

Perhydro-1, 6-dimethyl-2, 4, 5, 7-tetraoxoimidazo [1, 5-α] *s*-triazine (Hydrotheobromic acid anhydride)

Methylparabamic acid

Hydrotheobromic acid

B. *Three Condensed Rings. R.I.* 1557

Three compounds containing the *s*-triazinobenzimidazolidine structure in which the *s*-triazine ring is fused both to the imidazole ring and the benzene ring are known. Their physical and chemical properties are almost identical and they may be prepared by similar general procedure. All derivatives posses the triazepine ring system. Numbering starts clockwise at one of the nitrogen atoms common to two rings.

(1) 3,4-Dihydro-3-phenyl-10-p-tolylimino-1,5(2)-methano-1,3,5-benzotriazepine-2,4-dione (XII). This compound is a colorless crystalline solid melting at 254° which can be crystallized from benzene or ethanol.[9] It is prepared by the reaction of *o*-phenylenediamine and di(*p*-tolyl)carbodiimide to form *p*-tolyl-*o*-phenyleneguanidine. Treatment with phenyl isocyanate at 200° for one hour gives 3,4-dihydro-10-*p*-tolylimino-1,5(2)-methano-1,3,5-benzotriazepine-2,4-dione (XII). An equivalent of aniline is obtained as a reaction by-product[9] (14).

$$(XIA) + 2 C_6H_5NCO \xrightarrow[200°]{1 \text{ hr.}}$$

(14)

(2) 3,4-Dihydro-8-methyl-3-phenyl-10-phenylimino-1,5(2)-methano-1,3,5-benzotriazepine-2,4-dione. The colorless, crystalline solid melts at 234° when recrystallized from either benzene or ethanol. It is prepared by the reaction of 4-methyl-*o*-phenylenediamine and diphenylcarbodiimide to give phenyl-*p*-methyl-*o*-phenyleneguanidine which is then heated strongly with phenyl isocyanate in a manner similar to (14).

(3) 3,4-Dihydro-8-methyl-3-phenyl-10(p-tolylimino)-1,5 (2)-methano-1,3,5-benzotriazepine-2,4-dione. Like the two preceding compounds, this substance is a colorless crystalline solid.[9] Crystallized from benzene or ethanol, it melts at 232–233°.

Synthesis is accomplished by treating p-methyl-o-phenylene-diamine with di(p-tolyl) carbodimide and heating the substituted guanidine with p-tolyl isocyanate as illustrated above under (1).

This compound and others in the series are listed in Table VIII-1, together with the compounds discussed in the two previous sections.

3. Compound with Two Dihydroimidazole Rings

Incomplete structure proof has been offered[4a] for (XIIA). It was prepared by treatment of 2,4-bis(β-chloroethylamino)-6-chloro-s-triazine with ammonia and isolated as the dihydrochloride.

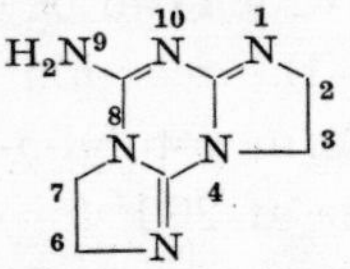

5 (XIIA)

4. Compound with Three Dihydroimidazole Rings

2,3,6,7,10,11-Hexahydrotrisimidazo[1,2-a; 1',2'-c; 1,″2″-e]s-triazine (XIIB) melts at 322–324° after recrystallization from water. It has been prepared in three ways[4a], two from triethylene melamine. The latter was heated at 100° for 7 hours in aqueous solution with Raney nickel under hydrogenation conditions to give compound (XIIB) in 40% yield. It can also be prepared from triethylene melamine by treatment with triethylamine hydrochloride in refluxing acetonitrile for 2½ hours. A third preparation consists in ring closure of tris(β-hydroxyethylamino)s-triazine with phosphorous oxychloride.

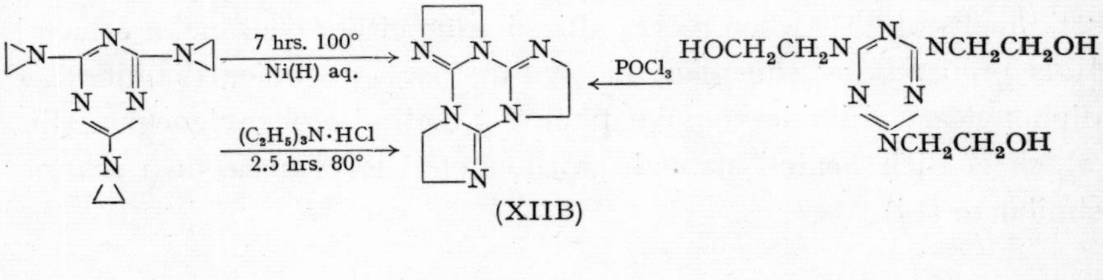

(XIIB)

Schaefer[4a] has discussed the rearrangement mechanism of the aziridine rings in compounds, such as IIIA, IIIB, XIIA, and XIIB, to

$$\begin{array}{c}
\text{(14A)}
\end{array}$$

give dihydroimidazole derivatives. Except for the hydrogenation synthesis above, the rearrangement can be explained readily by typical acid catalysis by triethylamine hydrochloride (14A).

3LE VIII-1. A. s-Triazinoimidazole Compounds

ural formula	Common name of parent compound	Systematic name of parent compound	Melting point/solvent used for recrystallization, °C.	Ref.
	Iminodicarbonyl-o-phenyleneguanidine or Phenylmelanuric acid	1,2,3,4-Tetrahydro-s-triazino(a)benzimidazo-2,4-dione or 2,4-Dihydroxy-s-triazino(a)benzimidazole	Over 320°/acetic acid (dec.) over 300°/H_2O	1
8-CH_3[a]	—	1,2,3,4-Tetrahydro-s-triazino(a)-7-methyl-benzimidazo-2,4-dione	Over 320°/acetic acid	2
8-Cl[a]	—	—	Over 320°/acetic acid	2
8-Br[a]	—	—	—	2
or 7,9-di Br[a]	—	—	—	2
8-OCH_3[a]	—	—	—	2
8-COOH[a]	—	—	—	2
	o-Phenyleneammelyl chloride	1,4-Dihydro-2-chloro-s-triazino(a)benzimidazole-4-imine	Over 200°; yellows at 220°	3
	o-Phenyleneisoammeline	1,2,3,4-Tetrahydro-4-oxo-s-triazino(a)-benzimidazole-2-imine	No m.p.; forms a hydrochloride salt which also has no M.p.	3
	o-Phenyleneisomelamine	1,2,3,4-Tetrahydro-s-triazino(a)benzimidazole-2,4-diimine	Over 300°	3
	o-Phenyleneamino-isomelamine	1,2,3,4-Tetrahydro-3-amino-s-triazino(a)-benzimidazole-2,4-diimine	Forms monohydrate, (dec.) 283°	3

(Table continued)

TABLE VIII-1A *(continued)*

Structural formula	Common name of parent compound	Systematic name of parent compound	Melting point/solvent used for recrystallization, °C.
	o-Phenylene-aminoisoam-meline	1,2,3,4-Tetrahydro-3-amino-4-oxo-s-tria-zino(a)benzimida-zole-2-imine	303°. Forms a mono-hydrochloride-monohydrate salt, M.p. 289°
	o-Phenylene-phenylisome-lamine	1,2,3,4-Tetrahydro-3-phenyl-s-triazino(a)-benzimidazole 2,4-diimine	Forms monohydrate, M.p. 241°
	o-Phenylene-phenylisoam-meline	1,2,3,4-Tetrahydro-3-phenyl-4-oxo-s-tri-azino(a)benzimida-zole-2-imine	Forms monohydrate (dec.) 292°. Forms ·NHO₃ salt (dec.) 225°
	o-Phenylene-benzalamino-isoammeline	1,2,3,4-Tetrahydro-3-benzalamino-4-oxo-s-triazino(a)benzi-midazol-2-imine	(Dec.) before melting
	—	1,4-Dihydro-1-anilino-s-triazino(a)benzimi-dazole-4-imine	Over 300°. Forms hydrochloride, M.p. over 300°
	—	1,4-Dihydro-2-anilino-s-triazino(a)benzimi-dazole-4-one	(Dec.) high tempe-rature. Forms hydrochloride
	—	1,4-Dihydro-2-(N-methylanilino)-s-triazino(a)benzi-midazole-4-imine	Forms hydrochlo-ride, M.p. over 300° (dec.)
	—	1,4-Dihydro-2-(N-methylanilino)-s-triazino(a)benzimi-dazole-4-one	235° (dec.). Forms hydrochloride, M.p. high tem-perature (dec.)
	Hydrotheobromic acid anhydride	Perhydro-1, 6-dime-thyl-2,4,5,7-tetraoxo-imidazo-s-triazine	264°/H₂O

a Positions of substituents not proved.

,3,5-Benzotriazepines

ural formula	Common name of parent compound	Systematic name of parent compound	Melting point/solvent used for recrystalliz-ation, °C.	Ref.
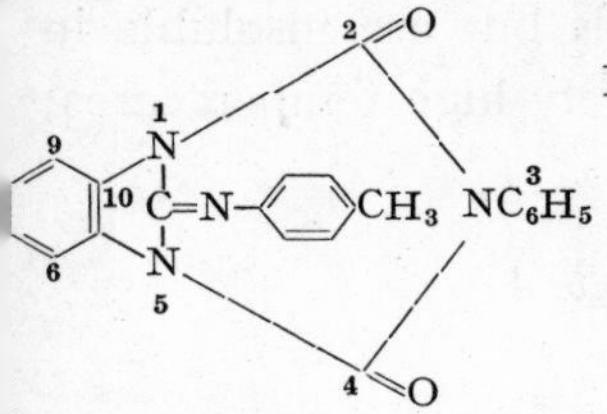	Phenylimido-dicarbonyl-*p*-tolyl-*o*-phenylene guanidine	3,4-Dihydro-3-phenyl-10-*p*-tolylimino-1,5-(2)-methano-1,3,5-benzotriazepine-2,4-dione	245°/benzene or ethyl alc.	6
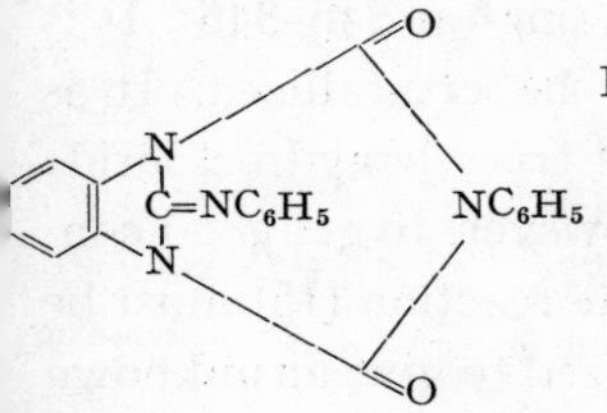	Phenylimido-dicarbonyl-phenyl-*o*-tolylene diamine	3,4-Dihydro-8-methyl-3-phenyl-10-phenyl-imino-1,5(2)-methano-1,3,5-benzotriazepine-2,4-dione	234°/benzene or ethyl alc.	6
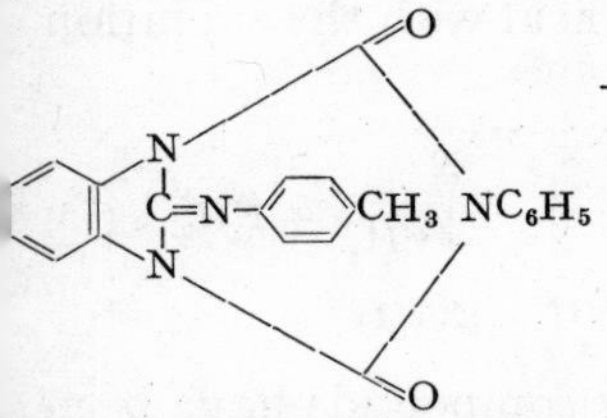	—	3,4-Dihydro-8-methyl-3-phenyl-10-(*p*-tolyl)-imino-1,5(2)-methano-1,3,5-benzotriazepine-2,4-dione	232–233°/ben-zene alc. or ethyl	6

1. P. Pierron, *Ann. chim. phys.*, (8), **15**, 196 (1908).
2. N. Heimbach and R. Clark, U.S. 2,444,609 (1948) to General Aniline & Film Co.
3. G. Pellizzari, *Gazz. chim. ital.*, **52**, (I), 199 (1922).
4. G. Pellizzari, *Gazz. chim. ital.*, **54**, (I) 177 (1924).
5. H. Blitz, *Ber.*, **67B**, 1856 (1934).
6. A. Keller, *Ber.*, **24**, 2512 (1891).

5. Compounds with One Triazole Ring, R.I. 701. 1,2,4-Triazolo-*s*-triazines

The compounds in this section are derivatives of 1,2,4-triazolo-[4,3a]1,3,5-triazine. Numbering is according to the following scheme:

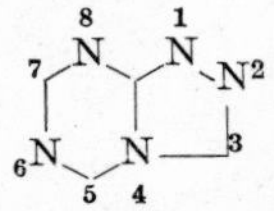

A number of condensed triazolo-*s*-triazines have been prepared. In general, these compounds can be synthesized by heating certain

1,2,4-triazoles with dicyandiamide or, in some cases, with biuret. The resulting compounds are generally characterized as white crystalline solids insoluble in cold water and most organic solvents. They are soluble to some extent in hot water and acids but are insoluble in alkalis. Most melt and/or decompose at relatively high temperatures; some have a tendency to sublime.

A. 3-Methyl-5,7-diamino-1,2,4-triazolo[4,3-a]-1,3,5-triazine (XIII)

Compound (XIII) is a white solid decomposing[9] at 345–346°. It is slightly soluble in water from which it can be crystallized. It is synthesized by refluxing 3-amino-5-methyl-1,2,4-triazole hydrochloride with dicyandiamide for six hours in water.[9] However, to get good consistent yields, in one case approaching 50%, the reaction (15) must be run[10] in methyl Cellosolve. (XIII) has been oxidized to give an unknown intermediate which was hydrolyzed to cyanuric acid with the evolution of nitrogen.[10]

$$H_3C \cdots N \quad HN \quad N \quad NH_2 \cdot HCl \quad + NH_2CNHCN \xrightarrow[\Delta]{HCl\ aq.} H_2N \cdots CH_3 \quad NH_2 \quad (XIII) \quad + NH_3 \quad (15)$$

The structures of (XIII) and the following compounds have been only recently proved.[10] As in some cases no approach to a logical structure has been made, the structural formulas indicated can only be the most probable ones. The structures of the 3-substituted-5,7-diamino-1,2,4-triazolo-[4,3-a]1,3,5-triazines, which are prepared from dicyandiamide and the corresponding 3-amino-5-substituted-1,2,4-triazole, are dependent on the structure of the starting triazole (16,17).

$$R-C \quad \longrightarrow \quad H_2N \cdots R \quad + NH_3 \quad (16)$$

$$\text{or} \qquad R-C \quad \longrightarrow \quad H_2N \cdots R \quad NH_2 \quad + NH_3 \quad (17)$$

$$(XV)$$

The substituent, R, which may be hydrogen or an aliphatic, a cycloaliphatic, or an aromatic radical, is on the 2- or the 3-position depending on the position of the double bonds in the triazole. The products are[11] either 1,2,4-triazolo-*s*-triazines (XIV) (16) or 1,3,4-triazolo-*s*-triazines (XV) (17). The former appear more likely in view of the fact that both nitrogen and cyanuric acid were obtained by hydrolysis of an unknown intermediate obtained by oxidation of 3-methyl-5,7-diamino-1,2,4-triazolo[4,3-a]1,3,5-triazine.This has been better demonstrated for 3,5,7-triamino-1,2,4-triazolo[4,3-*a*]1,3,5-triazine.

B. 3-n-Amyl-5,7-diamino-1,2,4-triazolo[4,3-a]–1,3,5-triazino (XVI)

The 3-*n*-amyl homolog is a colorless crystalline compound decomposing at 315–316° after recrystallization from Cellosolve.[11] It is synthesized in 35% yield by refluxing the nitrate of 2-amino-5-*n*-amyl-1,2,4-triazole with aqueous dicyandiamide for four hours.

C. 3-Phenyl-5,7-diamino-1,2,4-triazolo[4,3-a]–1,3,5-triazine (XVII)

3-Phenyltriazolo-*s*-triazine is a crystalline solid which decomposes[11] at 380°. It is slightly soluble in dilute hydrochloric acid and can be recrystallized from dimethylformamide.[11]

(XVII) can be prepared in 77% yield either by heating 3-amino-5-phenyl-1,2,4-triazole and dicyandiamide at 150–160° for two and one-half hours or refluxing with aqueous hydrochloric acid for three hours (17A).

D. 3,5,7-Triamino-1,2,4-triazolo[4,3-a]1,3,5-triazine (XVIII)

3,5,7-Triamino-1,2,4-triazolo[4,3-a]1,3,5-triazine, also called guanazoguanazole, has no melting point but sublimes at high temperatures. It can be prepared by heating hydrazine hydrochloride and di-

$$\text{NH}_2\text{NH}_2 + \text{H}_2\text{NCNHCN} \xrightarrow[\text{H}_2\text{O}]{\text{reflux}} \qquad \qquad (18)$$

cyandiamide in water in 83% yield[10] (18) or by heating guanazole with dicyandiamide (19).

$$\qquad \xrightarrow{\Delta} \qquad \qquad + \text{NH}_3 \qquad (19)$$

Compound (XVIII) forms[12] an adduct with silver nitrate, a chloroplatinate, $(C_4N_8H_6 \cdot HCl)_2 \cdot PtCl_4$, and a picrate which melts at 276°. Diacetyl,[12] triacetyl,[12] and tribenzoyl[10] derivatives are known. The benzoyl derivative was obtained[10] in 67% yield by heating 3,5,7-triamino-1,2,4-triazolo[4,3-a]1,3,5-triazine with benzoic anhydride at 185–200° for several hours. It is a tan powder melting at 172–175°. The material was soluble in hot acetic acid and butanol but difficult to recrystallize. It was insoluble in ethyl acetate.

Acid treatment of (XVIII) hydrolyzed one of the amino (or imino) groups to a carbonyl. Oxidation with acid permanganate gave a 62% yield of cyanuric acid with the evolution[10] of nitrogen, a reaction which establishes that (XVIII) and also other members of the series are 1,2,4- rather than 1,3,4-triazolotriazines. Were they instead 1,3,4-, then formation of nitrogen would have had to come about with splitting of the triazine nucleus which is improbable in this instance and without analogous precedent.

E. 3-Amino-5,7-dihydro-1,2,4-triazolo[4,3-a]-
1,3,5-triazine (XIX)

If guanazole is heated with biuret at 160°, the reaction takes a course similar to (19) except that the product is 3-amino-5,7-

dihydroxy-1,2,4-triazolo[4,3-a]1,3,5-triazine[12] also called urazoguana-
zole (20).

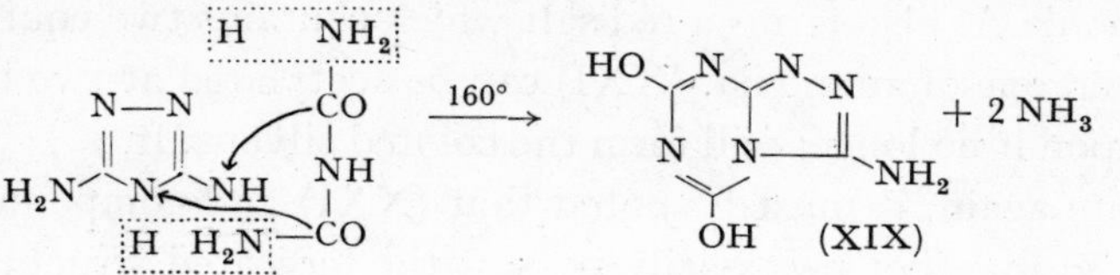

$$\text{(diagram)} \xrightarrow{160°} \text{(diagram)} + 2\,NH_3 \qquad (20)$$

(XIX)

F. 5-Amino-2,7-dihydroxy-1,2,4-triazolo[4,3-a]1,3,5-triazine

Pyroguanazole, which can be prepared[13] in good yield by pyrolysis
of guanazol or from dicyandiamide and hydrazine hydrate (see Section
II,4) yields 2,7-dihydroxy-5-amino-1,3,4-triazolo[2,3-a]1,3,5-triazine
(XX) when oxidized[13] with alkaline permanganate at 20°. Structure

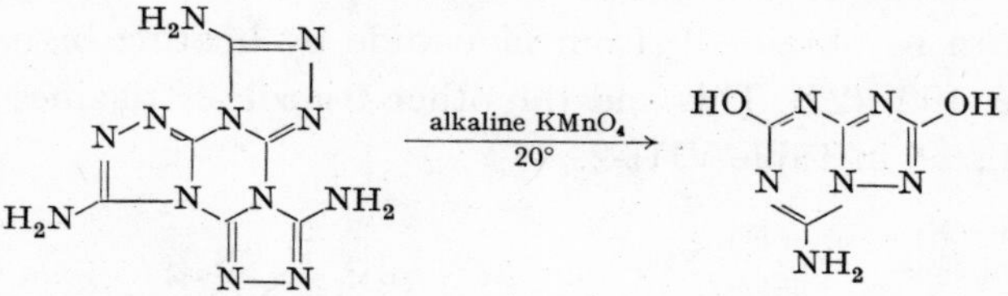

$$\text{Pyroguanazole} \xrightarrow[20°]{\text{alkaline } KMnO_4} \text{(diagram)}$$

Pyroguanazole   (XX)

(XX) is only tentative and the compound may actually be identical
with 3-amino-5,7-dihydroxy-1,2,4-triazolo[4,3-a]1,3,5-triazine (XIX)
above.

The 2,7-dihydroxy compound forms a disilver salt. Long heating
with potassium hydroxide removes the free amino (or imino) group as
ammonia.

G. 5,7-Diamino-3-hydroxy-1,2,4-triazolo[4,3-a]3,5-triazine (XXI)

This compound is also prepared from pyroguanazole. Hot alkali
or alkaline hydrogen peroxide converts[13] pyroguanazole to 5,7-diamino-
3-hydroxy-1,3,4,5-triazolo[2,3-a]1,3,5-triazine (21).

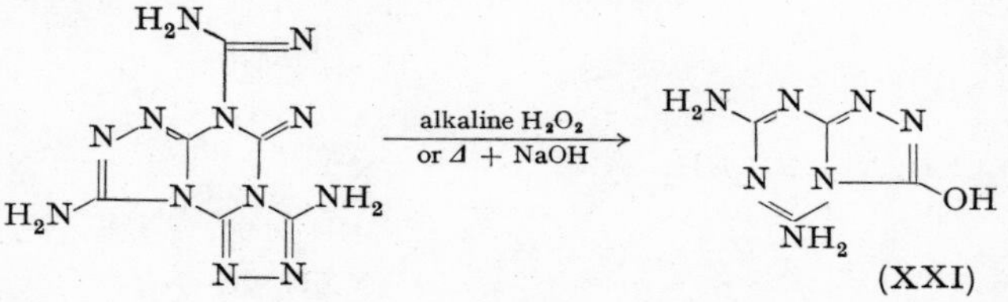

$$\text{(diagram)} \xrightarrow[\text{or } \Delta + NaOH]{\text{alkaline } H_2O_2} \text{(diagram)} \qquad (21)$$

(XXI)

Compound (XXI) usually crystallizes with one-half an equivalent of ammonia. It also forms a red salt which contains two equivalents of silver and one of ammonia. (XXI) can be acetylated at two hydrogens whereupon it no longer will form the colored silver salt.

Here again, it must be noted that (XXI) and compounds (XIX) and (XX) may not necessarily possess the indicated structures and it is possible that there are only two different compounds rather than the three described.

H. 7,8-Dihydro-5,7-diamino-3-hydroxy-1,2,4-triazolo-[4,3-a]1,3,5-triazine

7,8-Dihydro-5,7-diamino-3-hydroxy-1,2,4-triazolo[4,3-a]1,3,5-triazine can be obtained[12] from biguanide by heating biguanide with urazole at 190° (22). This and the other triazole-s-triazines in Section II,3 are listed in Table VIII-2.

$$\text{(22)}$$

6. Compounds with More Than One Triazole Ring, R. I. 2230

3,7,11-Triimino-tris-s-triazole[4,3-a, 4,3-c, 4,3-e]-s-triazine (XXII), more commonly called pyroguanazole, is the only compound of this category which has been identified. It can be prepared by two methods[13,14] both of which give almost quantitative yields. Heating dicyandiamide with hydrazine hydrate or hydrazine dihydrochloride produces pyroguanazole and ammonia. Pyrolysis (22A) of guanazole at 280° also produces good yields of pyroguanazole (XXII). Pyroguanazole gives a blue-violet color with alkali, a reaction by means of which the course of the pyrolysis may be followed. At 150° alkali gives a yellow color, at 200° yellow-red, at 215–230° light red, at 235–240° cherry red, at 260° violet-red, and at 270° an intense blue-violet.

$$3\ HN\!-\!NH \quad \xrightarrow{280°} \quad + 3\ NH_3 \qquad (22A)$$

TABLE VIII-2. Triazolo-*s*-triazines (3,5,7-Trisubstituted-1,2,4-triazolo[4,3-a]1,3,5-triazines)

uents	Conditions of synthesis[a]	Decomposition point, °C.	Yield, %	Solubility	Ref.
enyl-5,7-diamino-	Reflux 3 hours in aqueous HCl or heat at 150–160° for 2½ hours	380	77	S. sol. dilute HCl. Recrystallized from an acetic acid-H_2O-dioxane mixture	1
thyl-5,7-diamino-	Reflux 6 hours in aqueous HCl	345–346	—	Recrystallize from H_2O	1
Amyl-5,7-diamino-	Reflux nitrate salt 4 hours in water	315–316	—	Recrystallize from Cellosolve	1
-Triamino-	Fuse with dicyandiamide	Sublimes or depolymerizes at high temperatures	—		2
ino-5,7-dihydroxy-	Heat at 160° with biuret	—	—		2
droxy-5,7-diamin-	Heat at 190–200° with biguanide	—	—		2
Dihydroxy-5-amino-	Pyroguanazole and alkaline permanganate at 20°	—	—		3
droxy-5,7-diamino-	Pyroguanazole and alkaline hydrogen peroxide	—	—		3

[a] From substituted triazole and dicyandiamide.

1. D. Kaiser, U. S. 2,473,797 (1949) to American Cyanamid Co.
2. G. Pellizzari and C. Roncagliolo, *Gazz. chim. ital.*, **31**, I, 496 (1901).
3. K. Hofmann and O. Ehrhart, *Ber.*, **45**, 2733 (1912).

Pyroguanazole has the *s*-triazolo[4,3-a]-*s*-triazine structure and is numbered as indicated (22A). It could have structures (XXIII) or (XXII) depending on the structure of guanazole, but Hofmann and Ehrhart[13]

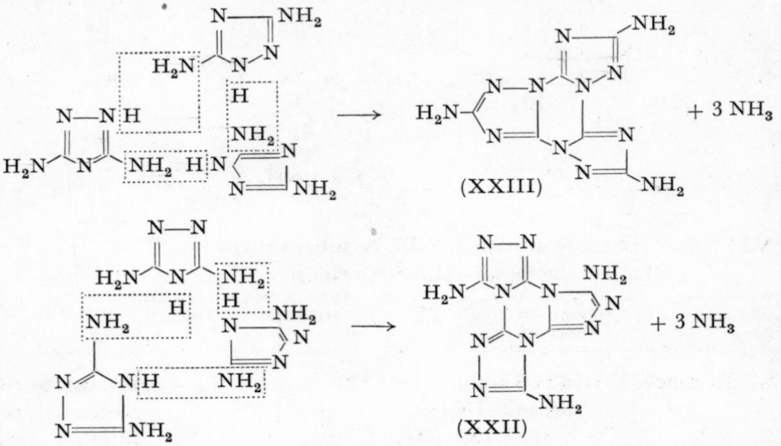

(XXIII)

(XXII)

isolated both cyanuric acid and nitrogen from the hot alkaline permanganate oxidation of pyroguanazole. The nitrogen could have come only from the hydrazine moiety.[10] Therefore, structure (XXIII) cannot be correct since nitrogen evolution requires rupture of the triazine ring. On the other hand structure (XXII) satisfactorily accounts for both nitrogen and cyanuric acid.[10]

Pyroguanazole is usually obtained as the monohydrate. A monohydrochloride results from treatment with dilute hydrochloric acid while with concentrated hydrochloric acid, a dihydrochloride forms. (XXII) also forms a chloroplatinate. A pentaacetyl derivative, $(C_6HN_{12}O)(Ac)_5$ can be obtained by treating (XXII) with acetic anhydride for ten hours at 125°. Pyroguanazole is very stable towards strong hot acids. Concentrated sulfuric acid at 190° oxidizes it to ammelide. Dilute aqua regia followed by hydrochloric acid degrades it to ammeline and some melam, while hot alkaline permanganate carries the degradation all the way to cyanuric acid.

Pyroguanazole is oxidized to 5-amino-2,7-dihydroxy-1,2,4-triazolo[4,3-a]1,3,5-triazine (XX) by alkaline permanganate at room temperature[13] and to 4,7-diamino-2-hydroxy-1,2,4-triazolo[4,3-a]1,3,5-triazine (XXI) by either alkaline hydrogen peroxide or hot caustic.[13]

7. Compounds with One Thiazole Ring
2,3,5-Trihydro-7-amino-5-iminothiazolo[2,3-a]1,3,5-triazine (XXV)

Thioammeline reacts with 1,2-dibromoethane in alcoholic solution at 120° in a closed vessel forming 2,3,5-trihydro-7-amino-5-imino-thiazole[2,3-a]1,3,5-triazine which is obtained[15,16] as the hydrobromide (23).

$$\text{(23)}$$

2,3,5-Trihydro-7-amino-5-iminothiazole[2,3-a]1,3,5-triazine, known also as ethylenethioammeline, undergoes rearrangement when a hydrochloric acid solution is oxidized with chlorine. Ring cleavage occurs at a sulfur-carbon bond on the triazine ring followed by recyclization forming 2,2-dioxo-3,4-dihydro-1,2,4-thiadiazino[4,3-a]1,3,5-triazine (24).

$$\text{(24)}$$

This reaction is also discussed in Section III,4. Thiadiazino-[4,3-a]-s-triazines.

III. Condensed Six-Membered Ring Compounds

1. Compounds with Piperidine Rings

*A. Perhydrotripyrido[1,2-a, 1',2'-c, 1",2"-e]-s-triazine
(α- and β-Tripiperideine)*

(1) Physical Properties. Perhydrotripyrido[1,2-a, 1',2'-c, 1",2"-e]-s-triazine exists as a cis-trans isomer pair known as α- and β-tripiperideine. The alpha form can be crystallized from acetone or ether. It melts at 61–62° and when distilled over alkali,[17,18] boils at 128–130° at 0.1 mm. The beta form can also be crystallized from acetone and melts at 72°.

(2) Preparation. If N-chloropiperidine is heated with alcoholic potassium hydroxide, a mixture of three trimeric compounds is obtained, two of which are *s*-triazines. The compounds have been named alpha-, beta- and isotripiperideine. The first two are cis-trans isomers although it is not yet known which is cis and which is trans. Isotripiperdeine is not an *s*-triazine derivative and is discussed only briefly in connection with the other two.

The first step occurring during the course of preparation is dehydrohalogenation of N-chloropiperidine to form Δ^1-piperideine (I).

(I)

Δ^1-Piperideine is an internal Schiffs' base or aldimine and, in keeping with the behavior of many of those compounds, (I) trimerizes very rapidly to give a mixture of the three isomers which distills at 60–140°/ 0.1 mm. Alpha- and beta-tripiperideine can be represented as cis-trans

cis   (II) and (III)   trans

isomers (II and III) or written in the general form (IV) or as a perhydro-tris-pyridino-*s*-triazine.

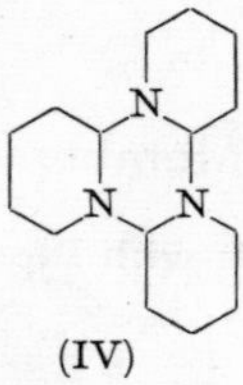

(IV)

(3) Reactions and Chemical Properties. (a) *Basicity and Salt Formation.* α-Tripiperideine or perhydrotripyrido[1,2-a, 1',2'-c, 1",2"-e]-*s*-triazine can be titrated with three equivalents of hydrochloric acid under normal conditions, however at —60° in methanol, it is titrated with only one equivalent of the acid.[20] In acid solution, α-tripiperideine exists as salts of Δ^1-piperideine while the trimer may be vacuum distilled from basic solution.

α-Tripiperideine forms a Reineckate salt, the only salt yet known, which melts at 211–213° (dec.) when crystallized from acetone-water or acetone-ether.

(b) *Detrimerization Rearrangements.* As is the case with other aldimine polymers, these triazines are sensitive to acids. Alpha-tripiperideine, which is the more stable form (although it is not known whether it is cis or trans), can be detrimerized by adding sufficient acid to neutralize the three nitrogen atoms and distilling out monomeric Δ^1-piperideine (I) b.p. 135–138°. This at once trimerizes. If the distillate is cooled, trimerization to the β-form only occurs; however, the warm distillate rearranges to the more stable α-form. The α-form can be distilled at 128–130°/0.1 mm but only if a small amount of powdered potassium hydroxide is added to neutralize traces of acid in the glass apparatus.[18]

The depolymerization is acid-catalyzed. Two theories of the mechanism have been offered[18] to account for the results observed, one involving an electron shift only, while the other involves both an electron shift and a proton shift. In both cases, the first step is addition of a proton. The second step may involve an electron shift whereby a quarternary nitrogen atom is formed. By the same shifts a molecule of Δ^1-piperideine forms and distills, and the residue breaks down as indicated below, the final step of the cycle being loss of a proton to another α- or β-tripiperideine molecule.

In case two, the second step may as well be proton migration to a nearby nitrogen atom, the driving force being the repelling of a proton

from the positively laden nitrogen atom. The difference between this
step in cases one and two is that in case two the migrating proton goes
to a nitrogen that has no positive charge. The third step in both cases
is addition of another proton. This step has an analogy since it has been
shown[21] that two protons are required for the acid-catalyzed depolymerization of paraldehyde. The last steps of detrimerization by this
mechanism are similar to the ones cited in the first mechanism and are
indicated below.

(c) *Rearrangement of the Beta to the Alpha Isomer.* The beta form
can be readily converted to the alpha quantitatively by distilling over
potassium acid sulfate.

The rearrangement of the β- to the α-form, a rearrangement which
is inhibited by alkali and cold and is therefore acid-catalyzed, has been
explained[18] by the same mechanisms which were discussed above for
detrimerization and trimerization and will not be described in detail
here (26).

(26)

(d) *Rearrangement of Alpha-Tripiperideine to Isotripiperideine.*
Isotripiperideine is one of the three isomeric trimers of Δ^1-piperideine
obtained in the synthesis of these substances. It is formed by aldol
condensation of the monomer followed by 1,2-addition of a third

monomer molecule (27). Acid depolymerization of isotripiperideine gives one equivalent of Δ^1-piperideine and one equivalent of decahydro-α,β-dipyridyl, the intermediate in equation (27), while the other

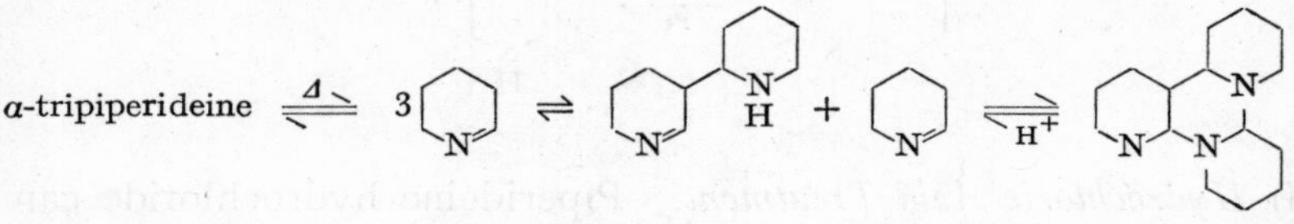

$$\alpha\text{-tripiperideine} \;\rightleftharpoons\; 3 \;\rightleftharpoons\; + \;\underset{H^+}{\rightleftharpoons}\; \tag{27}$$

two isomers give three equivalents of Δ^1-piperideine. Isotripiperideine can be prepared directly by heating the alpha isomer in cyclohexadiene for two days[17,18] at 110°, refluxing it in acetone[17,18] or allowing the alpha isomer to remain in alkaline solution at a pH of 9–10 for five hours at room temperature.[19] If, after five hours at 25° in the latter procedure, the mixture is made strongly alkaline and extracted with ether, an 84% yield of isotripiperideine can be realized.[19] The rearrangement is first order and a study of the kinetics has suggested[19] two possibilities for the mechanism.

(1) The α-tripiperideine molecule breaks down to three molecules of Δ^1-piperideine and forms isotripiperideine by the following reaction series, the first of which would be rate-determining (28).

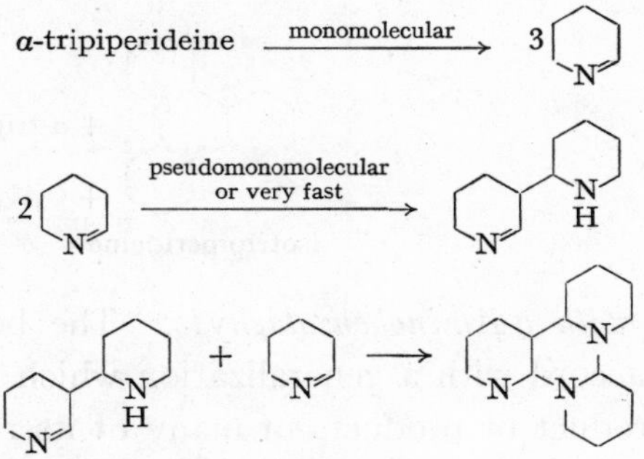

$$\alpha\text{-tripiperideine} \xrightarrow{\text{monomolecular}} 3$$

$$2 \xrightarrow[\text{or very fast}]{\text{pseudomonomolecular}} \tag{28}$$

$$+ \longrightarrow$$

(2) The α-tripiperideine molecule rearranges without detrimerization.[19] This reaction series is felt[19] to have somewhat more experimental support and a possible mechanism has been discussed.

(e) *Hydrogenation.* Hydrogenation of α-tripiperideine occurs in alcoholic solution with platinum and hydrogen. In twelve hours a 95% yield of piperidine resulted.[18] Detrimerization followed by hydrogenation or hydrogenolysis are the two means by which this

product can be obtained. The former is favored because of the relatively
mild conditions used.

(f) *Hydrochloric Acid Treatment.* Piperideine hydrochloride can
be isolated[18] in 95% yields by treating α-tripiperideine with $1N$ hydrochloric acid for one hour.

(g) *Reaction with Benzene Diazonium Chloride.* α-Tripiperideine is
converted to N-acetyl-Δ^2-piperideine at 100°. Treatment of the trimer
with benzene diazonium chloride followed by sodium acetate and acetic
acid gave a mixture of N-diazophenyl-Δ^2-piperideine (V) and its
3-isomer, 5,6-dihydro-3(4H)pyridone phenylhydrazone. (V) decomposes on heating forming α-tripiperideine and isotripiperideine.

(h) *Reaction with o-Aminobenzaldehyde.* The behavior of α-tripiperideine is in accord with a generalization which may be made of
aldimines. The product or products of many of its reactions indicate
that the reactive entity was the monomer rather than the polymer
or in this case trimer.

Treating the alpha or the beta isomer (which behaves in the same way chemically) with *o*-aminobenzaldehyde for a day at room temperature in neutral solution (29) produces 2,3-tetramethylene-1,2-dihydroquinazoline hydroxide, isolated as the picrate.

This compound rearranges to 2,3-tetramethylenequinoline-4. If the reaction is instead carried out at 100° or if the reactants are heated in the presence of acetic acid, 3(3-aminopropyl) quinoline dipicrate is the product.

(i) *Reaction with Phenylisothiocyanate (See Section B, below).*

B. Decahydro-5-phenyl-dipyrido[1,2-a, 1',2'-c]- s-triazine-6-(2H)-thion (VI)

Compound (VI) is a relative of α- and β-tripiperideine. It melts at 144–145° and can be recrystallized from ethanol.[17]

Synthesis of (VI) from α-tripiperideine is accomplished by means of reaction with phenylisothiocyanate at 25°. The temperature must be carefully controlled. Higher temperatures result in the formation of a different product. At 25° a 73% yield[17] of decahydro-5-phenyl-dipyrido[1,2a, 1',2'-c]-s-triazine-6(2H)-thion (VI) can be obtained, whereas at the temperature of boiling ethanol only a small amount of (VI) is produced and the principal product is a derivative of iso-

tripiperideine (VII). Formation of decahydro-5-phenyl-dipyrido-[1,2-a, 1',2'-c]-s-triazine-6(2H)-thion probably proceeds via hydration followed by condensation (30).

$$\text{(structure)} + 2 H_2O + C_6H_5NCO \longrightarrow \text{(structure: NH, OH)} + \text{HO}\text{(structure)} \longrightarrow \text{(structure VI)} \quad (30)$$

with structures showing $C=S$, HNC_6H_5, (VI) C_6H_5

2. Endo Compounds Derived from Cyclooctane

A. Endomethylene-s-Triazines. R.I. 931

As this group is composed for the most part of compounds derived from hexamethylenetetramine, this section should be consulted in connection with the chemistry of hexamethylenetetramine (Chapter X).

Endomethylenebicyclo-s-triazines may be named either as derivatives of 1,3,5,7-tetrazabicyclo[3,3,1]nonane or of 1,5-endomethylene-1,3,5,7-tetrazacyclooctane and are numbered as follows:

$$\begin{array}{c} \overset{1}{N} \\ 8 \qquad 2 \\ {}_7NH \quad {}^9CH_2 \quad HN_3 \\ 6 \qquad 4 \\ \underset{5}{N} \end{array}$$

The tetrazocyclooctane nomenclature system has been used almost exclusively in the literature and for this reason is retained in the present volume.

(1) 1,-5Endomethylene-3,7-dichloro-1,3,5,7-tetrazacyclooctane. (VIII).

In 1911, Delepine[22] isolated a compound which he called dichloropentamethylenetetramine from the reaction of hexamethylenetetramine and hypochlorous acid. More precisely named 1,5-endomethylene-3,7-dichloro-1,3,5,7-tetrazacyclooctane,[23] (VIII) is obtained as white scales[24] melting[23] at 79.5° and decomposing[24] at 140°. It is slightly soluble in water and alcohol;[24] the use of these solvents results in the loss of chlorine in four days.[24]

(VIII) has been synthesized from aqueous solutions of hexamethylenetetramine treated with potassium bicarbonate and sodium

$$(CH_2)_6N_4 + 2 HOCl \rightarrow [(CH_2)_6N_4] \cdot 2 HOCl \rightarrow [(CH_2)_6N_4Cl_2]^{++}[OH]_2^- \rightarrow$$

$$CH_2O + H_2O + ClN \begin{array}{c} N \\ | \\ CH_2 \quad NCl \\ | \\ N \end{array}$$

(VIII)

hypochlorite[24] in 77–80% yields. Hexamethylenetetramine forms an adduct with two equivalents of hypochlorous acid which breaks down giving formaldehyde, water and 1,5-endomethylene-3,7-dichloro-1,3,5,7-tetrazacyclooctane.[23]

Treatment of (VIII) with nitric acid and acetic anhydride replaces the chlorine atoms by nitro groups, and a 50% yield of 1,5-endo-methylene-3,7-dinitro-1,3,5,7-tetrazacyclooctane (IX) is obtained.[23]

| (VIII) | (IX) |

(2) 1,5-Endomethylene-3,7-dinitro-1,3,5,7-tetrazacyclooctane.

(a) *Physical Properties.* 1,5-Endomethylene-3,7-dinitro-1,3,5,7-tetrazacyclooctane (IX) is a white crystalline solid which melts[23] with decomposition at 208–209°. It may be recrystallized from alcohol, water or chloroform. Commonly it is abbreviated as DPT which stands for dinitropentamethylenetetramine.

(b) *Methonitrate: Knudsen's Base.* 1-Methyl-1,5-endomethylene-3,7-dinitro-1,3,5,7-tetrazacyclooctane-1-nitrate (X) m.p. 143°, has only recently[23,25] been shown to be identical with the so-called Knudsen's base. Some of the more important evidence for their identity is discussed below.

(X)

It has been established[25] that hexamethylenetetramine methonitrate produces (X) when treated with cold 98% nitric acid. Knudsen's base and (X) were found[25] to be identical. Moreover, the corresponding 1-picrates obtained[25] in 80% yield from (X) and from Knudsen's base were also identical, melting at 141°. Both (X) and Knudsen's base showed positive Thiele-Lochmann tests for N-nitro groups and negative Liebermann N-nitroso group tests. Hexamethylenetetramine methonitrate treated with 98% nitric acid and nitrogen tetroxide gives 1-methyl-1,5-endomethylene-3-nitro-1,3,5,7-tetrazacyclooctane-1-

nitrate. Therefore, hexamethylenetetramine methopicrate, under the same conditions should and did[25] give the same 1-picrate (XI); Knudsen's base also did.[25]

(XI)   m.p. 128–129°

1,5-Dimethylhexamethylenetetramine dipicrate melts at 193°. It is purified by dissolving in 70% nitric acid and precipitating with methanol. It can be prepared[25] in 80% yield by treating with picric acid, hexamethylenetetramine, or its dinitrate and methylamine nitrate; or in 30% yield from 1,3,5-trimethylhexahydro-s-triazine, formaldehyde, nitric acid, ammonium nitrate, and picric acid. Both hexamethylenetetramine methopicrate and Knudsen's picrate also yielded the dimethopicrate when they were heated at 50° in solution with methylamine hydrochloride, acetic acid, acetic anhydride and then treated with picric acid.

(c) *Methods of Preparation.* (1) *From Hexamethylenetetramine.* 1,5-Endomethylene-3,7-dinitro-1,3,5,7-tetrazacyclooctane (IX) can be prepared[27] by nitrating hexamethylenetetramine with 99–99.5% nitric acid, filtering to remove the chief product, 1,3,5-trinitrohexahydro-s-triazine, and neutralizing[28] to pH 5.6. Nitration can be carried out[29] in the presence of ammonium nitrate or sodium nitrate.

(IX)

1,5-Endomethylene-3,7-dinitro-1,3,5,7-tetrazacyclooctane (IX) is probably a precursor from which both part of the 1,3,5-trinitrohexahydro-s-triazine (RDX) and all of the 1,3,5,7-tetranitro-1,3,5,7-tetrazacyclooctane (HMX) obtained in the Bachmann nitration of hexamethylenetetramine are formed.[30]

Compound (IX) can also be prepared by treating hexamethylenetetramine with nitric anhydride,[28] N_2O_3, a process which produces water, carbon dioxide, and nitric oxide as by-products; or from hexamethylenetetramine dinitrate[29] in 31% yield by treating the salt with acetic anhydride at room temperature for three days, or with 90% sulfuric acid for fifteen minutes at 45°. It might be expected that dehydrating agents such as the latter two would convert hexamethylenetetramine dinitrate to (IX) since the two differ only by one equivalent of water and one of formaldehyde.

(2) *From bis-Dinitromethylenediamine.* Aqueous bis-dinitromethylenediamine reacts[31] with ammonia and formaldehyde forming 1,5-endomethylene-3,7-dinitro-1,3,5,7-tetrazacyclooctane (IX). Alkali reverses the reaction (31) and regenerates the starting materials.

$$CH_2(NHNO_2)_2 \text{ aq.} + NH_4OH + CH_2O \underset{\longleftarrow}{\overset{24 \text{ hrs.}}{\underset{NaOH}{\longrightarrow}}} O_2NN \begin{array}{c} \underset{\mid}{\overset{\text{—N—}}{\mid}} \\ CH_2 \\ \underset{\text{—N—}}{\mid} \end{array} NNO_2 \quad (31)$$

$$\text{(IX)}$$

(3) *From Nitramine.* Fresh solutions of formaldehyde and nitramine within the pH range 5.6–6.5 give[27] yields (32) of over 80% of (IX).

$$4 H_2NNO_2 + 6 CH_2O \longrightarrow O_2NN \begin{array}{c} \overset{\text{—N—}}{\mid} \\ CH_2 \\ \underset{\text{—N—}}{\mid} \end{array} NNO_2 \quad (32)$$

$$\text{(IX)} \quad 83\%$$

Addition of methylenediamine sulfate, from methylene diformamide, $CH_2(CONH_2)_2$, improves the yields. Wright and his workers have shown[27] that the instability of nitramine in acidic solutions excludes it from consideration as a precursor of 1,5-endomethylene-3,7-dinitro-1,3,5,7-tetrazacyclooctane. However, the addition of formaldehyde to nitramine vastly increases its stability. Since dimethylolnitramide is stable under the reaction conditions, it is the most likely precursor of (IX). The following equilibria exist:

$$H_2NNO_2 + 2 CH_2O \rightleftharpoons \begin{array}{c} CH_2OH \\ \mid \\ NNO_2 \\ \mid \\ CH_2OH \end{array} \begin{array}{c} HNH \\ \mid \\ CH_2 \\ \mid \\ HNH \end{array} \begin{array}{c} HOCH_2 \\ \mid \\ NNO_2 \\ \mid \\ HOCH_2 \end{array} \rightleftharpoons 2 CH_2O + H_2NNO_2$$

$$\downarrow$$

$$NO_2N \begin{array}{c} \overset{\text{—N—}}{\mid} \\ CH_2 \\ \underset{\text{—N—}}{\mid} \end{array} NNO_2 + 4 H_2O$$

$$\text{(IX)}$$

Additional support for the postulation that a diamine will condense with two mols of dimethylolnitramide to form a bridged 8-membered ring is available from the synthesis of 1,5-endoethylene-3,7-dinitro-1,3,5,7-tetrazacyclooctane (XII) from nitramine, ethylenediamine and formaldehyde.

$$H_2NNO_2 + CH_2O + H_2NCH_2CH_2NH_2 \xrightarrow{\text{O}°\ 16\ \text{hrs.}} O_2NN\ \underset{\text{CH}_2}{\overset{\text{N}}{\underset{\text{N}}{\overset{\text{CH}_2}{|}}}}\ NNO_2$$

(XII) m.p. 140° (dec.)

Dimethylolnitramide exists in equilibrium with formaldehyde and nitramide as indicated in the equations above. This can be further illustrated by a mixture of acetaldehyde and nitramine which did not undergo any reaction until formaldehyde was added, whereupon formation of 1,5-ethylidine-3,7-dinitro-1,3,5,7-tetrazacyclooctane proceeded (33).

$$4\,CH_3CHO + 2\,NH_2NO_2 + 4\,CH_2O \longrightarrow O_2NN\ \ HCCH_3\ NNO_2 \qquad (33)$$

(d) *Chemical Properties.* (1) *Reduction.* Reduction of 1,5-endo-methylene-3,7-dinitro-1,3,5,7-tetrazacyclooctane (IX) by sodium amalgam to the corresponding 3,7-diamino compound has been carried out,[32] although the latter has not been isolated. Acidification of its solutions gave hydrazine in addition to formaldehyde and ammonia; this shows the $>N$-NH_2 structure. Aromatic aldehydes produce derivatives which are substituted hydrazones of structure (XIII).

$$ArCH{=}N{-}N\ \ CH_2\ \ N{-}N{=}CHAr$$

(XIII)

(2) *Nitration Type Reactions.* Concentrated sulfuric acid added to a reaction mixture used to prepare 1,5-endomethylene-3,7-dinitro-1,3,5,7-tetrazacyclooctane[28] (IX) or excess nitric acid[27] added directly to (IX) produces 1,3,5,7-tetranitro-1,3,5,7-tetrazacyclooctane, also known as Homocyclonite or HMX (high melting explosive) (XIV).

When (IX) is treated with nitric acid and acetic anhydride, the product[33,35] is 1,3,7-trinitro-5-acetoxymethyl-1,3,5,7-tetrazacyclooctane

(XV). Further treatment of (XV) with nitrosyl chloride and acetic anhydride converts it to 1,3,7-trinitro-5-nitroso-1,3,5,7-tetrazacyclooctane (XVI) which is easily oxidized to the tetranitro compound (XIV) by means of 30% hydrogen peroxide and nitric acid.

If 1,5-endomethylene-3,7-dinitro-1,3,5,7-tetrazacyclooctane (IX) is subjected to the action of nitrosyl chloride and acetic anhydride, a 60% yield of 1,7-dinitro-3-nitroso-5-acetyl-1,3,5,7-tetrazacyclooctane (XVII) is obtained which can be oxidized by hydrogen peroxide to the 1,3,7-trinitro-5-acetyl compound (XVIII).

Three additional cleavage type reactions should be considered before discussion of these reactions. At 75°, nitric acid and ammonium nitrate convert 1,5-endomethylene-3,7-dinitro-1,3,5,7-tetrazacyclooctane (IX) to 1,3,5,7-tetranitro-1,3,5,7-tetrazacyclooctane (XIV) and 1,3,5-trinitrohexahydro-*s*-triazine, the ratio of the two products depending on the ratio of nitric acid to ammonium nitrate.[34]

Acetic anhydride and 1,5-endomethylene-3,7-dinitro-1,3,5,7-tetrazacyclooctane (IX) in the presence of nitric acid give 1,9 diacetyl-2,4,6,8-tetranitro-2,4,6,8-tetrazanonane; however if the acetic anhydride is replaced by nitrogen pentaoxide, N_2O_5, the principal product becomes 1,9-dinitroxy-2,4,6,8-tetranitro-2,4,6,8-tetrazanonone which can be converted to a 1,9-diether with alcohol. In order to form these linear compounds from (IX), a different pair of scissions must occur than can be specified for formation of the cyclic compounds 1,3,5,7-tetranitro-1,3,5,7-tetrazacyclooctane (XIV) and 1,3,5-trinitrohexahydro-*s*-triazine. There remain only two possibilities if structures are excluded in which two nitro groups are on one amino group, and no such compounds are known. Either a symmetrical scission at C and B or an unsymmetrical scission at A' and C may take place. The known

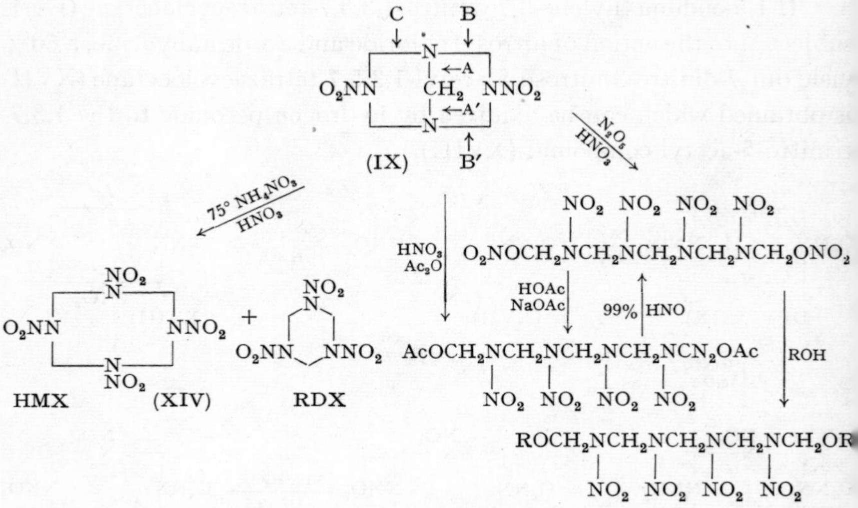

$$
\begin{array}{c}
C \quad B \\
\downarrow \quad \downarrow \\
\text{O}_2\text{NN}\;\begin{array}{c}-\text{N}-\\ |\;\;\leftarrow A \\ \text{CH}_2 \\ |\;\;\leftarrow A' \\ -\text{N}-\end{array}\;\text{NNO}_2 \\
(IX) \quad \uparrow \\
B'
\end{array}
$$

75° NH$_4$NO$_3$/HNO$_3$ →   N$_2$O$_5$/HNO$_3$ →

HNO$_3$/Ac$_2$O

$$
\begin{array}{cccc}
\text{NO}_2 & \text{NO}_2 & \text{NO}_2 & \text{NO}_2 \\
| & | & | & | \\
\end{array}
$$
O$_2$NOCH$_2$NCH$_2$NCH$_2$NCH$_2$NCH$_2$ONO$_2$

HOAc / NaOAc   99% | HNO

AcOCH$_2$NCH$_2$NCH$_2$NCH$_2$NCN$_2$OAc
$$
\begin{array}{cccc}
| & | & | & | \\
\text{NO}_2 & \text{NO}_2 & \text{NO}_2 & \text{NO}_2 \\
\end{array}
$$

ROH

ROCH$_2$NCH$_2$NCH$_2$NCH$_2$NCH$_2$OR
$$
\begin{array}{cccc}
| & | & | & | \\
\text{NO}_2 & \text{NO}_2 & \text{NO}_2 & \text{NO}_2 \\
\end{array}
$$

HMX:
$$
\text{O}_2\text{NN}\;\begin{array}{c}\text{NO}_2\\ -\text{N}-\\ \\ -\text{N}-\\ \text{NO}_2\end{array}\;\text{NNO}_2
$$
HMX (XIV)

$+$

RDX:
$$
\text{O}_2\text{NN}\;\begin{array}{c}\text{NO}_2\\ \text{N}\\ \end{array}\;\text{NNO}_2
$$
RDX

conversion of 1,3,7-trinitro-5-acetoxymethyl-1,3,5,7-tetrazacyclooctane (XV) to the N-acetate strongly suggests the unsymmetrical scission although no direct evidence is available. On this basis, the weakest linkage during nitrolysis is probably a bridge link; subsequently, the choice may depend upon the rapidity with which the free hydroxyl group is esterified. If, following scission at A', the pendulant hydroxyl group remains free for an appreciable time, the subsequent split is at A, liberation of formaldehyde accompanies the nitration. If the hydroxyl group is esterified, the linkage at A is strengthened and subsequent scission will occur at the only available linkage, C.

Ammonium nitrate addition to the reaction mixture produces 1,3,5,7-tetranitro-1,3,5,7-tetrazacyclooctane (XIV) instead of the 1,9-diacetoxynonane derivative. Apparently, ammonium nitrate either facilitates formaldehyde removal or demethylolation or else hinders esterification.

It should be noted that in the above reaction series, no evidence exists that acetyl nitrate acts as a nitrolyzing agent except when it has been converted to acetic anhydride and nitric acid by acetic acid.

Nitric acid—acetic anhydride and nitric acid—nitrogen pentoxide may both be considered simple solutions in which the absence of water has appreciably reduced the acidity of the nitric acid. In both instances, nitric acid is moreover considered as the nitrolyzing agent, while acetic anhydride or nitrogen pentoxide are the esterifying agents.

(3) 1,5-Endomethylene-3,7-dinitroso-1,3,5,7-tetrazacyclooctane. This colorless crystalline compound melts[33] at 207–215°. While treating hexamethylenetetramine with hydrochloric acid and sodium nitrite produces[36] mostly 1,3,5-trinitrosohexahydro-*s*-triazine, a quantity of 1,5-endomethylene-3,7-dinitroso-1,3,5,7-tetrazacyclooctane is also produced. The two compounds are readily separable. At pH 3–4 instead of the usual pH 1 employed for nitration, the ratio is shifted and a 75% yield of the endomethylene compound obtained.[33]

(4) 1,5-Endomethylene-3,7-diamino-1,3,5,7-tetrazacyclooctane and Derivatives.   The free amine has not been isolated from its solutions which are made by reductions of 1,5-endomethylene-3,7-dinitro-1,3,5,7-tetrazacyclooctane (IX) with sodium amalgam.[52] Acidification of solutions of 1,5-endomethylene-3,7-diamino-1,3,5,7-tetrazacyclooctane produces hydrazine, ammonia and formaldehyde, an indication of the >N-NH₂ structure. A number of derivatives of the 3,7-diamino compound are known. Aromatic aldehydes react in solutions of the diamine to

$$
\text{H}_2\text{NN} \quad \underset{\text{L}-\text{N}-\text{J}}{\overset{\text{[}-\text{N}-\text{]}}{\text{CH}_2}} \quad \text{NNH}_2 \; + \; 2\,\text{ArCHO} \; \longrightarrow \; \text{ArCH}{=}\text{N}{-}\text{N} \quad \underset{\text{L}-\text{N}-\text{J}}{\overset{\text{[}-\text{N}-\text{]}}{\text{CH}_2}} \quad \text{N}{-}\text{NCHAr} \quad (1)
$$
$$
+ \; 2\,\text{H}_2\text{O}
$$

produce substituted hydrazones (1). Table VIII-3 lists the aldehydes known[32] to form substituted dihydrazones of 1,5-endomethylene-3,7-diamino-1,3,5,7-tetrazacyclooctane together with their melting points.

TABLE VIII-3.   1,5-Endomethylene-3,7-di(arylidineamino)-
1,3,5,7-tetrazacyclooctanes

Aldehyde	M.p. Dihydrazone
Benzaldehyde	226–227°/Ethanol
m-Nitrobenzaldehyde	134°/Ethanol
Salicylaldehyde	213°/Chloroform-ether
Cinnamylaldehyde	207°-Ethanol

The compounds in Table VIII-3 are typical Schiff's bases. They are decomposed by acid, regenerating the aldehyde, hydrazine, formaldehyde and ammonia.

(5) 1,5-Endomethylene-3,7-dimethyl-1,3,5,7-tetrazacyclooctane. The 3,7-dimethyl derivative in this series has been isolated[37] as the picrate which melts with decomposition at 196° and can be recrystallized from ethanol. It is prepared (2) by heating hexamethylenetetramine picrate with formaldehyde.[37]

$$\text{Hexamethylenetetramine} + \text{CH}_2\text{O} \xrightarrow{\Delta} \text{CH}_3\text{N} \quad \text{CH}_2 \quad \text{NCH}_3 \cdot \text{Picrate} \quad (2)$$
$$\text{picrate}$$

(6) 1,5-Endomethylene-3,7-diacetyl-1,3,5,7-tetrazacyclooctane. 1,5-Endomethylene-3,7-diacetyl-1,3,5,7-tetrazacyclooctane (XIX) melts at 186–187° and can be crystallized from benzene. It has been reported[38] that treatment of hexamethylenetetramine in the cold with acetic anhydride produces a 30% yield of (XIX). Structure (XIX) is most probable.

$$(\text{CH}_2)_6\text{N}_4 + (\text{CH}_3\text{CO})_2\text{O} \xrightarrow{\text{cold}} \text{CH}_3\text{CON} \quad \text{CH}_2 \quad \text{NCOCH}_3$$
$$(\text{XIX})$$

(7) 1,5-Endomethylene-3,7-di(aryldiazo)1,3,5,7-tetrazacyclooctanes. (a) 1,5-Endomethylene-3,7-di(benzenediazo)-1,3,5,7-tetrazacyclooctane melts[32] with decomposition at 228°. It can be recrystallized from benzene.[32] This compound and the meta and para nitro derivatives below can be prepared from hexamethylenetetramine.[32]

Hexamethylenetetramine reacts with diazonium salts[3] in the cold in the presence of sodium acetate (to maintain neutrality) forming phenol-bis-diazobenzenes and 1,5-endomethylene-3,7-di(aryldiazo)-1,3,5,7-tetrazacyclooctanes (3).

$$+ \ 2 \ \text{ArN}_2^+ \text{Cl}^- \xrightarrow[\text{NaOAc}]{\text{cold}} \text{Ar}-\text{N}=\text{N} \quad \text{CH}_2 \quad \text{N}-\text{N}=\text{Ar} \quad (3)$$

(b) 1,5-Endomethylene-3,7-di(*m*-nitrobenzendiazo)1,3,5,7-tetrazacyclooctane melts[32] with decomposition at 184°. It can be crystallized from a chloroform-ethanol mixture and is prepared in the same way as the benzenediazo compound.

(c) 1,5-Endomethylene-3,7-di(p-nitrobenzenediazo)1,3,5,7-tetraza-cyclooctane, recrystallized from ethanol, melts[32] with decomposition at 244° and has been synthesized in the same way as the benzenediazo compound.

(d) 1,5-Endomethylene-3,7-di(p-sulfobenzenediazo)1,3,5,7-tetraza-cyclooctane has been obtained from water as the hexahydrated di-sodium salt.[32] A barium salt crystallizes with three molecules of water which are lost upon heating at 100°. Crystalline copper and nickel salts are known[32] as well as an amorphous silver salt.

The diazonium salt of sulfanilic acid reacts with hexamethylene-tetramine to give (XX).

(8) 1,5-Endomethylene-3,7-di(p-tolylsulfonyl)1,3,5,7-tetraza-cyclooctane (XXI).

Compound (XXI), a substituted sulfonamide, has also been named[39], 3,7-bis(p-tolylsulfonyl)1,3,5,7-tetrazabicyclo[3,3,1]-nonane. Compound (XXI) can be crystallized from nitromethane and melts at 236°. It is insoluble in most organic solvents but soluble in pyridine and hot nitromethane. It is prepared[39] by means of the reaction of p-toluenesulfonyl chloride and hexamethylenetetramine (4). Yields are 46%.

(9) 1,5 - Ethylidine - 3,7 - dinitro - 1,3,5,7 - tetrazacyclooctane.

1,5-Ethylidine-3,7-dinitro-1,3,5,7-tetrazacyclooctane melts at 175°. It can be synthesized[27] by the reaction of nitramine, acetaldehyde and formaldehyde (5).

B. Endoimino-s-Triazines, R.I. 932

The single member of this class of compounds, of which the parent compound is 2,4,6,8,9-pentazabicyclo[3,3,1]-nonane (XXII), is 1-amino-2,6-dimethyl-3,7-dioxo-2,4,6,8,9-pentazabicyclo[3,3,1]nonene-4.[40] It

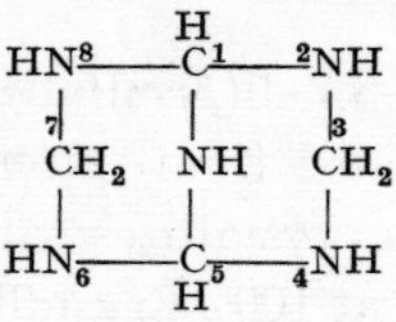

$$
\begin{array}{ccccc}
 & & \text{H} & & \\
\text{HN}^9 & \!\!\!\!-\!\!\!\! & \text{C}^1 & \!\!\!\!-\!\!\!\! & {}^2\text{NH} \\
{}_7| & & | & & |^3 \\
\text{CH}_2 & & \text{NH} & & \text{CH}_2 \\
| & & | & & | \\
\text{HN}_6 & \!\!\!\!-\!\!\!\! & \text{C}_5 & \!\!\!\!-\!\!\!\! & {}_4\text{NH} \\
 & & \text{H} & &
\end{array}
$$

(XXII)

decomposes at 320° and can be recrystallized from water. The bicyclic compound is insoluble in cold water, slightly soluble in acid, and soluble in warm base. It is produced in 25% yield by sulfuric acid-perchloric acid treatment of 2(methylcarbamino) 3-methyl-4-oxo-6-iminohexahydro-1,3,5-triazine (6). The synthesis is carried out by

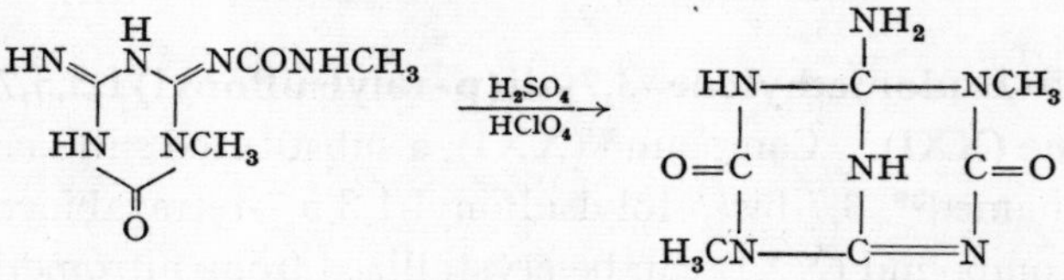

treating the substituted ammeline with concentrated sulfuric at 80–100° and then with perchloric acid, and finally neutralizing with sodium carbonate.

3. Compounds of Three Fused s-Triazine Rings: Cyamelurates, R.I. 1815

Compounds of this group all contain the cyameluric or tri-s-triazine nucleus which is numbered as follows:

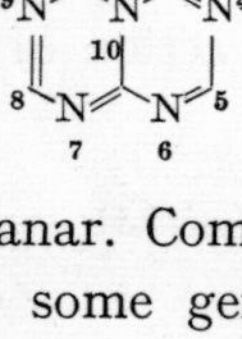

The three rings are coplanar. Compounds of this series are extremely stable, but undergo some general reactions in a manner analogous to the reactions of cyanuric acid derivatives. The stability of cyameluric derivatives is due to the large number of resonating forms which can exist. Pauling who has calculated[41] the resonance energy quantum mechanically by the method of molecular orbitals, finds a stabilization energy of 150,000 cal./mole, which completely removes the unsaturation to be expected if there were non-resonating molecules with six double bonds and accounts for the extraordinary stability of tri-*s*-triazine derivatives.

A. 2,5,8-Trihydroxytri-s-triazine: Cyameluric Acid

2,5,8-Trihydroxytri-*s*-triazine (XXIII) is commonly called cyameluric acid. It is an extremely stable substance which does not have a definite melting point, but decomposes at red heat. Owing to a greater resonance energy than cyanuric acid, (XXIII) is more stable and also a stronger acid. The magnetic susceptibility of cyameluric acid is -101.1×10^{-6} at 10°, twice that of cyanuric acid.[42]

2,5,8-Trihydroxytri-*s*-triazine (XXIII) is obtained when 2,5,8-tricyanamidotri-*s*-triazine, known also as hydromelamic acid, is treated with strong alkali. Ammonia is evolved and tripotassium cyamelurate results,[43,44] along with small amounts of ammelide and ammeline (6A).

Structure (XXIII) is favored[41,42] for cyameluric acid over structure (XXIV) although resonating electronic structures such as (XXV) also are probable.[42]

Most investigators have made little mention of the keto forms of cyameluric acid, but as considerations discussed in connection with cyanuric acid apply also to cyameluric acid, it is possible that all or a good part of cyameluric acid, either in crystalline form or in solution, exists in one or more of the keto forms, (XXVI), (XXVII) and (XXVIII).

(XXVI)   (XXVII)   (XXVIII)

The fact that alkylation with benzyl chloride produces exclusively the N-benzyl derivative furnishes evidence of the keto form. It should be noted that the triketo form of cyameluric acid still possesses three double bonds in the molecule unlike the triketo form of cyanuric acid in which the ring is completely saturated.

(1) Salts. Cyameluric acid is usually obtained as the penta-hydrate but becomes anhydrous if heated[45] at 100–120°. It forms a blue-lavender cupric ammonium salt,[45] $CuNH_4(C_6N_7O_3)NH_3$, comparable to the cupric ammonium salt, $CuNH_4(C_3N_3O_3)NH_3$, formed from cyanuric acid. This salt is useful for purifying cyameluric acid because the free acid can be readily regenerated by suspending the salt in water and acidifying with hydrochloric acid. Crystalline neutral salts of the following cations are known:[43] K^+, Ba^{++}, NH_4^+, Na^+, and Mg^{++}. The first two are water soluble; the barium salt loses its one equivalent of water of crystallization at 250°. Amorphous iron and silver salts, the latter with two equivalents of water which are lost[6] at 120°, are also known.

Cyameluric acid forms a potassium acid salt ($\cdot 4H_2O$, lost at 100°) in addition to the tripotassium salt ($\cdot 6H_2O$, lost at 120°) by heating the free acid with acetic acid-potassium acetate.

(2) Reactions. 2,5,8-Trihydroxytri-s-triazine (XXIII) is very stable. Hot nitric acid converts it to cyanuric acid. Heating to a dull red glow causes decomposition to cyanic acid (7). Potassium cyame-

lurate will not react with methyl iodide and reacts only sluggishly at
100° with allyl bromide giving an impure derivative. At a temperature

$$\text{HOCN} \xleftarrow{\text{red heat}} \text{(XXIII)} \xrightarrow[\Delta]{\text{HNO}_3} \qquad (7)$$

of 156°, benzyl chloride reacts, forming, in 36% yield, a tribenzyl
derivative, which is probably, 1,4,7-tribenzyltri-*s*-triazine (common
name 1,4,7-tribenzylisocyamelurate)[45] on the basis of the way in which
cyanuric acid alkylates.

Diazomethane and cyameluric acid react to form a mixture of
derivatives consisting mainly of the tri- and monomethyl-N-derivatives
and some mono-O-derivative.[45]

A mixture of a diamino and some impure triaminotri-*s*-triazine
results from the action of ammonia on cyameluric acid.[45] Tripotassium
cyamelurate produces a 93% yield of cyameluric chloride with phosphorous pentachloride[45] (8).

B. 2,5,8-Trichlorotri-s-triazine: Cyameluric Chloride

2,5,8-Trichlorotri-*s*-triazine (XXIX) is related to cyameluric acid as
cyanuric chloride is to cyanuric acid. It is isolated as thin yellow platelets
insoluble in organic solvents[45] such as chloroform, anisole, *o*-dichloroben-
zene, nitrobenzene, acetonitrile, and glacial acetic acid, with which it
reacts to form cyameluric acid and acetyl chloride. It has no melting
point, but gradually disappears on heating, probably as a result of a
combination of oxidation and sublimation.[45] (XXIX) has been commonly
named[45] cyameluryl or cyameluric chloride. It can be prepared in 93%
yield by the action of phosphorous pentachloride on the corresponding
trihydroxy compound, cyameluric acid (XXIII) or its tripotassium
salt[45] (8).

$$\text{(XXIII)} + 3\,\text{PCl}_5 \longrightarrow \text{(XXIX)} + 3\,\text{POCl}_3 + 3\,\text{HCl} \qquad (8)$$

Cyameluric chloride exhibits behavior typical of acid chlorides. It is analogous to cyanuric chloride but undergoes hydrolysis more readily since it is the chloride of a stronger acid. Both chlorides produce acetyl chloride and their respective free acids from acetic acid, and alkyl chlorides and the free acids from alcohols.

Cyameluric chloride undergoes no reaction[45] with sodium methoxide or sodium phenoxide which is surprising since (XXIX) appears to be more reactive than cyanuric chloride. This apparent unreactivity is very likely due to the insolubility of (XXIX) in common organic solvents.

C. 1,4,7-Tribenzyl-2,5,8-trioxo-1,2,4,5,7,8-hexahydrotri-s-triazine

1,4,7-Tribenzyl-2,5,8-trioxo-1,2,4,5,7,8-hexahydrotri-s-triazine (XXX) or 1,4,7-tribenzylisocyamelurate melts at 283–284°. It has been prepared in 36% yield by the reaction[45] of tripotassium cyamelurate with benzyl chloride at a temperature of 156°. Cyanuric acid forms isocyanurates under similar alkylation conditions.

Compound (XXX) produced benzylamine but no benzyl alcohol upon hydrolysis; this shows it to be a nitrogen substituted tri-s-triazine analogous to the isocyanurates.

D. 2,5,8-Tricyanamidotri-s-triazine: Hydromelonic Acid

2,5,8-Tricyanamidotri-s-triazine (XXXI), commonly named hydromelonic acid, is a white amorphous solid when pure. It does not melt but decomposes at temperatures approaching red heat. More commonly (XXXI) is isolated in a slightly yellow condition. It is insoluble in all common solvents but alkali.

Hydromelonic acid may be prepared by a number of procedures most of which are described in the older literature. They are rather tedious and the results are not readily reproduced. More reliable synthetic methods are needed. All of the available preparative methods make use of high temperature pyrolysis, in most cases the pyrolysis of thiocyanic acid derivatives. Hydromelonic acid is most commonly isolated as the potassium or sodium salts; the acid is difficult to obtain pure.

The following methods have been used to prepare 2,5,8-tricyana-amidotri-s-triazine (XXXI) or its salts:

(1) Fusion[46] of antimony trichloride and sodium thiocyanate.[46]

$$10\,SbCl_3 + 39\,NaSCN \xrightarrow[\text{30 minutes}]{\text{fuse}} 3\,Na_3C_3N_{13} + 5\,Sb_2S_3 + 12\,CS_2 + 30\,NaCl$$

(2) Fusion[47,48] of potassium ferrocyanide and sulfur.

(3) Heating[48] of thiocyanogen at 360°.

(4) Heating[48] of thiocyanogen with chlorine.

(5) Pyrolysis[43] of potassium thiocyanate.

(6) Fusion[49] of potassium thiocyanate with antimony or bismuth trichlorides, and

(7) Calcination[44] of the residue obtained from the thermal decomposition of ammonium thiocyanate or guanidine thiocyanate.

The similarity of 2,5,8-tricyanamidotri-s-triazine (XXXI) to tricyanamido-s-triazine (tricyanomelamine) revealed by X-ray examination, led Pauling to formulate[41] the structure of the cyameluric series. (XXXI) is the fundamental compound of the series synthetically speaking since all of the other members are prepared from it, directly or indirectly.

The free acid (XXXI) can be obtained as a dihydrated white amorphous powder by treating its sodium salt with silver nitrate and then heating the gelatinous silver salt in water while passing in hydrogen sulfide.[46] Hydromelonic acid (XXXI) forms salts with a great number of metals. The salts are crystalline in some cases but more often amorphous solids. All salts reported in the literature are listed in Table VIII-4, although in some cases no analyses were offered originally.

The potassium acid salt can be made[49] by treating a solution of the tripotassium salt with warm dilute hydrochloric acid or by heating it in acetic acid solution.

A silver-ammonia complex salt is made[46] by treating a solution of the sodium salt in liquid ammonia with silver nitrate.

TABLE VIII-4. Salts of 2,5,8-Tricyanamidotri-s-triazine

Cation	Hydrate, Moles H_2O	Temperature at which H_2O is lost, °C.	Remarks	Ref.
NH_4^+				1
Na^+	$5H_2O$		Recrystalline from hot H_2O. Sol. liq. NH_3	1, 3
K^+	$5H_2O$	—$4H_2O$ at 120°, —$5H_2O$ at 150°	Sol. H_2O	1
K^+ (acid)			Insol. cold H_2O, sol. K acetate sol'n.	2
Ag^+	Gelatinous	Dry at 180		1, 3
Pb^{++}				1
Hg^{++}				1
Ba^{++}	$6H_2O$	—$5H_2O$ at 130°		1
Sr^{++}				1
Ca^{++}	$4H_2O$	—$3H_2O$ at 120°		1
Mg^{++}				1
Cu^{++}	$5H_2O$	—$4H_2O$ at 120°		1
Mn^{++}				
Co^{+++}				1
Fe^{+++}				1
Cr^{+++}				1
Sb^{+++}				1
Ag^+	$6NH_3$		Insol. H_2O, dil. acids	3

1. J. Liebig, *Ann. Chem. Pharm.*, **50**, 337 (1844).
2. J. Liebig, *Ann. Chem. Pharm.*, **95**, 256 (1855).
3. W. Burdick, *J. Am. Chem. Soc.*, **47**, 1485 (1925).

2,5,8-Tricyanamidotri-s-triazine (XXXI) is hydrolyzed to 2,5,8-trihydroxytri-s-triazine (XXIII) by strong alkali treatment.[43, 44]

E. Melam, Melem, and Melon

Melam, melem and melon are three products of the pyrolytic degradation of melamine. They are also encountered to a minor extent in some of the synthetic methods for preparing melamine, principally those involving high temperatures.

Although melam does not possess a condensed ring structure, the three substances require mention here as well as in Chapter VI because the cyameluric acid structure proposed[41] by Pauling permits the formulation of an adequate structure for melam, as well as for melem and melon.[45]

Melam, $C_6H_9N_{11}$, is probably N^2-(4,6-diamino-2-s-triazinyl) melamine (XXXII). This structure accounts for the feeble basicity of melam

(XXXII)

and is consistent with its behavior at elevated temperatures with 30% aqueous ammonia to yield melamine and ammeline. Moreover boiling nitric acid converts[50] melam to cyanuric acid and ammonium nitrate.

Melem, $C_6H_6N_{10}$, is most probably 2,5,8-triaminotri-s-triazine (XXXIII). It bears the same relationship to cyameluric acid as does melamine to cyanuric acid. Structure (XXXIII) accounts for the formation of large quantities of ammelide upon hydrolysis and also for the greater resistance to hydrolysis of melem compared with melam.

Melon gives good yields of cyameluric acid on hydrolysis indicating that it contains the tri-s-triazine nucleus. A possible melon structure is (XXXIV) in which three molecules of ammonia have been lost from three triaminotri-s-triazine nuclei. The apexes of the triangles stand for the 2, 5, and 8 positions of the tri-s-triazine (cyameluric) nuclei.

(XXXIII)   (XXXIV)   (XXXV)

This structure is three times the formula of $C_6H_3N_9$ generally accepted for melon. Another possible structure is (XXXV) in which the tri-s-triazine nuclei, with the exception of the two terminal ones, are joined to only two other nuclei. Both of these possibilities can be extended to the proportions of a high polymer. Such extension may explain why the melon analyses in the literature have not been in better agreement.

Melon is probably a mixture of molecules of different sizes and shapes, a situation which gives rise to its amorphous character. It may be compared with graphite in that the molecules of both substances are planar and may be exceedingly large. The high stability of melon can be explained in terms of the enormous number of resonance forms which contribute to the structure.

4. Thiadiazino-s-Triazines:
2,2-Dioxo-3,4-dihydro-1,2,4-thiadiazino[4,3-a]-s-triazine

The single member of this group has been briefly mentioned before. It is produced by oxidative rearrangement[16] of 2,3,5-trihydro-7-amino-5-iminothiazolo[2,3-a]-s-triazine which is made from thioammeline and 1,2-dibromoethane.[15] If 2,3,5-trihydro-7-amino-5-iminothiazole[2,3-a]-s-triazine (XXXVI) is treated with chlorine in hydrochloric acid solution, cleavage at the sulfur-triazine ring carbon bond occurs. The mercapto group is oxidized by chlorine to a sulfonic acid

group. The ring carbon is also attacked, resulting in the introduction of a ring hydroxyl group. A molecule of water is reversibly eliminated and a new six-membered ring forms. The rearrangement may proceed through an intermediate sulfonyl chloride. Heating with water reopens the thiadiazine ring.

Barium hydroxide also cleaves the thiadiazine ring and hydrolyzes the resulting imino group, producing 2[4-amino-1,2-dihydro-6-hydroxy-2-oxo-1,3,5-triazine-1]ethylenesulfonic acid which melts at 265–270°.

5. Compounds Comprising Two Triazine Rings and One Thia-s-triazine Ring:
2-Thia-1,3,5,7-tetrazatricyclo[3,3,1,1³,⁷]decane-2,2-dioxide

2 - Thia - 1,3,5,7 - tetrazatricyclo [3,3,1,1³,⁷] decane - 2,2 - dioxide (XXXVIII) melts with decomposition at 224–225° after recrystalliza-

tion from 95% ethanol. It is prepared by the reaction of sulfamide, formaldehyde and ammonia.[51] The reaction is carried out in aqueous media at 55° and yields of 88% may be obtained.

Substitution of amines for ammonia results in the formation of 4-substituted thia-*s*-triazines (see Chapter IX, *Hexahydro-s-triazines*).

Compound (XXXVIII) behaves very much like hexamethylene-tetramine. It is decomposed by strong mineral acids into its constituents, forms salts with weak acids, and forms 1,3,5-trinitrohexahydro-*s*-triazine on nitration with nitric acid. Salts such as the phosphate, the picrate and the silver nitrate complex can be readily prepared.

On the basis of these properties and reactions, structure (XXXVIII) is probably correct. The compound has been given[51] the common name pentamethylenetetramine sulfone.

6. Compounds Comprising One Thiatriazine Ring and Two Triazacycloheptane Rings: 11-Thia-1,3,5,7-tetrazatricyclo[3,3,1,1³,⁷]-undecane-11,11-dioxide

The compound is a relative of hexamethylenetetramine. It can be recrystallized from water and melts with decomposition at 195–196°. The common name is homopentamethylenetetramine sulfone.[51] It can be prepared[51] from formaldehyde, sulfamide and ethylenediamine (see Sect. III,5 above). The reaction is carried out at 65–70° and yields of over 90% may be obtained.

$$CH_2O + H_2NCH_2CH_2NH_2 + (NH_2)_2SO_2 \xrightarrow{65-70°}$$

This compound behaves similarly to hexamethylenetetramine. It forms salts with weak acids and many inorganic compounds and is decomposed by strong mineral acids.

References

1. K. Slotta and R. Tschesche, *Ber.*, **62B**, 1390 (1929).
2. H. Stetter and K. Steinacker, *Ber.*, **85**, 451 (1952).
3. H. Stetter and W. Böckmann, *Ber.*, **84**, 834 (1951).
3a. R. Lukes and K. Syhora, *Coll. Czech. Chem. Communications*, **18**, 654 (1953).

4. P. Pierron, *Ann. chim. phys.*, **8**, **15**, 196 (1908).
4a. F. Schaefer, *J. Am. Chem. Soc.*, **77**, 5922 (1955).
5. N. Heimbach and R. Clark, U. S. 2,444,609 (1948) to Gen'l. Aniline and Film Co.
6. G. Pellizzari, *Gazz. chim. ital.*, **52**, (I) 199 (1922).
7. G. Pellizzari, *Gazz. chim. ital.*, **54**, (I) 177 (1924).
8. H. Blitz, *Ber.*, **67B**, 1856 (1934).
9. A. Keller, *Ber.*, **24**, 2512 (1891).
10. D. Kaiser, G. Peters and V. Wystrach, *J. Org. Chem.*, **18**, 1610 (1953).
11. D. Kaiser, U. S. 2,473,797 (1949) to American Cyanamid Co.
12. G. Pellizzari and C. Roncagliolo, *Gazz. chim. ital.*, **31**, (I) 496 (1901).
13. K. Hofmann and O. Ehrhart, *Ber.*, **45**, 2733 (1912).
14. K. Hofmann and O. Ehrhart, *Ber.*, **44**, 2713 (1911).
15. B. Rathke, *Ber.*, **20**, 1063 (1887).
16. B. Rathke, *Ber.*, **21**, 875 (1888).
17. C. Schöpf *et al.*, *Ann.*, **559**, 1 (1948).
18. C. Schöpf, H. Arm and H. Krimm, *Ber.*, **84**, 690 (1951).
19. C. Schöpf, H. Arm and F. Braun, *Ber.*, **85**, 937 (1952).
20. C. Schöpf, F. Braun and K. Otte, *Ber.*, **86**, 918 (1953).
21. R. Bell, D. Lidwell and M. Vaughn-Jackson, *J. Chem. Soc.*, **1936**, 1792.
22. M. Delepine, *Bull. soc. chim.*, (4), **9**, 1025 (1911).
23. J. Boivin and G. Wright, *Can. J. Research*, **28B**, 213 (1950).
24. A. Leulier and K. Cohen, *J. pharm. chim.*, **29**, 245 (1939).
25. M. Foss, *J. Chem. Soc.*, **1950**, 1691.
26. M. Foss, *J. Chem. Soc.*, **1950**, 624.
27. G. Wright et al., *Can. J. Research*, **27B**, 218 (1949).
28. Brit. 615,419 (1949; Brit. 615,793 (1949), to Honorary Council for Scientific and Industrial Research, Ottawa.
29. P. Griess and G. Harrow, *Ber.*, **21**, 2737 (1888).
30. S. Epstein and C. Winkler, *Can. J. Chem.*, **30**, 734 (1952).
31. A. Lamberton, C. Lindley and J. Speakman, *J. Chem. Soc.*, **1949**, 1650.
32. P. Duden and M. Scharff, *Ann.*, **288**, 218 (1895).
33. W. Bachmann and N. Deno, *J. Am. Chem. Soc.*, **73**, 2777 (1951).
34. A. McKay, H. Richmond and G. Wright, *Can. J. Research*, **27B**, 462 (1949).
35. R. Marcus and C. Winkler, *Can. J. Chem.*, **31**, 602 (1953).
36. F. Brockman, D. Downing and G. Wright, *Can. J. Research*, **27B**, 469 (1949).
37. J. Graymore, *J. Chem. Soc.*, **1931**, 1490.
38. M. Dominikiewicz, *Arch. Chem. Farm.*, **2**, 78 (1935).
39. A. McKay and G. Wright, *J. Am. Chem. Soc.*, **68**, 2116 (1946).
40. K. Slotta and R. Tschesche, *Ber.*, **62B**, 137 (1929).
41. L. Pauling and J. Sturdivant, *Proc. Natl. Acad. Sci.*, **23**, 616 (1937).
42. J. Maruha, *J. Chem. Soc. Japan, Pure Chem. Sect.*, **71**, 627 (1950), through *Chem. Abstracts*, **45**, 9067 (1951).
43. W. Henneberg, *Ann.*, **73**, 228 (1850).
44. J. Volhard, *J. prakt. Chem.*, (2), **9**, 6 (1874).
45. C. Redemann and H. Lucas, *J. Am. Chem. Soc.*, **62**, 842 (1940).
46. W. Burdick, *J. Am. Chem. Soc.*, **47**, 1485 (1925).
47. L. Gmelin, *Ann.*, **15**, 252 (1835).
48. J. Liebig, *Ann.*, **50**, 337 (1844).
49. J. Liebig, *Ann.*, **95**, 256 (1855).
50. J. Liebig, *Ann.*, **10**, 1 (1834).
51. A. Paquin, *Angew. Chem.*, **A60**, 316 (1948).

CHAPTER IX

Hexahydro-*s*-triazines

I. Introduction

This chapter includes those *s*-triazines and their immediate derivatives which have a saturated 1,3,5-triazacyclohexane ring with no functional derivatives such as: oxo, hydroxy, thion, amino, imino, etc., on ring carbon atoms. Necessarily, a few exceptions to this generalization had to be included. Compounds in this category may be regarded both chemically and structurally as cyclic secondary triamines, and indeed, in most instances, the reactions they undergo are indicative of their basic character. Basicity in the usual sense is not manifested in terms of salt formation due to the inherent instability of the compounds in the presence of acids.

II. Hexahydro-*s*-triazine and Nitrate

The first member of the series is hexahydro-*s*-triazine or 1,3,5-triazacyclohexane (I), which has not been isolated from solution. It had been postulated as an intermediate in the formation of hexamethylene-

tetramine from Duden-Scharf[1] and Henry[2] solutions of formaldehyde and ammonia since very early work in the field was carried out. Proof that compound (I) actually is an intermediate in such solution has been recently offered.[3] It might be well to discuss the mechanism of formation of the intermediate which gives rise to hexamethylenetetramine (hexamine) in order to gain a clearer understanding both of the compounds of this chapter and of hexamine itself. The solutions mentioned above are merely aqueous formaldehyde-ammonium chloride solutions

473

to which potassium carbonate has been added. Duden and Scharf solution differs from Henry solution in that it contains sodium chloride, is more dilute, and gives hexamine faster. In these solutions, the following equilibria exist (1). Note that the last step is irreversible.

$$3 \text{ CH}_2\text{O} + 3 \text{ NH}_3 \rightleftharpoons 3[\text{HOCH}_2\text{NH}_2] \rightleftharpoons 3[\text{CH}_2\text{=NH}] + 3 \text{ H}_2\text{O}$$

From this scheme it is apparent that a fresh solution should contain little or no hexamine. Newly prepared solutions do not form 1,5-endo-methylene-3,7-di(*m*-nitrobenzenediazo)-1,3,5,7-tetrazocyclooctane (II)

with benzene diazonium chloride as do hexamine solutions. Hexamine gives 1,3,5-tribenzoyl-1,3,5-triazapentane with benzoyl chloride, while the fresh solutions gave 1,3,5-tribenzoylhexahydro-*s*-triazine; this shows that hexahydro-*s*-triazine (I) was present as an intermediate (2).

Analysis of Henry solution further showed, by the $1:1$ ratio of CH_2O to NH_3, that hexahydro-*s*-triazine was the principal intermediate.

Hexamine in solution forms an insoluble characteristic salt with styphnic acid. Fresh Henry solution does not yield this salt unless more than one equivalent of the acid in added, in which case a reaction occurs whereby the acid decomposes the *s*-triazine ring.

Hexahydro-*s*-triazine exhibits a tendency to decompose to methylenediamine, $\text{CH}_2(\text{NH}_2)_2$, and the elements of hexamine. In strongly acid solutions, these fragments are partially stabilized as salts. In weakly acidic or basic solutions, they combine to give hexamine. The decomposition of methylenediamine under these conditions also contributes to the formation of hexamine.

The mono nitrate salt of hexahydro-*s*-triazine (I) has been isolated and characterized by Vroom and Winkler.[4] It is a solid melting at 98–100° and can be purified by dissolving in 75 % nitric acid at 20° and diluting with water at a temperature of —20°. It can be prepared by treating hexamethylenetetramine with 88 % nitric acid at 0° for four to five minutes. The salt is an explosive with about the same strength as 1,3,5-trinitrohexahydro-*s*-triazine (RDX).

There is good evidence for regarding (I) as the correct structure of the nitrate. Potassium iodide-iodine solution gave no precipitate of hexamethylenetetramine dinitrate tetraiodide from aqueous solutions—proof that it was not hexamethylenetetramine nitrate. No 1,3,5-trinitro-hexahydro-*s*-triazine residue was obtained after decomposition of the nitrate with boiling water indicating the absence of that substance. A qualitative diphenylamine test for nitrate ion was positive and it was shown quantitatively that one equivalent of nitrate per equivalent of (I) was present.

Hexahydro-*s*-triazine nitrate is readily converted to 1,3,5-trinitro-hexahydro-*s*-triazine, quantitatively when treated with five equivalents of 98 % nitric acid, and in good yield when a suspension of the salt in nitromethane is treated with boron trifluoride or a solution of it in 88 % nitric acid is treated with phosphorous pentoxide (3). Methylene bis-3,5-dinitrohexahydro-*s*-triazine (III) results when to an acetone

(3)

suspension of hexahydro-*s*-triazine nitrate is added 0.4 of an equivalent of dilute sodium hydroxide. A compound which may be 1,3-dinitrohexahydro-*s*-triazine results when (I) is dissolved in pyridine and pyridine nitrate and pyridine are successively removed.

A solid disinfectant prepared from aqueous formaldehyde and "hexahydro-*s*-triazine" has been described.[5]

III. 1,3,5-Trialkylhexahydro-*s*-Triazines

This group of ring-saturated triazines will be discussed in the following order: ascending homologous alkyl side chains, alkenyl side chain derivatives, and other variations of the 1,3,5-groups. Methods of preparation have not been repeated but rather referral is made to preceding derivatives inasmuch as the methods of preparation are limited in number and similar in nature.

The most common and simplest means of preparation of this group of 1,3,5-trialkyl derivatives of hexahydro-*s*-triazine is by the reaction of equimolar quantities of formaldehyde, usually 30–40% aqueous and the corresponding primary amine giving aliphatic aldimines which rapidly trimerize.

$$3 \, RNH_2 + 3 \, CH_2O \underset{H^+}{\rightleftharpoons} [3 \, RN{=}CH_2] + 3 \, H_2O \underset{H^+}{\rightleftharpoons} \quad (4)$$

It should be noted that the early workers, prior to 1900, regarded the condensation products of primary amines and formaldehyde as monomeric alkyl Schiff's bases or aldimines, $RCH{=}NH$. Although later cryoscopic work showed that the substances were trimeric, the fact that by careful techniques[6] these monomers can actually be obtained in a pure state and their Raman spectra measured before they undergo trimerization, does not allow us to exclude the possibility that in some cases early workers were dealing with monomers.

1. 1,3,5-Trimethylhexahydro-*s*-triazine

The first reliable descriptions of a method of preparation for 1,3,5-trimethylhexahydro-*s*-triazine (IV) were reported[2,7,8,9,10] in the middle-1890's, when (IV) was also indentified as a trimer of $CH_3N{=}CH_2$.

Compound (IV) has no melting point, but sublimes at 80°. In a closed tube, melting points of 84° and 94° have been reported.[1] It boils at 166°. at atmospheric pressure;[11,12] boiling points of 68° at 26 mm.[12] and at 11 mm[11] have both been reported. Refractive index, $n_D^{19} = 1.4632$ and density, $d_4^{19} = 0.9178$. (IV) forms a hydrate in water with the liberation of heat.

A. Preparation

(1) **Methylamine and Formaldehyde.** The easiest and the most widely used method for the synthesis of the trimethyl derivative and for most of the other members of the series of non-aromatic substituents as well, is the condensation of an amine with formaldehyde. This reaction normally proceeds best in the presence of an alkaline catalyst to give an almost quantitative yield of 1,3,5-trialkylhexahydro-*s*-triazine which typical of other numbers in the homologous series, is stable in neutral or alkaline solution but is rapidly decomposed by mineral and other strong acids to the starting materials with the evolution of considerable quantities of heat (4). The trimethyl derivative is formed as rapidly as methylamine is added to aqueous formaldehyde.[2,6,7,8,9,10,11,12,13]

(2) **From Hexamine.** If the quarternary salt formed by hexamethylenetetramine and methyl iodide is heated with alkali, 1,3,5-trimethylhexahydro-*s*-triazine is reported to be formed.[14] Hexamethylenetetramine can serve as a source of ammonia in ammonation. This probably occurs in the second step of the synthesis producing methylamine. Methylamine could react with the formaldehyde which is also produced by the decomposition of hexamethylenetetramine to give (IV).

(3) **From Dimethylchloramine.** A somewhat poorer yield of 1,3,5-trimethylhexahydro-*s*-triazine than that given by either of the two preceeding methods results when dimethylchloramine is treated[15] with copper-bronze in ether; tetramethylmethylenediamine is also obtained (5).

B. Reactions

(1) Decomposition. 1,3,5-Trimethylhexahydro-s-triazine and also the other cyclic alkylamines of this series, in addition to their previously mentioned instability to acids, may be decomposed to the amine and formaldehyde by heating strongly with water.

(2) Formation of Salts and Addition Compounds. 1,3,5-Trialkylhexahydro-s-triazines form salts readily under anhydrous conditions and a large number of salts are known, particularly in the case of the lower homologues. Among the salts most commonly prepared are hydrohalides, picrates, oxalates, methiodides, and alkiodides. The salts are tabulated with the parent compounds in Table IX-1.

1,3,5-Trimethylhexahydro-s-triazine forms a deliquescent hydrochloride[8] and a hydroiodide[13] in anhydrous media when one equivalent of hydrogen halide is passed into the solution. It also forms a picrate,[9,15] an addition compound with sodium iodide,[15] and quarternary salts with methyl,[13] ethyl,[16] and n-butyl iodides.[15] The formation of quarternary halides is an important reaction. n-Alkyl iodides react readily (6) with

$$
\begin{array}{ccc}
\underset{\substack{\text{N} \\ | \\ \text{H}_3\text{CN} \quad \text{NCH}_3}}{\overset{\text{CH}_3}{\bigcap}} + \text{RI} \longrightarrow & \underset{\substack{\text{N}^+ \\ | \\ \text{H}_3\text{CN} \quad \text{NCH}_3}}{\overset{\text{RCH}_3 \text{ I}^-}{\bigcap}} & \quad\quad (6)
\end{array}
$$

(IV)

1,3,5-trimethylhexahydro-s-triazine in the cold,[15] however, the rate of formation of the quarternary base diminishes with increasing molecular weight of the R group. Ethyl iodide reacts vigorously in the cold. If the reaction mixture is allowed to become too hot, the only solid product which can be isolated is the diiodo adduct, $C_6H_{15}N_3I_2$, which melts at 162°. The quarternary compound evidently decomposes under such conditions. n-Butyl iodide reacts very slowly. No heat is evolved, and the product obtained is probably a mixture of the diiodide and the quarternary compound. Attempts to improve low yields of quarternary bases obtained from such sluggishly reacting compounds as isopropyl iodide by refluxing, resulted in the formation of di- and tetraiodides.[16] No reaction was obtained between 1,3,5-trialkylhexahydro-s-triazines and ethyl, n-propyl or n-butyl chlorides. The quarternary bases, like the amines themselves, are decomposed by acids to the primary amine and formaldehyde and the alkyl halide (7).

$$\text{(ring structure: } \underset{RN \quad NR}{\overset{R \; R'}{N^+ I^-}}) \quad \xrightarrow[\text{H}_2\text{O}]{\text{H}^+} \quad 3\,CH_2O + R'I + 3\,RNH_2 \tag{7}$$

When 1,3,5-trimethylhexahydro-s-triazine is treated with benzyl chloride in the cold, a mixture of products is obtained[17] from which can be isolated after treatment with hydrochloric acid, benzylmethyl-amine and dibenzyldimethylammonium chloride in addition to form-aldehyde and methylamine. It is likely that a quarternary base is formed first which is then decomposed by the acid. If splitting occurs

$$\underset{(IV)}{\overset{CH_3}{\underset{H_3CN \quad NCH_3}{N}}} + C_6H_5CH_2Cl \longrightarrow \left[\underset{H_3CN \quad NCH_3}{\overset{CH_2C_6H_5}{\underset{N^+ I^-}{\overset{CH_3}{|}}}}\right] \xrightarrow{HCl}$$

$$C_6H_5CH_2NHCH_3 + \underset{Cl}{(C_6H_5CH_2)_2{-}N(CH_3)_2} + CH_2O + CH_3NH_2$$

in such a way as to include a ring methylene group, as is possible, then reaction of this fragment, a tertiary amine, with another molecule of benzyl chloride would give dibenzyldimethylammonium chloride. Since only small amounts of the tertiary amine derivative were obtained, it is clear that a very limited number of methylene groups can ultimately appear as methyl groups on the tertiary amine. Further evidence that at least some of this type of fission occurs, sometimes even at the expense to the $>$N—R bond, is found in the isolation of benzylmethyl-amine as well as benzylethylamine from decomposition of the reaction product of 1,3,5-triethyl-s-triazine and benzyl chloride.

The reaction with benzyl chloride is no doubt similar to the reaction with benzoyl chloride in which case a quarternary salt[18] is known to

$$\underset{(IV)}{\overset{CH_3}{\underset{H_3CN \quad NCH_3}{N}}} + C_6H_5COCl \xrightarrow{dry} \underset{H_3CN \quad NCH_3}{\overset{COC_6H_5}{\underset{N^+ Cl^-}{\overset{CH_3}{|}}}} \xrightarrow{H_2O} C_6H_5CONHCH_3 \tag{8}$$

be produced. If the product is treated with water or if the reaction is carried out in aqueous media, methylbenzamide is obtained (8).

The reactivity of the 1,3,5-trialkylhexahydro-s-triazines to active halogen-containing substances is further demonstrated by their reactivity toward the nitrogen mustards.[19] For example with methyl-bis (β-chlorethyl) amine, $ClCH_2CH_2N(CH_3)CH_2CH_2Cl$, 1,3,5-trimethyl-s-triazine (IV) undergoes 99% reaction, which may be compared with the 68% reactions of the triethyl compound, and the 54% of the triisopropyl homolog.

(3) Reaction with Halogens. The cyclic bases react with free halogens. Treating 1,3,5-trimethylhexahydro-s-triazine (IV) with chlorine[17] in chloroform solution gives a dichloro adduct, $C_6H_{15}N_3Cl_2$, which melts at 128–130° with decomposition and decomposes in moist air. Similarly, iodine in carbon tetrachloride give a diiodo adduct, $C_6H_{15}N_3I_2$, previously mentioned.

(4) Reduction. Reduction of the 1,3,5-trialkylhexahydro-s-triazines with zinc and HCl to the respective alkylmethylamine occurs smoothly,[4] undoubtedly proceeding first by acid decomposition to the

$$\text{(ring structure)} \xrightarrow[\text{Zn}]{\text{HCl}} [3\ RN{=}CH_2] \xrightarrow{[H]} 3\ RNHCH_3 \qquad (9)$$

methyleneimine followed by actual reduction (9). Dimethylamine results from (IV). Reduction can be accomplished by means of sodium and alcohol,[21] but such a procedure results in a variety of products.

(5) Reaction with Hydrogen Sulfide and Carbon Disulfide. 1,3,5 - Trimethylhexahydro - s - triazine (IV) reacts with hydrogen sulfide[22,23] and also with carbon disulfide.[22,23] In the case of carbon disulfide, an addition compound $C_4H_{10}N_2CS_2$, m.p. 96°, is obtained, but the reaction is in need of more modern evaluation. With hydrogen sulfide, a similar addition compound forms. Alkali decomposes it, and

$$\text{(IV)} + H_2S \longrightarrow [H_2S\ add'n.\ cmpd.] \xrightarrow[\text{aq.}]{\text{NaOH}} [CH_3NHCH_2OH] \qquad (10)$$

gives N-methyl-3-thiaazacyclobutane. The reaction proceeds first as a hydrolysis in the presence of base (10) giving methylolmethylamine which reacts with H_2S to give methylamine and hydroxymethyl-mercaptan. These undergo condensation to the cyclobutane derivative:

$$[CH_3NHCH_2OH] + H_2S \longrightarrow CH_3NH_2 + HS—CH_2OH \longrightarrow \overset{\displaystyle S—CH_2}{\underset{\displaystyle H_2C—NCH_3}{|\qquad|}} + 2\,H_2O$$

(6) Electrolytic Reduction. If the 1,3,5-trialkylhexahydro-*s*-triazines are subjected to electrolysis, the free amine is regenerated.[24]

2. 1,3,5-Triethylhexahydro-*s*-triazine

The triethyl homologue (V) was described in 1893–1895 at the same time has the trimethyl compound (IV).[2,8,10] It is a liquid at room temperature, boiling at 207–208° at one atmosphere.[2,8,10] Boiling points at reduced pressures are given as 92–97° at 11 mm[25] and 81.7–83.4° at 10 mm of mercury.[2,8,10]

Like the trimethyl compound, (V) is prepared[2,6,8,13,25] by the condensation of an aliphatic amine, ethylamine, with aqueous form-aldehyde producing an aldimine which immediately trimerizes (11).

$$3\,C_2H_5NH_2 + 3\,CH_2O \longrightarrow 3\,[C_2H_5N{=}CH_2] + 3\,H_2O \longrightarrow \overset{\displaystyle C_2H_5}{\underset{\displaystyle H_5C_2N\qquad NC_2H_5}{\overset{\displaystyle N}{\bigcirc}}} \qquad (11)$$

(V)

The decomposition of the hexamethylenetetramine salt of ethyl iodide has also been used[14] to prepare 1,3,5-triethylhexahydro-*s*-triazine (V). Again, in the same manner as the trimethyl compound (IV), 1,3,5-triethylhexahydro-*s*-triazine (V) forms a hydroiodide,[14] a picrate,[14] and a quarternary salt with methyl iodide.[14] However, in addition, it also forms a hydrobromide,[14] a dipicrate,[14] and quarternary salts with allyl iodide[17] and ethyl bromide.[17] The latter melts at 112–114° with decomposition, and although obtained in 10 % yields, is the only such salt in the series formed from a bromide.

A comparison with the trimethyl compound is continued. A reaction mixture from the interaction of benzyl chloride and 1,3,5-triethyl-hexahydro-*s*-triazine (V) yields benzylethylamine among its hydrochloric acid decomposition products,[17] the significance of which has been discussed.

(V)

1,3,5-Triethylhexahydro-s-triazine reacts with carbon disulfide[22,23] giving a 30% yield of 3,5-diethyltetrahydro-1,3,5-thiadiazine-2-thion.[25] This reaction occurs with most of the trialkylhexahydro-s-triazines and usually gives poor yields[25] (12).

$$\tag{12}$$

Recently, 1,3,5-triethylhexahydro-s-triazine has shown potentialities[26] as a vulcanization accelerator. It is effective in the final hard rubber phase of the rubber-sulfur reaction. Other members of the series might display similar properties.

3. 1,3,5-Triisopropylhexahydro-s-triazine

The triisopropyl derivative is a liquid distilling at 115–122° at 11 mm, prepared[25] in 63% yield by condensing formaldehyde and isopropylamine.

Treatment[25] of 1,3,5-triisopropylhexahydro-s-triazine with carbon disulfide in acetone gave a 42% yield of 3,5-diisopropyltetrahydro-1,3,5-thiadiazine-2-thion. When the latter was heated near its boiling point, rearrangement took place, the product of which was 1,3,5-triisopropylhexahydro-s-triazine-2-thion (VI). Compound (VI) was iden-

tified by molecular weight, elemental analysis, and ultraviolet absorption spectra which showed the thiourea-type linkage. Compound (VI), recrystallized from acetone, melts at 99.4–100.2°.

4. 1,3,5-Tri-*n*-butylhexahydro-s-triazine

1,3,5-Tri-*n*-butylhexahydro-s-triazine was prepared in 1896 by Franchimont and Van Erp.[21] It boils at 285° at atmospheric pressure,[21] 141–143° at 11 mm[21] and 132–134° at 4–5 mm.[25]

Like all the other members of this series, the tri-*n*-butyl compound can be most conveniently prepared from formaldehyde and the respective aliphatic amine[6,20,21] (58% yield).[25]

It forms a picrate and a deliquescent hydrochloride. Like the trimethyl compound, the tri-*n*-butyl homologue is reduced by sodium and alcohol, but in the case of the tri-*n*-butyl compound, butyl hydrazine has been reported[20] as well as methylbutylamine and butylamine.

Although 1,3,5-tri-*n*-butylhexahydro-s-triazine appears[25] to undergo reaction with carbon disulfide, the products have not been identified.

5. 1,3,5-Triallylhexahydro-s-triazine

The triallyl derivative was prepared in 1935 from formaldehyde and allylamine.[27] The colorless liquid boils at 138–141°. It forms a picrate melting at 139°, stable to hot water and stable to sodium hydroxide.[27]

When 1,3,5-triallylhexahydro-s-triazine was treated with a methanolic solution of mercuric acetate, the reagents added[27] across the side-chain double bonds to give 1,3,5-tri(2'-methoxypropyl mercury acetate) hexahydro-s-triazine (VII). If (VII) is dissolved in sodium

$$CH_2CH{=}CH_2$$
$$\overset{\displaystyle N}{\underset{\displaystyle \smile}{}}$$
$$CH_2{=}CHCH_2N \quad NCH_2CH{=}CH_2 + Hg(OAc)_2 \qquad \xrightarrow{\text{MeOH}}$$

$$OCH_3$$
$$CH_2CHCH_2HgOAc$$
$$H_3CO \quad N \quad OCH_3$$
$$AcOHgCH_2CHCH_2N \quad NCH_2CHCH_2HgOAc$$

(VII)

hydroxide and carbon dioxide is bubbled through the solution, the acyl group is removed giving 1,3,5-tri(2'-methoxypropyl mercury hydroxide) hexahydro-s-triazine (VIII), a yellow powder, alkaline solutions of which are stable.

$$
\begin{array}{c}
OCH_3 \\
| \\
CH_2CHCH_2HgOH \\
OCH_3 \quad \overset{N}{\frown} \quad OCH_3 \\
| \qquad\qquad | \\
HOHgCH_2CHCH_2N \quad NCH_2CHCH_2HgOH \\
\smile
\end{array}
$$

(VIII)

6. 1,3,5-Tricyanomethylhexahydro-s-triazine (IX)

In 1894, Jay and Curtis[28] obtained a compound melting at 129° by the reaction of ammonium cyanide and formaldehyde which they called methyleneaminoacetonitrile. Klages[29,30] repeated the preparation in 1902–1903. The molecular weight corresponding to the dimer of methyleneaminoacetonitrile determined in 1902–1903 was redetermined[31,32] and found to be three times that of methyleneaminoacetonitrile. The compound was given[31,32] the tentative name of α-hydroformamine cyanide and is believed to posses the hexahydro-s-triazine ring structure.

It forms orthorhombic[32] crystals which can be recrystallized from alcohol,[28,33] acetone,[32] or water,[28,33] It is very slightly soluble[28] in water, alcohol, ether, and benzene, but soluble in hot water,[28] alcohol[28] or acetone.[32]

A most reliable method for preparing 1,3,5-tricyanomethylhexahydro-s-triazine (IX) is given in Organic Syntheses.[33] Aqueous sodium cyanide is added to a mixture of formaldehyde and ammonium chloride at 0° with vigorous stirring. When one-half of the solution of sodium cyanide has been added, glacial acetic acid is added concurrently

$$
6\,CH_2O + 3\,NaCN + 3\,NH_4Cl \xrightarrow[\text{vigorous stirring}]{\text{0°AcOH}}
\begin{array}{c}
CH_2CN \\
\overset{N}{\frown} \\
NCCH_2N \quad NCH_2CN \\
\smile
\end{array}
+ 3\,NaCl + 6\,H_2O
$$

(IX)

and proportionately with the remainder. The product partially crystallizes towards the end of the reaction and addition of water completes the precipitation. After filtration, the product melts at 129° and is pure enough for most purposes. It may be further purified[33] by recrystallization from water, but the accompanying losses are large.

Potassium cyanide may be used in place of sodium cyanide[18,30,31,32,33] or aminoacetonitrile hydrochloride[29] may be used with formaldehyde, both methods giving essentially the same results as above.[33]

The aqueous filtrate, upon standing,[32] gives a 10% yield of a compound thought[18,32] to be an isomer of (IX) and called[28,32] β-hydroformamine cyanide (m.p. 86°) but which is actually[35] methylene bisiminodiacetonitrile, $CH_2[N(CH_2CN)_2]_2$. The molecular weight (204) of 1,3,5-tricyanomethylhexahydro-*s*-triazine has been determined cryoscopically in naphthalene and ebulliscopically in acetone;[32] it furnishes good evidence that (IX) is a trimer of methylene aminoacetonitrile. The saturated ring structure cannot[31] be readily reduced to give methylamine fragments, but it is rapidly broken down by hydrochloric[28] acid to products which are hydrolyzed in varying degrees. Cold aqueous hydrochloric acid yields aminoacetonitrile hydrochloride,[28] alcoholic hydrochloric acid gives the imido ether hydrochloride[34] and boiling hydrochloric acid produces ethylaminoacetate.[28,30]

$$CH_2CN$$
$$\overset{N}{\underset{\smile}{\big\lceil \quad \big\rceil}}$$
$$CNCH_2N \qquad NCH_2CN$$

(IX)

$+ 3\,HCl + 3\,H_2O \xrightarrow{\text{cold}} 3\,NCCH_2NH_2 \cdot HCl + 3\,CH_2O$

$$\overset{NH}{\overset{\|}{}}$$

$+ 3\,C_2H_5OH + 3\,HCl + 3\,H_2O \xrightarrow{\text{cold}} 3\,C_2H_5OCCH_2NH_2 \cdot HCl + 3\,CH_2O$

$+ 3\,C_2H_5OH + 6\,HCl + 6\,H_2O \xrightarrow{\Delta} 3\,C_2H_5OOCCH_2NH_2 \cdot HCl + 3\,CH_2O + 3\,NH_4Cl$

Treatment of (IX) with an alcoholic solution of 96% sulfuric acid[30] gives aminoacetonitrile sulfate. Behavior towards hydrogen sulfide is not entirely clear. One equivalent of hydrogen sulfide adds readily giving a compound which has the formula $C_8H_{12}N_5CSNH_2$, probably compound (X). It is a colorless or pink crystalline solid, melts

$$CH_2CN$$
$$\overset{N}{\underset{\smile}{\big\lceil \quad \big\rceil}}$$
$$CNCH_2N \qquad NCH_2CN$$

(IX)

$+ H_2S \longrightarrow$

$$\overset{S}{\overset{\|}{CH_2CNH_2}}$$
$$\overset{N}{\underset{\smile}{\big\lceil \quad \big\rceil}}$$
$$CNCH_2N \qquad NCH_2CN$$

(X)

at 152–153°, and is recrystallized from ethanol. Purification is difficult because the adduct is decomposed by heat as well as dilute alkali. It is insoluble in water, ether, acetone, benzene, and chloroform, and soluble in ethanol to the extent[31] of five parts per thousand at room temperature.

Prolonged treatment of (IX) with hydrogen sulfide[31] leads to the formation of dithiopiperazine or thiopolypeptide combinations.

1,3,5-Tricyanomethylhexahydro-s-triazine readily reacts[36,37] with hydrogen cyanide (12) as a monomer in the presence of a trace of hydrochloric acid, without which no reaction takes place.[37] The product is iminoacetonitrile.[36,37]

$$\begin{array}{c} CH_2CN \\ | \\ N \\ \diagup \quad \diagdown \\ CNCH_2N \quad NCH_2CH \\ \diagdown \quad \diagup \end{array} \longrightarrow 3\,(CH_2{=}NCH_2CN) + HCN \xrightarrow[48\,hrs.\,20°]{HCl} NH(CH_2CN)_2 \quad (12)$$

(IX)

7. 1,3,5-Tri(β-hydroxy)ethylhexahydro-s-triazine (XI)

Compound (XI) is a viscous oil distilling at 1 mm. It can be prepared[38] in 90% yield by adding 133 g of 96% ethanolamine to 200 g of 30% aqueous formaldehyde over a period of one and one-half hours at 40–45°.

$$3\,CH_2O + HOCH_2CH_2NH_2 \xrightarrow[40-45°]{1.5\,hrs.} \begin{array}{c} CH_2CH_2OH \\ | \\ N \\ \diagup \quad \diagdown \\ HOCH_2CH_2N \quad NCH_2CH_2OH \\ \diagdown \quad \diagup \end{array}$$

(XI)

An unusual reversible rearrangement occurs when (XI) is distilled at 1 mm. Apparently, formation of the triazine is reversed giving the monomer [$HOCH_2CH_2N{=}CH_2 + H_2O$] as well as the original components. Either the monomer or the original compounds may recyclize

$$\begin{array}{c} (CH_2)_2OH \\ | \\ N \\ \diagup \quad \diagdown \\ HO(CH_2)_2N \quad N(CH_2)_2OH \\ \diagdown \quad \diagup \end{array} \underset{\substack{\text{spontaneous} \\ \text{rearrangement}}}{\overset{\text{distill, 1 mm.}}{\rightleftarrows}} 3\begin{array}{c} O \\ \diagup \diagdown \\ HN \\ | \quad | \\ \diagdown \diagup \end{array}$$

to form oxazolidine. This five membered ring has only a transitory existence under conditions of the experiment and rearranges at once back to (XI). Oxazolidine may be stable at low temperatures.

TABLE IX-1. 1,3,5-Trialkylhexahydro-s-triazines and Salts

RN–NR (with NR)

R	Boiling point, °C./mm. Hg.	Preparation Method[a]	Reference	Yield	Ref.	Salt	Melting point, °C.	Solvent	Ref.
CH_3	166/1 atm.	A	1,2,4,5,7,8			(a) Picrate[b]	127–128	—	5, 6
	50/11 mm.	B	2			Hydrochloride (deliq.)	120–124	—	4
		C	6			Ethyl iodide	72 (dec.)	—	11
						Methyl iodide	—	—	3
						n-Propyl iodide	105 (dec.)	—	11
						Hydroiodide	122	—	3
						n-Butyl iodide	123–125 (dec.)	—	11
						Sodium iodide	—	—	11
C_2H_5	207–208/1 atm.	A	3,4,7,8,19	25%	19	(b) Picrate[c]	65	Ether	3
	92–97/11 mm.	B	2			Hydroiodide	120–121	Absolute alc.	3
	81.7–83.4/10 mm.					Hydrobromide	132	Absolute alc.	3
						Methyl iodide	98–99	Chloroform	3
						Ethyl bromide	112–114 (dec.)	—	11
						Allyl iodide	—	—	11
						Dipicrate	—	—	3
$n\text{-}C_3H_7$	248–249/1 atm.	A	4,7,8						
	132–134/18 mm.								
	122–123/11 mm.								
$iso\text{-}C_3H_7$	102–104/11 mm.	A	7,18	63%	19				
	115–122/11 mm.								
$n\text{-}C_4H_9$	285/1 atm.	A	7,9,10,19	58%	19	Picrate	75–76	Ethyl alc.	10
	141–143/11 mm.	D	12			Hydrochloride (deliq.)	—	—	10
	132–134/4–5 mm.								

(Table continued)

TABLE IX-1 (*continued*)

R	Boiling point, °C./mm. Hg.	Preparation Method[a]	Ref.	Yield	Ref.	Salt	Melting point, °C.	Solvent	Ref.
iso-C$_4$H$_9$	255/1 atm. 128.7–130.6/12 mm.	A	7, 8, 10			Picrate	107	Ethyl alc.	10
						Oxalate	165	Aq. ethyl alc.	10
iso-C$_5$H$_{11}$	299–300/1 atm. 151–154/10 mm.	A	7, 8, 10			Picrate	75	Acetone	10
						Oxalate	115	Aq. ethyl alc.	10
HOCH$_2$CH$_2$	Viscous oil distills 1 mm.	A	13			Urate	(dec.) high temperature		10
CH$_2$=CHCH$_2$	138–141	A	14						
CNCH$_2$	M.p. 129 recryst. water, acetone, or ethyl alc.	A	16, 19			Picrate			14
	M.p. 86 recryst. ethyl alc. or acetic acid	A	17			Mercuriacetate			14
C$_6$H$_{11}$ (Cyclohexyl)	M.p. 72.7–72.8	A	19	82%	19	Hydrochloride	152–153	—	17

a Methods of preparation:

A = Condensation of amine with formaldehyde.

B = Degradation of quaternary salt of hexamine and alkyl halide.

C = Dialkylchloramine and copper-bronze.

D = Reduction of unsaturated acyl side chain.

b Another complete series of isomeric salts has been reported[3] in addition to the ones listed above. Thus, heating the hydroiodide for 45 minutes at 80–90° gave an isomeric hydroiodide, M.p. 199–200°. Picric acid converts the hydroiodide to a picrate (M.p. 108° recrystallized from absolute

melting at 182° when recrystallized from alcohol-acetic acid. A chloroplatinate (·H$_2$PtCl$_6$), which melted at 215° (dec.) when crystallized from dilute alcohol, resulted when the hydroiodide was treated with silver chloride followed by platinum chloride. Treatment of the hydroiodide (M.p. 199–200°) with iodoform gave an addition salt (HI·CHI$_3$), M.p. 133–4° recrystallized from chloroform, a reaction which the other isomeric hydroiodide (M.p. 120–121°) did not undergo.

c An isomeric hydroiodide, M.p. 166°, has been reported[3] by heat isomerization of the above hydroiodide. From it, an isomer, M.p. 159–160° crystallized from ethanol, of the above picrate (M.p. 107–109°) has been prepared

1. A. Brochet and R. Cambier, *Compt. rend.*, **120**, 452 (1895).
2. K. Hock, *Ger.*, **139**, 394 (1903).
3. A. Einhorn and A. Prettner, *Ann.*, **334**, 210 (1904).
4. R. Cambier and A. Brochet, *Bull. soc. chim.*, (3), **13**, 404 (1895).
5. P. Duden and M. Scharff, *Ber.* **28**, 936 (1895).
6. F. Klager, F. Kircher and M. Bock, *Ann.*, **547**, 23 (1941).
7. L. Kahovec, *Z. Physik. Chem.*, **B43**, 364 (1939).
8. L. Henry, *Bull. Acad. Belg.*, (3), **26**, 200 (1893).
   L. Henry, *Bull. Acad. Belg.*, (3), **29**, 23 (1895).
9. A. Franchimont and H. Van Erp, *Rec. trav. chim.*, **15**, 66 (1896).
10. J. Graymore, *J. Chem. Soc.*, **1932**, 1353.
11. R. Blundell and J. Graymore, *J. Chem. Soc.*, **1939**, 1787.
12. C. Price and L. Krishmamurti, *J. Am. Chem. Soc.*, **72**, 5334 (1950).
13. A. Paquin, *Ber.*, **82**, 316 (1949).
14. M. Dominikiewicz, *Arch. Chem. Farm.*, **2**, 160 (1935), through *Chem. Abstracts*, **30**, 1030 (1936).
15. J. Burchenal, S. Johnson, M. Cremer, L. Webber and C. Stock, *Proc. Soc. Exptl. Biol. Med.*, **74**, 708 (1950).
16. R. Adams and W. Langley, *Organic Syntheses Coll.*, *Vol. I*, 2nd Ed., John Wiley and Sons, New York 1946, p. 355.
17. T. Johnson and H. Rinehart, *J. Am. Chem. Soc.*, **46**, 768 (1944).
18. A. Klages, *Ber.*, **36**, 1506 (1903).
19. A. Schnitzer, *Dissertation*, Oklahoma A. and M. College, 1951.

8. 1,3,5-Tricyclohexahydro-*s*-triazine

1,3,5-Tricyclohexylhexahydro-*s*-triazine[25] is a solid melting at 72.2–72.8° and distilling around[25] 110° at 40 mm. It can be prepared in 82% yield by the formaldehyde-cyclohexylamine condensation. Synthesis has also been reported[25] by heating cyclohexylamine with methylenedichloride and potassium hydroxide, but another unidentified compound is also produced by this indirect method.

1,3,5-Tricyclohexylhexahydro-*s*-triazine reacts with carbon disulfide and produces a 57% yield of 3,5-dicyclohexyltetrahydro-1,3,5-thiadiazine-2-thion which, on further heating, is transformed into 1,3,5-tricyclohexylhexahydro-*s*-triazine-2-thion (m.p. 158.2–160, recrystallized from acetone).

Table IX-1 gives a summary of the 1,3,5-trialkylhexahydro-*s*-triazines discussed above and also of the other known compounds of this series prepared by methods identical with those described above. Physical properties, salts and compounds, and methods of preparation are listed.

IV. Aryl and Arylalkylhexahydro-s-Triazines

1. Introduction

The aryl- and arylalkylhexahydro-s-triazines are synthesized most commonly by condensation of the respective amine with formaldehyde, the method most widely used for the alkyl compounds. Synthesis in the aryl group results in two isomeric products, at least in cases of the more thoroughly studied members such as the triphenyl and tritolyl compounds. The appearance of isomers is not entirely foreign to the alkyl series, however. Footnotes to Table XI-1 mention the appearance of two isomers in the case of salts of the triethyl and trimethylhexahydro-s-triazines. A higher melting free base[39] (m.p. 98–99° crystallized from chloroform) can be obtained by treating the methiodide of 1,3,5-triethylhexahydro-s-triazine with ether. The high melting base undoubtedly corresponds to the hydroiodide which melts at 199° and not to the normal or low melting hydroiodide. The latter melts at 121° and corresponds to the normal base, a liquid.

2. 1,3,5-Triphenylhexahydro-s-triazine

1,3,5-Triphenylhexahydro-s-triazine (XI) was prepared and characterized about ten years before the lower members of the alkyl series. In 1884, Paterno[41] and Tollens[40], working independently, treated aniline with formaldehyde solution and obtained the trimeric Schiff's base.

1,3,5-Triphenylhexahydro-s-triazine (XI) is a white crystalline solid melting[42] at 141°. It can be recrystallized from ligroin. Although it is stable at room temperature, it is capable of dissociating at higher temperatures and shows a molecular weight in camphor which is only twice that of the monomer. The molecular weight of the vapor is stated to correspond to that of the monomer.[59]

A. Methods of Preparation

(1) From Amines and Formaldehyde. The simplest and most widely used means of preparing (XI) is by the condensation of aniline with formaldehyde. The treatment of primary amines with formaldehyde was shown to be a general method of preparation for most of the alkyl compounds and for almost all of the triaryl and triarylalkyl compounds as well. The reaction takes place with ease in the presence of a basic catalyst. In neutral dilute aqueous solution, products of indefinite composition are obtained unless conditions are carefully

$$3\ C_6H_5NH_2 + CH_2O\ (\text{excess}) \xrightarrow{\text{base}}$$

$$\begin{array}{c} C_6H_5 \\ N \\ H_5C_6N \qquad NC_6H_5 \end{array}$$

(XI)

controlled. This explains some of the confusion and contradictions that obtained for many years. Moreover in synthesizing (XI) by the condensation of aniline and formalin, an isomeric high melting (225–227°) compound is also produced. As mentioned in the introduction to this section, isomers of several triarylhexahydro-s-triazines are known. Although these isomers have the same analyses as the more commonly available normal low melting compounds, their general insolubility has led to neglect insofar as molecular weight determinations are concerned, but enables simplified separation procedures to be used to obtain the isomers in pure condition. The high melting isomers of the triarylhexahydro-s-triazines are tabulated along with the low melting isomers in Table XI-2.

In addition to the standard method of condensation of the primary amine, aniline in this case, with formaldehyde, a number of variations in this synthetic approach to the triphenyl compound and other members of the series is available.

A secondary amine may often be available and can be used with formaldehyde in the same manner at the primary amine. Thus, a mixture of N, N'-diphenylmethylenediamine and formaldehyde[43] gave 1,3,5-triphenyl-hexahydro-s-triazine (13).

$$3\ (C_6H_5NH)_2CH_2 + 3\ CH_2O \longrightarrow 2\ \begin{array}{c} C_6H_5 \\ N \\ H_5C_6N \qquad NC_6H_5 \end{array} + 3\ H_2O \qquad (13)$$

The secondary amines are intermediates in the formation of the cyclic structures. They can be obtained by dissolving the primary amine in alcohol and water, and treating the solution with formaldehyde. Occasionally, the secondary amines become the chief product which is an indication that the reaction must be conducted at a higher temperature to complete the cyclization. In other cases, a highly hindered amine will not cyclize. Examples of these situations are given later in this section.

(2) From Hexamethylenetetramine. Heating aniline and hexa-methylenetetramine at 150–190° has been reported[45] to yield (XI). As will be seen later, the Delepine method is much more generally used.

(3) By the Curtius Reaction. A Curtius reaction can be used[46] to prepare 1,3,5-triphenylhexahydro-*s*-triazine (XI). Either acidic or basic decomposition of benzyl azide ultimately results in about an 80% yield of (XI), the other 20% appearing as benzaldehyde from the un-rearranged portion.

$$C_6H_5CH_2N_3 \xrightarrow{\text{H}^+ \text{ or OH}^-} [C_6H_5CH_2N<] + N_2 \nearrow \xrightarrow{20\%} [C_6H_5CH=NH]$$

$$\downarrow \text{H}_2\text{O}$$

$$C_6H_5CHO + NH_3$$

$$[C_6H_5N=CH_2] \xleftarrow{\text{H}_2\text{O}} C_6H_5NH_2 + CH_2O \longrightarrow (XI)$$

(4) From Aniline and Methylchloromethyl Sulfate. Methyl-chloromethyl sulfate has been used[47] as a source of formaldehyde in the synthesis of (XI) from aniline. The method is of historical significance only.

$$C_6H_5NH_2 + \underset{ClCH_2O}{\overset{CH_3O}{>}}SO_2 \longrightarrow (XI)$$

(5) From 1,1-Bis(phenylamino)ethane. An unspecified yield of (XI) has been reported[25] along with some of the high melting isomer when 1,1-bis(phenylamino)ethane, formaldehyde and carbon disulfide were heated together.

B. Structure

1,3,5-Triphenylhexahydro-*s*-triazine was shown by cryoscopic measurements[42] definitely to possess structure (XI), trimer of the Schiff's base from aniline and formaldehyde: $[C_6H_5N=CH_2]_3$. Since aniline and formaldehyde can be regenerated by acid decomposition of (XI), there can be little doubt of its structure.

Reduction of 1,3,5-triphenylhexahydro-*s*-triazine with zinc and hydrochloric acid at 5–10°—conditions for Clemmensen reduction—gives[42,48] a mixture of aniline, methylaniline and dimethylaniline.

$$(XI) \xrightarrow[5-10°]{Zn + HCl} C_6H_5NH_2 + C_6H_5NHCH_3 + C_6H_5N(CH_3)_2$$
$$\text{(as hydrochlorides)}$$

Appearance of the mixture is significant from the structural viewpoint, and is indicative of a nitrogen joined to two methylene groups.

C. Reactions

Chemical properties and reactions of the triaryl and the triarylalkylhexahydro-*s*-triazines are for the most part similar to those of the trialkyl compounds. In many instances, reactions have been carried out on one member of one series which would also work with members of both series. Below, emphasis has been placed on the first member of the series, the triphenyl compound (XI), and the section on it should be consulted when information concerning other members of the series is desired.

A reaction is discussed most completely under the lowest member of the series for which information in most completely available and less known compounds are referred to that discussion.

(1) Acid Decomposition. The triaryl compounds are easily as unstable to the action of acids as their alkyl analogs. Formaldehyde and the primary amine are the usual products.

$$(XI) \xrightarrow[H_2O]{H^+} 3C_6H_5NH_2 + 3CH_2O$$

(2) Oxidation. 1,3,5-Triphenylhexahydro-*s*-triazine is said[8] to yield phenylcarbylamine when subjected to oxidation (14).

$$(14)$$

(3) Reduction. As with the trialkyl compounds, treatment of the triaryl compounds with reducing agents gives mostly secondary amine. In the case of compound (XI), the simplest member of the series, zinc and hydrochloric acid at 5–10° produces aniline and dimethylaniline as well as methylaniline. (See *Structure* above).

(4) Reaction with Hydrocyanic Acid. When (XI) is treated with hydrocyanic acid, three moles of N-phenylglycinonitrile result.[8,49] Weakly acidic hydrocyanic acid in effect catalyzes the decomposition of 1,3,5-triphenylhexahydro-s-triazine to the aldimine and then adds across the double bond.

$$(XI) \xrightarrow{HCN} 3 C_6H_5N{=}CH_2 + 3 HCN \longrightarrow C_6H_5NHCH_2CN$$

A variety of interesting reactions have been reported in the literature around the turn of the century which should be reinvestigated before they are accepted without strong reservations. In this light, the following reactions are listed.

(5) Reaction with Isocyanates. 1,3,5-Triphenylhexahydro-s-tri-azine reacts[50] with phenylisocyanate to give 1,3-diphenyl-1,3-diaza-cyclobutanone-2 (XII), m.p. 197.5–198.5°, recrystallized from benzene.

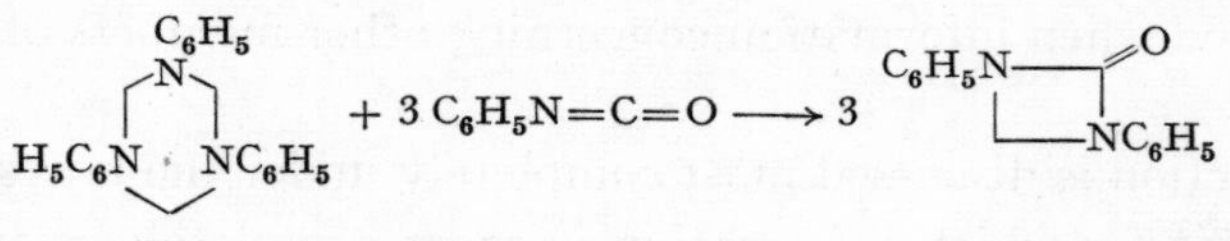

(IX)   (XII)

(6) Reaction with Phenol. 1,3,5-Triphenylhexahydro-s-triazine undergoes reaction[51] with phenol which consists of a 1, 2-addition of phenol across the double bond of the monomer. Zinc chloride hastens the reaction (15).

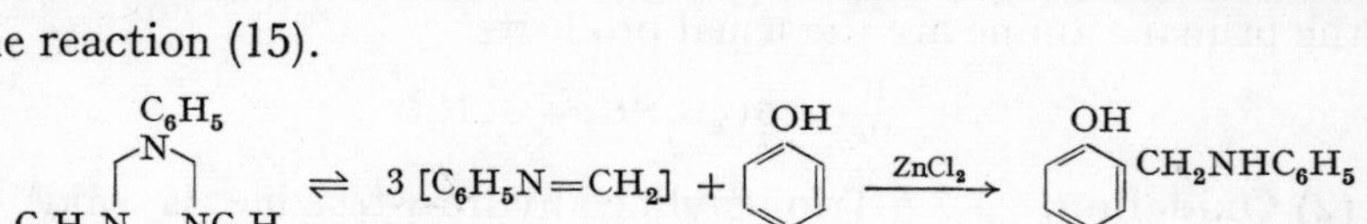

(7) Reaction with Bisulfite. The same type (15) of reaction occurs with sodium bisulfite,[52] and the product may undergo further reaction with potassium cyanide giving a substituted glycinonitrile.

$$(XI) \rightleftharpoons [C_6H_5N{=}CH_2] + NaHSO_3 \longrightarrow C_6H_5NHCH_2SO_3Na$$

$$\downarrow KCN$$

$$C_6H_5NHCH_2CN$$

(8) Reaction with Benzaldehyde and Cyanides. Reaction products from the triaryl bases, benzaldehyde and potassium cyanide are known[1] but not well characterized. The triphenyl compound (XI) gives a substance melting at 219° from benzene-alcohol.

D. Applications

1,3,5-Triphenylhexahydro-s-triazine and also other 1,3,5-triaryl-hexahydro-s-triazines have been found[54] useful in promoting stabilization of plasticized synthetic rubber; 1–3 % of a member of this series is added to the rubber.

3. 1,3,5-Tritolylhexahydro-s-Triazines

The three position isomers of the tritolyl compounds are known, but no compounds have been reported in which different position isomers exist in the same molecule. The tri-ortho isomer, first described[55] in 1894, is a solid melting at about 100°. The tri-p-tolyl compound prepared in the same year[55] can be crystallized from ligroin and melts at 128° while 1,3,5-tri(m-tolyl)hexahydro-s-triazine was not known[56] until 1903. It melts at 148–149° when crystallized from ether.

Dissociation of these compounds parallels that of (XI). For example, the para isomer exists[65] as a trimer from 5–80°; has the molecular weight of a dimer in molten camphor; and is a monomer above 250°. During distillation of any of the hexahydro-s-triazines, overheating causes detrimerization. The resulting monomer vapor is superheated and its boiling point incorrectly observed. On condensation of the product, the trimer forms only slowly unless base is added or unless recrystallization is used. Angyal[65] concludes that the trimeric form is more stable because the bond energy of six carbon-nitrogen single bonds (48.6 Kcals./mole/bond) is greater than for three carbon-nitrogen double bonds (94 Kcals./mole/bond).

All three isomers can be synthesized by the condensation of the respective toluidine with formaldehyde. In the case of all three compounds, high melting isomers are produced which are similar to the one obtained in the synthesis of (XI). The high melting isomers have been the subjects of only limited investigation because of their insolubility in common solvents. This property, however, makes then easy to remove from the normal compounds. For example, the high melting (m.p.

225–227°) isomer of 1,3,5-tri(p-tolyl)hexahydro-s-triazine is insoluble[58] in ligroin whereas the low melting hexahydro-s-triazine is soluble.[a]

The tris-p-tolyl compound can also be synthesized using the secondary amine, N,N'-di(p-tolyl)methylenediamine.[51]

The tritolyl bases are decomposed by acids and undergo oxidation and reduction in a fashion similar to that of 1,3,5-triphenylhexahydro-s-triazine although the reactions have not been extensively examined.

1,3,5-Tri(p-tolyl)hexahydro-s-triazine reacts also with benzaldehyde and potassium cyanide, giving a substance of uncertain structure[60] melting at 245° when crystallized from alcohol.

1,3,5-Tri(p-tolyl)hexahydro-s-triazine and other "anhydrobases," the name by which hexahydro-s-triazines were known before their trimeric character was established, undergo reaction[61,62] with β-naphthol to produce polycyclic compounds. This reaction is said to be

m.p. 190–193·5°/C_6H_6

applicable to a mixture of the aryl amine and formaldehyde or other aldehydes. The intermediate dihydro compound may be oxidized very readily; a stream of air is in most cases entirely adequate. With p-toluidine and aldehydes other than formaldehyde, the reaction gives alkyl substituted tetracyclic derivatives (XIII).

(XIII)

It is reported[63] that treatment of the hexahydro-s-triazine obtained from p-toluidine with cold aniline hydrochloride gave p,p'-diaminodiphenylmethane. On the other hand, if, to the same two starting

---

[a] It is possible that dimethylformamide or Cellosolve might prove suitable as solvents for the high melting isomers.

materials were added azobenzene or a nitroaromatic and ferric chloride, parafuchsin was obtained.[63] Similarly, the intermediate methylene-diamine is said to react[64] with diphenylamine, the hydrochloride thereof, and *o*-nitrotoluene in the presence of ferric chloride at 170° to give triphenyl-*p*-rosaniline. The reactions are mentioned here for completeness only and are of doubtful authenticity.

4. 1,3,5-Tri(p-ethoxyphenyl)hexahydro-s-triazine

This recently reported[25] compound was isolated as whitish yellow needles melting at 156.2–157° in 13% yield from *p*-phenetidine and formaldehyde.

Treatment with carbon disulfide in boiling acetone produced 3,5-di(*p*-ethoxyphenyl)tetrahydro-1,3,5-thiadiazine-2-thion which, when boiled, gave[25] a 29% yield of 1,3,5-tri(*p*-ethoxyphenyl)hexahydro-*s*-triazine-2-thion; when this compound was boiled it gave a 2% yield of 1,3,5-tri(*p*-ethoxyphenyl)hexahydro-*s*-triazine melting at 173–174.2°.

5. 1,3,5-Tri(p-chlorophenyl)hexahydro-s-triazine (XIV)

1,3,5-Tri(*p*-chlorophenyl)hexahydro-*s*-triazine (XIV) was made[56] in 1903 by the condensation of *p*-chloroaniline and aqueous formaldehyde. It is a solid, m.p. 154°.

Mention was previously made of the fact that methylenediamine derivatives are possible intermediates in the synthesis of 1,3,5-trisubstituted hexahydro-*s*-triazines and that, in the case of certain amines, the reaction with formaldehyde halted at this stage. The chloroanilines are an example. Thus, *o*-chloroaniline reacts with formaldehyde only as far as N,N'-di(*o*-chlorophenyl)methylenediamine. On the other hand,

the *p*-chloro analog, when heated in alcohol with formaldehyde, gives
1,3,5-tri-*p*-chlorophenylhexahydro-*s*-triazine (XIV). If the reaction is
not run in alcohol, however, the high melting (228°) modification of
(XIV) results.[56]

The intermediate, N,N'-di(*p*-chlorophenyl)methylenediamine may
be converted to (XIV) by further reaction with formaldehyde or by
distillation. Some *p*-chloroaniline is also produced (16).

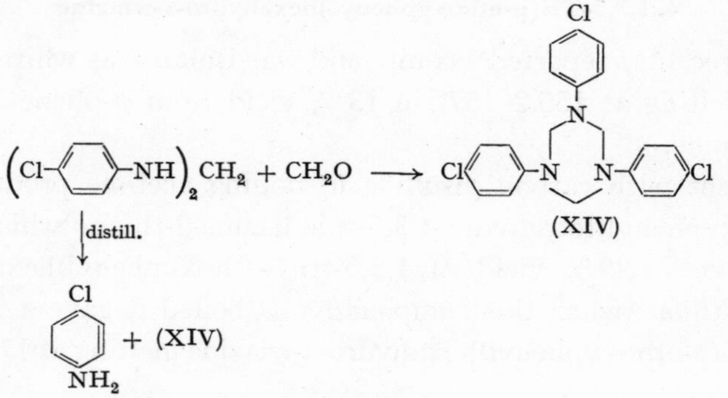

$$\left(Cl{-}\bigcirc{-}NH\right)_2 CH_2 + CH_2O \longrightarrow Cl\bigcirc{-}N \quad N{-}\bigcirc Cl \tag{16}$$

(XIV)

Cl

+ (XIV)

NH₂

6. 1,3,5-Tri(6-tetralyl)hexahydro-*s*-triazine

The tetralin compound is also prepared by the amine-formaldehyde
method.[66] It is a colorless crystalline compound melting at 121° when
crystallized from acetone-ligroin.[66] An isomer melting at 164–165° is
also produced in the synthesis.[66]

The tri-6-tetralyl compound undergoes reduction with sodium
amalgam to give[66] N-methyl-5,6,7,8-tetrahydro-*β*-naphthylamine almost exclusively (17).

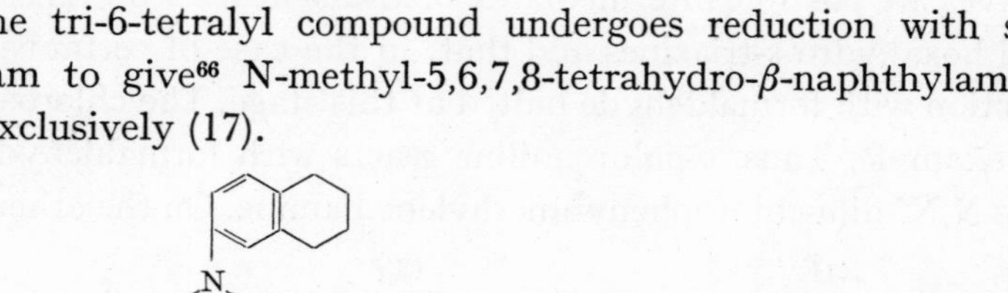

$$+ \text{Na(Hg)} \xrightarrow{\text{[H]}} 3 \quad \text{NHCH}_3 \tag{17}$$

7. 1,3,5-Tri(2-pyridyl)hexahydro-*s*-triazine

This derivative of hexahydro-*s*-triazine melts at 96°. It can be
recrystallized from ligroin and is synthesized[67] by the condensation of
2-aminopyridine and formaldehyde.

Instead of the usual complete decomposition to starting materials that occurs when a hexahydro-s-triazine is refluxed with formic acid

$$\text{(structure)} \xrightarrow[\Delta]{\text{HCOOH aq.}} \left[\text{structure} \right]_2 -CH_2 + \text{structure} NH_2 + CH_2O \qquad (18)$$

(18), 1,3,5-tri(2-pyridyl)hexahydro-s-triazine gave a small amount of bis-N-methyl-N-pyridylmethylenediamine, which is a probable reaction intermediate in both the synthesis and the decomposition of this hexahydro-s-triazine.

8. 1,3,5-Tribenzylhexahydro-s-triazine and derivatives (XV)

The tribenzyl compound, one of the earliest known members of this group, was made[10] in 1895 by the amine-formaldehyde method.[10,20] It is a low melting solid (43°) and boils at 245°.

In addition to the benzylamine-formaldehyde method, 1,3,5-tribenzylhexahydro-s-triazine (XV) may also be prepared, it is reported,[14]

$$\text{Hexamine} + \text{structure} CH_2I \longrightarrow \text{IV}° \text{ salt} \xrightarrow[\text{or } K_2CO_3]{\Delta \text{ KOH}} H_5C_6CH_2-N \quad N-CH_2C_6H_5 \qquad (19)$$

(XV)

by means of the Delepine method of treating the quarternary salt of hexamine and benzyl iodide with hot alkali (19).

Compound (XV) forms a methiodide which melts at 160–161° recrystallized from ethanol. At 80° this salt is decomposed by water and gives benzylmethylamine hydroiodide, formaldehyde, and a dimeric aldimine (20).[68]

$$\text{(XV structure)} + CH_3I \longrightarrow \text{structure} \quad I^- \xrightarrow[80°]{H_2O} C_6H_5CH_2NHCH_3 \cdot HI + CH_2O + (C_6H_5CH_2N=CH_2)_2 \qquad (20)$$

(XV)

Hexamethylenetetramine is a source from which some of the substituted tribenzylhexahydro-s-triazines have been prepared by degradative procedures. Hexamine is attacked by o-nitrobenzyl chloride.[69] If the reaction is carried out under reflux in 60% ethanol for 4 hours, 1,3,5-tri(o-nitrobenzyl)hexahydro-s-triazine (m.p. 112° recrystallized from methanol) is obtained. On the other hand, if the starting compounds are refluxed in carbon tetrachloride for 45 minutes, a 61% yield of an intermediate melting with decomposition at 184° is obtained. The latter can be converted to the s-triazine by heating for

an hour in 60% ethanol and probably is the methylenediamine derivative.[70] Some of the higher melting isomer is also obtained.

Other substituted benzylhexahydro-s-triazines which can be prepared[68] by this method, although in indeterminate yield, are: p-nitrobenzyl, p-methylbenzyl, and p-chlorobenzyl and 2,4,6-trimethylbenzyl.

Recently,[71] 1,3,5-tribenzylhexahydro-s-triazine (XV) and the ortho and para nitro derivatives have been prepared in good yields (see Table IX-2) by alkaline cleavage of benzylaminomethylsulfonic acids. These sulfonic acids are made by cleavage of the corresponding benzyl- or nitrobenzylhexamethylenetetramonium halides with sulfur dioxide.[a]

$$C_6H_5CH_2I + (CH_2)_6N_4 \longrightarrow [[(CH_2)N_4](C_6H_5CH_2)]^+I^- \xrightarrow{SO_2} C_6H_5CH_2NHCH_2SO_3H$$

$$3C_6H_5CH_2NHCH_2SO_3H + NaOH, 15\% \text{ aq.} \longrightarrow (XV)$$

[a] The sulfonic acids may well be sulfite esters, but the sulfonate structure is thought to be more reasonable.

9. 1,3,5-Triphenylethylhexahydro-s-triazine (XVI)

This colorless liquid, b.p. 255°, is made[18],[25] by the amine-form-aldehyde process.

Benzoyl chloride reacts with 1,3,5-triphenylethylhexahydro-s-triazine (XVI) to give N-benzoyl-β-phenylethylamine.[18] It will be recalled that benzoyl chloride reacts differently with 1,3,5-trimethyl-hexahydro-s-triazine, forming an addition compound initially. Its action in this case is similar to the reaction of hydrogen cyanide on 1,3,5-triphenylhexahydro-s-triazine (see Section IV.2 *Reactions*).

$$C_6H_5CH_2CH_2N \quad NCH_2CH_2C_6H_5 \quad (CH_2CH_2C_6H_5 \text{ on N}) + 3\, C_6H_5COCl \longrightarrow 3\, C_6H_5CH_2CH_2NHCOC_6H_5$$

(XVI)

Compound (XVI) can be converted[25] in 41% yield to 3,5-di-(phenylethyl)tetrahydro-1,3,5-thiadiazine-2-thion by heating with carbon disulfide. When the thiadiazine derivative was boiled, a 59% yield[25] of 1,3,5-tri(phenylethyl)hexahydro-1,3,5-triazine-2-thion resulted. When this compound was crystallized from acetone, it melted at 157–157.8°.

10. 1,3,5-Trithenylhexahydro-s-triazines

A. 1,3,5-Tri(2-thenyl) hexahydro-s-triazine

This compound melts at 55° when recrystallized from ethyl alcohol. It forms a hydrochloride which melts at 118° and is stable in dry air, and a picrate which melts at 133° and can be crystallized from anhydrous ethanol.[65] It may be prepared by the amine-formaldehyde method or by means of the Mannich reaction[72] discussed below (Section IV,10.B). A temperature of 65° is necessary.

B. 1,3,5-Tri(5-methyl-2-thenyl)hexahydro-s-triazine

The S-methyl derivative melts at 87–88° upon recrystallization from absolute ethanol. It has been prepared[72] by a Mannich reaction (20). The stable intermediate monomers are isolated as hydrochloride salts in excellent yields. Treatment with alkali completes the trimerization.

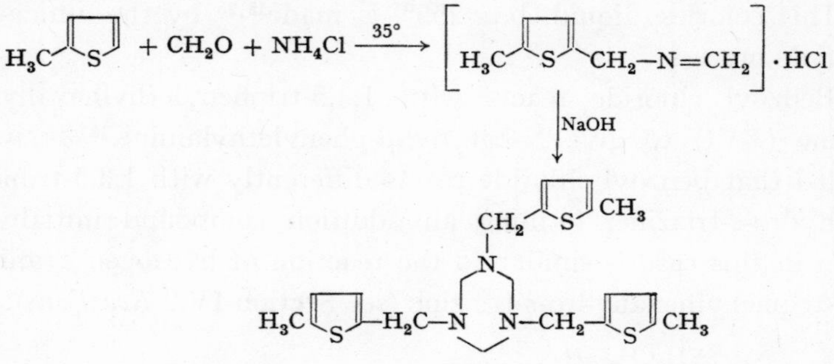

$$H_3C\text{-}S\text{-thiophene} + CH_2O + NH_4Cl \xrightarrow{35°} \left[H_3C\text{-}S\text{-}CH_2\text{—}N\text{=}CH_2 \right] \cdot HCl$$

$$\downarrow NaOH$$

(20)

$$H_3C\text{-}S\text{-}H_2C\text{—}N\quad N\text{—}CH_2\text{-}S\text{-}CH_3$$

C. 1,3,5-Tri(5-tert-butyl-2-thenyl)hexahydro-s-triazine (XVII)

Compound (XVII) is a solid, recrystallized from ethanol, which melts at 106–106.5°.

In the case of *tert*-butylthiophene, a modification[73] of the aminomethylation reaction is used with sulfurous acid as catalyst. To a mixture of 2-*tert*-butylthiophene, ammonium chloride and 36 % aqueous formaldehyde, is added a stream of sulfur dioxide at 70°. The first product which can be isolated is 5-*tert*-butyl-2-thenylaminomethylsulfonic acid. This compound yields 1,3,5-tri(5-*tert*-butyl-2-thenyl)-hexahydro-s-triazine when heated with excess sodium hydroxide (21).

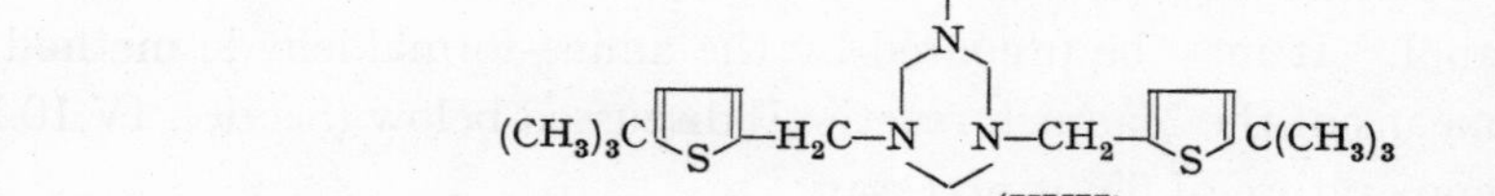

$$(CH_3)_3C\text{-}S\text{-thiophene} + NH_4Cl + CH_2O \text{ aq.} \xrightarrow[70°]{SO_2} (CH_3)_3C\text{-}S\text{-}CH_2NHCH_2SO_3H$$

$$\downarrow \Delta\,NaOH$$

(21)

$$(CH_3)_3C\text{-}S\text{-}H_2C\text{—}N\quad N\text{—}CH_2\text{-}S\text{-}C(CH_3)_3$$

(XVII)

The triaryl and triarylalkylhexahydro-s-triazines discussed above and, in addition, several others which are similar in regard to properties, reactions, and methods of preparation, are listed in Table IX-2 together with their physical properties, derivatives, and references to methods of preparation.

LE IX-2. Triaryl and Trialkylaryl hexahydro-*s*-triazines

	Melting or Boiling point/ recrystallization solvent	Method of prep.*a*-ref.	Remarks
yl	M.p. 141°/ligroin Isomer, M.p. 210°	A–1, 6, 7, 12, 13, 15, 17, 18, 23, 24, 29 C–14 D–16 F–25	
yl	M.p. ca. 100°	A–23, 25	
lyl	M.p. 128°/ligroin. Isomer, M.p. 225–7°	A–1, 2, 3, 4, 12, 23, 30	
lyl	M.p. 148–9°/ether. Isomer, M.p. 182–3°	A–3	
lorophenyl)	M.p. 154°. Isomer, M.p. 228°/ether-acetone	A–3	
hoxyphenyl)	M.p. 156.2–157°	A–29	Yield, 13 %–A
rboxyphenyl)	M.p. 175–200°	A–8	
rboxyphenyl)	—	A–3	
trophenyl)	M.p. 113°/methyl alc. Isomer, M.p. 153.5°/ ether-alcohol	B–5, 27 G–27	Yield, 83 %–G
trobenzyl)	M.p. 161.5°/phenol	B–5, 26, 27, 30 G–27	Yield, 88 %–G
Methoxyquinoline)	M.p. 203–205°/pyridine	A–8	
yl	M.p. 50°/aq. ethyl alc. at —10° B.p. 240–245°/1 atm.	A–10, 11, 26, 30 B–26, 27 C–9 G–27	Salts: Hydrochloride, M.p. 125°. Picrate, M.p. 110°. Oxalate, M.p. 135°, cryst. aq. ethyl alc. Methiodi- de, M.p. 160–161°, cryst. ethyl alc. Yield 95 %–A; 60 %–G
ylethyl	B.p. 255°	A–19, 29	Cmpd. a viscous yellow liq. Yield, 85 %–A
-Trimethylbenzyl	M.p. 150°	B–30	
ralyl	M.p. 121°/acetone-ligroin. Isomer, M.p. 164–165°	A–20	
ridyl	M.p. 96°/ligroin	A–21	
enyl	M.p. 55–56°/EtOH	E–22 B–30	Salts: Hydrochloride, M.p.180°, stable in dry air. Picrate, M.p. 133°, cryst. anhy. ethyl alc. Yield, 90 %–B

(*Table continued*)

TABLE IX-2 *(continued)*

Ar	Melting or Boling point/ recrystallization solvent	Method of prep.[a]-ref.	Remarks
2-(5-Methylthenyl)	M.p. 87–88°/dry ethyl alc.	E–22	
p-Methylbenzyl	—	B–26	
p-Chlorobenzyl	—	B–26	
2-(S-*tert*-Butylthenyl)	M.p. 106–106.5%/ethyl alc.	E–28	

$$H_3CCCH_3$$
$$CH_3$$
S CH_2–

[a] *Methods of Preparation*

A Condensation of primary amine and formaldehyde.
B Reaction of hexamine and substituted benzyl chloride.
C Decomposition of quarternary salt from hexamine.
D Curtius rearrangement.
E Mannich reaction.
F Using methylchloromethyl sulfate.
G Alkaline cleavage of methylol sulfites.

1. C. Bishoff, *Ber.*, **31**, 3248 (1899).
2. E. Wagner and J. Simons, *J. Chem. Ed.*, **13**, 265 (1936).
3. C. Bischoff and F. Reinfeld, *Ber.*, **36**, 41 (1903).
4. A. Eibner, *Ann.*, **302**, 335 (1898).
5. F. Mayer and F. English, *Ann.*, **417**, 60 (1918).
6. C. Goldschmidt, *Chem. Zeit.*, **28**, 1229 (1904).
7. A. Senier and F. Shepheard, *J. Chem. Soc.*, **95**, 441 (1909).
8. G. Bachman, G. Bennett and R. Barker, *J. Org. Chem.*, **15**, 1278 (1950).
9. K. Hock, *Ger.*, **139**, 394 (1903).
10. L. Henry, *Bull. Acad. Belg.*, (3), **29**, 23 (1895).
11. J. Graymore, *J. Chem. Soc.*, **1932**, 1353.
12. J. Miller and E. Wagner, *J. Am. Chem. Soc.*, **54**, 3698 (1932).
13. E. Paterno, *Gazz. chim. ital.*, **14**, 351 (1884).
14. L. Hartung, *J. prakt. Chem.*, (2), **46**, 19 (1892).
15. W. von Miller and J. Plöchl, *Ber.*, **25**, 2020 (1892).
16. T. Curtius and A. Darapsky, *J. prakt. Chem.*, (2), **63**, 428 (1901).
17. G. Pulvermacher, *Ber.*, **25**, 2762 (1892).
18. B. Tollens, *Ber.*, **17**, 657 (1884).
19. J. Graymore, *J. Chem. Soc.*, **1935**, 865.
20. C. Smith, *J. Chem. Soc.*, **85**, 732 (1904).
21. H. Kahn et al., *J. Chem. Soc.*, **1945**, 858.
22. H. Hartough, S. Meisel, E. Kopf and J. Schick, *J. Am. Chem. Soc.*, **70**, 4013 (1948).
23. C. Eberhardt and A. Welter, *Ber.*, **27**, 1804 (1894).
24. R. Cambier, and A. Brochet, *Bull. soc. chim.*, (3), **13**, 404 (1895).
25. J. Houben and H. Arnold, *Ber.*, **41**, 1577 (1908).
26. J. Graymore, *J. Chem. Soc.*, **1947**, 1116.
27. B. Reichert and W. Domis, *Arch. Pharm.*, **282**, 109 (1944), through *Chem. Abstracts*, **45**, 1969 (1951).
28. H. Hartough, J. Schick and J. Dickert, *J. Am. Chem. Soc.*, **72**, 1572 (1950).
29. A. Schnitzer, *Dissertation*, Oklahoma A. & M. Coll., 1951.
30. S. Angyal, D. Penman and G. Warwick, *J. Chem. Soc.*, **1953**, 742.

V. 2,4,6-Trialkyl- and Triarylhexahydro-s-Triazines

Relatively few compounds of this category are known and most of these have been obtained by the interaction of aldehydes with ammonia. When aliphatic aldehydes of low molecular weight are treated in ether with ammonia, crystalline solids are obtained which correspond in composition to simple addition compounds. These are the aldehyde-ammonias. They are relatively unstable substances, for, on standing in moist air or on treatment with dilute acids, they readily revert to their constituents. On standing over concentrated sulfuric acid or on heating in a vacuum, they lose water and give imines, which are usually trimeric.[59]

When acetaldehyde is treated with concentrated aqueous ammonia, a compound is isolated (as the trihydrate, m.p. 95–97°; recrystallized from water) which has been considered[74] to be a saturated s-triazine. The three methyl groups are symmetrically distributed on the ring methylene groups required by (XIX), 2,4,6-trimethylhexa-

hydro-s-triazine. Evidence indicates,[75] however, that the s-triazine structure is at best transitory and more likely, the trimeric product isolated has the linear structure (XX).

Further consideration of the possible trimeric structure of acetaldehyde-ammonia is deferred until Section VI.

It appears reasonably certain that an s-triazine results from the action of ammonia on pyridine-2-carboxaldehyde (21).

(21)

2,4,6-Tri(2-pyridyl)hexahydro-s-triazine is obtained as yellow crystals which melt with decomposition at 126°. The compound is soluble in organic solvents, exhibits basic properties, and has a molecular weight[76] corresponding to the trimeric structure $(C_6H_6N_2)_3$. Long heating in aqueous alcohol reverses the synthesis reaction.

1,3,5-Trimethyl-2,4,6-triphenylhexahydro-s-triazine (XXI) is a colorless oil, boiling at 68–75° at 30 mm. Unlike the other members of this group it is not prepared directly from ammonia, but by heating[77] hexamethylenetetramine and chlorobenzene in chloroform solution and distilling the reaction product (22).

$$(CH_2)_6N_4 \; + \; \bigodot^{Cl} \; \longrightarrow \; [\;\;] \; \xrightarrow{\text{distill.}} \; \substack{C_6H_5 \\ H_3CN \quad NCH_3 \\ H_5C_6 \diagdown \diagup C_6H_5 \\ | \\ N \\ CH_3 \quad (XXI)} \tag{22}$$

Treatment of (XXI) with hydrochloric acid gives three moles of methylamine, two moles of benzaldehyde and some formaldehyde, a result consistent with the structure as written.

$$\substack{C_6H_5 \\ H_3CN \quad NCH_3 \\ H_5C_6 \diagdown \diagup C_6H_5 \\ | \\ N \\ CH_3 \quad (XXI)} \xrightarrow{\text{HCl aq.}} 3\,CH_3NH_2 + 2\,C_6H_5CHO + CH_2O$$

2-Formyl-2,3-dihydropyran condenses with ammonia at 0–5° to give an 81 % yield[71a] of 2,4,6-tris(2-pyranyl)hexahydro-s-triazine. It is a crystalline solid which melts at 125–126° after recrystallization from acetic acid. Hydrogenation over Raney nickel in the presence of ammonia yields 2-methylamino-2,3-dihydropyran. If the ammonia is omitted, the major reduction product becomes imino-bis(2-methylpyran).

VI. Halogen Derivatives of Hexahydro-s-triazine and Alkylhexahydro-s-triazines

1. 1,3,5-Trichlorohexahydro-s-triazine

This labile white solid was first prepared[78] in 1911 from hexamethylenetetramine.

1,3,5-Trichlorohexahydro-s-triazine (XXII) has a melting point of

78° when recrystallized from ether and forms long shiny needles melting at 75° from chloroform. The purity of the recrystallized product is 95–99 % by titration.

Hydrogen cyanide and carbylamine evolved from (XXII) on standing, leaving a residue of ammonium chloride. Compound (XXII) is hygroscopic and unstable. It loses chlorine to give water soluble products, but may be kept for 1–2 days if maintained under absolutely anhydrous conditions. Thereafter it smells of chlorine.

1,3,5-Trichlorohexahydro-*s*-triazine (XXII) may be prepared by either of two methods. Monochloramine and formaldehyde react near 0° to form methylenechlorimine in five minutes. Trimerization occurs in about one hour[79] (23). Compound (XXII) may also be prepared from

$$NH_2Cl + CH_2O \xrightarrow[\text{5 min.}]{0°} CH_2{=}NCl \xrightarrow[\text{1 hr.}]{0°} \quad\text{(XXII)}\qquad (23)$$

hexamethylenetetramine[78] either by first treating that compound with hypochlorite and then heating the resulting dichloropentamethylene-tetramine with ten times its weight of acetic acid, or, more directly, by treating hexamine with aqueous hypochlorite and acetic acid.

$$\text{hexamine} + 2\,NaOCl + H_2O \longrightarrow (CH_2)_5N_4Cl_2 + 2\,NaOH + CH_2O$$

$$\xrightarrow{aq.\ NaOCl\ +\ HOAc}\qquad \Big\downarrow \begin{array}{c}HOAc\\ \Delta\end{array}$$

(XXII)

If (XXII) is treated with sodium ethoxide, decomposition occurs according to reaction (23).

$$(XXII) + 3\,NaOC_2H_5 + 9\,H_2O \longrightarrow$$
$$3\,NaCl + 3\,HCOOH + 3\,C_2H_5OH + 3\,NH_3 \qquad (23)$$

2. 1,3,5-Trichloro-2,4,6-trimethylhexahydro-s-triazine

If acetaldehyde is treated with chloramine and the product treated with sodium hypochlorite, only a cyclic dioxa compound results,[81] but if the hypochlorite treatment is followed by the addition of acetic acid,[81,82] 1,3,5-trichloro-2,4,6-trimethylhexahydro-s-triazine (XXIII) is obtained. Its structure (XXIII) is not completely certain.

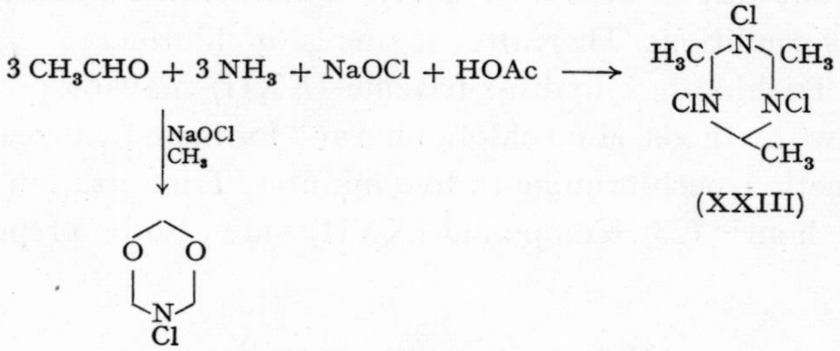

$$3\ CH_3CHO + 3\ NH_3 + NaOCl + HOAc \longrightarrow$$

(XXIII)

3. 2,4,6-Tribromomethylhexahydro-s-triazine

2,4,6-Tribromomethylhexahydro-s-triazine (XXIV) melts with decomposition at 100°. It is obtained by adding[82] ammonia gas to a solution of bromoacetaldehyde in benzene over a period of two hours.

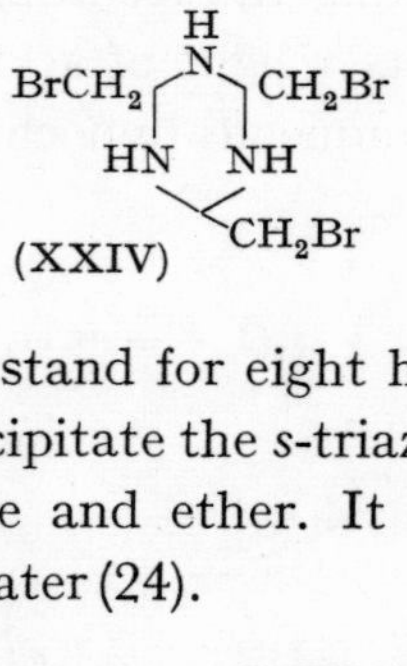

(XXIV)

The mixture is allowed to stand for eight hours at room temperature before adding water to precipitate the s-triazine. Compound (XXIII) is slightly soluble in benzene and ether. It is converted back to the starting materials by hot water (24).

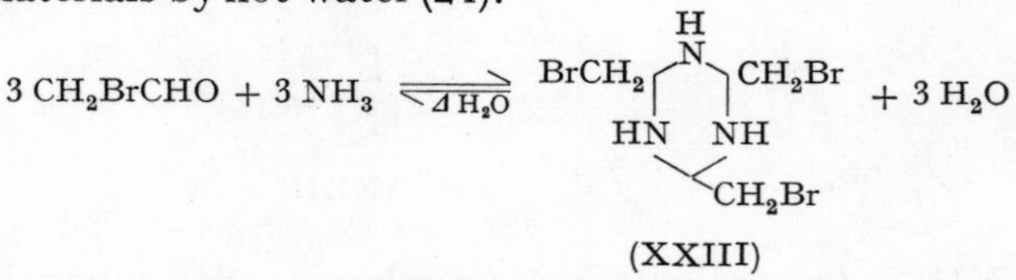

$$3\ CH_2BrCHO + 3\ NH_3 \underset{\Delta\ H_2O}{\rightleftharpoons} \quad\quad + 3\ H_2O \tag{24}$$

(XXIII)

4. 2,4,6-Tri(trichloromethyl)hexahydro-s-triazine

While early[84,85] work indicated that the reaction of trichloroacetaldehyde with ammonia produced an s-triazine along with a linear dimer and the usual aldehyde-ammonia monomer, analysis, reactions and instability do not[6] substantiate the presence of an *s*-triazine ring. They rather indicate[75] that a linear trimer exists analogous to that postulated as formed from acetaldehyde and ammonia; as, with the acetaldehyde-ammonia compound (XIX), decomposition to the dimer

$$CCl_3—\overset{\displaystyle\nearrow OH}{\underset{\displaystyle\searrow NH_2OH}{CH}}$$
$$CCl_3—\overset{\displaystyle}{\underset{\displaystyle\searrow NH_2}{CH}}$$

occurs only one day after synthesis.

5. 2,4-Di(trichloromethyl)6-thionhexahydro-*s*-triazine

Chloral and ammonium thiocyanate are reported[86] to react to give 2,4-di(trichloromethyl)6-thionhexahydro-*s*-triazine, m.p. 180° (dec.). However, it appears likely that the same considerations apply to the probable structure of this compound as to the reaction products of chloral with ammonia (Sect. VI.4) and of acetaldehyde and ammonia (Sect. V).

VII. Nitro- and Nitrosohexahydro-*s*-Triazines

The nitro and nitroso derivatives are discussed together in this section. These two classes of compounds are much more closely inter-related in the hexahydro-*s*-triazines series than are the more commonly encountered aromatic and aliphatic nitroso and nitro compounds, owing to their common origin in hexamethylenetetramine. Attention is directed to Chapter X—Hexamethylenetetramine—which should be consulted in conjunction with this Chapter. A good deal of hexamine chemistry is discussed in this Chapter; some is duplicated in both Chapters for completeness.

A discussion of the chemistry of 1,3,5-trinitroso- and 1,3,5-trinitro-hexahydro-*s*-triazine is presented below followed by a discussion of other nitroso and nitrohexahydro-*s*-triazines. The physical properties of the nitroso and nitrohexahydro-*s*-triazines are summarized in Table IX-3.

1. 1,3,5-Trinitrosohexahydro-s-triazine (I)

1,3,5-Trinitrosohexahydro-s-triazine (I) was prepared in 1895 by the action of nitrous acid[8] on hexamethylenetetramine and by oxidation[87] of hexamethylenetetramine. It is not altogether stable and melts at 105–107°. Heats of explosion and methods of purification of (I) have been reported.[104] The heats of combustion and formation are 3.4 Kcal./mole and —68 Kcal./mole, respectively.[89]

If hexamethylenetetramine is treated with nitrous acid, 60 % yields of 1,3,5-trinitrosohexahydro-s-triazine (I) result.[8,88] This method is discussed further below. Derivative (I) can also be prepared by other methods. Methylenediamine dihydrochloride and aqueous sodium nitrate give 1,3,5-trinitrosohexahydro-s-triazine[90] (1). The product is not pure, however, nor can it be obtained completely pure by controlled oxidation of hexamine,[87] which is another means of preparing compound (I).

$$ (1) $$

Reduction of the trinitrosohexahydro-s-triazine with sodium amalgam gives 1,3,5-triaminohexahydro-s-triazine[87] (2). Other reactions of

$$ (2) $$

(I) will be discussed with the reactions of 1,3,5-trinitrohexahydro-s-triazine [and in conjunction with the following brief treatment of that substance].

2. 1,3-Dinitrohexahydro-s-triazine

The existence of 1,3-dinitrohexahydro-s-triazine is not certain, but a yellow viscous oil, isolated after removal of pyridine nitrate and then pyridine from hexahydro-s-triazine nitrate dissolved in pyridine, may be the compound in question.[1] Treatment with excess 97 % nitric acid gave RDX (see 3 below) in good yields. The nitrate salt is known,[91a] however (see sections 3 and 4 below).

3. 1,3,5-Trinitrohexahydro-*s*-triazine and 1-Nitroso-3,5-dinitrohexahydro-*s*-triazine

The trinitro compound was first described but not identified in 1899 in a German patent[92] for preparing it by nitric acid treatment of hexamethylenetetramine. It is the well known explosive RDX or hexogen.

1,3,5-Trinitrohexahydro-*s*-triazine (II) is a difficultly purified crystalline solid melting at 205° in the pure state. More commonly, melting points of 198–202° may be encountered unless special purification techniques are employed. (II) is insoluble in water and alcohol and slightly soluble in acetone and acetic acid. It is insoluble in dilute alkalis and acids.

The heat of vaporization is 26 Kcal/mole[93] and the boiling point is estimated[93] to be 340° by extrapolating from the boiling point at 15–20 mm and 80–100 mm and by measuring the time of evaporation of drops from a metal block at various temperatures. The heats of combustion and formation are 2281.0 cal./mole and —15.7 Kcal./mole, respectively.[95] Ultraviolet and visible absorption spectra are amply discussed for all the *s*-triazines and condensed ring *s*-triazines containing primary and secondary nitramine, secondary nitrosamine, nitroxy and nitrate ion groups by Jones and Thorn[94] and by Schroeder.[117]

Molecular weight determination[95] on (II) in triphenyl phosphate gave values of 244 and 272, which are higher than the theoretical 222. The purity of the material employed is unknown, however.

One of the best laboratory and commercial preparations[96] for the manufacture of 1,3,5-trinitrohexahydro-*s*-triazine consists in adding hexamine in acetic acid and a solution of ammonium nitrate in 97% nitric acid to acetic anhydride at temperatures of 60–65°. The reaction is essentially complete in 15 to 20 minutes. These reagents will also form (II) from any compound[97] which can generate the active methylene group of formaldehyde under reaction conditions. Thus, even such a compound as methylene bismorpholine will give[98] small amounts of (II) with ammonium nitrate, nitric acid, acetic acid, and acetic anhydride.

If the oxidation of hexamethylenetetramine is carried out under stronger oxidizing conditions than are used for preparing 1,3,5-trinitrosohexahydro-s-triazine (I), 1,3,5-trinitrohexahydro-s-triazine is obtained.[99] It can also be obtained by the action of nitric acid on a derivative of a hexahydro-s-triazine, such as the condensation product of formaldehyde and methylamine,[5] or by dropping dry hexamethylene-tetramine nitrate[100] into concentrated nitric acid. The heats of reaction[101] involved in the synthesis of RDX from hexamethylenetetramine are listed in the following table, where (c) stands for solid and (s) represents solution in 97.5 % acid:

Reaction	ΔH (Kcal./mole)
$(CH_2)_6N_4$ (c) + HNO_3 $\longrightarrow$ RDX (s)	— 88.0
$(CH_2)_6N_4 \cdot HNO_3$ (c) + HNO_3 $\longrightarrow$ RDX (s)	— 69.2
$(CH_2)_6N_4 \cdot 2HNO_3$ (c) + HNO_3 $\longrightarrow$ RDX (s)	— 41.7
$(CH_2)_6N_4$ (s) + Bachmann reagents $\longrightarrow$ RDX (s)	—140
$(CH_2)_6H_4 \cdot HNO_3$ (s) + Bachmann reagents $\longrightarrow$ RDX (s)	—126
$(CH_2)_6N_4 \cdot 2HNO_3$ (s) + Bachmann reagents $\longrightarrow$ RDX (s)	—118

These measurements, together with those of the heats of solution of the reagents involved, indicate that hexamethylenetetramine dinitrate is an intermediate in the direct nitrolysis of hexamethylene-tetramine to RDX, but that the mononitrate is probably intermediate in Bachmann conversion of hexamethylenetetramine to RDX.[101] The mechanism of nitrolysis is discussed in Chapter X.

A German process for the production of 1,3,5-trinitrohydro-s-triazine consists of preparing potassium methylene sulfamate and converting it to (II) with nitric acid and sulfur dioxide.[102] The reaction proceeds in the following manner:[103]

$$CH_2O + NH_2SO_3K \longrightarrow CH_2=NSO_3K + H_2O$$

$$\downarrow \begin{matrix} HNO_3 \\ SO_2 \end{matrix}$$

$$(CH_2=NNO_2)_3 \longrightarrow (II)$$
$$+$$
$$KHSO_4$$

Yields of 80 % are said to be possible.

1,3,5-Trinitrohexahydro-s-triazine (II), prepared by nitrolysis of hexamine, always contains the difficultly removable impurity 1,3,5,7-tetranitro-1,3,5,7-tetrazacyclooctane,[105] erroneously identified[88,90] by earlier workers as dinitroso-pentamethylenetetramine. While compound

(II) can be purified by such procedures as refluxing in aqueous sodium perborate for 6 hours at 73–76° with agitation at a pH of 7.5–8.0, filtering, washing and drying,[104] a more convenient method of obtaining pure product is by oxidation of the trinitroso precursor. (1) When the latter is obtained from hexamine by nitrous acid treatment, it is contaminated only by 1,5-endomethylene-3,7-dinitroso-1,3,5,7-tetrazacyclooctane, which is formed at the same time. Despite the instability of the trinitroso compound, the impurity can be readily removed, after which the use of 99% nitric acid and 30% hydrogen peroxide at —40° converts (I) to (II), melting at 205° and quite pure. If less than the theoretical amount of oxidant is used, the intermediate 1-nitroso-3,5-dinitrohexahydro-s-triazine (III) can be isolated. It has a melting point of 176.6°, crystallized from nitromethane. These relationships are shown in (3).

$$(3)$$

Ultraviolet light turns the white crystals of 1,3,5-trinitrohexahydro-s-triazine yellow but no volatile products capable of oxidizing potassium iodide are produced.[107] (II) is readily decomposed by alkali. One normal, or even one-tenth normal, sodium hydroxide or potassium hydroxide acts[102] at 60° in several hours giving hexamine, nitrates, nitrites, organic acid, ammonia, nitrogen, and formaldehyde.

1,3,5-Trinitrohexahydro-s-triazine (II) can function as a nitrating agent.[109] For example, a solution of (II) in 95 % sulfuric acid gave a 45 % yield of p-nitroacetanilide from acetanilide. A number of other nitro compounds have been examined[109] as nitrating agents, but the efficiency of RDX is at least twice that of any of the others examined and, in strong acid at least, compares not too unfavorably with potassium nitrate.

Other reactions of 1,3,5-trinitrohexahydro-s-triazine are presented in the following pages, and in Chapters X and VIII, *Hexamethylenetetramine*, and *Condensed Ring Compounds*, respectively.

1,3,5-Trinitro-s-triazine became widely known during World War II as Cyclonite or RDX, a powerful and versatile explosive. It is amenable to safe handling and its use in a plastic form has found wide adaptation[110] for specialized tasks as well as fulfilling the qualifications of a good general explosive. In addition to its explosive properties, RDX is a spasmodic.[111] It acts on the central nervous system causing, acute poisoning manifested by haematapoetic interference, and causes changes in the vascular walls accompanied by secondary nerve cell degeneration. In cases of chronic poisoning, the liver, lungs and heart are also affected by a mechanism which involves interference with lipoid metabolism; probably this, in turn, is caused by an inhibition of the biological oxidation processes. The toxicity seems to be due to the nitrated amine groups, because the $-\overset{|}{\underset{|}{C}}-NO_2$ grouping alone has no spasmodic effect.

A variety of interesting and informative intermediates and derivatives of compounds (I) and (II) have been isolated as a result of the exhaustive investigations of the mechanism of formation, the structure and the reactions of Cyclonite carried out during and after World War II by Dunning and Dunning[112,113,114] and by Wright and co-workers.[115,116] Under carefully controlled nitration conditions, a number of products besides Cyclonite are obtained from hexamethylenetetramine.

4. 1,3-Dinitrohexahydro-s-triazine nitrate (IV)

The colorless crystalline salt (IV) m.p. 129°, is obtained as six-sided plates and prisms of the orthorhombic system[112] when hexamethylenetetramine is treated with 97% nitric acid. It is unstable in sulfuric acid solution, decomposing to nitrous oxide and undergoing nitration to Cyclonite in 29% yield at 88% acid strength.[91a]

$$\text{(4)}$$

Compound (IV) can also be made[114] by treating 1-methoxymethyl-3,5-dinitrohexahydro-s-triazine with 100% nitric acid at —30° in dry ether. Water is added at the end of twelve minutes causing salt (IV) to precipitate. The salt undergoes reactions which establish it as an intermediate, isolated in some cases and hypothetical in others, in a number of syntheses and degradations of this series.

If, to an acetone solution of (IV) at 5–7°, is added 6.6% sodium hydroxide, methylene bis-1,3-dinitrohexahydro-s-triazine (V) is ob-

(IV) + [CH₂O] → (V) m.p. 136°(dec.), recryst. from dry acetone then petroleum ether

tained. When 1,3-dinitrohexahydro-s-triazine nitrate (IV) is prepared from hexamine by means of 97% nitric acid, addition of methanol or ethanol to the reaction mixture gives the respective 1-alkoxymethyl compounds. They may also be obtained by treating purified (IV) with formaldehyde and methanol or ethanol (5). Use of an alcohol without formaldehyde gives mostly starting material.

$$\text{(5)}$$

If the same nitrate is treated with acetic acid and sodium acetate (6), one obtains 1-acetyl-3,5-dinitro-s-triazine (VI).

$$\text{(6)}$$

5. Methylene bis-3,5-dinitrohexahydro-s-triazine (V)

The colorless compound (V) crystallizes from dry acetone to which petroleum ether is added in the form of monoclinic needles melting at 136° with decomposition. It can be obtained by four methods. The first, described above under Section 3, consists in adding cold dilute alkali to a solution of 1,3-dinitrohexahydro-s-triazine nitrate (IV). The second method is as follows: If hexamine dinitrate is slowly added to 97% nitric acid at −45—28° and the resulting solution quenched with cold ether, a white gum precipitates.[112] Treatment of the gum with water gives (V).

$$\text{Hexamethylenetetramine} + \atop 97\% \text{ HNO}_3 \text{ dinitrate} \xrightarrow[\text{quench in ether}]{-45 \text{ to } -60°} \text{white gum}$$

(V)

The third procedure utilized 3,5-dinitro-3,5-diazapiperidinium nitrate in acetone solution.[116] Treating this compound with aqueous 6.6% sodium hydroxide at 5–7° and a pH below 5.6, gave[116] a 40% yield of the pure bis-compound (V).

A fourth procedure consists[91] of treating hexahydro-s-triazine nitrate in acetone suspension with four tenths of an equivalent of dilute sodium hydroxide (7).

(7)

The bis-compound (V) may be acetylated with acetic anhydride at room temperature or at 80° giving 1-acetyl-3,5-dinitro-s-triazine (VI), but if acetic acid is added at a reaction temperature of 70–85°, the corresponding 1-acetoxymethyl compound results.

Strong (96%) nitric converts (V) to Cyclonite (II); alcohols have no effect on (V). Treatment[116] of (V) with 98% nitric acid and acetic anhydride at 35–40° first, then at 28° for an hour gives a 35% yield of

1,7-diacetyl-2,4,6-trinitrohexahydro-2,4,6-triazacycloheptane. These reactions are summarized (8).

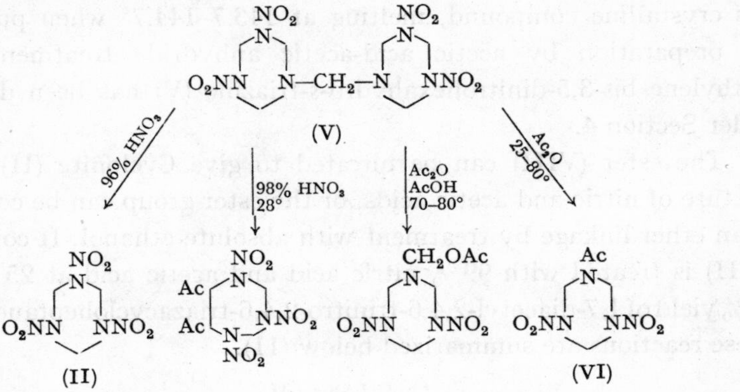

NO₂ → NO_2

$$\text{(8)}$$

(V)

96% HNO₃

98% HNO₃
28°

Ac₂O
AcOH
70-80°

Ac₂O
25-80°

NO₂

(II)

Ac

NO₂
NNO₂
NO₂

(CH₂OAc)

(Ac)

(VI)

6. 1-Acetyl-3,5-dinitrohexahydro-s-triazine

1-Acetyl-3,5-dinitrohexahydro-s-triazine (VI) forms[112,116] colorless needles melting at 156°.

Schroeder[117] has discussed maxima and minima in the ultraviolet and visible spectra of (VI), measured in ethanol. Compound (VI) is obtained as a product in reactions illustrating the chemistry of a number of compounds in Section VII. For example its preparation from methylene bis-3,5-dinitrohexahydro-1,3,5-triazine (V) is listed as a reaction of that compound. Yields are 50%. The 1-acetyl compound can also be made[115] from 1,3-dinitrohexahydro-s-triazine nitrate (9).

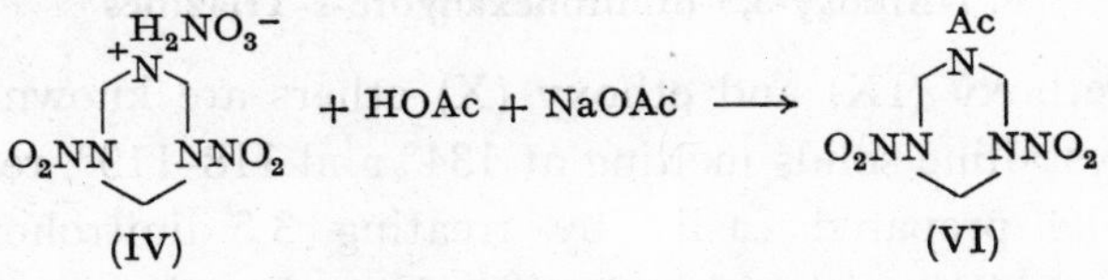

$$+ \text{HOAc} + \text{NaOAc} \longrightarrow \qquad (9)$$

(IV)   (VI)

Treating[114] di(3,5-dinitrohexahydro-1,3,5-triazinyl-1-methyl) ether (VII) with acetic anhydride at room temperature is another means (10) of preparing 1-acetyl-3,5-dinitrohexahydro-s-triazine (VI).

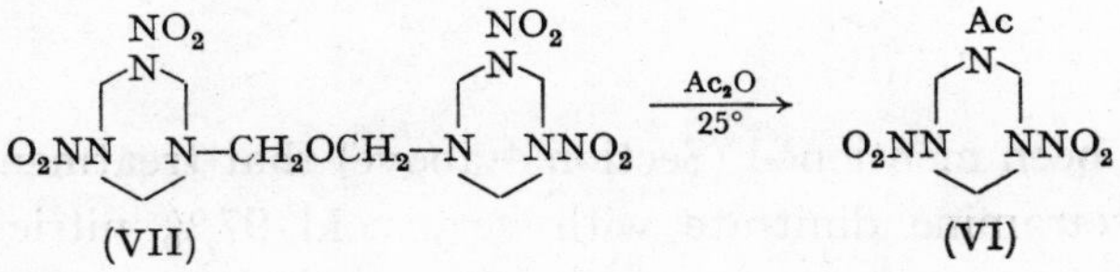

$$\xrightarrow{\text{Ac}_2\text{O}}_{25°} \qquad (10)$$

(VII)   (VI)

7. 1-Acetoxymethyl-3,5-dinitrohexahydro-*s*-triazine

1-Acetoxymethyl-3,5-dinitrohexahydro-*s*-triazine (VIII) is a color-less crystalline compound, melting at 143.7–144.7° when pure.[114,116] Its preparation by acetic acid-acetic anhydride treatment of 1-methylene bis-3,5-dinitrohexahydro-*s*-triazine (V) has been discussed under Section 4.

The ester (VIII) can be nitrated to give Cyclonite (II) with a mixture of nitric and acetic acids, or the ester group can be converted to an ether linkage by treatment with absolute ethanol. If compound (VIII) is treated with 99% nitric acid and acetic acid at 25–50°, an 81% yield of 1,7-diacetyl-2,4,6-trinitro-2,4,6-triazacycloheptane results. These reactions are summarized below (11).

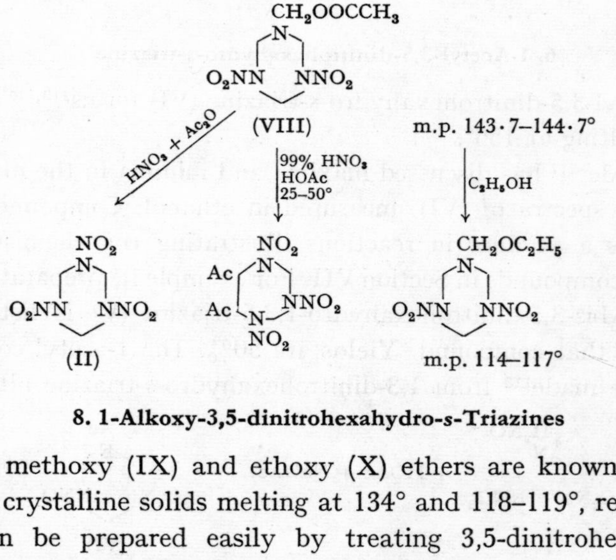

$$CH_2OOCCH_3$$

O_2NN   NNO_2

(VIII)   m.p. 143·7–144·7°

$HNO_3 + Ac_2O$

99% HNO_2
HOAc
25–50°

C_2H_5OH

NO_2	NO_2	CH_2OC_2H_5
O_2NN NNO_2	Ac NNO_2 Ac NO_2	O_2NN NNO_2
(II)		m.p. 114–117°

(11)

8. 1-Alkoxy-3,5-dinitrohexahydro-*s*-Triazines

The methoxy (IX) and ethoxy (X) ethers are known; both are colorless crystalline solids melting at 134° and 118–119°, respectively. They can be prepared easily by treating 3,5-dinitrohexahydro-*s*-triazine nitrate (IV) with either methanol or ethanol.

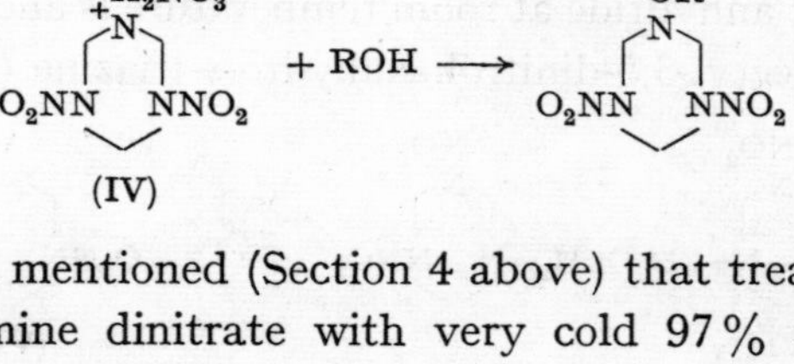

$$+H_2NO_3^-$$

O_2NN   NNO_2   + ROH ⟶   O_2NN   NNO_2

(IV)

It has been mentioned (Section 4 above) that treatment of hexa-methylenetetramine dinitrate with very cold 97% nitric acid and quenching the solution with cold ether[112] produced a white gum. Adding methyl or ethyl alcohol to this gum gives mostly 3,5-dinitro-dimethylenetriamine nitrate but some (20%) of the respective 1-alkoxymethyl-3,5-dinitro-s-triazines (IX) and (X) are obtained (12).

$$\text{Hexamine dinitrate} + 97\% \text{HNO}_3 \xrightarrow[\text{quench in ether}]{-45 \text{ to } -60°} \text{white gum}$$

(12)

$$
\begin{array}{ccc}
\text{CH}_2\text{OC}_2\text{H}_5 & & \text{CH}_2\text{OCH}_3 \\
\text{O}_2\text{NN} \quad \text{NNO}_2 & + \text{ mostly} \quad \text{O}_2\text{NNHCH}_2\text{NCH}_3{}^+\text{NO}_3{}^- & \text{O}_2\text{NN} \quad \text{NNO}_2 \\
& \underset{\text{NO}_2}{|} & \\
\text{(X)} & & \text{(IX)} \\
\text{m.p. } 118\text{--}119° & & \text{m.p. } 134°
\end{array}
$$

The ethyl ether (X) has also been made by treating 1-acetoxy-methyl-3,5-dinitrohexahydro-s-triazine with absolute ethanol (13).

$$
\begin{array}{ccc}
\text{CH}_2\text{OAc} & & \text{CH}_2\text{OC}_2\text{H}_5 \\
\text{O}_2\text{NN} \quad \text{NNO}_2 & + \text{ C}_2\text{H}_5\text{OH} \longrightarrow & \text{O}_2\text{NN} \quad \text{NNO}_2 \\
& & \text{(X)}
\end{array}
\qquad (13)
$$

The 1-alkoxy-3,5-dinitrohexahydro-s-triazines undergo reactions useful for preparation of some of the remaining members of the series. Both alkoxy compounds give 90 % yields of Cyclonite (11) when treated with 96 % nitric acid. Treating Compound (IX) with 99%

$$
\begin{array}{ccc}
\text{CH}_2\text{OCH}_3 & & \text{NO}_2 \\
\text{O}_2\text{NN} \quad \text{NNO}_2 & \xrightarrow[0 \text{ to } -40°]{99\% \text{ HNO}_3} & \text{O}_2\text{NN} \quad \text{NNO}_2 \\
\text{(IX)} & & \text{(II)}
\end{array}
\qquad (14)
$$

$$\downarrow \text{HOAc} + \text{HNO}$$

$$
\begin{array}{cc}
\text{NO}_2 & \\
\text{O}_2\text{NN} \quad \text{NNO}_2 & + \text{ CH}_3\text{OCH}_2\text{NCH}_2\text{NCH}_2\text{NCH}_2\text{OCH}_3 \\
& \qquad\quad \underset{\text{NO}_2}{|} \; \underset{\text{NO}_2}{|} \; \underset{\text{NO}_2}{|} \\
\text{(II)} &
\end{array}
$$

nitric acid also gives Cyclonite. Acetyl nitrate gives Cyclonite but some α,ω-dimethoxy-N,N′,N″-trinitrotetramethylenetriamine as well (14).

Other reactions of the two alkoxy compounds are discussed in the following two sections which are written as continuations of this one.

9. 1-Halomethyl-3,5-dinitrohexahydro-s-Triazines

The alkoxy compounds (IX) and (X) are labile and react readily with a variety reagents.[114] Acetic anhydride and acetyl halides react easily with the ether linkages. At —10°, acetyl bromide gives a 62 % yield of 1-bromomethyl-3,5-dinitrohexahydro-s-triazine (XII), m.p. 127° (dec.). Acetyl chloride at 10–20° gives an 88 % yield of the 1-chloromethyl compound (XI) which melts at 147°. Acetic anhydride requires 3 days at room temperature to give 1-acetyl-3,5-dinitrohexahydro-s-triazine (VI) from (IX) or (X). Compound (VI) is also produced by the action of acetic anhydride on either of the halomethyl compounds (XI) or (XII). These reactions are summarized below (15).

$$
\begin{array}{ccc}
\text{CH}_2\text{OCH}_3 & & \text{Ac} \\
\text{(IX)} & \xrightarrow[-25° \text{ 3 da.}]{\text{Ac}_2\text{O}} & \text{(VI) m.p. 156°} \\
& \text{CH}_2\text{Cl} & \\
& \text{(XI) m.p. 147°} & \\
& \xrightarrow[-10°]{\text{AcBr}} & \text{CH}_2\text{Br} \\
& & \text{(XII)}
\end{array} \tag{15}
$$

Compounds (XI) and (XII) may be used to regenerate the methyl or ethyl ethers (IX) and (X) by treating them with the corresponding alcohol. Compounds (XI) and (XII) can be nitrated, as can most of the compounds discussed in Section VII, to give Cyclonite in 70–90 % yield by the use of 96–98 % nitric acid at temperature from —10° to +20°.

10. Di(3,5-dinitrohexahydro-1,3,5-triazinyl-1-methyl) ether (VII)

Compound (VII) melts with decomposition[114] at 150°. It can be made from 1-chloromethyl-3,5-dinitrohexahydro-s-triazine (XI). Aqueous sodium acetate effects a condensation between two molecules of (XI) to give methylene bis-3,5-dinitrohexahydro-s-triazine (VII). If instead of sodium acetate, compound (XI) is treated carefully with 100% nitric acid at —40°, a symmetrical ether representing the condensation of two molecules with elimination only of the chlorine atoms results (16).

$$2 \quad \underset{(XI)}{\left[\begin{array}{c} CH_2Cl \\ N \\ O_2NN \quad NNO_2 \end{array} \right]} \xrightarrow[-40°]{100\% \ HNO_3} \underset{(VII) \ m.p. \ 150° \ (dec.)}{\left[\begin{array}{c} NO_2 \qquad NO_2 \\ N \qquad N \\ O_2NN \quad NCH_2OCH_2N \quad NNO_2 \end{array} \right]} \qquad (16)$$

The ether (VII) is also obtained by treating 1-methoxymethyl-3,5-dinitro-s-triazine for exactly 15 minutes with 100% HNO_3 at —30° in dry ether. Unstable products are reported[114] if the time is varied. At the end of 15 minutes a white precipitate is obtained which gives no Cyclonite but only decomposes when heated with water. Careful recrystallization from anhydrous acetone-chloroform gives (VII). At the end of 12 minutes of the nitration reaction, water will cause the precipitation of 3,5-dinitrohexahydro-s-triazine nitrate (IV).

Compound (VII) behaves in the same manner as most of the other derivatives of this series. By reaction with acetyl nitrate, 25% yields each of Cyclonite and a triazacycloheptane derivative are obtained; 100% nitric acid gives mostly Cyclonite; and acetic anhydride at room temperature gives 1-acetyl-3,5-dinitro-s-triazine (VI).

The conclusion that has been drawn[112,113,114] from the reactions exhibited by this series of derivatives is that neither 3,5-dinitrohexahydro-s-triazine nitrate (IV) nor the ether (VII) is a true intermediate in the nitrolysis of 1-chloromethyl or 1-methoxymethyl-3,5-dinitrohexahydro-s-triazine, but rather arise by the interaction of the diluents, water and R_2O respectively, with the true intermediates.

Table XI-3 contains a list of the known nitro and nitroso hexahydro-s-triazines exclusive of those which contain unsubstituted alkyl groups.

TABLE IX-3.   Nitro and Nitrosohexahydro-*s*-triazines

Compound	Melting point, °C.	Yield	Ref.
ONN⟩⟨NNO / N–NO	105–107		2
O_2NN⟩⟨NNO_2 / N–NO_2	205. B.p. 340°/1 atm.		1, 2, 8, 10
O_2NN⟩⟨NNO / N–NO_2	176.6. Recryst. nitromethane		2
CH_3 / O_2NN⟩⟨NNO / H_3C–,–CH_3 / N–NO	161		3, 4
O_2NN⟩⟨NNO_2 / N–H_2^+ NO_3^-	129		5, 8, 10
[O_2NN⟩⟨N–CH_2 / N–NO_2]$_2$	136 (dec.)	40 %	5, 6, 9, 11
O_2NN⟩⟨$NCOCH_3$ / N–NO_2	156–157	50 %	9
O_2NN⟩⟨NCH_2OOCCH_3 / N–NO_2	143.7–144.7		7, 9
O_2NN⟩⟨$NCH_2OC_2H_5$ / N–NO_2	118–119	17 %	5
O_2NN⟩⟨NCH_2OCH_3 / N–NO_2	134	24 %	5
O_2NN⟩⟨NCH_2Br / N–NO_2	127 (dec.)	62 %	6

(Table continued)

TABLE IX-3 (*continued*)

Compound	Melting point, °C.	Yield	Ref.
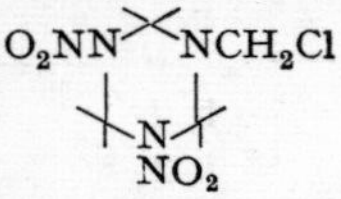 O_2NN⤫NCH_2Cl ｜N｜ NO_2	147	88 %	6
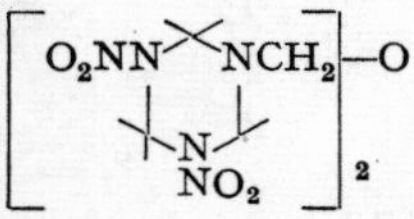 [O_2NN⤫NCH_2—O ｜N｜ NO_2]$_2$	150 (dec.)		7
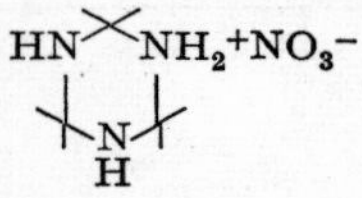 HN⤫$NH_2{}^+NO_3{}^-$ ｜N｜ H	98–99		11
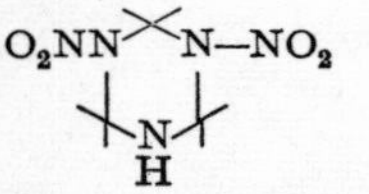 O_2NN⤫N—NO_2 ｜N｜ H	Yellow oil (?)		11

1. A. Belyaev, *J. Phys. Chem.*, **22**, 91 (1948), through *Chem. Abstracts*, **42**, 5227 (1948).
2. F. Brockman, D. Downing and G. Wright, *Can. J. Research*, **27B**, 469 (1949).
3. M. Delepine, *Compt. rend.*, **144**, 853 (1907).
4. M. Delepine, *Bull. soc. chim.*, (4), **1**, 590 (1907).
5. K. Dunning and W. Dunning, *J. Chem. Soc.*, **1950**, 2920.
6. K. Dunning and W. Dunning, *J. Chem. Soc.*, **1950**, 2925.
7. K. Dunning and W. Dunning, *J. Chem. Soc.*, **1950**, 2928.
8. G. Wright et al., *Can. J. Research*, **27B**, 218 (1949.
9. W. Chute et al., *Can. J. Research*, **27B**, 503 (1949).
10. G. Myers and G. Wright, *Can. J. Research*, **27B**, 489 (1949).
11. A. Vroom and C. Winkler, *Can. J. Research*, **28B**, 701 (1950).

11. Alkyl and Dialkylnitrohexahydro-*s*-Triazines

The alkyl and dialkylnitrohexahydro-*s*-triazines differ from other members of Section VII with respect to the methods used for their preparation and have therefore been listed separately.

A. *Physical Properties*

Table IX-4 lists compounds of the two following types:

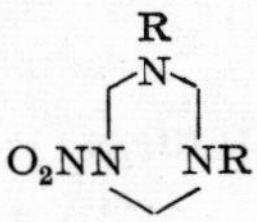

R
｜N｜
O_2NN NR
Type A

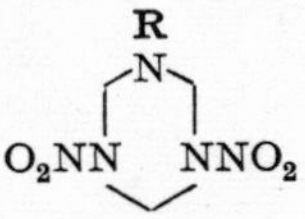

R
｜N｜
O_2NN NNO_2
Type B

TABLE IX-4.   1-Alkyl-3,5-dinitrohexahydro-s-triazines and
                      1,3-Dialkyl-5-nitrohexahydro-s-triazines

Type[a]	R.[b]	M.p., °C./solvent used	Ref.
A	$C_6H_5CH_2$-	108–110 (dec.)/acetone	1, 2
A	C_6H_{11}-	101–102/ligroin	1, 2
B	$C_6H_5CH_2$-	127–130 (dec.)/acetone	2
B	CH_3-	100–104 (dec.) or 98–99 (dec.)	2
B	C_2H_5-	88–89 (dec.)	2
B	H-	Solid	2

[a] See previous paragraph.
[b] Preparative methods are discussed below.

1. G. Wright et al., *Can. J. Research*, **27B**, 218 (1949).
2. F. Chapman, *J. Chem. Soc.*, **1949**, 1638.

B. Methods of Preparation

(1) Dimethylolnitramide.   Dimethylolnitramide appears to be a compound which may offer a general method of synthesis of 1,3-dialkyl-5-nitrohexahydro-s-triazines. The reaction involved has been applied with success to cyclohexylamine[115] and benzylamine.[115] When 10% aqueous cyclohexylamine is added to excess dimethylolnitramide and the mixture treated with formaldehyde at 0°, an 80% yield of the

$$
\text{C}_6\text{H}_{11}\text{NH}_2 + \begin{array}{c}\text{CH}_2\text{OH}\\|\\\text{N}-\text{NO}_2\\|\\\text{CH}_2\text{OH}\end{array} + \text{CH}_2\text{O} \xrightarrow{0°} \quad \text{(17)}
$$

respective s-triazine results (17). With benzylamine, stoichiometric quantities are used, and some 1,5-dinitro-3,7-dibenzyl-1,3,5,7-tetraza-cyclooctane results (18).

$$
\text{C}_6\text{H}_5\text{CH}_2\text{NH}_2 + 2\begin{array}{c}\text{CH}_2\text{OH}\\|\\\text{NNO}_2\\|\\\text{CH}_2\text{OH}\end{array} + 12\,\text{CH}_2\text{O} \longrightarrow \quad \text{(18)}
$$

(2) Methylenedinitramine. A similar mode of synthesis of 1-alkyl-3,5-dinitro- and 1,3-dialkyl-5-nitrohexahydro-*s*-triazines consists in starting with methylenedinitramine, the respective alkyl amine, and gaseous or aqueous formaldehyde. By variations[118] of this method, a number of the compounds listed in Table IX-4 can be prepared (19).

$$O_2NNHCH_2NHNO_2 + CH_2O + RNH_2 \xrightarrow{0°}$$

(19)

Type A   Type B

(3) Dimethylolmethylenedinitramine. Dimethylolmethylenedinitramine gives the same products (20) as methylenedinitramine and formaldehyde. Undoubtedly it is one of the first intermediate reaction products formed from dinitramine and formaldehyde when the two are used in a reaction with an alkylamine.

$$\underset{O_2NN-CH_2-NNO_2}{\overset{CH_2OH \quad CH_2OH}{|\qquad\quad |}} + CH_3NH_2 \xrightarrow[2\,hrs.]{0°}$$

(20)

(XIII)

C. Reactions

The compounds in Section 11 usually melt with decomposition giving the starting materials; barium hydroxide also effects synthesis reversal. Linear methyleneamines are obtained by subjecting 1-methyl (or ethyl)-3,5-dinitrohexahydro-*s*-triazine to nitrating conditions. Thus ammonium nitrate, 98 % nitric acid, acetic acid and acetic anhydride give N,N′,N″-trinitro (acetoxymethylaminomethyl) (methylaminomethyl)-amine from the 1-methyl (XIII) or 1-ethylhexahydro-*s*-triazines.[119]

$$(XIII) + 98\% \, HNO_3 + NH_4NO_3 \xrightarrow[50-60°]{\overset{HOAC}{Ac_2O}} \underset{CH_3NCH_2NCH_2NCH_2OOCCH_3}{\overset{NO_2 \quad NO_2 \quad NO_2}{|\qquad |\qquad |}}$$

On the other hand, 98 % nitric acid alone gives the nitrate ester, N,N′,N″-trinitro (nitroxymethylaminomethyl) (methylaminomethyl)-amine. The latter may be converted to the acetoxymethyl compound with sodium acetate-acetic acid or to the methyl ether with hot methanol. Similar treatment of 1,3-dicyclohexyl-3-nitrohexahydro-*s*-triazine with nitric acid alone gives only cyclohexylamine while, by addition of the other reagents as well, Cyclonite (II) is isolated.

The solid which is obtained from methylenediamine, formaldehyde and ammonia may be converted to 3-acetyl-1,5-dinitrohexahydro-*s*-triazine with acetyl chloride.

12. 1,3,5-Trinitroso-2,4,6-trimethylhexahydro-s-triazine

This compound melts at 161°. It is obtained[80],[120] by treating an acetaldehyde-ammonia mixture in chloroform with nitric anhydride, N_2O_3, at —23°, a temperature at which the monomer $CH_3CH=NH$ slowly polymerizes (21).

$$[CH_3CH=NH] + N_2O_3 \xrightarrow{-23°} \begin{matrix} NO \\ H_3C \overset{N}{\frown} CH_3 \\ ONN \quad NNO \\ \underset{CH_3}{\diagdown} \end{matrix} \qquad (21)$$

VIII. Amino Derivatives of Hexahydro-s-Triazines

Unlike the amino derivatives of the *s*-triazines (melamines) which constitute such a voluminous group that they must be treated in a separate chapter (VI) rather than as direct derivatives of cyanuric acid, the amino derivatives of hexahydro-*s*-triazine are but few in number.

1. 1,3,5-Triaminohexahydro-s-triazine (XIV)

Compound (XIV) is slightly soluble in water and alcohol; insoluble in ether. It can be prepared by two methods:

$$3\,CH_2O\ aq. + 3\,NH_2NH_2 \cdot H_2O \xrightarrow{\Delta} \begin{matrix} NH_2 \\ N \\ H_2NN \quad NNH_2 \end{matrix} + 6\,H_2O \qquad (22)$$

(XIV)

(A) Formaldehyde or paraformaldehyde and hydrazine[12] (22) and
(B) Reduction[87] of 1,3,5-trinitroso-*s*-triazine (23).

$$\begin{matrix} NO_2 \\ N \\ O_2NN \quad NNO_2 \end{matrix} \xrightarrow{Na(Hg)} \begin{matrix} NH_2 \\ N \\ H_2NN \quad NNH_2 \end{matrix} \qquad (23)$$

(II) (XIV)

1,3,5-Triaminohexahydro-*s*-triazine (XIV) appears to be a trimer of $NH_2N=CH_2$ although, very much in keeping with the properties of other members of Chapter IX, some of its reactions also indicate that it can react as a monomer. It forms a salt with two molecules of silver nitrate, an indication that it is a trimer, and reacts very much in the manner of a hydrazine giving a derivative (XV) upon reaction with three moles of salicylaldehyde which melts at 139–140°, crystallized from chloroform.

2. 1,3,5-Triamino-2,4,6-trimethylhexahydro-*s*-triazine

Acetaldehyde and hydrazine react in alcoholic solution (24) to give the 2,4,6-trimethyl derivative[122] of 1,3,5-triaminohexahydro-*s*-triazine. Reaction (24) is reversed with acid, but the compound is stable to alkali. It gives a trisilver salt, but yields no azide when treated with amyl nitrite and sodium ethoxide.

3. 1,3,5-Triaminomethylhexahydro-*s*-triazine (XVI)

Bromoacetaldehyde in benzene will react with ammonia at room temperature to give 2,4,6-tribromomethylhexahydro-*s*-triazine but in ether at —5 to 10°, the reaction[83] proceeds further (25) with ammonia. The product is the trihydrobromide of 1,3,5-triaminomethylhexahydro-*s*-triazine (XVI). Compound (XVI) decomposes at 50° or in moist air. With phenylhydrazine, glyoxal phenylosazone is said[83] to be obtained.

4. 2,4,6-Tri-α,α',α"-triketo-2,4,6-triacetonitrile-hexahydro-1,3,5-triazine trioxime (XVII)

Compound (XVII) is obtained in the form of yellow needles which turn brown at 240° and decompose at 321°. The starting material, which is prepared in ethanol at 0° from malononitrile, amyl nitrite, and sodium ethoxide, condenses when heated in the same solvent,[123] with

$$\begin{array}{c}CN\\CH_2\\\ \ CN\end{array} + C_5H_{11}ONO + NaOC_2H_5 \xrightarrow[0°]{C_2H_5OH} HON=\overset{\overset{\displaystyle OC_2H_5}{|}}{\underset{\underset{\displaystyle CN\ \ OH}{|\ \ \ |}}{C-C-NH_2}} \xrightarrow[\Delta]{C_2H_5OH}$$

$$\begin{array}{c}NC\ \ \ \ \ \ \ \ CN\\ |\ \ \ \ H\ \ \ |\\ HON=C\ \ \ N\ \ \ C=NOH\\ H\diagup\ \ \ \ \diagdown H\\ HN\ \ \ \ NH\\ \diagdown\underset{|}{C}=NOH\\ H\diagup\ \ \ CN\end{array}$$

$$(XVII)$$

$$(26)$$

elimination of ethanol (26). The product of reaction (26) is believed to have the indicated provisional structure (XVII) which is 2,4,6-tri-α,α',α"-triketo-2,4,6-triacetonitrilehexahydro-1,3,5-triazine trioxime.

IX. Sulfonyl Derivatives

1. Tripotassium hexahydro-s-triazine-1,3,5-trisulfonate (XVIII)

The salt (XVIII) does not have a good melting point. It is insoluble in non-aqueous solvents. Titration of (XVIII) with aqueous mineral acid shows[130] that the acid is comparable in strength to hydrochloric acid, but that it is unstable.

The salt (XVIII) is obtained as an intermediate in a German process[102] for the production of Cyclonite. Formaldehyde and potassium sulfamate react giving (XVIII) which, upon treatment with nitric acid and sulfur trioxide, is said to give 80 % overall yields of Cyclonite (27).

$$3\ CH_2O + 3\ NH_2SO_3K \longrightarrow (XVIII) + 3\ H_2O$$

$$\begin{array}{c}SO_3K\\ |\\ \diagup N \diagdown\\ |\ \ \ \ \ \ \ |\\ KO_3SN\ \ \ NSO_3K\\ \diagdown\diagup\end{array} \xrightarrow[SO_3\ or\ P_2O_5]{HNO_3} [\ \ ] \longrightarrow \begin{array}{c}NO_2\\ |\\ \diagup N \diagdown\\ |\ \ \ \ \ \ \ |\\ O_2NN\ \ \ NNO_2\\ \diagdown\diagup\end{array}$$

$$(XVIII) \hspace{6cm} (27)$$

It has been found, however, that only 50 % yields could be obtained in the synthesis of the salt and then only by reworking the mother liquors.

Binnie, Cohen and Wright[103] have shown that potassium methylene sulfamate, $CH_2=NSO_3K$, is trimeric, by molecular weight and goniometric studies. In solution the ionic equilibrium (28) exists as infinite dilution is approached.

$$
\begin{array}{c}
\text{SO}_3\text{K} \\
\overset{\displaystyle N}{\underset{\displaystyle \text{KO}_3\text{SN} \quad \text{NSO}_3\text{K}}{\bigwedge}}
\end{array}
\;\rightleftharpoons\; 3\,\text{K}^+ \;
\left[
\begin{array}{c}
\text{SO}_3 \\
\overset{\displaystyle N}{\underset{\displaystyle \text{O}_3\text{SN} \quad \text{NSO}_3}{\bigwedge}}
\end{array}
\right]^{\equiv}
\qquad (28)
$$

(XVIII)

The salt (XVIII) is recovered unchanged after attempts[103] to convert it to a sulfonyl chloride with thionyl and sulfuryl chlorides. Nothing was recovered after attempts[103] to nitrosate with nitrous acid or to methylate with dimethyl sulfate. Reduction with platinum and hydrogen was likewise fruitless.[103] Nitric acid and sulfur trioxide yield Cyclonite; phosphorous pentoxide may be used[103] in place of sulfur trioxide (27).

2. 1,3,5-Tri(sulfonylethyl)hexahydro-s-triazine

Alkyl sulfonamides have not been fully investigated. However ethylsulfonamide and ethylsulfonic acid react (29) with formaldehyde giving[124] an isomeric mixture melting at 120–145°, which is probably 1,3,5-tri(ethylsulfonyl)hexahydro-s-triazine.

$$
\text{CH}_3\text{CH}_2\text{SO}_3\text{H} + \text{CH}_3\text{CH}_2\text{SO}_2\text{NH}_2 + \text{CH}_2\text{O} \xrightarrow[\text{H}_2\text{SO}_4]{\text{Ac}_2\text{O}}
\begin{array}{c}
\text{SO}_2\text{C}_2\text{H}_5 \\
\overset{\displaystyle N}{\underset{\displaystyle \text{H}_5\text{C}_2\text{O}_2\text{SN} \quad \text{NSO}_2\text{C}_2\text{H}_5}{\bigwedge}}
\end{array}
\qquad (29)
$$

3. 1,3,5-Tri(arylsulfonyl)hexahydro-s-Triazines

Arylsulfonamides react with formaldehyde or paraformaldehyde in much the same manner as do primary amines giving 1,3,5-tri(arylsulfonyl)hexahydro-s-triazines (XIX). An acid catalyst is necessary.

$$
3\,\text{ArSO}_2\text{NH}_2 + 3\,\text{CH}_2\text{O} \xrightarrow[\text{HOAc 80°}]{\text{H}_2\text{SO}_4}
\begin{array}{c}
\text{SO}_2\text{Ar} \\
\overset{\displaystyle N}{\underset{\displaystyle \text{ArO}_2\text{SN} \quad \text{NSO}_2\text{Ar}}{\bigwedge}}
\end{array}
+ 3\,\text{H}_2\text{O}
$$

(XIX)

The synthesis of the benzenesulfonamide derivative by this method is accompanied by the appearance of an alkali soluble dimer of the starting sulfonamide which can readily be separated by fractional crystallization.

A second method of preparing the tri(arylsulfonyl)hexahydro-s-triazines is by means of hexamethylenetetramine and the arylsulfonyl chloride.[125] In place of

$$3\,ArSO_2Cl + (CH_2)_6N_4 + 3\,NaOH \xrightarrow{60°} (XIX)$$

hexamethylenetetramine, formaldehyde and ammonia may be sub-stituted in a mole ratio of 1 : 2, respectively, however yields are lowered thereby. If the reaction is run in chloroform, the reactants may pre-cipitate as salts or as addition compounds. The products obtained by the second method have reported melting points which disagree with the results of investigators using the acid-sulfonamide procedure. Both sets of physical constants are listed in Table IX-5 with the methods of preparation and known derivatives. These hexahydro-s-triazines are considerably more stable than the saturated s-triazines previously discus sed. For example, hydrochloric acid at 160° is required to regenerate ammonia, formaldehyde and the respective sulfonic acid. The sulfonyl hexahydro-s-triazines form unstable addition compounds with aniline.

Attempts[115] to recrystallize the p-tolyl compound from acetic acid or acetic anhydride cause detrimerization and N-acetyl-p-tolylsulfonamide is obtained (30).

4. 1,3,5-Tri[p-(sulfonamido-2-thiazole)phenyl]-hexahydro-1,3,5-triazine (XX)

This compound does not have the sulfonyl groups attached directly to the triazine ring but is included in this category nevertheless. It is formed by the reaction of formaldehyde with sulfathiazole[126] and probably possesses structure (XX).

Compound (XX) has been described[126] as a chemotherapeutic agent.

TABLE IX-5.   1,3,5-Tri(arylsulfonyl)hexahydro-s-triazines

Compound	Preparation	Melting point, °C./solvent used	Melting point of addition compound with aniline, °C.
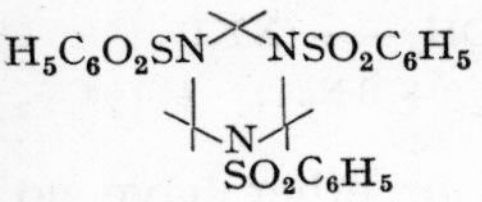 $H_5C_6O_2SN$ $NSO_2C_6H_5$ N $SO_2C_6H_5$	HCl gas into ethanol sol'n.[1] Hexamine method[2]	217°/Acetic acid. 228°/ Chloroform (80 % yield)	—
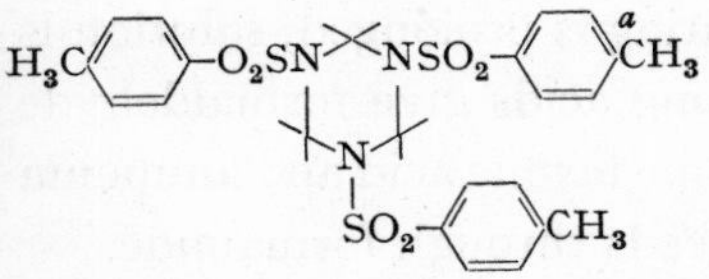 H_3C—O_2SN NSO_2—CH_3 ^{a} N SO_2—CH_3	Sulfuric-acetic[3] acids at 80°. Hexamine method[2]	169.5–170.5°/ Acetone or toluene. 236° (dec.)/Chloroform	73°
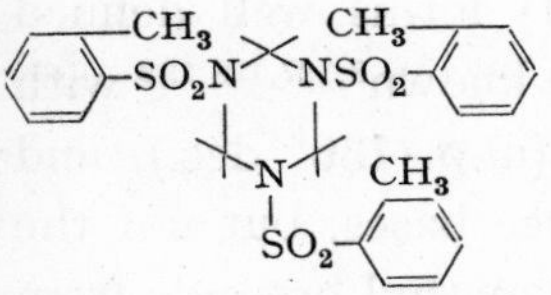 CH_3 CH_3 —SO_2N NSO_2— N CH_3 SO_2—	Sulfuric-acetic[3] acids at 80°. Hexamine method[2]	245.5–246.5°/ Xylene. 222°/ Acetic acid 80 % yield	259°

[a] The crystallographic characteristics of this compound have been extensively examined. See E. Flint, *Trudy Inst. Krist.*, 1947, No. 2, 17 through *Chem. Abstracts*, **44**, 7614 (1950).

1. A. Magnus-Levy, *Ber.*, **26**, 2148 (1893).
2. C. Hug, *Bull. soc. chim.*, (5), **1**, 1004 (1934).
3. L. McMaster, *J. Am. Chem. Soc.*, **56**, 204 (1934).

X. Hydroxy Derivatives:

1,3,5-Trihydroxyhexahydro-s-triazine

The simplest member of this series, 1,3,5-trihydroxhexahydro-s-triazine (XXI) is the only member of the series whose structure appears established,[8,127,128,129] to any convincing extent.

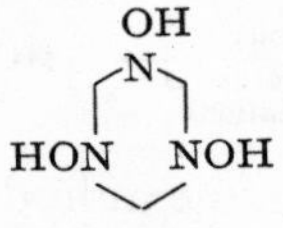

$$\begin{array}{c} OH \\ N \\ HON \quad NOH \end{array}$$

(XXI)

The compound was first prepared in 1891 by Scholl[127] from formaldehyde and hydroxylamine. It is an amorphous solid which decomposes without melting. The method of preparation consists[8,127,128,129] of heating an aqueous solution of formaldehyde and hydroxylamine hydrochloride with an alkaline acceptor added to liberate the hydroxylamine, cooling, and then separating the gelatinous product at room temperature.

$$3\,CH_2O + 3\,NH_2OH \cdot HCl + 1\tfrac{1}{2}\,Na_2CO_3 \longrightarrow 3[CH_2{=}NOH] \longrightarrow (XXI)$$
$$+ 4\tfrac{1}{2}\,H_2O \;+\; 3\,NaCl \;+\; 1\tfrac{1}{2}\,CO_2$$

Short periods of heating with water, alcohol or ether have no action on compound (XXI), but, if the heating is prolonged, solution is effected leaving only a small residue. Strong acids give formaldehyde and hydroxylamine, but weak acids give some formic acid and ammonia indicating that the reaction probably proceeds through formamide.

1,3,5-Trihydroxyhexahydro-s-triazine (XXI) forms well defined salts with monobasic anhydrous acids. Salts are known[8,127,128,129] with hydrochloric acid (m.p. 136°), hydriodic acid (m.p. 136° dec.), and hydrobromic acid. As might be expected, the free bases, but not the hydrohalides, form[128] salts with methyl iodide or methyl bromide from

$$(31)$$

(XXI)   m.p. 102° (dec.)/ether

methanol solution (31). Heating these salts with water gave the following substances, showing that the $>$ N—OCH$_3$ group was present: NH$_2$OH, CH$_2$O and NH$_2$OCH$_3$.

Heating 1,3,5-trihydroxyhexahydro-s-triazine (XXI) to 140° gives[128] formaldoxime (31), but if (XXI) is heated at burner temperatures,[129] it detonates giving water and hydrogen cyanide (32).

$$(XXI) \xrightarrow{\;140°\;} 3\,CH_2{=}NOH \tag{31}$$

$$(XXI) \xrightarrow[\substack{temperature\ \varDelta\\ (detonation)}]{burner} 3\,HCN + 3\,H_2O \tag{32}$$

Acetic anhydride and benzoic anhydride react with (XXI) to give compounds melting with decomposition at 133° from water and 168.5° from ethanol, respectively. The structure of the triacetyl and tribenzoyl derivatives is not certain and little has been published on their chemical properties.

XI. Carbonyl (Acyl) Derivatives

Carbonyl derivatives of hexahydro-s-triazines almost exclusively include the class of methyl substituted 1,3,5-triacylhexahydro-s-triazines, listed in Table IX-6. These compounds (XXII) are conveniently prepared[124,130-134] by heating alkyl, aryl, halogen substituted, or unsaturated nitriles with formaldehyde or trioxane, usually in the presence of an acidic catalyst such as sulfuric or chlorsulfonic acid (32).

$$\text{RCN} + \underset{\text{(Ar)}}{} \quad \begin{array}{c} O \quad O \\ \diagdown \quad \diagup \\ O \end{array} \quad \xrightarrow{H_2SO_4 \text{ or } ClSO_3H} \quad \underset{\text{(XXII)}}{RCON \diagup \overset{\overset{\displaystyle COR}{|}}{N} \diagdown NCOR} \tag{32}$$

BLE IX-6.   1,3,5-Triacylhexahydro-s-triazines $RCO-N{\diagup}{\diagdown}N-COR$ / $\underset{COR}{\overset{|}{N}}$

	Solvent for reaction	Reaction temperature, °C.	Yield, %	Melting point, °C.	Solvent for recrystallization	Ref.
3-	—	95	66	96–98	90 % Ethyl alc.	1, 2
-5-	CCl₄	77	86	169–171	Ethyl alc.	1, 2, 5
=CH-ᵃ	CCl₄	46	89	100 (Slowly polymerizes)	Ethyl alc., water, acetic anhydride, pyridine	1, 2, 5
H₂CH₂-	—	95	75	170–171	Ethyl alc.	1
=C(CH₃)-	—	95	15–40	149.5–151	Ethyl alc.	1, 2, 4
=CH—CH₂-	—	Reflux	Poor	191–192	Water	3
-5-	CCl₄	77	95	220–222	Chloroform and ppt. with ether	1, 2, 5, 6
C₆H₄CH₂-	—	—	—	175	—	1
C₆H₅-	CCl₄	77	98	216–217	Carbon tetrachloride + ether	5
H₃OC₆H₄-	CCl₄	77	87	216–217	Ethyl acetate	5
OCH₂CH₂-	—	—	—	—	—	2

ᵃ Compound is soluble in ethanol, acetone, chloroform, tetrahydrofuran, pinacols, acetone and water, and tetrahydrofuran and water; insoluble in ether, benzene, chlorobenzene.[2]

1. M. Gradsten and M. Pollock, *J. Am. Chem. Soc.*, **70**, 3079 (1948).
2. P. B. 73894, frames 5769–5778.
3. C. Price and L. Krishnamurti, *J. Am. Chem. Soc.*, **72**, 5334 (1950).
4. T. Gresham and T. Steadman, *J. Am. Chem. Soc.*, **71**, 1872 (1949).
5. W. Emmons, H. Rolewicz, W. Cannon and R. Ross, *J. Am. Chem. Soc.*, **74**, 5524 (1952).
6. P. Duden and M. Scharff, *Ann.*, **288**, 218 (1895).

A procedure described[134] in Organic Syntheses consists of heating an equimolar mixture of formaldehyde (as trioxane) and propionitrile with concentrated sulfuric acid at 95–105° for $3\frac{1}{2}$ to 4 hours. A 65% yield of white crystals of 1,3,5-tripropionylhexahydro-s-triazine melting at 170–172° upon recrystallization from 95% ethanol is obtained. The melting point can be raised to 173–174° by another recrystallization from 95% ethanol. Although this procedure is a firmly established one, better yields of 1,3,5-triacylhexahydro-s-triazines can be obtained by changing the solvent[133] used. Thus Emmons has shown carbon tetrachloride to be a good general solvent. The triazines (XXII) are insoluble in it and precipitate either as formed or when the mixture is cooled. Table IX-7 lists the effects of different solvents on the yields of products from the reaction between formaldehyde and propionitrile, acrylonitrile and benzonitrile.

TABLE IX-7.   Effects of Solvents on Yields of 1,3,5-Triacylhexahydro-s-triazines[a]

Solvents	Reaction temperature, °C.	Yields, % using:		
		C_2H_5CN	$CH_2=CHCN$	C_6H_5CN
CCl_4	77	86	89	95
CS_2	46	66	64	8
C_6H_5Cl	100	64	37	78
CH_3NO_2	102	64	21	79
$CHCl=CCl_2$	87	63	38	56
CH_3CCl_3	74	53	9	56
CH_2ClCH_2Cl	84	45	69	73
CCl_3CCl_3	100	42	76	81
$C_6H_5NO_2$	—			
$O\diagdown\!\!\!\begin{smallmatrix}CH_2CH_2\\CH_2CH_2\end{smallmatrix}\!\!\!\diagup O$	—	P		
$ClCH_2COOH$	—		O	
Cl_3CCOOH	—		O	
CH_3COOH	—		R	
$HCOOH$	—	0	0	0
$(C_2H_5)_2O$	—	0	0	0
$C_2H_5OOCCH_3$	—	0	0	0

[a] W. Emmons, H. Rolewicz, W. Cannon and R. Ross, *J. Am. Chem. Soc.*, **74**, 5524 (1952).

Benzamide in a solvent may be used in place of benzonitrile; the yield is 32% of 1,3,5-tribenzoylhexahydro-s-triazine instead of the 38% which is obtained with benzonitrile without a solvent. 1,3,5-Tribenzoylhexahydro-s-triazine has also been prepared by the action of benzoyl chloride on hexamine[1] or ammonium chloride[1] and formaldehyde.

$$C_6H_5COCl + \underset{\text{or } NH_4Cl + CH_2O}{(CH_2)_6N_4} \xrightarrow{\text{NaOH}} [(CH_2)_3N_3(COC_6H_5)_3]$$

The triacylhexahydro-s-triazines are more stable towards acids than most of the other perhydro-s-triazines; however, the end products of hydrochloric acid treatment are usually formaldehyde, ammonium chloride and the respective alkanoic acid. For example, the tripropionyl

$$\underset{C_2H_5CON \quad NCOC_2H_5}{\overset{\overset{\displaystyle COC_2H_5}{N}}{\bigcirc}} \xrightarrow[\Delta]{\text{HCl·aq.}} 3\,CH_2O + 3\,NH_4 + 3\,CH_3CH_2COOH \qquad (33)$$

derivative gives[135] propionic acid (33). Alkali treatment has been known to give similar results. Thus refluxing 1,3,5-tri-n-butyrylhexahydro-s-triazine in 20% aqueous alkali gives[124] sodium butyrate (34).

$$\underset{H_7C_3CON \quad NCOC_3H_7}{\overset{\overset{\displaystyle COC_3H_7}{N}}{\bigcirc}} + NaOH \;20\%\text{ aq.} \xrightarrow{\Delta} 3\,C_3H_7COONa \qquad (34)$$

Reduction of a side chain olefinic linkage in a hexahydro-s-triazine without reducing a carbonyl group may be accomplished[124,135] by hydrogenating in methanol at 80–90° using a nickel-cobalt catalyst or by using platinum and hydrogen (35).

$$\underset{CH_2=CHCON \quad NCOCH=CH_2}{\overset{\overset{\displaystyle COCH=CH_2}{N}}{\bigcirc}} \xrightarrow[\text{Ni–Co or Pt}]{[H]} \underset{CH_3CH_2CON \quad NCOCH_2CH_3}{\overset{\overset{\displaystyle COCH_2CH_3}{N}}{\bigcirc}} \qquad (35)$$

(XXII)

1,3,5-Triacrylylhexahydro-s-triazine (XXII) is stable in dilute acid solution, but in alkaline solution the active hydrogens of compounds such as amines, imines, alcohols, amide and water add across the double bonds producing polymerizable products.[135] One, two or three equivalents of sodium bisulfite can be added[136] giving solid products which do not melt up to 250°. After a third equivalent has been added, the bisulfite addition product can no longer be polymerized. Adducts with the following substances have been obtained:[136] butanol, butadiene, decylamine, and diethylamine. When fewer than three vinyl groups have been saturated, the product obtained may be polymerized.

Only in the case of addition of one equivalent of diethylamine to (XXII) does the product consists of a solid with a definite melting point[136] (XXIII).

$$CH_2=CHCON\underset{(XXII)}{\overset{COCH=CH_2}{NCOCH=CH_2}} + (C_2H_5)_2NH \xrightarrow{CHCl_3} CH_2=CHCON\underset{(XXIII)\ \text{m.p. }146-149°/\text{Toluene}}{\overset{COCH_2CH_2N(C_2H_5)_2}{NCOCH=CH_2}}$$

1,3,5-Triacylhexahydro-s-triazines with vinyl groups in the side-chains such as methacrylyl, acrylyl, and α-chloroacrylyl have found application[137] as polymeric products alone and copolymerized with styrene. 1,3,5-Trimethacrylylhexahydro-s-triazine shows[138] a slight beneficial effect on Ak_4 mouse leukemia.

XII. Oxo and Thion Derivatives

1. 1-Substituted-4-Oxohexahydro-s-Triazines; 1-Substituted-Hexahydro-s-triazine-4-thion and Derivatives

This group of compounds have in common four characteristics. All are synthesized by the same procedure or a variation thereof, all have either an oxo or a thion group in the 4-position, all have substituents on the 1-position which include alkyl, β-hydroxyethyl, cyclohexyl, and β-dimethylaminoethyl groups, and all are crystalline solids melting over 100°. Two compounds are also included one of which has, in addition, 1,5-diphenyl substitution and the other 2,6-dimethyl-substitution. The compounds are listed in Tables IX-8 A and B.

Both urea and thiourea react with an amine and two equivalents of formaldehyde giving 1-substituted-4-oxo (or thion) hexahydro-s-triazine, respectively[139] (36). This group of compounds has been

TABLE IX-8   A. 1-Substituted-4-oxohexahydro-*s*-triazines and Derivatives

$$\text{HOCH}_2\text{NHCONHCH}_2\text{OH} + \text{RNH}_2 \longrightarrow \begin{array}{c} \text{HN} \diagup \diagdown \text{NR} \\ \bigm| \quad \bigm| \\ \text{O} \diagup \diagdown \underset{\text{H}}{\text{N}} \diagup \end{array} + 2\,\text{H}_2\text{O}$$

R- or Compound	Yield, %	Melting point, °C.	Solvent for recrystallization
CH$_3$	62	210	95 % Ethanol
(CH$_3$)$_2$CHCH$_2$	34	200	Ethyl acetate
HOCH$_2$CH$_2$	57	158	95 % Ethanol
(CH$_3$)$_2$NCH$_2$CH$_2$	36	114	95 % Ethanol

B. 1-Substituted Hexahydro-*s*-triazine-4-thion

$$\text{H}_2\text{N}\overset{\text{S}}{\overset{\|}{\text{C}}}\text{NH}_2 + 2\,\text{CH}_2\text{O} + \text{RNH}_2 \longrightarrow \begin{array}{c} \text{HN} \diagup \diagdown \text{NR} \\ \bigm| \quad \bigm| \\ \text{S} \diagup \diagdown \underset{\text{H}}{\text{N}} \diagup \end{array} + 2\,\text{H}_2\text{O}$$

R- or Compound	Yield, %	Melting point, °C.	Solvent for recrystallization
CH$_3$	69	180	95 % Ethanol
(CH$_3$)$_2$CHCH$_2$	72	139	Trichlorethylene
C$_6$H$_{11}$	85	172	95 % Ethanol
Dodecyl	95	153	95 % Ethanol
HOCH$_2$CH$_2$	50	162	95 % Ethanol
C$_6$H$_5$N⟨NCH$_2$CH$_2$OH, S=⟨N⟩C$_6$H$_5$	72	178	95 % Ethanol
HN⟨CH$_3$⟩NCH$_2$CH$_2$OH, S=⟨N⟩CH$_3$ H	13	168	95 % Ethanol

included in this chapter because it may be regarded as the condensation of formaldehyde with mixed amines, in analogy with the general condensation of aldehydes with ammonia treated earlier. The reaction is

$$\begin{array}{c} \text{CH}_2 \vert \text{O} \quad \text{H} \vert \text{NR} \\ \vert \text{H} \qquad \text{H} \vert \\ \text{HN} \qquad \text{O} \vert \text{CH}_2 \\ \text{O} \diagup \diagdown \underset{\text{H}}{\text{N}} \vert \text{H} \end{array} \longrightarrow \begin{array}{c} \text{R} \\ \text{N} \\ \diagup \diagdown \\ \text{HN} \quad \text{NH} \\ \diagdown \diagup \\ \text{O} \end{array} + 2\,\text{H}_2\text{O} \qquad (36)$$

general. It can be applied to substituted amines such as ethanolamine and N,N-dimethylethylenediamine, or urea and formaldehyde can be conveniently replaced by dimethylolurea, $CH_2OHNHCOHNCH_2OH$. Thiourea reacts even more readily then urea (at room temperature compared to 70–100°); even 1,3-diphenylurea will undergo condensation. Acetaldehyde can replace formaldehyde. The structure of the condensation product obtained from thiourea is based on the analogous behavior of urea and thiourea toward acetaldehyde and ammonia.

Tables IX-8 A and B contain the yields and physical data on condensations of the type illustrated above.

2. 1,5-Di-*p*-tolyl-3-phenyl-4-oxohexahydro-*s*-triazine (XXIV)

This compound was made by Ingold and Piggott[140] in 1923. It is a crystalline solid melting at 148° when crystallized from benzene-ligroin. Formaldehyde and *p*-toluidine form a dimer, 1,3-di-*p*-tolyl-cyclobutane, at 45°. If the dimer is treated at 100° with phenyl isocyanate, a transformation (37) occurs giving (XXIV).

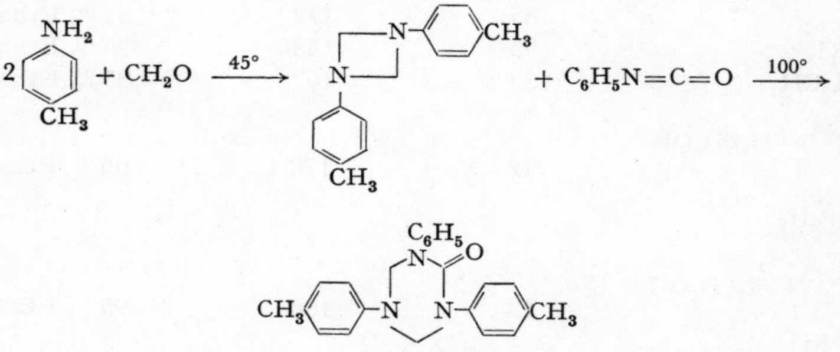

(37)

(XXIV)

1,3-Di-*p*-tolyl-5-phenyl-4-oxohexahydro-*s*-triazine (XXIV) has weakly basic properties and shows the instability to acids displayed by other 1,3,5-triarylhexahydro-*s*-triazines, decomposing to a mixture of formaldehyde, *p*-toluidine and phenyl-*p*-tolylurea (38).

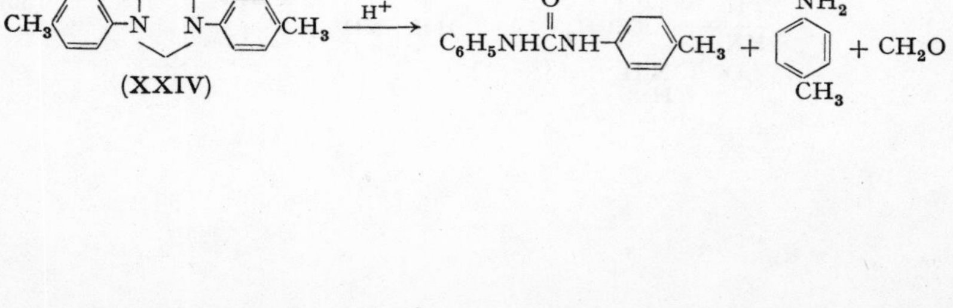

(38)

(XXIV)

XIII. Carboxylic acid derivatives

1. Esters

1,3,5-Tricarbethoxyhexahydro-*s*-triazine (XXV) is a crystalline solid melting at 101–102° upon recrystallization from ligroin.[141]

Compounds containing amino groups as well as other functional groups are often found to react with formaldehyde. The preparation of (XXV) furnished an additional example of such a condensation. Thus urethane condenses[141] with formaldehyde undoubtedly first forming the usual monomeric intermediate which then trimerizes to (XXV).

$$3\ H_2NCOOC_2H_5 + 3\ CH_2O \longrightarrow 3\ [CH_2{=}NCOOC_2H_5] \longrightarrow$$
$$+\ 3\ H_2O$$

$$\begin{array}{c} COOC_2H_5 \\ N \\ C_2H_5OOCN \qquad NCOOC_2H_5 \end{array}$$

(XXV)

2. Amides (Triazinylacetamides)

A. *1,3,5-Tri(carbamylmethyl)hexahydro-s-triazine (XXVI)*

Compound (XXVI) melts at 162° upon recrystallization from methyl alcohol.[143] It can be prepared in 82 % yield by the condensation of formaldehyde and aminoacetamide (39).

$$3\ NH_2CH_2COONH_2 + 3\ CH_2O \longrightarrow$$

$$\begin{array}{c} CH_2CONH_2 \\ N \\ NH_2COCH_2N \qquad NCH_2CONH_2 \end{array} +\ 3\ H_2O \quad (39)$$

(XXVI)

B. *1,3,5-Tri(N-methylcarbamylmethyl)-* *hexahydro-s-triazine*

1,3,5-Tri[*N*-methylcarbamylmethyl]hexahydro-*s*-triazine, which melts at 167.5–169° when recrystallized from butanol, is prepared in a manner quite analogous to the synthesis above of 1,3,5-tricarbethoxy-hexahydro-*s*-triazine (XXVI). Glycylmethylamide reacts[141] with form-aldehyde. The intermediate methyleneimine can be isolated before it trimerizes, if desired.

One of the theories of formation of urea-formaldehyde resins involves the hexahydro-*s*-triazine structure.[141] In the condensation, urea is thought to behave as an amino acid amide. The amino portion condenses with formaldehyde to give a methylene imine which trimerizes, while the amide group reacts with formaldehyde to yield methylene bis-amide links between the rings. This results is a crosslinked polymer (XXVIII).

XIV. 1-Sulfo-4-alkylhexahydro-2,4,6-Triazines

This group consists of a number of compounds, listed in Table IX-9, all of which are prepared[142] by the reaction of formaldehyde and

$$CH_2O + RNH_2 + (NH_2)_2SO_2 \xrightarrow{30°} \quad \overset{\overset{\displaystyle O_2}{\underset{\displaystyle |}{S}}}{HN \diagdown NH} \qquad (40)$$

an alkylamine with either sulfamide or a mono or symmetrically disubstituted sulfamide (40).

TABLE IX-9.　　1-Sulfo-4-alkylhexahydro-2,4,6-triazines

4-Substituent	Melting point, °C.	Yield, %
—CH$_3$	185–186 (dec.)	66
—C$_3$H$_7$	134	78
—C$_4$H$_9$	120	86
(cyclohexyl)	155	84
—CH$_2$CH$_2$OH	Soft, amorphous solid obtained from ethyl hydroxylamine	—

These compounds are weak bases. They form salts with many different substances including weak acids, but are decomposed by mineral acids.

Acetate and benzoate esters of the β-hydroxyethyl compound are known as is a benzyl ether prepared from the chloride. All three derivatives are amorphous, soft solids.

References

1. P. Duden and M. Scarf, *Ann.*, **288**, 218 (1895).
2. L. Henry, *Bull. Acad. Belg.*, (3), **26**, 200 (1893).
3. H. Richmond, S. Myers and G. Wright, *J. Am. Chem. Soc.*, **70**, 3659 (1949).
4. A. Vroom and C. Winkler, *Can. J. Research*, **28B**, 701 (1950).
5. P. Horvath and L. Stein, *Hungar.*, **133**, 835 (1947), through *Chem. Abstracts*, **45**, 4874 (1951).
6. L. Kahovec, *Z. physik. Chem.*, **B43**, 364 (1939).
7. A. Brochet and R. Cambier, *Compt. rend.* **120**, 452 (1895).
8. R. Cambier and A. Brochet, *Bull. soc. chim.*, (3), **13**, 404 (1895).
9. P. Duden and M. Scharff, *Ber.*, **28**, 936 (1895).
10. L. Henry, *Bull. Acad. Belg.*, (3), **29**, 23 (1895).
11. F. Scheffer, *Z. physik. Chem.*, **72**, 466 (1910).
12. J. Brühl, *Ph. Ch.*, **22**, 381.
13. A. Einhorn and A. Prettner, *Ann.*, **334**, 210 (1904).
14. K. Hock, *Ger.*, 139,394 (1903).
15. F. Klager, F. Kircher and M. Bock, *Ann.*, **547**, 23 (1941).
16. R. Blundell and J. Graymore, *J. Chem. Soc.*, **1939**, 1787.
17. J. Graymore, *J. Chem. Soc.*, **1941**, 39.
18. J. Graymore, *J. Chem. Soc.*, **1935**, 865.
19. S. Gurin, A. Deluva and D. Crandell, *J. Org. Chem.*, **12**, 612 (1947).
20. J. Graymore, *J. Chem. Soc.*, **1932**, 1353.
21. A. Franchimont and H. Van Erp, *Rec. trav. chim.*, **15**, 66 (1896).
22. M. Delepine, *Bull. soc. chim.*, (3), **15**, 889 (1896).
23. M. Delepine, *Ann. chim. phys.*, (7), **9**, 119 (1896).
24. P. Knudsen, *Ger.* 143,197 (1902).
25. A. Schnitzer, *Dissertation*, Oklahoma A. and M. College, 1951.
26. D. Fisher, R. Newton, R. Norman and J. Scott, *J. Rubber Research*, **17**, 161 (1948).
27. M. Dominekiewicz, *Arch. Chem. Farm.*, **2**, 160 (1935), through *Chem. Abstracts*, **30**, 1030 (1936).
28. R. Jay and T. Curtius, *Ber.*, **27**, 59 (1894).
29. A. Klages, *J. prakt. Chem.*, (2), **65**, 192 (1902).
30. A. Klages, *Ber.*, **36**, 1506 (1903).
31. H. Rinehart and T. Johnson, *J. Am. Chem. Soc.*, **46**, 1653 (1924).
32. T. Johnson and H. Rinehart, *J. Am. Chem. Soc.*, **46**, 768 (1924).
33. R. Adams and W. Langley, *Organic Synthesis, Coll. Vol.*, **I**, 2nd Ed., John Wiley and Sons, New York, 1946, p. 355.
34. R. Jay and T. Curtius, *Ber.*, **31**, 2490 (1898).
35. H. Rinehart, *J. Am. Chem. Soc.*, **48**, 2794 (1926).

36. J. Bailey and D. Snyder, *J. Am. Chem. Soc.*, **37**, 935 (1915).
37. J. Bailey and L. Lochte, *J. Am. Chem. Soc.*, **39**, 2443 (1917).
38. A. Paquin, *Ber.*, **82**, 316 (1949).
39. A. Einhorn and A. Prettner, *Ber.*, **35**, 2942 (1902).
40. B. Tollens, *Ber.*, **17**, 657 (1884).
41. E. Paterno, *Gazz. chim. ital.*, **14**, 351 (1884).
42. J. Miller and E. Wagner, *J. Am. Chem. Soc.*, **54**, 3698 (1932).
43. C. Bischoff, *Ber.*, **31**, 3248 (1899).
44. C. Eberhardt, and A. Welter, *Ber.*, **27**, 1804 (1894).
45. L. Hartung, *J. prakt. Chem.*, (2), **46**, 19 (1892).
46. J. Curtius and A. Darapsky, *J. prakt. Chem.*, (2), **63**, 428 (1901).
47. J. Houben and H. Arnold, *Ber.*, **41**, 1577 (1908).
48. C. Goldschmidt, *Chem. Z.*, **28**, 1229 (1904).
49. Ger. 157,617 (1904) to Badische Anilin & Soda Fabrik.
50. A. Senier and F. Shepheard, *J. Chem. Soc.*, **95**, 504 (1909).
51. Ger. 109,498 (1900) to Meister, Lucius and Brüning.
52. Ger. 132,621 (1902) to Badische Anilin and Soda Fabrik.
53. W. von Miller and J. Plöchl, *Ber.*, **31**, 2708 (1899).
54. E. Gartner and A. Kock, U. S. 2,365,405 (1944).
55. C. Eberhardt and A. Welter, *Ber.*, **27**, 1804 (1894).
56. C. Bischoff and F. Reinfeld, *Ber.*, **36**, 41 (1903).
57. A. Eibner, *Ann.*, **302**, 335 (1898).
58. E. Wagner and J. Simons, *J. Chem. Ed.*, **13**, 265 (1936).
59. M. Sprung, *Chem. Revs.*, **26**, 297 (1940).
60. W. von Miller and J. Plöchl, *Ber.*, **25**, 2020 (1892).
61. F. Ullmann and E. Naef, *Ber.*, **33**, 1905 (1900).
62. F. Ullmann, Ger. 117,472 (1900).
63. Ger. 53,937 (1890) to Meister, Lucius and Brüning.
64. Ger. 67,013 (1893) to Meister, Lucius and Brüning.
65. S. Angyal, D. Penman and G. Warwick, *J. Chem. Soc.*, **1953**, 742.
66. C. Smith, *J. Chem. Soc.*, **85**, 732 (1904).
67. H. Kahn et al., *J. Chem. Soc.*, **1945**, 858.
68. J. Graymore, *J. Chem. Soc.*, **1947**, 1116.
69. F. Mayer and F. English, *Ann.*, **417**, 60 (1918).
70. C. Eberhardt and A. Welter, *Ber.*, **27**, 1804 (1894).
71. B. Reichert and W. Domis, *Arch. Pharm.*, **282**, 109 (1944), through *Chem. Abstracts*, **45**, 1969 (1951).
71a. H. Schultz and H. Wagner, *Angew. Chem.*, **62**, 105 (1950).
72. H. Hartough, S. Meisel, E. Kopf and J. Schick, *J. Am. Chem. Soc.*, **70**, 4013 (1948).
73. H. Hartough, J. Schick and J. Dickert, *J. Am. Chem. Soc.*, **72**, 1572 (1950).
74. Ger. 290,808 (1916) to F. Bayer and Co.
75. O. Aschan, *Ber.*, **48**, 874 (1915).
76. C. Harries and G. Lenart, *Ann.*, **410**, 100 (1915).
77. J. Graymore and D. Davies, *J. Chem. Soc.*, **1945**, 293.
78. M. Delepine, *Bull. soc. chim.*, (4), **9**, 1025 (1911).
79. M. Lindsay and F. Saper, *J. Chem. Soc.*, **1946**, 791.
80. M. Delepine, *Bull. soc. chim.*, (4), **1**, 590 (1907).
81. M. Delepine, *Bull. soc. chim.*, (3), **21**, 58 (1899).
82. M. Delepine, *Compt. rend.*, **128**, 105 (1899).
83. A. Chichibabin and M. Shchukina, *Ber.*, **62B**, 1075 (1929).
84. R. Schiff, *Gazz. chim. ital.*, **21**, 492 (1891).

85. A. Behal and Choay, *Ann. phys. chim.*, (6), **26**, 1 (1892).
86. M. Nencki and F. Schaffer, *J. prakt. Chem.*, (2), **18**, 430 (1878).
87. P. Duden and M. Scharff, *Ann.*, **288**, 223 (1895).
88. F. Mayer, *Ber.*, **21**, 2883 (1888).
89. M. Delepine and M. Badoche, *Compt. rend.*, **214**, 777 (1942).
90. P. Knudsen, *Ber.*, **47**, 2698 (1914).
91. A. Vroom and C. Winkler, *Can. J. Research*, **28B**, 701 (1950).
91a. C. Holstead, A. Lamberton and P. Wyatt, *J. Chem. Soc.*, **1953**, 3341.
92. Henning, Ger. 104,280 (1899).
93. A. Belyaev, *J. Phys. Chem.*, **22**, 91 (1948), through *Chem. Abstracts*, **42**, 5227 (1948).
94. N. Jones and G. Thorn, *Can. J. Research*, **27B**, 828 (1949).
95. F. Gaelli and G. Racciu, *Atti. Acad. Lincei*, **16**, 54 (1932); through *Chem. Abstracts*, **27**, 2370 (1933).
96. G. Wright, H. Richmond and D. Downing, U. S. 2,434,879 (1948), to Council Scientific and Industrial Res., Ottawa, Canada; through *Chem. Abstracts*, **42**, 9180 (1948).
97. R. Schiesler and J. Ross, U. S. 2,434,230 (1948); through *Chem. Abstracts*, **42**, 2292 (1948).
98. F. Chapman, *J. Chem. Soc.*, **1949**, 1631.
99. E. von Herz, Brit. 145,791 (1920).
100. D. Nobel, Fr. 736,591 (1932).
101. V. Gilpin and C. Winkler, *Can. J. Chem.*, **30**, 743 (1952).
102. W. Crater, *Ind. Eng. Chem.*, **40**, 1627 (1948).
103. W. Binnie, H. Cohen and G. Wright, *J. Am. Chem. Soc.*, **72**, 4457 (1950).
104. L. Medard and M. Thomas, *Mem. poudres*, **31**, 173 (1949); through *Chem. Abstracts*, **46**, 11684 (1952).
105. F. Brockman, D. Downing and G. Wright, *Can. J. Research*, **27B**, 469 (1949).
106. J. Burttle, U. S. 2,418,733 (1947) to Olin Industries.
107. T. Urbanski, *Roczniki Chem.*, **21**, 120 (1947); through *Chem. Abstracts*, **42**, 4856 (1948).
108. F. Somlo, *Z. Schiess-u Sprengstoffw.*, **35**, 175 (1940); through *Chem. Abstracts*, **35**, 349 (1941).
109. C. Holstead and A. Lamberton, *J. Chem. Soc.*, **1952**, 1886.
110. G. Wright and W. Allan, U. S. 2,439,328 (1948) to Imperial Chemical Industries; through *Chem. Abstracts*, **42**, 4359 (1948).
111. R. Sklyanahaya and F. Pozhariskii, *Farmakol. i Tokikol.*, **3**, 43 (1944); through *Chem. Abstracts*, **39**, 3073 (1945).
112. K. Dunning and W. Dunning, *J. Chem. Soc.*, **1950**, 2920.
113. K. Dunning and W. Dunning, *J. Chem. Soc.*, **1950**, 2925.
114. K. Dunning and W. Dunning, *J. Chem. Soc.*, **1950**, 2928.
115. G. Wright et al., *Can. J. Research*, **27B**, 218 (1949).
116. W. Chute et al., *Can. J. Research*, **27B**, 503 (1949).
117. W. Schroeder et al., *Anal. Chem.*, **23**, 1740 (1951).
118. F. Chapman, *J. Chem. Soc.*, **1949**, 1638.
119. F. Chapman, P. Owston, and D. Woodcock, *J. Chem. Soc.* **2950**, 1647.
120. M. Delepine, *Compt. rend.*, **144**, 853 (1907).
121. R. Stollé, *Ber.*, **40**, 1505 (1907).
122. R. Stollé, *Ber.*, **44**, 1134 (1911).
123. O. Diels and E. Borgwordt, *Ber.*, **54B**, 1334 (1921).
124. R. Wegler and A. Ballauf, *Ber.*, **81**, 527 (1948).
125. C. Hug, *Bull. soc. chim.*, (5), **1**, 1004 (1934).

126. V. Nadkarny, S. Bhatnager, A. Kothare and F. Fernandes, *Current Sci. (India)*, **18**, 441 (1949).
127. R. Scholl, *Ber.*, **24**, 573 (1891).
128. N. Dunstan and E. Goulding, *J. Chem. Soc.*, **71**, 573 (1897).
129. W. Dunstan and A. Bossi, *J. Chem. Soc.*, **73**, 353 (1898).
130. M. Gradsten and M. Pollock, *J. Am. Chem. Soc.*, **70**, 3079 (1948).
131. T. Gresham and T. Steadman, *J. Am. Chem. Soc.*, **71**, 1872 (1949).
132. C. Price and L. Krishnamurti, *J. Am. Chem. Soc.*, **72**, 5334 (1950).
133. W. Emmons, H. Rolewicz, W. Cannon and R. Ross, *J. Am. Chem. Soc.*, **74**, 5524 (1952).
134. W. Teeters and M. Gradsten, *Org. Syntheses*, **30**, 51 (1950).
135. P. B. 73894, frames 5769–5778.
136. E. Zerner and M. Pollock, U. S. 2,615,889 (1952) to Sun Chemical Corp.
137. E. Zerner and M. Gradsten, U. S. 2,559,694 (1951) to Sun Chemical Corp.
138. J. Burchenal, S. Johnston, M. Cremer, L. Webber and C. Stock, *Proc. Soc. Exptl. Biol. Med.*, **74**, 708 (1950).
139. W. Burke, *J. Am. Chem. Soc.*, **69**, 2136 (1947).
140. C. Ingold and H. Piggott, *J. Chem. Soc.*, **1923**, 2745.
141. C. Marvel, J. Elliot, F. Boettner and H. Yuska, *J. Am. Chem. Soc.*, **68**, 1681 (1946).
142. A. Paquin, *Angew. Chem.*, **A60**, 316 (1948); through *Chem. Abstracts*, **43**, 2573 (1951).
143. A. Davis and A. Levy, *J. Chem. Soc.*, **1951**, 3479.

CHAPTER X

Hexamethylenetetramine

I. Introduction

Since the first recorded synthesis of hexamethylenetetramine in 1859 by Butlerow[1] and his demonstration[2] that the empirical formula was $C_6H_{12}N_4$, a tremendous number of salts, molecular compounds, and coordination complexes of hexamethylenetetramine involving a large majority of the elements and innumerable organic compounds have appeared in the literature. Pertinent information on these substances, some of the chemistry of hexamethylenetetramine, and a great deal of valuable information on the industrial and physiological uses of the substance are already available in book form.[3,4,4a] For this reason, Chapter X will deal briefly with the older chemistry, not at all comprehensively with the compounds or uses, but rather carefully with more recent developments in the organic chemistry of hexamethylenetetramine.

Hexamethylenetetramine is also known by the names hexamine, aminoform, formin, hexamethyleneamine, urotropine in the older literature, and methenamine in pharmaceutical usage. It is a tertiary amine and shows the properties of a monoacidic base in its salt formation.

II. Structure

The structures which have been offered by investigators to explain the chemical reactions of hexamethylenetetramine are considerably varied. Structures postulated by Butlerow,[2] Lösekann,[5] Guareschi,[6] Duden and Scharff,[7] van 't Hoff,[8] Cohn[9] and Dominikiewicz[10] are shown.

The Duden and Scharff structure is commonly accepted[11] and is in closest agreement with the experimental facts. X-ray data substantiate this representation and indicate[12] that hexamethylenetetramine in

545

solid crystalline form has a structure in which each carbon atom is surrounded by four atoms at least two of which, nitrogen atoms, are approximately at the vertices of a regular tetrahedron. Each nitrogen

$$N(N{<}^{CH_2}_{CH_2})_3$$

Butlerow

$$N{-}^{CH_2N=CH_2}_{CH_2N=CH_2}$$ with $CH_2N=CH_2$

Lösekann

Guareschi

$$CH_2{=}C{-}CHCH(NH_2)CH(NH_2)CH=NH$$ with $\underset{H}{N}$

Cohn

Duden-Scharff

van 't Hoff

Dominikiewicz

atom is equidistant from three carbon atoms, but is not in the same plane as the carbon atoms. The minimum N–C distance is 1.44 Å. Thus the structure is shown[13] to be a combination of a four-membered nitrogen tetrahedron with a six-membered carbon hexahedron. Spatially,[a] it can be represented by the figure of Dickinson and Raymond.[14] This structure is undoubtedly a true picture of hexamethylenetetramine in the crystalline state and alone in neutral or basic solution, but the influence of hydrogen ions and various reagents and the fact that the compound acts as a monoacidic base can be better explained by the Lösekann structure which may enjoy a transitory existence, particularly in the formation of simple salts.

III. Formation

Hexamethylenetetramine formation from formaldehyde and ammonia in aqueous solution proceeds rapidly and essentially to completion according to equation (1)

$$6\,CH_2O + 4\,NH_3 \longrightarrow (CH_2)_6N_4 + 6\,H_2O \tag{1}$$

at temperatures of 0–50° in the presence of excess formaldehyde or

[a] A full discussion of the spatial configuration of hexamethylenetetramine is presented in R. Reinicke, *Zeit. Krist.*, **87**, 417 (1934); *Chem. Abstracts*, **28**, 6605 (1934).

ammonia. The mechanism of the formation may involve several paths,[15] but it is likely that the following one is predominant:

$$3\,CH_2O + 3\,NH_3 \xrightarrow{\text{fast}} 3CH_2=NH + 3\,H_2O \tag{1}$$

$$3\,CH_2 = NH \xrightarrow{\text{fast}} \text{(structure)} \tag{2}$$

Hexahydro-s-triazine

$$\text{(structure)} + 3\,CH_2O \xrightarrow{\text{slow}} \text{(structure)} \tag{3}$$

1,3,5-Trimethylolhexahydro-s-triazine

$$\text{(structure)} + NH_3 \xrightarrow{\text{slow or fast}} (CH_2)_6N_4 + 3\,H_2O \tag{4}$$
$$\text{(I)}$$

The synthesis reaction is considered by Baur and Ruetschi[15] to be third order with an initial uptake of two moles of formaldehyde to one of ammonia, a view which is consistent with the third or rate determining step plus the first two very fast steps. It has been shown that the final step of the reaction is not measurably reversible in alkaline media.[16] Evidence for the above mechanism is strong. Freshly prepared mixtures of formaldehyde and ammonia behave differently than hexamethylenetetramine (I) solutions. The latter forms 1,5-endomethylene-3,7-di-(m-nitrobenzenediazo)-1,3,5,7-tetrazocyclooctane (II) by reaction with diazotized m-nitroaniline while freshly prepared ammonia-formaldehyde mixtures do not. Hexamethylenetetramine gives 1,3,5-tribenzoyl-1,3,5-triazapentane (III) with benzoyl chloride, while the ammonia-formaldehyde mixture gives only a trace of compound (III) and mostly 1,3,5-tribenzoylhexahydro-s-triazine (IV).

Both starting solutions give 1,3,5-trinitrosohexahydro-s-triazine (V) with nitric acid but the yield from hexamethylenetetramine is only one half that obtained from the Duden-Scharff solution[1,2] of formaldehyde, ammonia and sodium chloride. These relationships are illustrated in (2). Henry solution,[17] which is merely a more concentrated formaldehyde-ammonia mixture containing potassium carbonate, will give small amounts of methylene-bis-benzamide in addition to 1,3,5-

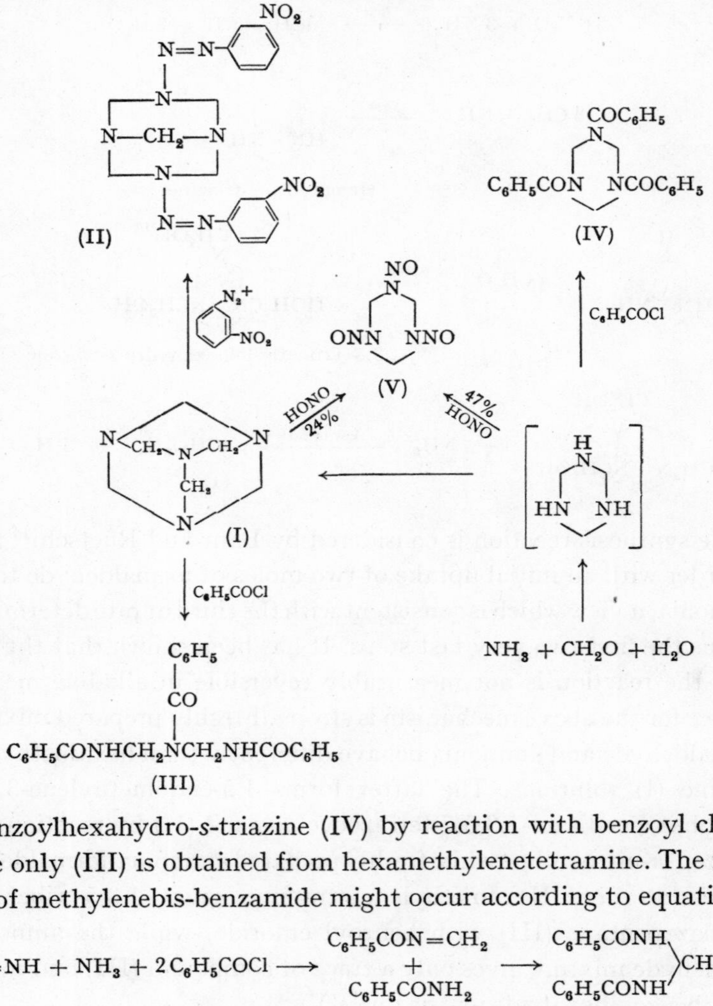

tribenzoylhexahydro-s-triazine (IV) by reaction with benzoyl chloride while only (III) is obtained from hexamethylenetetramine. The formation of methylenebis-benzamide might occur according to equation (3),

$$CH_2=NH + NH_3 + 2\,C_6H_5COCl \longrightarrow \begin{matrix} C_6H_5CON=CH_2 \\ + \\ C_6H_5CONH_2 \end{matrix} \longrightarrow \begin{matrix} C_6H_5CONH \\ \diagdown \\ C_6H_5CONH \diagup \end{matrix} CH_2 \quad (3)$$

or from methylenediamine which might be found according to reaction (4) and

$$24\,CH_2=NH \rightleftharpoons 8\,(CH_2=NH)_3 \longrightarrow 3\,C_6H_{12}N_4 + 6\,NH_2CH_2NH_2 \quad (4)$$

evidence for which has been obtained[16] in the form of its sulfate salt. Although no hexamethylenetetramine can be isolated from the acidic filtrate of this salt, reaction (4) is not impossible in weakly acid or neutral solution. Indications are that hexahydro-s-triazine tends to decompose into methylenediamine and the elements of hexamethylenetetramine. These fragments recombine to give hexamethylenetetramine. Evidence for the postulated third order kinetics of the formation of hexamethylenetetramine is on less certain ground. It is difficult to reconcile the considerable difference in rate between formation of hexahydro-s-triazine and its subsequent conversion[16] to hexamethylenetetramine with the third order kinetics of Baur and Ruetschi.[15]

Ammonium salts as well as free ammonia react with formaldehyde to form hexamethylenetetramine. The reaction appears to be general with both the rate and yield increasing with pH. At a given buffered pH, most ammonium salts give the same rates and yields. Higher temperatures or excess formaldehyde increase the formation of stable by-product. As a result of an investigation[18] of the mechanism and scope of this method of synthesis, the mechanism in (4) was suggested.

$$
\mathrm{CH_2O + NH_3 \rightleftharpoons HOCH_2NH_2 \xrightarrow{\;CH_2O\;} CH_2NH_2 + HCOOH} \tag{4}
$$

$$
\mathrm{CH_2O} \Big\Updownarrow
$$

$$
\mathrm{HOCH_2NHCH_2OH \xrightleftharpoons{\;NH_3\;} OHCH_2NHCH_2NH_2 + H_2O}
$$

$$
\Big\Updownarrow \mathrm{CH_2O}
$$

$$
\text{Hexamethylenetetramine} \rightleftharpoons \mathrm{HOCH_2NHCH_2NHCH_2OH}
$$

+   Hemi-hexamethylenetetramine
H$_2$O   (methylol form)

The experimental fact that hexamethylenetetramine formation is more sensitive to the concentration of formaldehyde than to the concentration of ammonia has been interpreted as an indication that the reaction between formaldehyde and primary amino groups is rate determining. From scheme (4) it is apparent that if formaldehyde were to react with methylolamine in an oxidation-reduction reaction, methylamine and formic acid would result. Furthermore, if it is considered that the methylolamine reacts with ammonia instead of with formaldehyde, methylenediamine would result which could then react with formaldehyde also to give hemi-hexamethylenetetramine.

The view has been expressed[19] that hexamethylenetetramine

exists as an entity only as a solid and its solutions are made up of a series of products similar to the above intermediates in equilibrium with ammonia and formaldehyde, with the equilibrium far in the direction of hexamethylenetetramine in all but acidic solutions.

The reaction of formaldehyde and ammonium nitrate in glacial acetic acid to form hexamethylenetetramine has been studied kinetically[20]. Rate curves at temperatures of 25°, 35°, 45° and 55° were determined over a range of initial mole ratios of formaldehyde to ammonia of from 0.75:1 to 9.0:1 for reaction (5).

$$6\,CH_2O + 4\,NH_4NO_3 \longrightarrow (CH_2)_6N_4 + 6\,H_2O + 4\,HNO_3 \tag{5}$$

At 25° there is a definite induction period for hexamethylenetetramine formation, the length of which is not changed by increasing the ammonium nitrate concentration above the theoretical 1.5:1, but which may be shortened by initial addition of excess formaldehyde or sodium acetate. Above 35°, no inhibition period is apparent.

A new continuous commercial process for hexamethylenetetramine production, which allows the direct addition of the formaldehyde and the ammonia in the gaseous phase to the reactor, has recently been described.[15a]

IV. Physical Properties

Hexamethylenetetramine is a colorless, odorless compound which crystallizes in rhombic dodecahedrons[21] ordinarily without water of crystallization. It sublimes without melting when heated; in a sealed tube decomposition occurs above 280°. Hexamethylenetetramine is readily soluble in water—about 45 % at 50°—forming weakly basic solutions of pH 8–8.5. It is interesting to note that this solubility is a reverse function of temperature,[22] a property possessed by some other tertiary amines and due to decreasing association with water as the temperature increases. It is somewhat soluble in the lower alcohols,[23] only slightly soluble in most organic solvents[23] but about 13 % soluble in chloroform,[23] which therefore is the solvent most commonly used for organic reactions.

Ammonia rapidly decreases the solubility of hexamethylenetetramine in water,[24] a fact which enables very pure material[25] to be readily prepared. Ammonia is added to aqueous hexamethylenetetramine solutions and the precipitate filtered.

Hexamethylenetetramine is stable in water at room temperature, a stability which is increased by the addition of small amounts of a weak base, decreased slightly at higher temperatures, and rapidly decreased with lower pH's. For example, hydrolysis of hexamethylenetetramine to ammonia and formaldehyde is complete[26] in six hours in the presence of 0.1 N hydrochloric acid, the rate being a direct function of the hydrogen ion concentration[26] in acid solutions. From a series of determinations of the freezing point lowering of solutions of hexamethylenetetramine with acids, it has been shown[27] that the immediate reaction of acid is one of addition and that only later does the hydrolytic action of the hydrogen ion predominate with increasing hydrolysis (6).

$$(CH_2)_6H_4 + 4\,HCl + 6\,H_2O \longrightarrow 4\,NH_4Cl + 6\,CH_2O \qquad (6)$$

Relative intensities of the Raman lines characteristic of bases and their hydrochlorides make possible demonstration of the effect[28] of hydrolysis in solutions of the hydrochlorides of weak bases such as urea and hexamethylenetetramine. The results indicate that the latter is even a weaker base than urea.

V. Preparation

Hexamethylenetetramine is prepared almost quantitatively by the reaction of ammonia with aqueous formaldehyde.[29] A slight excess of ammonia must be used to avoid the formation of trimethylamine. The reaction may be carried out as readily in the gas phase,[30] again in nearly quantitative yields.

As mentioned in the preceding Section III, hexamethylenetetramine can be prepared from formaldehyde and most ammonium salts.[18,31] This reaction is a general one. Ammonium carbonate gives a pure product in 66% yield. Passing carbon dioxide into ammonium carbonate in 10% less than theoretical amounts and treating the resulting bicarbonate with formaldehyde has been recommended as giving excellent results.[32] The product is concentrated under reduced pressure on a water bath. Other ammonium salts that have been tried include the acetate, nitrate, hydrogen phosphate, sulfate and oxalate.

Other less important methods of preparing hexamethylenetetramine include oxidation of methane in a mixture with ammonia by means of a visible non-dampened discharge of high tension, high frequency alternating current,[33],[34] or by means of oxygen over oxidation catalysts;[35] passing carbon monoxide, hydrogen and ammonia at a temperature of 250–280° over reduced nickel on diatomaceous earth;[36] and by reaction of ammonia and methylene chloride,[37],[38] a reaction in which large amounts of ammonia are converted to ammonium chloride (7).

$$6 CH_2Cl_2 + 16 NH_3 \longrightarrow (CH_2)_6N_4 + 12 NH_4Cl + 6 H_2 \qquad (7)$$

VI. Reactions

Hexamethylenetetramine functions in a great many instances as a source of formaldehyde which then reacts as if it had been added initially. The other general characteristic of hexamethylenetetramine in reactions is its function as a tertiary amine. The following series of reactions are grouped according to the reagents or reactants acting on hexamethylenetetramine. The inorganic substances are followed by the organic reactants.

1. Reactions with Inorganic Compounds

A. Hydrolysis

When hexamethylenetetramine is heated with aqueous solutions of strong acids, hydrolysis occurs[7],[39-43] at a rate which is dependent on the temperature and on the acid strength. The reaction (8) is quantitative and is the basis of numerous methods of analysis for hexamethylenetetramine, usually involving the use of sulfuric acid.

$$C_6H_{12}N_4 + 2 H_2SO_4 + 6 H_2O \longrightarrow 2 (NH_4)_2SO_4 + 6 CH_2O \qquad (8)$$

If prolonged heating with hydrochloric acid is carried out, methylamine is obtained[43] undoubtedly either by an oxidation-reduction reaction involving methylolamine hydrochloride and formaldehyde (8, 9) or involving methyleneimine and formaldehyde (10). Thus, when hexamethylenetetramine hydrolyzes, the resulting ammonia and formaldehyde may recombine. The overall reaction with

$$CH_2O + NH_4Cl \longrightarrow HOCH_2NH_2 \cdot HCl \qquad (8)$$

$$HOCH_2NH_2 \cdot HCl + CH_2O \longrightarrow CH_3NH_2 \cdot HCl + HCOOH \qquad (9)$$

or $\quad CH_2{=}NH \cdot HCl + CH_2O + H_2O \longrightarrow CH_3NH_2 \cdot HCl + HCOOH \qquad (10)$

hydrochloric acid proceeds with the evolution of carbon dioxide (11):

$$C_6H_{12}N_4 + HCl + H_2O \longrightarrow 4CH_3NH_2 \cdot HCl + 2CO_2 \tag{11}$$

B. Reduction

Reduction of hexamethylenetetramine with zinc in either acid,[44,45] or alkaline media[46] gives ammonia and trimethylamine as principal products with smaller amounts of methylamine and dimethylamine. Electrolytic reduction gives similar results[47] with larger proportions of the primary and secondary amines. A mechanism postulated[45] for the reduction, at least in the case of zinc and hydrochloric acid is as follows:

$$(CH_2)_6N_4 \xrightarrow[\text{Zn + HCl}]{(H)} \begin{bmatrix} H \\ N \\ HN \quad NH \end{bmatrix} + N(CH_3)_3$$

$$(I) \qquad\qquad\qquad\qquad (II)$$

$$\begin{bmatrix} H \\ N \\ HN \quad NH \end{bmatrix} + 3\,CH_2O \longrightarrow 3\,CH_2O + 3\,NH_3$$

$$(II)$$

$$CH_2O + NH_3 \longrightarrow (CH_2{=}NH) + H_2O$$

Reduction of the methyleneimine would give methylamine, while condensation of the latter with formaldehyde followed by reduction gives the secondary amine.

$$CH_2{=}NH \xrightarrow{(H)} CH_3NH_2$$

$$CH_3NH_2 + CH_2O \longrightarrow CH_3N{=}CH_2 + H_2O$$

$$CH_3N{=}CH_2 \xrightarrow{(H)} (CH_3)_2NH$$

It is certain that none of the amine comes from the reaction of formaldehyde with more hexamethylenetetramine (I) since when the picrate salt of (I) was treated with formaldehyde, the only product obtained was dimethylpentamethylenetetramine picrate and no methylamines. Sodamide has no action on hexamethylenetetramine.[48]

C. Reaction with Hydrogen Peroxide

Two major products may be obtained from the reaction of hexamethylenetetramine and hydrogen peroxide. When (I) is treated with

30% hydrogen peroxide in the presence of considerable quantities of acid, formation of the primary explosive, hexamethylenetriperoxide-diamine, HMTD, (VI) occurs in almost quantitative yield.[49-53] Aqueous formaldehyde and ammonia give the same peroxide (VI) when heated with hydrogen peroxide at 55°. Compound (VI) is soluble in benzene, acetic acid, chloroform and ethyl acetate, from which beautiful crystals may be obtained.[54] The crystals are extremely subject to detonation in a dry state. Hot water or hot dilute acids[54] decompose (VI) with evolution of formaldehyde while with hot bases, ammonia is evolved. The mechanism of formation of (VI) may well proceed in a

$$2 \text{ (I)} + 3 \text{ H}_2\text{O}_2 \text{ (30\%)} \xrightarrow{\text{HOAc}} \text{(VI)} + 6 \text{ (CH}_2\text{=NH)}$$

fashion similar to that of the acid catalyzed decomposition of hexa-methylenetetramine, with the trimethylamine portion participating in the peroxide formation according to Marotta and Alessandrini.[49] From the filtrate on treatment with benzoyl chloride and alkali, was isolated 1,3,5-tribenzoylhexahydro-s-triazine (IV). This would apparently substantiate the mechanism, but the yield of the triperoxide is stated to be 100%, and whether the basis used is one mole or two moles of hexa-methylenetetramine is not clear. It would be necessary that the inter-mediate by-product in the decomposition mechanism, the hypothetical hexahydro-s-triazine (II), serve as a source for the formation of some of the triperoxide inasmuch as only a trace of (IV) can be obtained. It is further reported that a substance with the same properties as hexa-methylenetriperoxidediamine may be obtained from "trioxytrimethyl-amine" and 30% hydrogen peroxide.

The second reaction product of (I) and hydrogen peroxide is obtained[52] by low temperature (below 50°) vacuum evaporation of a solution of the two substances with a small amount of acid added to increase product stability. The product is the addition compound or hydroperoxide of formula $((\text{CH}_2)_6\text{N}_4) \cdot \text{H}_2\text{O}_2$. It is a colorless, crystalline, water or alcohol soluble compound which liberates chlorine from hydro-chloric acid. It explodes when treated with concentrated sulfuric acid.

D. Salt Formation with Inorganic Compounds

Hexamethylenetetramine forms a hexahydrate[44] obtainable by cooling a saturated aqueous solution gradually to 0°. It decomposes at 13.5° and is not the usual product obtained upon vacuum evaporation of aqueous hexamethylenetetramine solutions.

Salts of hexamethylenetetramine with inorganic acids may be isolated if non-aqueous solvents or in some cases cold aqueous solutions are used. As mentioned in a preceding section, salts are the primary products formed and when conditions which enhance their stability are employed, they are easily isolated. Hexamethylenetetramine is a monoacidic base and may be titrated with mineral acids using methyl orange indicator. Salts with more than one equivalent of acid as for example[55] the "salt" $C_6H_{12}N_4 \cdot 2HCl$ indicate that the true salt has formed an addition compound with the second equivalent of acid. Salts are known[55,56] with such acids as HCl, HBr, HI, H_2SO_4, HNO_3, H_3PO_4, $HClO_4$, $H_2Cr_2O_7$, etc. Salts with nitric acid are discussed in more detail under E below.

It was established[61,62] that Knudsen's base, the base obtained by treating hexamethylenetetramine dinitrate with hot solvents, and the methylhexamethylenetetramine cation are the same. A consideration of this identity is presented in Chapter VIII, III,2A(3). A possible mechanism by which the conversion of hexamethylenetetramine dinitrate may proceed to the dipicrate has been suggested by Foss,[62] who favors an open cage structure as the basis for the transformation. Certainly there may be many variations in the scheme and in the order of the steps. All steps are considered reversible with the exceptions of the reductions and the ring closure, the latter because the nitrogen involved in ring closure is constrained to the quarternary tetraalkyl-ammonium state and $> \overset{+}{N}$—C bonds are stronger than $>$ N—C bonds.

With the notable exception of lead, hexamethylenetetramine forms addition compounds or complexes which involve a great majority of the available elements of the periodic table including salts of the metals, the alkali metals, the alkaline earths and the rare earths. Most of these have been described by Altpeter.[3] No one formula can adequately express a general relationship between the number of molecules of hexamethylenetetramine and the particular compound in question because very often a difference in concentration of the solvent used or in the concentration[63] of the organic base leads to the formation of

$$
\begin{array}{c}
NO_3^- \\
^+HN \diagdown_{CH_2-N-CH_2} \diagup N \\
| \\
CH_2 \\
| \\
N^+ \\
H \quad NO_3^-
\end{array}
\quad \xrightarrow[H_2O]{H^+NO_3^-} \quad
\begin{array}{c}
CH_2OH \\
HN \diagdown_{CH_2-N-CH_2} \diagup N \\
| \\
CH_2 \\
| \\
N^+ \\
H \quad NO_3^-
\end{array}
\quad + \quad
\begin{array}{l}
\text{some decomposition to} \\
(6\,CH_2O + 4\,NH_3 + 2\,HNO_3)
\end{array}
$$

$$
\begin{array}{c}
CH_2OH \\
HN \diagdown_{CH_2-N-CH_2} \diagup N \\
CH_2 \\
N^+ \\
H \; NO_3^-
\end{array}
+ CH_2O \rightarrow
\begin{array}{c}
CH_2OH \qquad CH_2OH \\
N \diagdown_{CH_2-N-CH_2} \diagup N \\
CH_2 \\
N^+ \\
H \; NO_3^-
\end{array}
\xrightarrow[\text{reduction}]{\substack{\text{intramolecular} \\ \text{oxidation-} \\ \text{reduction}}}
\begin{array}{c}
CH_3 \qquad CHO \\
N \diagdown_{CH_2-N-CH_2} \diagup N \\
CH_2 \\
N^+ \\
H \; NO_3^-
\end{array}
$$

reduction CH$_4$O → (diagonal)

reduction CH$_4$O ↓ (vertical)

$$
\begin{array}{c}
CH_3 \\
NO_3^-{}^+N \diagdown_{CH_2-N-CH_2} \diagup N \\
CH_2 \\
N^+ \\
H \; NO_3^-
\end{array}
\xleftarrow{HNO_3}
\begin{array}{c}
CH_3 \\
OH^+{}^+N \diagdown_{CH_2-N-CH_2} \diagup N \\
CH_2 \\
N^+ \\
H \; NO_3^-
\end{array}
\xleftarrow{\text{ring closure}}
\begin{array}{c}
CH_2OH \\
H_3CN \diagdown_{CH_2-N-CH_2} \diagup N \\
CH_2 \\
N^+ \\
H \; NO_3^-
\end{array}
$$

Picric acid −HNO$_3$ →

$$
\left[
\begin{array}{c}
\overset{+}{H_3CN} \diagdown_{CH_2-N-CH_2} \diagup N \\
CH_2 \\
N
\end{array}
\right]
\quad \text{(picrate)}^-
$$

several different complexes from the same inorganic compound. In cases where several colored salts result, the coloration is most intense in the salt in which the base is present in lower or lowest proportions. The complexity of many of the salts is such that the Werner theory of coordinate complexes does not appear[64] to furnish an adequate explanation for their existence.

The complex salts and addition compounds of hexamethylene-tetramine are generally[65] water soluble but insoluble in most organic solvents. Many are hydrated and some complexes form with one or more molecules of solvent in the complex.[63]

E. Nitration Reactions

Studies of the nitration of hexamethylenetetramine carried out during World War II in connection with the production of 1,3,5-tri-nitrohexahydro-s-triazine, (VII), known as RDX or Cyclonite, con-tributed in detail to the knowledge of the chemistry of the process. A good portion of the work is discussed in Chapter IX, Section VII and in Chapter VIII, Section 3a, both of which should be consulted con-comitantly with this section.

Hexamethylenetetramine, upon reaction with nitric acid under a variety of conditions, gives several products,[51,58,59,60] Formation of mono- and dinitrate salts has been described. (I) can undergo two principal types of cleavage during nitration: 1) cleavage to compounds containing three amino nitrogen atoms which include six-membered ring compounds such as 1,3,5-trinitrohexahydro-s-triazine (VII), (RDX or Cyclonite) and, in the presence of acetic anhydride the linear tri-nitramine, 1,7-diacetoxy-2,4,6-trinitro-2,4,6-triazaheptane (VIII), and 2) cleavage to compounds containing four amino nitrogen atoms which include eight membered ring compounds such as 1,5-endomethylene-3,7-dinitro-1,3,5,7-tetrazacyclooctane (IX), known as DPT (dinitro-pentamethylenetetramine), and 1,3,5,7-tetranitro-1,3,5,7-tetrazacyclo-octane (X) known as HMX (high melting explosive) and also the linear compound 1,9-diacetoxy-2,4,6,8-tetranitro-2,4,6,8-tetrazanonane (XI). The first type cleavage is favored[66] by high acidity or high activity of the nitrating agent while, conversely, the second type cleavage occurs where the acidity and activity of the nitrating agent are relatively low. Cyclonite (VII) is the most commonly obtained product in either case, but some DPT (IX) is always obtained in amounts that vary according to the procedure. (IX) may be obtained pure from nitration mixtures of hexamethylenetetramine by filtering [67] to remove the Cyclonite and neutralizing to a pH of 5.6. Compound (IX) can also be obtained[67] by treating hexamethylenetetramine dinitrate with acetic anhydride at

room temperature for three days (31 % yield) or with 90 % sulfuric acid
at 15° for 45 minutes. It is also formed when hexamethylenetetramine

$$
\begin{array}{c}
\text{NO}_2 \\
\text{N} \\
\text{O}_2\text{NN} \quad \text{NNO}_2 \\
\smile \\
\text{(VII)}
\end{array}
\qquad
\begin{array}{c}
\text{CH}_3\text{COOCH}_2\text{N(NO}_2)\text{CH}_2\text{N(NO}_2)\text{CH}_2\text{OOCCH}_3 \\
\text{(VIII)}
\end{array}
$$

$$
\begin{array}{c}
\text{O}_2\text{NN} \quad \text{CH}_2 \quad \text{NNO}_2 \\
\text{(IX)}
\end{array}
\qquad
\begin{array}{c}
\text{NO}_2 \\
\text{O}_2\text{NN} \quad \text{NNO}_2 \\
\text{NO}_2 \\
\text{(X)}
\end{array}
$$

$$
\text{CH}_3\text{COOCH}_2\text{N(NO}_2)\text{CH}_2\text{N(NO}_2)\text{CH}_2\text{N(NO}_2)\text{CH}_2\text{N(NO}_2)\text{CH}_2\text{OOCCH}_3
$$
$$(\text{XI})$$

$$
\begin{array}{c}
\text{H}_2 \quad \text{NO}_3^- \\
^+\text{N} \\
\text{HN} \quad \text{NH} \\
\smile \\
\text{(XII)}
\end{array}
$$

is treated with concentrated nitric acid containing added sodium
nitrate, or with nitric anhydride,[68] N_2O_3. The latter is a reagent that
also can be used[69] to prepare Cyclonite (VII) from a chloroform solution
of hexamethylenetetramine.

By suitable modification of reaction conditions, the so-called by-
products of the solvolysis (nitrolysis) of (I) can be prepared in such a
way that they become the principal products.[66] Thus, 1,5-endomethy-
lene-3,7-dinitro-1,3,5,7-tetrazacyclooctane (IX), which melts at 213°
upon recrystallization from nitromethane, can be made in 48 % yield;
1,7-diacetoxy-2,4,6-trinitro-2,4,6-triazaheptane (VIII) in 51 % yield;
and 1,9-diacetoxy-2,4,6,8-tetranitro-2,4,6,8-tetrazanonane (XI) in 32 %
yield by use of the proper conditions. 1,3,5,7-Tetranitro-1,3,5,7-tetraza-
cyclooctane (X) can be prepared in 70 % yield from (IX). The chemistry
of the bicyclic s-triazine derivatives is discussed under the appropriate
section in Chapter VIII.

Treating hexamethylenetetramine with 88 % nitric acid at 0° for four to five minutes produces[70] hexahydro-s-triazine nitrate (XII) (see Chapter IX). The further nitration of hexamethylenetetramine is accomplished by three chief methods: 1) the Schiessler-Ross process in which acetic acid, acetic anhydride and formaldehyde give 50–60 % yields of RDX, 2) the Hale process wherein less than 100 % yields of RDX are obtained from hexamethylenetetramine and nitric acid, and 3) the Bachmann process by use of which greater than 100 % yields of RDX are obtained from hexamethylenetetramine, acetic acid, acetic anhydride, ammonium nitrate and 99 % nitric acid. Hexamethylene-tetramine may also be nitrated to RDX in good yields with nitric acid containing less than 25 % phosphoric anhydride[71] but dilute solutions starting with hexamethylenetetramine concentrations of less than 16 % must be used. All methods but the Bachmann[72] process form 1,3,5-trinitrohexahydro-s-triazine according to the simplified equation:

$$C_6H_{12}N_4 + 3HNO_3 \longrightarrow C_3H_6O_6N_6 + 3CH_2O + NH_3,$$

which shows that the process is obviously wasteful of one half of the formaldehyde, whereas in the Bachmann method the stoichiometric equation is (12).

$$C_6H_{12}N_4 + 4HNO_3 + 2NH_4NO_3 + 6(CH_3CO)_2O \rightarrow 2C_3H_6O_6N_6 + 12CH_3COOH \quad (12)$$

Reaction (12) is conducted at 75°. Hexamethylenetetramine and 98–100 % nitric acid are gradually added to the reaction mixture. It is possible to obtain yields of (VII) of over 80 % (based on 2 moles of hexamethylenetetramine) and as high[66] as 90%. In addition, economy of concentrated nitric acid may be achieved by starting with hexamethylenetetramine dinitrate, which is preparable[76] from 70 % nitric acid.

Before consideration of the mechanism by which the Bachmann process can give two moles of RDX from one mole of hexamethylene-tetramine, it is well to consider some other general aspects of the nitration reaction which show the function of the components of the Bachmann mixture. It should be noted for subsequent reference below that even the apparently obvious degradation products are not formed simply. For example, one of the ways by which hexamethylenetetra-mine may be converted to 1,5-endomethylene-3,7-dinitro-1,3,5,7-tetrazacyclooctane[76] (IX, DPT) is first by formation of the stable

dinitrate[73] followed by the salt dinitrohexamethylenetetraminium diacetate which may exist as an entity or as a path to DTP (13).

$$(13)$$

Myers and Wright[74] have synthesized the seven-membered homolog
of Cyclonite by the nitrolysis of methylene-bis(3,6-dinitro-1,3,6-triaza-
cycloheptane) which was synthesized from N,N'-dimethylol-1,2-di-
nitraminoethane, formaldehyde, and ammonia. Some generalizations
for hexamethylenetetramine degradation were indicated by a study
of the chemistry of nitration in the seven-membered series and the
fact that analogies hold for the six-membered compounds. The normal
Hale solvolysis of hexamethylenetetramine with 99.6% nitric acid
yields chiefly RDX (VII) and dimethylolnitramine.[75] If acetic anhydride is used together with nitric acid, the chief products are 1,7-
diesters of 2,4,6-trinitro-2,4,6-triazaheptane. The ester groups are
acetoxy or nitroxy or both depending on the reactant proportions.
How these products are formed may be seen from the scheme below.
Hexamethylenetetramine gives rise to Compound (XIII), the primary
intermediate. If (XIII) is formed under conditions which minimize
demethylolization, that is, a deficiency of ammonium nitrate and an
abundance of acetic anhydride, then esterification occurs and the
intermediate (XIIIa) results. Subsequent scission occurs largely at
bond A producing RDX dimethylolnitramide. Cleavage at bonds C
and B also takes place to a lesser extent to give (XIIIb) and (XIV),
ultimately accounting for limited amounts of linear esters when followed
by scission at D and E. If (XIII) does not esterify, step-wise demethylolation down to RDX probably occurs and intermediate (XIIIb) is
excluded from significance in the formation of RDX since it is known
from triazacycloheptane chemistry that scission at D occurs to an
appreciable extent. Thus we may infer that under conditions promoting
esterification and inhibiting demethylolation, cleavage at C and
especially B may become preponderant, while conversely cleavage at
A most readily occurs when demethylolation proceeds normally. It

should moreover be noted that solvolysis (nitrolysis) is a fast reaction and esterification a slow one.[73] Ammonium nitrate inhibits both reactions. It decreases the reactivity of nitric acid and, while esterification

is thus largely prevented, nitrolysis is not inhibited below a useful rate. Without esterification, demethylolation can proceed. There is evidence[76] that 1-methyl-3,5-dinitrohexahydro-s-triazine is an important stable intermediate.

That the ring bonds at D in intermediates (XIIIb) and (XIV) are readily susceptible to rupture in comparison to the linkage at E is shown by the thermal decomposition of methylene bis(3,5-dinitrohexahydro-s-triazine) (XV) to 1,5-dinitro-3,7-endomethylene-1,3,5,7-tetrazacyclooctane (IX) through the formation of an intermediate followed by loss of the elements of methylenenitrimine and recombination to the cyclooctane derivative (13). Compound (XV) is analagous to intermediate (XIII) above, dimethylolaminomethyl dinitrohexahydro-s-triazine, and the reactions of the latter, which has never been isolated, can be deduced from the former.

$$(13)$$

Another mechanism[77] by which hexamethylenetetramine can give rise to heptane derivatives is based on successive cleavages occurring always at the bond most distant from a nitramine[80] grouping and nearest to a nitrogen atom attached to an acetoxymethyl group. Hexamethylenetetramine undergoes cleavage at any bond and the resulting intermediate undergoes successive attack according to the rule above

$$(14)$$

(14). It should be noted that the reaction is complex and many pathways exist. For example, in Hale nitrolysis of hexamethylenetetramine where anhydride is ostensibly not involved, a small amount of 1,9-diethoxy-2,4,6,8-tetranitro-2,4,6,8-tetrazanonane can be isolated by boiling the product in ethanol. This compound may come directly from (IX), DPT; however, another way it could arise is first by nitrolysis-demethylolation of dimethylolaminodinitrohexahydro-s-triazine (XIII) but esterification before a second demethylolation. The product can solvolyze (nitrolyze) at A to give RDX and hydroxynitroxydimethyl nitramine or at B to give a compound which is then esterified and which would give the diethyl ester with hot alcohol (not shown).

The question of how the Bachmann process of nitrating hexamethylenetetramine can give yields of greater than 100 % is reduced to these possibilities: Hexamethylenetetramine is degraded by a Hale solvolysis to RDX, formaldehyde and ammonia. These fragments may a) recombine by the Schiessler-Ross process to give more hexamethylenetetramine which is again solvolyzed in the same manner or

b) the fragments may yield linear methylenenitramine units and these unite to form RDX.

It has been shown that methylenedinitramine can be formed in a Schiessler-Ross reaction mixture, however not under conditions[78] favorable to the formation of RDX. Wright and his workers[78] therefore question the significance of a reaction mechanism involving the direct construction of RDX from small methylenenitramine units. Moreover, the fact that RDX yields are considerably enhanced by the addition of methylenedinitramine to Schiessler-Ross reactions can be explained otherwise than by assuming direct participation in the formation of RDX. Its strong tendency toward methylolation may have the effect of withholding formaldehyde from the direct reaction until it is needed, thus reducing the side reactions of formaldehyde. One of the principal Schiessler-Ross side reactions is acetylation. It is therefore likely that methylenedinitramine is effective in reducing the tendency toward formation of non-RDX forming methylenediacetate.

It is known[15,78] that hexamethylenetetramine is formed to some extent in acid solution, but no direct proof exists that it can do so under Bachmann or Schiessler-Ross conditions. Kinetic studies[79] using paraformaldehyde, ammonium nitrate and acetic anhydride show that hexamethylenetetramine dinitrate is formed and solvolyzed to RDX by nitric acid which is also formed in the reaction mixture. The entire cycle of reactions requires about two and one half hours. Indirect evidence of hexamethylenetetramine formation under Bachmann conditions is available.[78] Two by-products, 1-aceto-3,5,7-trinitro-1,3,5,7-tetrazacyclooctane (XVII) and 1-aceto-3,5-dinitrohexahydro-s-triazine (XVIII), are always found together in Bachmann and Schiessler-Ross reactions in the RDX filtrate in yields of 3% and 1%, respectively. The nature of these products indicates that acetamide is involved in their formation. Excellent yields of acetamide can be obtained from

(XVII)   (XVIII)

acetic anhydride and ammonium nitrate. Adding excess acetic anhydride to a Bachmann mixture raises the yield of by-products (XVII
and XVIII). The same result can be obtained by adding acetamide
itself or propionamide—in which case the 1-propionyl analogs result.
Neither of the by-products (XVII and XVIII) can be obtained from
solutions of acetamide, formaldehyde, and ammonia indicating that
hexamethylenetetramine or a substance or substances derived from
hexamethylenetetramine is the source. Two possible intermediates,
not preparable from acetamide, formaldehyde and ammonia, are 1-acet-
amidomethylhexamethylenetetramine-1-nitrate (XIX) and 1,5-endo-
methylene-3,7-diacetyl-1,3,5,7-tetrazacyclooctane (XX) which is obtained[81] from hexamethylenetetramine and acetic anhydride. Compound
(XIX), which melts at 183–184°, can be prepared by a variety of
methods[82] from hexamethylenetetramine and its nitrate salt. Nitron
chloride converts the nitrate (XIX) to the corresponding chloride which
melts at 188–189°. The propionamide analog of the nitrate salt (melting
point 183–184°) can be made by equivalent procedures utilizing propionic acid and propionic anhydride. Compound (XIX), a quarternary
salt of established structure yields RDX (VII) and 1,3,5,7-tetranitro-
1,3,5,7-tetrazacyclooctane (X), but no (XVIII) when treated with
Bachmann reagents; this indicates that compound (XVIII) comes from

a different source. To explain the formation of the first two compounds
without the second, Wright[78] proposes rearrangement of (XIX) to 1,5-
endomethylene- 3,7(endodimethylene - N - acetamido) - 1,3,5,7- tetraaza-

cyclooctane (XXI) by means of a 1,3-shift of methylene accompanied by a 1,3-shift of hydrogen and proceeding with inversion from tetrahedral apex to base. In a manner analagous to the solvolysis (nitrolysis) of hexamethylenetetramine, the product of rearrangement undergoes cleavage at A to give an intermediate which has not been isolated (15). The latter, with ammonium nitrate present to inhibit esterification, undergoes degradation as far as linkage D to give (XIX) while, in the presence of excess anhydride, cleavage at B followed by cleavage

$$(15)$$

at C occurs giving 1,9-diacetoxy-6-aceto-2,4,8-trinitro-2,4,6,8-tetraazanonane (XXII) and diacetoxydimethylnitramine. All of the end products have been isolated.

The other aceto compound (XVIII), 1-aceto-3,5-dinitrohexahydro-s-triazine, melts at 158° when recrystallized from alcohol–acetone solvent. It cannot be obtained from the quarternary salt (XIX) but can be prepared from 1,5-diaceto-3,7-endomethylene-1,3,5,7-tetrazacyclooctane (XXIII) which, in turn, can be obtained from hexamethylenetetramine. Compound (XXIII) can give rise to 1-aceto-3,5-dinitrohexahydro-s-triazine by solvolytic cleavage at A (16). Cleavage at B and C gives 1,5-diaceto-3,7-dinitro-1,3,5,7-tetraazacyclooctane (XXIIIA) and its products of further solvolysis, the tri- and tetranitrocyclooctane derivatives (XVII) and (X). With a deficiency of ammonium nitrate, cleavage at B or C followed by cleavage at either A linkage gives the corresponding linear tetraazanonane (XXIIA).

$$
\begin{array}{ccc}
\text{(XXIII)} & \xrightarrow[\text{Ac}_2\text{O}]{\substack{\text{HNO}_3 \\ \text{NH}_4\text{NO}_3}} & \text{(XVIII)} \longrightarrow \text{(VII)}
\end{array}
$$

(XXIII):
$$
\begin{array}{c}
\text{A} \downarrow \\
\text{CH}_3\text{CON} \quad \text{CH}_2 \; \text{NCOCH}_3 \\
\leftarrow \text{C} \\
\leftarrow \text{B} \\
\text{A} \nearrow
\end{array}
$$

(XVIII):
$$
\begin{array}{c}
\text{COCH}_3 \\
\text{N} \\
\text{O}_2\text{NN} \quad \text{NNO}_2
\end{array}
$$

(VII):
$$
\begin{array}{c}
\text{NO}_2 \\
\text{N} \\
\text{O}_2\text{NN} \quad \text{NNO}_2
\end{array}
$$

$$
\text{(XXIIIA)} \rightarrow \text{(XVII)} \rightarrow \text{(X) (16)}
$$

(XXIIIA):
$$
\begin{array}{c}
\text{NO}_2 \\
\text{N} \\
\text{CH}_3\text{CON} \quad \text{NCOCH}_3 \\
\text{N} \\
\text{NO}_2
\end{array}
$$

(XVII):
$$
\begin{array}{c}
\text{NO}_2 \\
\text{N} \\
\text{O}_2\text{NN} \quad \text{NCOCH}_3 \\
\text{N} \\
\text{NO}_2
\end{array}
$$

(X) HMX:
$$
\begin{array}{c}
\text{NO}_2 \\
\text{N} \\
\text{O}_2\text{NN} \quad \text{NNO}_2 \\
\text{N} \\
\text{NO}_2
\end{array}
$$

(XXIII) $\xrightarrow[\text{Ac}_2\text{O}]{\text{HNO}_3}$ (XXIIA)

(XXIIA):
$$
\begin{array}{c}
\text{O}_2\text{NN—CH}_2\text{—NCOCH}_3 \\
| \qquad\qquad | \\
\text{CH}_2 \qquad\quad \text{CH}_2 \\
| \qquad\qquad | \\
\text{CH}_3\text{CON} \qquad \text{NNO}_2 \\
| \qquad\qquad | \\
\text{CH}_2 \qquad\quad \text{CH}_2\text{OAc} \\
\text{OAc}
\end{array}
$$

The evidence then is overwhelming with respect to the aceto compounds and all major and minor reaction products of Bachmann and Schiessler-Ross reactions that their synthesis proceeds by first the reformation of hexamethylenetetramine followed by selective solvolytic (nitrolytic and acetolytic) cleavage rather than by synthesis of these products directly from fragments. The Schiessler-Ross reaction represents the second phase of the Bachmann reaction and constitutes a synthesis of hexamethylenetetramine followed by a Hale type solvolysis.

The reactions which result in the formation of 1,3,5-trinitrohexahydro-s-triazine (VII, RDX) and 1,3,5,7-tetranitro-1,3,5,7-tetraza-cyclooctane (X, HMX) from hexamethylenetetramine in Bachmann type mixtures are comparable to each other with respect to optimum nitric acid concentrations and in the fact that optimal amounts of acetic anhydride and ammonium nitrate are necessary for maximum yields of either substance.[83] Activation energies for the formation of either are the same—15 ± 1 Kcal./mole. However, withholding ammonium nitrate has a more deleterious effect on RDX formation than on HMX formation. On the basis of this and other evidence accumulated during a kinetic study[83] of the reaction, the following scheme has been offered as best fitting the existing facts. Steps (1), (2), and (3) involve

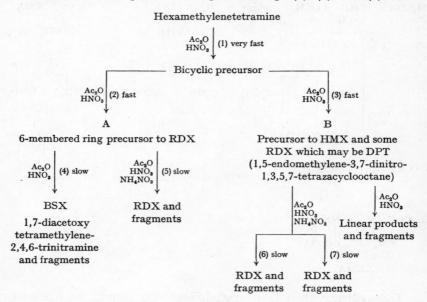

hexamethylenetetramine mononitrate and perhaps acetic anhydride and acetic acid, but are not influenced by ammonium nitrate. Although it was found that one third of the potential RDX is destroyed in a few minutes without ammonium nitrate, RDX and HMX (X) can be produced from their common precursor, B, after several hours. It therefore appears that the reaction proceeds even without ammonium nitrate to A and B. A goes to RDX in the presence of ammonium nitrate but is otherwise rapidly destroyed. However B, common to RDX and (X), is destroyed at a slower rate with parallel destruction of potential RDX and (X). Also in the absence of ammonium nitrate, the destruction of potential RDX and (X) at 55° becomes much slower after four hours. This may be due to destruction of most of B after four hours leaving only the relatively stable fragments to go to RDX and (X). These facts taken collectively indicate that steps (5), (6), and (7) are rate controlling in RDX synthesis by the Bachmann method.

Aristoff[78] has pointed out that 3,5-dinitro-3,5-diaza-1-oxacyclo-hexane obtained only during Hale nitrolysis is the one byproduct of hexamethylenetetramine nitration which has never been synthesized from simpler substances nor produced by degradation of any substance other than hexamethylenetetramine; consequently it remains as the one question mark in the otherwise complete mechanism of nitrolysis. For additional descriptions of the nitration mechanism see references 86 and 87. Schroeder[88] has presented the results of ultraviolet and visible spectra studies on many compounds involved in the nitration reaction.

F. Nitrosation

Nitrous acid reacts with hexamethylenetetramine to give two chief products similar in structure to the main products of nitration. In nitrosation, as in nitrolysis, acidity is the key to the product obtained. If the reaction is carried out in a medium of high acidity,[66,84] pH = 1, a 50 % yield of 1,3,5-trinitrosohexahydro-s-triazine (XXIV) is obtained while at low acidity, pH = 3–4, a 75 % yield of 1,5-endomethylene-3,7-dinitroso-1,3,5,7-tetrazacyclooctane (XXV) occurs. At a pH = 2, both products are formed in substantital amounts.

50% (XXIV) $(CH_2)_6N_4$ + HONO   (XXV) 75%

G. Reaction with Halogens and Compounds
Containing Active Halogens

Hexamethylenetetramine reacts with halogens; chlorine gives un-stable substitution products difficult to purify whereas bromine and iodine form compounds with two or four halogen atoms loosely united but isolable.

(1) Chlorine.   Chlorine in chloroform solvent forms very unstable substitution derivatives of hexamethylenetetramine which decompose into ammonium chloride and chlorinated hydrocarbons.[85] In aqueous solution explosive nitrogen trichloride is formed.[89] It is indicated[90] that dichloropentamethylenetetramine is produced, so it may be that milder workup procedures would enable the isolation of definite derivatives from hexamethylenetetramine and chlorine, especially in view of recent low temperature work on hexahydro-s-triazines discussed in Chapter IX.

(2) Bromine.   In aqueous solutions, a yellow dibromide of hexamethylenetetramine is formed[85,91] with bromine, while in chloroform[92] or with a large excess of bromine in acetic acid,[85] a red crystalline tetrabromide results. On standing in air or in the presence of caustic or water the tetrabromide loses one equivalent of bromine and gives the dibromide.

(3) Iodine.   As with bromine, hexamethylenetetramine reacts with iodine[85,92] to give di- and tetraiodo addition derivatives. The diiodide, prepared from aqueous hexamethylenetetramine and alcoholic iodine, is a reddish, crystalline water insoluble solid. The tetraiodide is a brown crystalline solid, insoluble in water but soluble in acetone and chloroform. It results from the action of iodine on hexamethylenetetramine in alcohol solution. A hexaiodide[93] results $(C_6H_{12}N_4I_6)$ when hexamethylenetetramine is treated with ammonia and iodine. It is a violet-red powder explosively sensitive to heat or shock.

(4) Mixed Halogens.   Mixed halogens generally produce tetrahalo adducts. With Schützenberger's compound, $HICl_2$, the dichlorodiiodo compound, a pale yellow, amorphous powder melting at 161–162° with the evolution of iodine, is produced.[94] Similarly, BrI gives a dibromodiiodo derivative[95] of hexamethylenetetramine. This adduct is a yellow solid, insoluble in most common solvents.

(5) Hypochlorites.   When aqueous hexamethylenetetramine is treated with hypochlorous acid, a sequence of reactions (17) occurs ultimately giving 1,5-endomethylene-3,7-dichloro-1,3,5,7-tetrazacyclooctane[73],[96],[97] commonly called dichloropentamethylenetetramine (XXVI). The yield is about 80%. Compound (XXVI) is slightly soluble

$$C_6H_{12}N_4 + 2 HOCl \longrightarrow C_6H_{12}N_4 \cdot 2 HOCl \longrightarrow [C_6H_{12}N_2(NCl)_2]^{++} \, 2 \, OH^-$$

$$\longrightarrow CH_2(OH)_2 + \begin{array}{c} \text{—N—} \\ | \\ ClN \quad CH_2 \quad NCl \\ | \\ \text{—N—} \end{array} \tag{17}$$

M.p. 79.5° (dec.)

(XXVI)

in water and in alcohol, and may be converted to the 3,7-dinitro derivative (IX) in 50 % yield with nitric acid and acetic anhydride.

A tetrachloro addition compound has been reported to be produced by evaporating aqueous solutions of sodium hypochlorite and hexamethylenetetramine[98] and by adding hexamethylenetetramine to phosphoric acid-sodium hypochlorite solutions.[99] Sodium hypobromite reacts with hexamethylenetetramine in acid solution to give the same dibromide,[85] $C_6H_{12}N_4Br_2$, as is obtained by the action of aqueous bromine on hexamethylenetetramine.

(6) Phosphorous Pentachloride. Phosphorous pentachloride decomposes[7] hexamethylenetetramine to ammonia, formaldehyde and methylamine, probably due to the formation of hydrochloric acid in the presence of even a little moisture.

(7) Others. Hexamethylenetetramine is converted to a white crystalline monochloro derivative, when treated with any of the following[10] reagents: $COCl_2$, SCl_2, S_2Cl_2, $SOCl_2$ or SO_2Cl_2. It is crystallized from methanol and melts of 193–194°. With sulfur dichloride, the addition compound $(C_6H_{12}N_4)_2SCl_2$ is also obtained and with thionyl chloride, the compound $C_6H_{12}N_4SOCl_2$ is a by-product.

2. With Organic Compounds

A. Alcohols

Hexamethylenetetramine reacts with alcohols in the presence of acids. The reaction is one of the many instances of hexamethylenetetramine acting as a source of formaldehyde or ammonia both of which are produced by acid decomposition of (I). In the aliphatic series, the formal of the alcohol is obtained along with the ammonium salt of the

respective mineral acid.[100] If excess formaldehyde is added as paraformaldehyde, the reaction products are tertiary alkoxymethyl-
amines;[101] for example, the reaction with butanol is illustrated (18):

$$(CH_2)_6N_4 + 6\,CH_2O + 12\,C_4H_9OH \longrightarrow 4\,(C_4H_9OCH_2)_3N + 12\,H_2O \qquad (18)$$

B. Salts; Reaction with Organic Acids

Quarternary salts are discussed in Section E below.

Organic acids form salts with hexamethylenetetramine. Salt
formation is usually rapid and yields are nearly quantitative. Equimolar
mixtures of the acid and hexamethylenetetramine are dissolved in a
common solvent, preferably water, and the solvent removed under
vacuum or by application of gentle heating. Strong heating is to be
avoided in order to minimize decomposition, particularly with strong
acids. Thus heating with aqueous formic acid results in the evolution of
carbon dioxide and the formation of methylamines,[102] reduction
products of hexamethylenetetramine.

Salts of sulfonic acids and phenolsulfonic acids are also easily
formed. In instances where a phenolsulfonic acid is treated with hexamethylenetetramine, the resulting salt is stable[103] and has definite
physical characteristics. Further heating beyond the melting point
of the hexamethylenetetramine salt of o-hydroxybenzenesulfonic acid
results in the liberation of phenol and formaldehyde but not directly
in polymer formation.

Hexamethylenetetramine forms molecular complexes with such
diverse compounds as benzoyl peroxide,[104] iodoacetamide,[105] sugars[103]
(such as sucrose, lactose and galactose) and alkyl esters of arylsulfonic
acids.[107] Heating the otherwise stable salts formed from adipic or
sebacic acids for five to six hours ar 220–240° in a solvent or aqueous
solution results in the formation[108] of polymers. The salts have melting
points of 190–191° and 172–172.5°, respectively.

Hexamethylenetetramine acts as a source for ammonia and formaldehyde when salts of such dibasic acids as succinic and phthalic acids
are heated.[109] Methylene bis-imides are produced (19).

C. Hydrogen Cyanide and Methylnitramine

Aqueous hexamethylenetetramine reacts with hydrogen cyanide (20) giving imidoacetonitrile and ammonia.[106] Catalytic amounts of strong mineral acids are required for optimum results.[102] If large amounts of strong hydrochloric acid are

$$(CH_2)_6N_4 + 6\,HCN \xrightarrow[H_2SO_4]{HCl\ or} 3\,HN(CH_2CN)_2 + NH_3 \qquad (20)$$

used, the chief product becomes nitriloacetonitrile, $N(CH_2CN)_3$, which can also be obtained by acidifying with hydrochloric acid an aqueous solution of hexamethylenetetramine and potassium cyanide.

Methylnitramine behaves like hydrogen cyanide toward hexamethylenetetramine. The analogous product[110] is tris(methylnitramino)trimethylamine (21).

$$CH_3NHNO_2 + (CH_2)_6N_4\ aq. \longrightarrow N(CH_2N(CH_3)NO_2)_3 \qquad (21)$$

The same product is obtained when ammonia and formaldehyde are used in place of hexamethylenetetramine; this affords good evidence that (I) breaks down before reaction.

D. Compounds Containing Active Methylene Groups

The weakly acid properties of hydrogen atoms in compounds containing such groups as $-CO-CH_2-CO-$, $-CO-CH_2-\overset{|}{C}=C <$, and $-CO-CH_2-\overset{|}{C}=N-$ cause their rapid reaction with hexamethylenetetramine in aqueous or non-aqueous media.[111] Decomposition of hexamethylenetetramine by the active methylene probably proceeds in the above fashion and gives two principal product types A and B. Not all active methylene groups react with hexamethylene-tetramine. Groups of the types $RCOCH_2R'$ and cyclopentadiene do not react. The order of reactivity corresponds roughly to the activity of the methylene hydrogens. In the series of groups of ascending methylene activity (malonic ester, acetoacetic ester, acetylacetone, indanedione, dimethyl and phenyldihydroresorcinol, phenylmethyl-pyrazalone and its analogs biindone, etc.), the least active, malonic ester, does not react at all while the others do so with increasing vigor.

In addition to the two main products, a third type is often pro-duced. The methylene bis-compound B may lose hydrogen during the course of the reaction giving the grouping $> C{=}CH{-}CH <$. The three types are illustrated in the following examples. In the case of acetoacetic ester, two products are obtained, both formed by reaction type B, one by means of dehydrogenation. Ammonia is present in the reaction medium and enters into combination with the two inter-mediates giving diethyldihydrolutadine dicarboxylate and diethyl-lutadine dicarboxylate, respectively (22). Acetylacetone reacts more

$$(CH_2)_6N_4 +$$
$$+ \; CH_3COCH_2COOC_2H_5 \rightarrow$$

(22)

vigorously with hexamethylenetetramine than acetoacetic ester and again gives a bis-type product which in this case loses an equivalent of hydrogen and reacts further with ammonia to finally give 4,6-diacetyl-m-toluidine (23).

$$(CH_2)_6N_4 + CH_3COCH_2COCH_3 \longrightarrow$$

(23)

With either dimethyl- or phenyldihydroresorcinol, "B" type condensation occurs giving bismethylene compounds and these in turn condense with ammonia in a manner similar to that described in reactions (22) and (23) resulting in the formation of substituted dihydrocarbazoles. Indanedione and phenylmethylpyrazolone both react (24, 25) extremely rapidly with (I). In the case of indanedione the reaction (24) is even faster than the rapid autocondensation to biindone. Both compounds give bismethylene compounds which dehydrogenate and react no further.

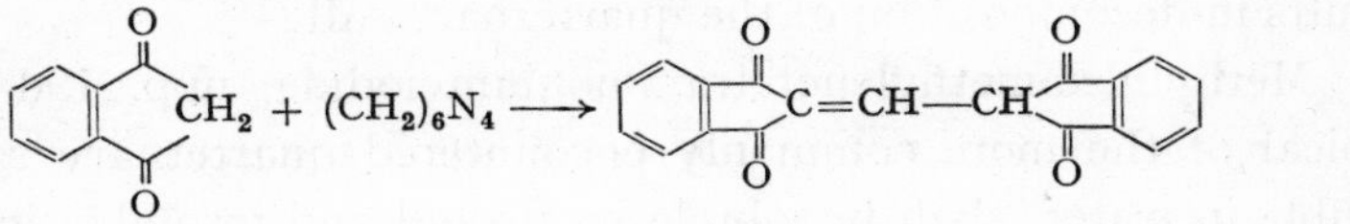

$$ (24) $$

and

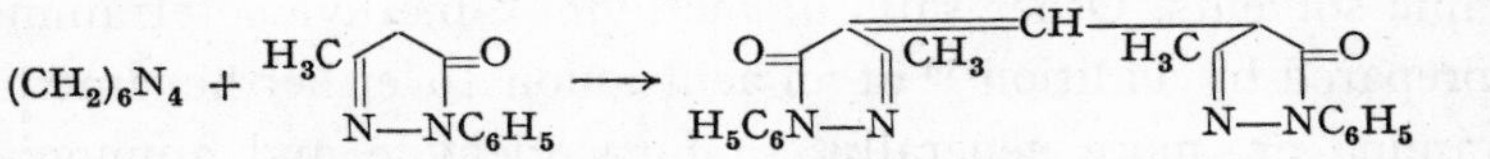

$$ (25) $$

Biindone ($\Delta1,2$-biindane-1',3,3'-trione) contains the most reactive of all the methylene groups of this series. It reacts with hexamethylenetetramine giving principally a product (XXVII) formed by an "A"

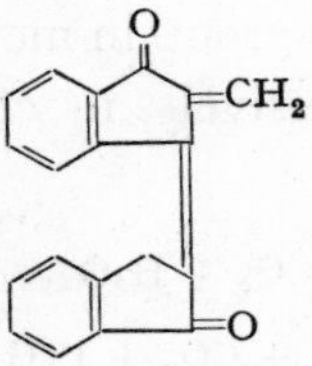

(XXVII) 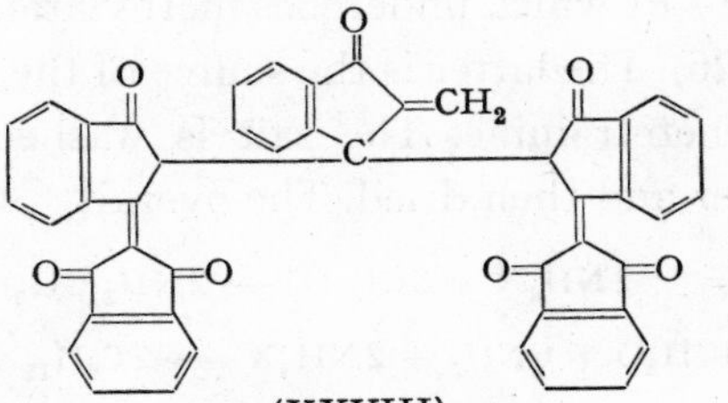　　　　　　　　(XXVIII)

type reaction. Compound (XXVII) may further react[111] to some extent with more biindone in a two step reaction producing methylene-indandionyliden-bis-biindone (XXVIII). This reaction is the basis for a qualitative test[112] for hexamethylenetetramine. A solution containing hexamethylenetetramine turns green when biindone is added.

E. Organic Halogen Compounds

(1) Alkyl Halides Hexamethylenetetramine forms quarternary salts upon reaction with equivalent quantities of alkyl halides. Straight chain alkyl bromides and iodides of low molecular weight react readily and give high yields of quarternary salts. Aliphatic bromides of more than four carbon atoms do not react readily; with longer chains, even the iodides form salts with decreasing ease. Angyal has found[116] that most alkyl halides react only slowly with hexamethylenetetramine. Alkyl bromides and iodides required twenty-four hours refluxing in chloroform; alkyl chlorides more. Of the secondary and tertiary halides, isopropyl iodide was the only compound[113] which would form readily characterized salts. Use of higher boiling solvents to force reaction results in decomposition of the quarternary salt.

Methylhexamethylenetetrammonium iodide, m.p. 190° (dec.) is typical of the more commonly encountered quarternary salts. It is soluble in water, slightly soluble in alcohol and insoluble in common organic solvents. Other salts of methylhexamethylenetetramine may be prepared by addition[114] of an acid anion to either hexamethylene-tetramine or, more generally, to formaldehyde and ammonia. The reaction can be conveniently carried out in chloroform, a solvent in which hexamethylenetetramine is fairly soluble and the resulting salt usually is not.[115] When the acid anion is added it will form an ammonium salt which undergoes methylation to produce a salt of methyl-amine (26). The latter is the source of the methyl group in methylhexa-methylenetetramine. The salt is washed successively in chloroform and ether and then dried. The overall

$$2\,NH_4X + 3\,CH_2O \longrightarrow 2\,NH_2(CH_3)\cdot HX + CO_2 + H_2O \tag{26}$$

$$15\,CH_2O + 6\,NH_3 + 2\,NH_4X \longrightarrow 2\,C_6H_{12}N_4\cdot CH_3X + CO_2 + 13\,H_2O \tag{27}$$

reaction is expressed in equation (27). Most salts of methylhexa-methylenetetramine are neutral. A few like the borate are feebly alkaline. All possess the property of generating formaldehyde even in alkaline solution when they are heated. These properties distinguish the methyl or alkyl quarternary salts from the salts of hexamethylene-tetramine and inorganic acids. The latter are acidic and do not give formaldehyde when heated. Formaldehyde and ammonium nitrate are reported to give methylhexamethylenetetrammonium nitrate.[61]

Treatment of methylhexamethylenetetrammonium iodide with silver oxide produces[101] the strongly basic hydroxide, behavior characteristic of tertiary amines. Mixtures of hexamethylenetetramine, sodium iodide, and ethyl or methyl iodides or bromides form the primary alkylamines in 70–80 % yields[117] after standing about a week. Heating the quarternary alkyl iodides with alkali is also reported[118] to result in the formation of 1,3,5-trialkylhexahydro-s-triazines.

(2) Benzyl and Other Arylalkyl Halides. Benzyl halides, substituted benzyl halides, benzyl thiocyanates,[115] and naphthalene and thiophene compounds containing the halomethyl group form addition compounds with hexamethylenetetramine that are the basis for a number of synthetically important reactions.

(a) *Reduction with Formic Acid.* Heating the addition compounds of hexamethylenetetramine and benzyl chloride slowly with formic acid gives[119] yields of the corresponding dimethylbenzylamine which vary depending on the halide used. The method offers obvious advantages for the preparation of this type tertiary amine since neither the primary nor the secondary predecessor need be available. Carbon dioxide is evolved during the synthesis.

(b) *Action of Acids.* If the addition compounds are treated with acid, good yields, subject however to considerable variation, of the corresponding benzylamine are obtained. A 96 % yield of benzylamine can be obtained.[120] Primary amines result also when mixtures of hexamethylenetetramine and a benzyl or a phenylethyl halide are allowed to stand in aqueous solution with sodium iodide.[117] Yields of primary amine and times required for reaction are as follows: benzyl chloride, 82%, 2 hours; p-nitrobenzyl chloride, 61%, 1 day; and β-phenylethyl chloride, 54%, 3 weeks.

(c) *Sommelet Reaction.* Hexamethylenetetramine forms addition compounds with benzyl halides and also with many other halogen containing compounds. The addition compounds undergo rearrangement followed by hydrolysis when heated in aqueous solution, giving as products aldehydes and ketones.

A mechanism for the reaction as proposed by Graymore[121] is indicated below and is an interpretation supported by the fact that

$$ArCH_2X + (CH_2)_6N_4 \longrightarrow (CH_2)_6N_4 \cdot ArCH_2X \longrightarrow ArCH_2NH_2 \longrightarrow$$
$$ArCH_2N{=}CH_2 \longrightarrow ArCH{=}NCH_3 \xrightarrow{H_2O} ArCHO$$

the corresponding intermediate amines may be employed and, upon treatment with formaldehyde, acid and hexamethylenetetramine, yield the same aldehydes. For example, α-phenylethylamine treated in this manner, gave acetophenone which can also be made from α-chloroethylbenzene, hexamethylenetetramine and hydrochloric acid. Moreover, certain amino acids when heated in acid with formaldehyde evolve methylamine,[122] presumably due first to the transposition of a double bond in a Schiff's base (28).

$$CH_2=N-CHRCOOH \longrightarrow CH_3N=CRCOOH \tag{28}$$

More recently, Angyal[125] and his workers reexamined the Sommelet reaction and concluded that it was essentially a hydrogenation-dehydrogenation process in which a Schiff's base is hydrogenated at the expense of an amine. The active intermediate is the conjugate acid of a Schiff's base, the mesomeric cation $R^+-N=CH_2 \longleftrightarrow RNHCH_2^+$. The strongly electrophilic carbon can then attack water in the hydrolysis of a Schiff's base or it can abstract a hydride ion (29).

$$
\begin{aligned}
&R'N = CH_2 \\
&\quad \updownarrow \\
[R&-NH \cdots CH_2]^+ + RCH-\overset{\frown}{N}H_2 \rightleftharpoons R'NHCH_3 + [RCH \cdots NH_2]^+ \\
&\qquad\qquad\qquad\quad\; H \\
&R'NHCH_2OH \underset{}{\overset{H^+}{\rightleftharpoons}} R'NH_2 + CH_2O \qquad\qquad\qquad RCHO + NH_3
\end{aligned}
\tag{29}
$$

When hexamethylenetetramine is used, $R' = H$.

In acid solution, hydrolysis occurs and the vertical scheme of (29) holds. Only in pH range of 3–7 where amine and Schiff's base coexist does the Sommelet reaction occur. This mechanism is supported by (1) demonstration that the conjugate acids of methyleneamines have a definite although short existence in aqueous solution and (2) the fact that the Sommelet reaction occurs when conjugate acids of Schiff's bases are heated in the absence of a solvent.

If the addition compound of hexamethylenetetramine and a benzyl halide, for example, is treated with ammonia and formaldehyde, there are formed[123] monomeric and dimeric (and also probably trimeric or hexahydro-s-triazines) anhydromethylene bases. These react normally with hydrochloric acid giving the respective carbonyl derivative but with steam and hydrochloric acid the respective amine hydrochloride results (30).

$$(CH_2)_6N_4ArCH_2X + NH_3 + CH_2O \longrightarrow (ArCH_2N{=}CH_2)_n \xrightarrow[\text{dil. HCl}]{\text{HCl, steam}} \begin{array}{l} ArCH_2NH_2 \cdot HCl \\ \qquad\qquad (30) \\ ArCHO \end{array}$$
$$n = 1 \text{ or } 2$$

Table X-1 contains some of the more recently prepared representative compounds from hexamethylenetetramine and substituted benzyl halides.

An abnormal reaction in the Sommelet aldehyde synthesis occurs[124] with 2,4,6-trimethylbenzyl chloride. Decomposition of the quarternary ammonium salt instead of producing mesitaldehyde gives N,N'-di-α^2-isodurylmethanediamine. According to Fuson,[124] this indicates that the mechanism of the reaction may involve at least one step which is inhibited by the mesityl group.

TABLE X-1. Some addition compounds of Hexamethylenetetramine $(CH_2)_6N_4 \cdot ArCH_2X$

CH₂X		Melting point, °C.	Yield, %	Aldehyde prepared	Amine prepared	Ref.
Benzyl chlorides,						
—CH₂Cl	o-Chloro	205		×	×	1
	m-Chloro	204–205		×	×	1
	p-Chloro	198		×	×	1
	2-Methoxy-5-car-boxyldehyde			×		3
Benzyl bromides,						
—CH₂Br	p-Methyl	168 (dec.)		×		2
	p-Nitro					1
	2,6-Dichloro		80	Could not		6
	2-Chloro-6-nitro		55	Could not		6
Benzyl iodide,						
CH₂I —NO₂	2-Nitro	154, Yellow needles				1
β-Bromoethylbenzene,						
CH₂CH₂Br		177–178	72		×	10
	4-Nitro	181–182	67		×	10
ω-Bromophenetole,						
OCH₂CH₂Br	2,4-Dimethyl	176–179				11
	2,4-Dichloro	164				11

(*Table continued*)

TABLE X-1 (*continued*)

ArCH$_2$X		Melting point, °C.	Yield, %	Aldehyde prepared	Amine prepared	Ref.
ω-Bromacetophenone,					×	14
COCH$_2$Br	4-Methyl				×	14
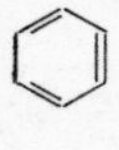	4-Fluoro	126–128 (dec.)				17
	4-Chloro	180 (dec.) Cryst. ethyl alc.; also 153 (dec.) reported	95–98		×	16
	4-Bromo	153–154 (dec.)				17
	4-Iodo	172 (dec.)				17
	3-Nitro	175 (dec.). Cryst. from ethyl alc.	95–98		×	14,
	4-Nitro	118–120 (dec.)	95		×	13
	2,4-Dichloro	167–168 (dec.)				17
	4-Methoxy				×	14
	p-Phenyl	153–154 (dec.)				17
ω-Iodoacetophenone,						
COCH$_2$I	4-Chloro	172–173 (dec.)				17
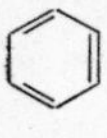	4-Bromo	170–171 (dec.)				17
	4-Iodo	180–181 (dec.)				17
	4-Phenyl	176–187 (dec.)				17
α-Chloromethylnaphthalene				×		9
CH$_2$Cl						
α-Bromomethylnaphthalene		175–179. Cryst. from ethyl alc.				8
CH$_2$Br						
β-Bromomethylnaphthalene,		160 (dec.)		×		8
α-Bromo				×		8
CH$_2$Br						
α-Naphthaldehyde,		85, Cryst. from ethyl alc.		×		8
CHO 4-Bromo						
Br						
α-Bromacetylnaphthalene,						
COCH$_2$Br β-Methoxy		188	89			12
4-Methoxy						

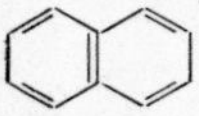

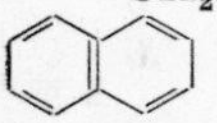

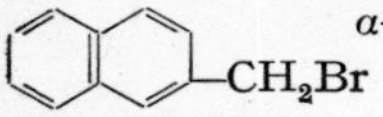

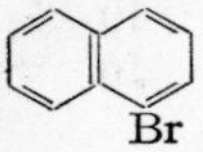

(*Table continue*

TABLE X-1 (continued)

H₂X	Melting point, °C.	Yield,%	Aldehyde prepared	Amine prepared	Ref.
Bromacetylnaphthalene COCH₂Br	152 (dec.)				17
Iodoacetyl-5,7,7,8-tetrahydro-naphthalene COCH₂I	165–166 (dec.)				17
Chloromethylthiophene CH₂Cl		94–99	×		5
Bromomethylthiophene CH₂Br	150		×		4
Chloro-3-bromomethyl-thiophene CH₂Br Cl	165, Cryst. from ethyl alc.	84	×		7
	Cryst. from ethyl alc.	75	×		7

1. J. Graymore and D. Davis, *J. Chem. Soc.*, **1945**, 293.
2. J. Graymore, *J. Chem. Soc.*, **1947**, 1116.
3. B. Reichert and H. Marquardt, *Pharmazie*, **5**, 10 (1950).
4. E. Campaigne and N. LeSuer, *J. Am. Chem. Soc.*, **70**, 1555 (1948).
5. K. Wiberg, *Org. Syntheses*, **29**, 87 (1949).
6. S. Angyal, P. Morris, R. Rassack and J. Waterer, *J. Chem. Soc.*, **1949**, 2704.
7. E. Campaigne and N. LeSeur, *J. Am. Chem. Soc.*, **71**, 333 (1949).
8. R. Mayer and A. Sieglitz, *Ber.*, **55B**, 1835 (1922).
9. D. Bertin, *Compt. rend.*, **229**, 660 (1949).
10. K. Slotta and W. Altner, *Ber.* **64B**, 1510 (1931).
11. R. Jones, T. Metcalfe and W. Sexton, *Biochem. J.*, **45**, 143 (1949).
12. B. Reichert and H. Baege, *Pharmazie*, **3**, 209 (1948), through *Chem. Abstracts*, **42**, 5889 (1949).
13. M. Rebstock, H. Crooks, J. Controulis, and Q. Bartz, *J. Am. Chem. Soc.*, **71**, 2473 (1949).
14. B. Reichert and H. Baege, *Pharmazie*, **2**, 451 (1947), through *Chem. Abstracts*, **42**, 3743 (1948).
15. N. Buu-Hoi and N. Khoi, *Compt. rend.*, **229**, 1343 (1949).
16. N. Buu-Hoi, P. Jacquignon and N. Khoi, *Compt. rend.*, **230**, 662 (1950).
17. C. Bahner, M. Pickens, D. Pickens and N. Easley, *J. Am. Chem. Soc.*, **72**, 2266 (1950).

F. Reaction with Miscellaneous Organic Compounds

(1) Acid Halides. Hexamethylenetetramine reacts with acetyl and benzoyl chlorides to give addition compounds from which hexamethylenetetramine may readily be regenerated.[7,126] Dominikiewicz has reported[127] that hexamethylenetetramine and benzoyl chloride react in the presence of pyridine giving chlorobenzoylhexamethylenetetramine, m.p. 188–189°, and some dichloropyridinedibenzoyl-hexamethylenetetramine, but in the absence of pyridine, 1,3,5-tribenzoylhexahydro-s-triazine and other products are formed.

(2) Halogen Derivatives of Alcohols and Esters. Hexamethylenetetramine forms related addition compounds with halogen derivatives of alcohols[128] and esters. Compounds with esters of the type $RCHICOO(CH_2)_nCH_3$ where $R = H$ or CH_3 and $n = 7, 11, 15$ or 17 may easily be made[129] and are convenient starting materials for preparation of the corresponding amines.

(3) Betaine Formation. Betaines are formed when hexamethylenetetramine and chloracetic acid in warm chloroform are treated with silver oxide,[130] or when hexamethylenetetramine and β-brompropionic acid stand with bicarbonate overnight. Refluxing the betaine with alcoholic hydrochloric acid produces β-alanine.[131]

(4) Other Halogen Containing Compounds. Among the great variety of addition compounds that hexamethylenetetramine may form are compounds with the following: 1,5-dibromo-2,4-dinitrobenzene[132], 4-hydroxy-ω-iodoacetonaphthalene,[133] 4-methyl-5-bromoacetylimidazole,[134] 4-chloracetylamino-1-phenyl-2,3-dimethyl-5-pyrazolone,[135] such nitrogen mustards as tris-β-chloroethylamine, and ethyl and methyl bis-β-chloroethylamine,[136] α-bromobutyrolactone,[137] m-chloracetylaminobenzamide,[138] 1-bromo-2-decene,[139] chloracetic ester, etc.

(5) Addition Compounds With Sulfur Containing Compounds. Hexamethylenetetramine forms addition compounds with alkyl sulfates,[115] alkyl nitrates,[115] methyl and benzyl thiocyanates,[115] and alkylaryl sulfonates.[115] Unstable addition compounds are formed with arylsulfonyl chlorides. These decompose giving 1,3,5-triarylsulfonylhexahydro-s-triazines[140] and 3,7-bis-arylsulfonyl-1,3,5,7-tetrazabicyclo-(3,3,1)nonane.[141]

(6) Reaction With Methylenequinones. Phenolic alcohols possess the property of vulcanizing rubber. This property is a result of the formation of methylenequinones (XXIX). However, the vulcanization properties are completely destroyed[142] when hexamethylenetetramine (I) is added due to combination of ammonia derived from (I)

HOCH$_2$—[ring, O top, CH$_3$ right]—CH$_3$ + (CH$_2$)$_6$N$_4$ $\longrightarrow$ HOCH$_2$—[ring, OH top, CH$_3$ right]—CH$_3$ (31)

CH$_2$ CH$_2$NH$_2$

(XXIX)   (XXX)

with the methylenequinones (31). Thus methylenequinones are captured by the ammonia from hexamethylenetetramine before they react with rubber, formation of bridge linkages between rubber chains is prevented and no vulcanization occurs.

G. Action of Sulfur Dioxide on Quarternary Addition Compounds

Treatment of the adducts of haloacetyl compounds and hexamethylenetetramine with sulfur dioxide proceeds[143,144] by replacement

$$ArCOCH_2X + (CH_2)_6N_4 \longrightarrow \text{Addition compound} \xrightarrow{SO_2}$$
$$ArCOCH_2NHCH_2OSO_2H \xrightarrow{HCl} ArCOCH_2NH_2$$

of the halogen atoms with the grouping —NHCH$_2$OSO$_2$H; acid hydrolysis produces the free amine.[132] N-Haloacetylarylamines may also be used.[145] The products are α-(sulfomethylamino)acetanilides, ArNHCOCH$_2$NHCH$_2$SO$_3$H.

H. Reactions with Phenolic Compounds

(1) With Phenol. Hexamethylenetetramine reacts with phenol first forming molecular compounds containing either one[146,147] or, more commonly, as when the two components are mixed at room temperature, three[148] molecules of phenol to one of hexamethylenetetramine. The crystalline triphenol adduct can also be prepared from ammonia, formaldehyde and phenol[149] or by heating p-hydroxybenzyl alcohol with ammonia and phenol.[150] It is a condensation intermediate when formaldehyde and phenol are used together to manufacture resins with ammonia as a catalyst.[151] Heating hexamethylenetetramine ·3C$_6$H$_5$OH at 130° causes ammonia to be evolved and produces a substance[149] similar to Bakelite "A."

(2) With Other Phenols. Substituted phenols behave in much the same manner as phenol itself, forming first molecular compounds with one, two or three equivalents of the phenol[152,153,154] and then, on further heating, many form resinous materials. Phenol sulfonic acids react with hexamethylenetetramine forming stable molecular compounds,[155] probably involving the —SO$_3$H group. A series of stable crystalline phenolated ammonium compounds is obtained[156,157] when hexamethylenetetramine is refluxed in an alcohol or a chloroform solution with excess alkyl halide and excess monohydric phenol. The products are soluble in water but insoluble in alcohol.

(3) Reactions Involving Introduction of the Carboxaldehyde Group. Hexamethylenetetramine reacts with certain phenols giving the carboxaldehyde derivative of the phenol. For example, refluxing hexamethylenetetramine with salicylic acid for sixteen hours in aqueous solution gives a mixture of salicylic-3-carboxaldehyde which is benzene soluble and salicylic acid-5-carboxaldehyde, which is benzene insoluble.[158] Neither meta nor para-hydroxybenzoic acids gives tractable products. Methyl-β-resorcylate refluxed in acetic acid for ten hours with hexamethylenetetramine and then for three hours with hydrochloric acid gives a 45% yield[159] of 2,4-dihydroxy-5-carboxaldehyde benzoic acid.

A more general method of preparing the aldehyde derivatives of such phenols as p-chlorophenol, m-xylenol, β-naphthol, carvacrol, and phenol itself consists of using glyceroboric acid[160] as a catalyst. Here again hexamethylenetetramine serves as an ultimate source for formaldehyde. Methylamine and ammonia are by-products of the reaction in every case. A possible reaction pathway is indicated in equations (32 and 33).

$$\text{ArH} + (\text{CH}_2)_6\text{N}_4 \xrightarrow{\text{glyceroboric acid}} \text{NH}_3 + 3\ \text{ArCH}_2\text{N}{=}\text{CH}_2 \tag{32}$$

$$\text{ArCH}_2\text{N}{=}\text{CH}_2 \xrightarrow{\text{isomerization}} \text{ArCH}{=}\text{NCH}_3 \xrightarrow{\text{HOH}} \text{ArCHO} + \text{CH}_3\text{NH}_2 \tag{33}$$

The reaction is rapid and in some cases better yields than with the Reimer-Tiemann method may be obtained. A boric acid in Cellosolve catalyst may also be employed.[161] The first product that is isolable, on heating phenol, for example, with hexamethylenetetramine and boric acid in Cellosolve, is bis-*p,p'*-dihydroxyphenyldimethylamine. The latter can undergo dehydrogenation when heated with additional hexamethylenetetramine in acetic acid and the resulting Schiff's base gives *p*-hydroxybenzaldehyde and *p*-hydroxybenzylamine hydrochloride with hydrochloric acid cleavage. Further reactions giving the

same products ultimately are outlined below. It is interesting to note that the step involving dehydrogenation,

$$-CH_2NHCH_2- \longrightarrow -CH=N-CH_2-,$$

has been shown[161] to be *the essential step* in the Sommelet reaction. See Section (4) below for a further discussion of the bis compounds.

(4) Formation of Bis-Compounds. Several bisymmetrical products result from heating naphthols or certain phenols with hexamethylenetetramine; the yields and especially the compounds formed depend on the duration of heating, the time of reaction and, more important, the solvent.[163,164] In aqueous-alcoholic media, α- and β-naphthol and hexamethylenetetramine give 2,2'-methylene-1,1'-dinaphthol and 1,1'-methylene-2,2'-dinaphthol, respectively, while if the solvent is instead acetic acid, the product; for example with α-naphthol, is 2,2'-dihydroxy-1-naphthylidene-1'-naphthylmethylamine. If a mixture of acetic acid and alcohol is used as solvent, the reaction takes still another course and bis—naphthyoxydimethylamines are produced. These generalizations concerning the effect of the solvent must be qualified of course. Bis-2,2—naphthoxydimethylamine is obtained from β-naphthol in 95 % alcohol and some Schiff's base is produced with alcohol-acetic acid.

Still a fourth type of product results from heating p-nitrophenol at 100° with aqueous hexamethylenetetramine. The product is N-hydroxymethyl-bis(5-nitro-2-hydroxybenzylamine) (33).

$$\tag{33}$$

(6) Reaction with Thiophenols. Hexamethylenetetramine and thionaphthols react giving products analogous to the ones obtained from naphthols and discussed in Section (4), with substituted dimethylamines and azomethines predominating.[164] In the case of thiophenols and benzylmercaptan, however, the reaction usually proceeds one step further and the products[164,165,166] are tertiary amines (34).

$$(CH_2)_6N_4 + 6 C_6H_5SH \longrightarrow (C_6H_5SCH_2)_3N + 2 NH_3 \tag{34}$$

I. Reaction with Amines

Aniline and hexamethylenetetramine react to give 1,3,5-triphenyl-hexahydro-s-triazine[167] when heated at 150–190°. Benzylamines, treated with formaldehyde first and later with hexamethylenetetramine, form benzaldehydes in the presence of hydrochloric acid.[121] This reaction serves as proof of the mechanism for formation of benzaldehydes from benzyl halides and hexamethylenetetramine [see Section VI,2,E(1)].

Dialkylarylamines react[162,168] with hexamethylenetetramine in glacial acetic acid in the presence of formic acid. After an initial period of heating, the reaction mixture is heated with dilute hydrochloric acid to obtain 20–40 % yields of p-(N,N-dialkylamino)benzaldehyde.[168,169] The following N,N-di-substituted anilines have been used successfully: dimethyl, methylethyl, diethyl, di-n-propyl, di-n-butyl, methylbenzyl, and ethylbenzyl. No formaldehyde is found in the vapor from these reactions, but methylamine is always produced in a 1:1 mole ratio with the substituted benzaldehyde. For these reasons, the reaction mechanism is different from that offered by Angyal and Russak.[169] Duff[162,168] feels that the older mechanism (35–37) is more probably representative of the course of the reaction.

$$3 R_2NC_6H_5 + (CH_2)_6N_4 \longrightarrow NH_3 + 3 R_2NC_6H_4CH_2N=CH_2 \qquad (35)$$

$$R_2NC_6H_4CH_2N=CH_2 \longrightarrow R_2NC_6H_4CH=NCH_3 \qquad (36)$$

$$R_2NC_6H_5CH=NCH_3 + H_2O \longrightarrow R_2NC_6H_4CHO + CH_3NH_2 \qquad (37)$$

When the reaction was conducted in formic acid and ethanol, in addition to the usual aldehyde, there was also obtained some p-(dimethylaminomethyl)-N,N-dimethylaniline probably formed by reduction and methylation of the intermediate $R_2NC_6H_4CH_2N=CH_2$ through the combined action of formic acid and formaldehyde.[162,168]

Mannich bases of the type $ArCH_2NRR'$ (where Ar = indole as in gramine) or β-naphthol react[170] in acid solution (38) to give salts of the type encountered in the Sommelet synthesis. The solvent may be glacial acetic or hot 66% aqueous acetic, propionic or butyric acids.

$$(ArCH_2N^+HRR')X^- + (CH_2)_6N_4 \longrightarrow (ArCH_2N^+(CH_2)_6N_4)X^- + RR'NH \qquad (38)$$

Decomposition of the salts again produces an aldehyde. The reaction proceeds by a typical Sommelet mechanism (35–37) and has been used to replace the secondary amino groups of the compounds in Table X-2 by an aldehyde function.[170]

TABLE X-2.   Replacement of Secondary Amino Groups with Carboxaldehyde Groups

Starting material	Product	Yield
Gramine	Indole-3-carboxaldehyde	50%
1-Dimethylaminomethyl-β-naphthol	2-Hydroxy-α-naphthaldehyde	32%
1-Piperidino-β-naphthol	2-Hydroxy-α-naphthaldehyde	20%

J. Reaction with Grignard's Reagent

Benzylmagnesium chloride and hexamethylenetetramine form only complex resinous products from which the following compounds have been isolated:[171] methylamine, toluene, benzyl chloride, methylphenylethylamine, bibenzyl, styrene, and alcohols.

K. *Reaction with Thiophene*

An example of the ammoniation properties of hexamethylene-tetramine is provided by its reaction with thiophene[172] in the presence of acid. The products are 7 % 2-thienylamine, 25 % 2,2'-dithienylamine and 68 % polymeric amine containing methylol groups.

VII. Detection and Analysis of Hexamethylenetetramine

Hexamethylenetetramine in extremely low concentration can be detected by the precipitation of its mercuric chloride salt by excess mercuric chloride in neutral or slightly acid solution.[174] If the precipitation is conducted at a pH of 4.0, it provides a quantitative gravimetric method of analysis, accurate[20] to within 0.2%. Hexamethylene-tetramine can be extracted from aqueous solutions with chloroform,[173] and determined quantitatively by precipitation with picric acid. Precipitation of the tetraiodo derivative by addition of a solution of iodine and potassium iodide in water furnishes a useful test having wide application.[175] The yellow dibromide readily forms when sodium hypobromite is added to a solution of dilute hydrochloric acid and hexamethylenetetramine.[176] The dibromide liberates iodine from potassium iodide.[177]

Other useful tests are the compound[177] with antipyrine and the phenates which form upon mixing hexamethylenetetramine solutions with alcoholic phenol.[177] The most useful and readily carried out test is to heat hexamethylenetetramine with dilute sulfuric acid. If no other sources of formaldehyde are present, its characteristic odor or the Schiff's base reaction readily provide identification. Sulfuric acid decomposition is the basis for the usual and most reliable methods[178-182] for quantitative analysis for hexamethylenetetramine. Formaldehyde is usually removed during several hours heating[178] or may be analyzed by Nessler's reagent.[179] The unneutralized standard sulfuric acid is titrated with standard alkali using as indicator methyl orange or rosolic acid.[181]

VIII. Uses of Hexamethylenetetramine

The uses of hexamethylenetetramine have been amply covered by Walker[4,4a] and Altpeter.[3] Brief mention is made here of a few major ones.

1. Medicine

Under the name Methenamine U.S.P., hexamethylenetetramine has been used widely as a urinary antiseptic but it has been replaced in large measure by more effective drugs. However, compounds and salts of hexamethylenetetramine and the base alone are the active ingredients in over two hundred pharmaceutical preparations.[185,186] Under various trade names, the salt of hexamethylenetetramine with anhydro-methylenecitric acid,[187] made from citric acid and paraformaldehyde, has also been used as a urinary antiseptic.

2. Resins

The largest and most important use of hexamethylenetetramine is in the resin industry. No attempt will be made to discuss those applications which may be found in a number of books dealing more completely with this subject. Brief mention is made below concerning some of the recent work on the chemical aspects.

Hexamethylenetetramine reacts with simple molecules such as phenol, urea,[191] methylolureas,[192] nitropropane,[193] etc. to form synthetic resins. It may also act as a source of formaldehyde in the modification of high molecular weight resinous materials, either synthetic or natural such as lignin or casein. It is the condensation with phenolic materials which is now considered. In the formation of resins from phenols and hexamethylenetetramine, the first step is the formation of a nitrogen containing resin, with the nitrogen in the form of polybenzylamine[194] linkages, $ArCH_2NHCH_2-$. At higher temperatures or with a larger proportion of the phenolic component, nitrogen is eliminated as ammonia and perhaps as amines so that the overall reaction may give a nitrogen free resin. The hardening process is a result of this liberation of ammonia and netting of the resin with bonds[195] such as

$$-CH_2NHCH_2- > CH_2\underset{|}{N}CH_2- \quad \text{and} \quad -CH_2-$$
$$CH_2-$$

The resinification process is analogous to the hardening of resoles which first form polyesters and then undergo secondary reactions, especially loss of water and formaldehyde. At higher temperatures, reduction and oxidation reactions occur giving strongly colored azomethine derivatives. Hydrogenation and dehydrogenation reactions may also take place leading to new terminal methyl groups and unsaturated strongly phenolic bases. When the primary resins are heated in a dry air stream at 130–230°, gases, sublimates and still other resins are obtained. The nitrogen contents of resins from hexamethylenetetramine and phenol, p-cyclohexylphenol, and p-tert-butylphenol all range from 5 % to 11%. The main reaction product of hexamethylenetetramine and phenol at 190° contains 10.2 % nitrogen of which more than one half is lost upon further heating with three times its weight of phenol.

The crystalline product of hexamethylenetetramine and 2,4-xylenol is stable at 190° but when it is heated with three times its weight of phenol at 190°, all the nitrogen is lost in two hours. The course

$$(39)$$

of these reactions may be illustrated by considering[196] the case of 2,4-xylenol (39). The structure of the compounds involved has been proved, as well as similar intermediate starting with 2,6-xylenol.

3. Miscellaneous Uses

Hexamethylenetetramine has been found to increase the water solubility of formaldehyde polymers when used in 0.25–10% concentrations.[197] On the other hand, salts of hexamethylenetetramine with long chain acyl halides[198] impart water repellant properties to textiles.

Heatabs is the widest known brand name for the satisfactory solid fuel pellets which can be compounded from hexamethylenetetramine and inorganic or organic scorifying agents of low melting point such as sodium potassium tartrate[199] potassium nitrate[200] or others.[201]

Hexamethylenetetramine has been used in the vulcanization of rubber.[202]

It has been found to be an effective catalyst for the reaction between diethylchlorothionophosphate and sodium p-nitrophenolate in chlorobenzene to form parathion. Apparently it functions in the following manner[203] where R_3N can be hexamethylenetetramine:

$$(C_2H_5O)_2PSCl + R_3N \longrightarrow [(C_2H_5O)_2PSNR_3]^+Cl^-$$

$$[(C_2H_5O)_2PSNR_3]^+Cl^- + Na^+\bar{O}C_6H_4NO_2 \longrightarrow NaCl + [(C_2H_5O)_2PSNR_3]^+ (OC_6H_4NO_2)^-$$

$$\longrightarrow (C_2H_5O)_2PS{-\!\!-}C_6H_4NO_2 + R_3N$$

References

1. A. Butlerow, *Ann.*, **111**, 250 (1859).
2. A. Butlerow, *Ann.*, **115**, 322 (1860).
3. J. Altpeter, *Das Hexamethylenetetramin und Seine Verwendung*, Verlag von Wilhelm Knapp, Halle, 1931.
4. J. Walker, *Formaldehyde*, Reinhold, New York, 1944, Chapt. 18, pp. 276–300.
4a. J. Walker, *Formaldehyde*, 2d Ed., Reinhold, New York, 1953.
5. G. Lösekann, *Chem. Zeit.*, **14**, 1409 (1890).
6. J. Guareschi, *Einfuhrung in das Studium Alkaloide*, H. Kunz-Krausse, Berlin, 1897, p. 620.
7. P. Duden and M. Scharff, *Ann.*, **288**, 218 (1895).
8. J. van 't Hoff, *Ausichte über organische Chemie*, I, Braunschweig, 1881, p. 121.
9. G. Cohn, *J. prakt. Chem.*, **56**, 345 (1897).
10. M. Dominikiewicz, *Arch. Chem. Farm.*, **4**, 1 (1939), through *Chem. Abstracts*, **34**, 714 (1940).
11. A. Oskerko, *Farm. Zhur.*, **1938**, No. 3, p. 35, through *Chem. Abstracts*, **34**, 2325 (1940).
12. S. Hendricks, *Chem. Revs.*, **7**, 431 (1930).
13. R. Reinicke, *Zeit. Elektrochem.*, **35**, 895 (1925).
14. R. Dickinson and A. Raymond, *J. Am. Chem. Soc.*, **45**, 28 (1923).
15. E. Baur and W. Ruetschi, *Helv. chim. Acta*, **24**, 754 (1941).
15a. E. Meissner, E. Schweidessen and D. Othmer, *Ind. Eng. Chem.*, **46**, 724 (1954).
16. H. Richmond, G. Myers and G. Wright, *J. Am. Chem. Soc.*, **70**, 3659 (1948).
17. L. Henry, *Bull. Acad. Belg.*, (3), **26**, 200 (1893).
18. J. Polley, C. Winkler and R. Nicholls, *Can. J. Research*, **25B**, 525 (1947).
19. T. Colon, *Bol. acad. cienc. exactes, fis.(quym.) nat. (Madrid)*, No. 2, p. 7 (1935), through *Chem. Abstracts*, **30**, 2919 (1936).
20. T. Ingraham and C. Winckler, *Can. J. Chem.*, **30**, 687 (1952).
21. R. Fittig and A. Schwärtzlin, *Ann.*, **331**, 105 (1904).
22. B. Grützner, *Arch. Pharm.*, **236**, 370 (1898).
23. F. Utz, *Süddeut. Apotheker-Z.*, **59**, 832 (1919), through *Chem. Abstracts*, **14**, 3345 (1920).
24. C. Carter, U. S. 1,566,820 (1935) to S. Karpen & Bros.
25. T. Ohara, *J. Soc. Rubber Ind. Japan*, **10**, 438 (1937).
26. B. Trendelenberg, *Biochem. Z.*, **95**, 146 (1919).
27. A. Rattu, *Ann. chim. Applicata*, **29**, 22 (1939), through *Chem. Abstracts*, **34**, 41 (1940).
28. P. Krishnamurti, *Indian J. Physics*, **6**, 345 (1931), through *Chem. Abstracts*, **26**, 1190 (1932).

29. F. Chemnitius, *Chem.-Ztg.*, **52**, 735 (1928).
30. S. Kolosov, *Novosti Tekhniki*, **1936**, No. 40–41, p. 42, through *Chem. Abstracts*, **31**, 3002 (1937).
31. A. Sandor, *Z. angew. Chem.*, **33**, I, 84 (1920).
32. W. Herzog, *Z. angew. Chem.*, **33**, 48 (1920).
33. P. Nachan, U. S. 1,930,210 (1933) to Gutehoffnungshütte, A-G.
34. Fr. 687,735 (1930) to Gutehoffnungshütte, A-G.
35. H. Plauson, U. S. 1,408,826 (1922).
36. L. Rombaut and J. Nieuwland, *J. Am. Chem. Soc.*, **44**, 2061 (1922).
37. C. Carter and A. Coxe, U. S. 1,499,001 (1924) to S. Karpen & Bros. C. Carter, U. S. 1,499,002; 1,566,822 (1925); 1,630,782 (1927); 1,635,707 (1927).
38. Ger. 521,456 (1927) to S. Karpen & Bros.
39. D. Defrance, *J. Pharm. Belg.*, **3**, 605 (1921), through *Chem. Abstracts*, **15**, 3891 (1921).
40. E. Slowick and R. Kelley, *J. Am. Pharm. Assoc.*, **31**, 15 (1942).
41. M. Rapine, *Ann. chim. anal.*, **25**, 113 (1943).
42. R. Gros, *J. pharm. chim.*, **22**, 241 (1935), through *Chem. Abstracts*, **30**, 3362 (1936).
43. A. Brochet and R. Cambier, *Bull. soc. chim.*, (3), **13**, 395 and 534 (1895).
44. M. Delepine, *Bull. soc. chim.*, (3), **13**, 135 (1895).
45. J. Graymore, *J. Chem. Soc.*, **1931**, 1490.
46. G. Grassi, *Gazz. chim. ital.*, **36**, II, 505 (1906).
47. P. Knudsen, *Ber.*, **42**, 3994 (1909).
48. Picon, *Compt. rend.*, **175**, 695 (1922).
49. D. Marotta and M. Alessandrini, *Gazz. chim. ital.*, **59**, 942 (1929).
50. C. von Girsewald and H. Sugens, *Ber.*, **54B**, 490 (1921).
51. D. Marotta and M. Alessandrini, *Gazz. chim. ital.*, **61**, 977 (1931).
52. C. von Girsewald, *Ber.*, **45**, 2571 (1912).
53. L. Legler, *Ber.*, **18**, 3343 (1885).
54. A. Baeyer and V. Villiger, *Ber.*, **33**, 2486 (1900).
55. J. Altpeter, *Das Hexamethylenetetramin und Seine Verwendung*, Halle, Verlag von Wilhelm Knapp, Halle, 1931, p. 26.
56. J. Walker, *Formaldehyde*, Reinhold, New York, 1944, Chapt. 18.
57. R. Cambier and A. Brochet, *Bull. soc. chim.*, (3), **13**, 394 (1895).
58. M. Delepine, *Bull. soc. chim.*, (3), **13**, 353 (1895).
59. G. Hale, *J. Am. Chem. Soc.*, **47**, 2754 (1925).
60. V. Gilpin and C. Winkler, *Can. J. Chem.*, **30**, 743 (1952).
61. M. Foss, *J. Chem. Soc.*, **1950**, 624.
62. M. Foss, *J. Chem. Soc.*, **1950**, 1691.
63. G. Scagliarini and M. Monti, *Atti accad. Lincei*, (6), **4**, 210 (1926), through *Chem. Abstracts*, **21**, 213 (1927).
64. G. Scagliarini, *Atti accad. Lincei*, (6), **2**, 269 (1925) through *Chem. Abstracts* **20**, 156 (1926).
65. R. Ripan, *Bull. soc. stiinte Cluj*, **4**, 28 (1928), through *Chem. Abstracts*, **22** 3104 (1928).
66. W. Bachmann et al., *J. Am. Chem. Soc.*, **73**, 2769 (1951).
67. Brit. 615,419 and 615,793 (1949) to Honorary Council for Scientific & Industrial Research (Canada).
68. P. Griess and G. Harrow, *Ber.*, **21**, 2137 (1888).
69. G. Caesar and M. Goldfrank, U. S. 2,398,080 (1946) to Stein, Hall & Co.
70. A. Vroom and C. Winkler, *Can. J. Research*, **28B**, 701 (1950).

71. J. Wyler, U. S. 2,355,770 (1944) to Trojan Powder Co.
72. W. Bachmann and J. Sheehan, *J. Am. Chem. Soc.*, **71**, 1842 (1949).
73. J. Boivin and G. Wright, *Can. J. Research*, **28B**, 213 (1950).
74. G. Myers and G. Wright, *Can. J. Research*, **27B**, 489 (1949).
75. W. Chute et al., *Can. J. Research*, **27B**, 218 (1949).
76. L. Berman, R. Meen and G. Wright, *Can. J. Chem.*, **29**, 767 (1951).
77. W. Bachmann and E. Jenner, *J. Am. Chem. Soc.*, **73**, 2773 (1951).
78. E. Aristoff et al., *Can. J. Research*, **27B**, 520 (1949).
79. A. Gillies, H. Williams and C. Winkler, *Can. J. Research*, **29**, 377 (1951).
80. W. Dunning, B. Millard, and C. Nutt, *J. Chem. Soc.*, **1952**, 1264.
81. M. Dominikiewicz, *Arch. Chem. Farm.*, **2**, 78 (1935), through *Chem. Abstracts*, **30**, 1029 (1936).
82. W. Bachmann, E. Jenner and L. Scott, *J. Am. Chem. Soc.*, **73**, 2775 (1951).
83. S. Epstein and C. Winkler, *Can. J. Chem.*, **30**, 734 (1952).
84. W. Bachmann and N. Deno, *J. Am. Chem. Soc.*, **73**, 2777 (1951).
85. D. Marotta and M. Alessandrini, *Gazz. chim. ital.*, **59**, 947 (1929), through *Chem. Abstracts*, **24**, 3987 (1930).
86. W. Jones, *J. Am. Chem. Soc.*, **76**, 829 (1954).
87. M. Kirsch and C. Winkler, *Can. J. Research*, **28B**, 715 (1950).
88. W. Schroeder et al., *Chem.*, **23**, 1740 (1951)
89. M. Hoehuel, *Arch. Pharm.*, **237**, 693 (1899).
90. M. Likhosheratov, *J. Gen. Chem.*, **3**, 164 (1933), through *Chem. Abstracts*, **28**, 1675 (1934).
91. L. Legler, *Ber.*, **18**, 3350 (1885).
92. H. Horton, *Ber.*, **21**, 1999 (1888).
93. R. Scheuble, *Ger.* 583,478 (1933).
94. E. Werner, *J. Chem. Soc.*, **89**, 1639 (1906).
95. A. Mouneyrat, *Compt. rend.*, **136**, 1472 (1903).
96. M. Delepine, *Bull. soc. chim.*, (4), **9**, 1025 (1911).
97. A. Leulier and R. Cohen, *J. pharm. chim.*, **29**, 245 (1939).
98. R. Buratti, Swiss 90,703 (1923), through *Chem. Abstracts*, **17**, 2119 (1923).
99. R. Buratti, U. S. 1,416,606.
100. T. Birchall and S. Coffey, U. S. 2,021,680 to Imperial Chem. Ind. Ltd.
101. A. Wohl, *Ber.*, **19**, 1840 (1886).
102. J. Walker, *Formaldehyde*, Reinhold Publishing Corp., New York, 1944, p. 293.
103. J. Laborde, *Chim. ind.*, Special No., p. 504 (Feb. 1929), through *Chem. Abstracts*, **23**, 1488 (1929).
104. A. Perret and A. Krawczynaki, *Compt. rend.*, **194**, 376 (1932).
105. P. Malatesta, L. Scurs and F. Sorice, *Farm. sci. e tec.*, **4**, 145 (1949), through *Chem. Abstracts*, **43**, 5824 (1949).
106. W. Eschweiler, *Ann.*, **278**, 230 (1894).
107. M. Frerejacque, *Ann. chim.*, **14**, 147 (1930), through *Chem. Abstracts*, **25**, 3222 (1931).
108. V. Korshak and S. Rafikov, *J. Gen. Chem.*, **14**, 974 and 983 (1944), through *Chem. Abstracts*, **39**, 4593 (1945).
109. M. Passerini, *Gazz. chim. ital.*, **53**, 333 (1923).
110. A. Franchimont, *Rec. trav. chim.*, **29**, 355 (1910).
111. M. Ionescu and V. Georgescu, *Bull. soc. chim.*, (4), **41**, 881 (1927).
112. G. Vanags, *Z. anal. Chem.*, **122**, 119 (1941).
113. M. Delepine and P. Jaffeux, *Bull. soc. chim.*, (4), **31**, 108 (1922).
114. R. Tschunk, U. S. 1,336,709 (1920) to The Chemical Foundation.

115. F. Hahn and H. Walter, *Ber.*, **54B**, 1531 (1921).

116. S. Angyal, D. Penman and G. Warwick, *J. Chem. Soc.*, **1953**, 1737.

117. A. Galat and G. Elion, *J. Am. Chem. Soc.*, **61**, 3585 (1939).

118. K. Hock, Ger. 139,394 (1903).

119. M. Sommelet and J. Guioth, *Compt. rend.*, **174**, 687 (1922).

120. M. Delepine, *Bull. soc. chim.*, (3), **17**, 290 (1897).

121. J. Graymore and D. Davies, *J. Chem. Soc.*, **1945**, 293.

122. H. Clarke, H. Gillespie and S. Weisshaus, *J. Am. Chem. Soc.*, **55**, 4571 (1933).

123. J. Graymore, *J. Chem. Soc.*, **1947**, 1116.

124. R. Fuson and J. Denton, *J. Am. Chem. Soc.*, **63**, 654 (1941).

125. S. Angyal, D. Penman, and G. Warwick, *J. Chem. Soc.*, **1953**, 1742.

126. J. Hartung, *J. prakt. Chem.*, (2), **46**, 1 (1892).

127. M. Dominikiewicz, *Arch. Chem. Farm.*, **2**, 78 (1935), through *Chem. Abstracts*, **30**, 1029 (1936).

128. Ger. 346,383 (1923) to J. R. Riedel, A-G. through *Chem. Abstracts*, **17**, 1248 (1923).

129. A. Baniel, M. Frankel, I. Friedrich and A. Katchalsky, *J. Org. Chem.*, **13**, 791 (1948).

130. F. Boedecker and J. Sepp, *Ber. pharm. Ges.*, **32**, 339 (1922), through *Chem. Abstracts*, **17**, 195 (1923).

131. N. Wendler, *J. Am. Chem. Soc.*, **71**, 375 (1949).

132. C. Adaveeshia and H. Jois, *J. Indian Chem. Soc.*, **22**, 49 (1945).

133. B. Dey and S. Rajagopalan, *Arch. Pharm.*, **277**, 359 (1939).

134. Y. Tamanuisi, *J. Pharm. Soc. Japan*, **60**, 189 (1940), through *Chem. Abstracts*, **34**, 5446 (1940).

135. Austr. 86,136 (1923) to Meister, Lucius, and Brüning, through *Chem. Abstracts*, **17**, 1305 (1923).

136. S. Gurin, A. Deluva and D. Crandell, *J. Org. Chem.*, **12**, 612 (1947).

137. I. Kaye, *J. Am. Chem. Soc.*, **73**, 5002 (1951).

138. W. Jacobs and M. Heidelberger, *J. Am. Chem. Soc.*, **39**, 1439 (1917).

139. R. Delaby, *Bull. soc. chim.*, (5), **3**, 2375 (1936).

140. E. Hug, *Bull. soc. chim.*, (5), **1**, 990, 1004 (1934).

141. A. McKay and G. Wright, *J. Am. Chem. Soc.*, **68**, 2116 (1946).

142. S. van der Meer, *Rev. trav. chim.*, **63**, 157 (1944).

143. B. Reichert and H. Baege, *Pharmazie*, **2**, 451 (1947), through *Chem. Abstracts*, **42**, 3743 (1948).

144. B. Reichert and H. Baege, *Pharmazie*, **3**, 209 (1948), through *Chem. Abstracts*, **42**, 5889 (1948).

145. B. Reichert and H. Baege, *Pharmazie*, **4**, 149 (1949), through *Chem. Abstracts*, **43**, 6586 (1949).

146. L. Smith and K. Welch, *J. Chem. Soc.*, **1934**, 729.

147. T. Miyoshi, *J. Soc. Chem. Ind. Japan*, **45**, 1080 (1942), through *Chem. Abstracts*, **42**, 6154 (1948).

148. H. Moschatos and B. Tollens, *Ann.*, **272**, 280 (1893).

149. S. Sugimoto, *Repts. Imp. Ind. Research Institute Osaka, Japan*, **11**, No. 21 (1931), through *Chem. Abstracts*, **25**, 3778 (1931).

150. S. Sugimoto, *Repts. Imp. Ind. Research Institute Osaka, Japan*, **10**, No. 11 (1929), through *Chem. Abstracts*, **24**, 837 (1930).

151. T. Shono, *J. Soc. Chem. Ind.*, **32**, 2128 (1929), through *Chem. Abstracts*, **24**, 1940 (1930).

152. M. Harvey and L. Baekeland, *J. Ind. Eng. Chem.*, **13**, 135 (1921).

153. D. Defrance, *J. Pharm. Belg.*, **3**, 605 (1921), through *Chem. Abstracts*, **15**, 3891 (1921).
154. J. Altpeter, *Das Hexamethylenetetramin und Seine Verwendung*, Verlag von Wilhelm Knapp, Halle, 1931, p. 80–83.
155. J. Laborde, *Chim. ind.* Special No., p. 504 (Feb. 1929), through *Chem. Abstracts*, **23**, 4188 (1929).
156. P. Bouchereau, *J. pharm. chim.*, **4**, 162 (1936), through *Chem. Abstracts*, **31**, 4773 (1937).
157. P. Bouchereau, *J. pharm. chim.*, **25**, 159 (1937), through *Chem. Abstracts*, **31**, 4773 (1937).
158. J. Duff and E. Bills, *J. Chem. Soc.*, **1932**, 1987.
159. R. Desai and K. Radha, *Proc. Indian Acad. Sci.*, **11A**, 422 (1940), through *Chem. Abstracts*, **34**, 7883 (1940).
160. J. Duff, *J. Chem. Soc.*, **1941**, 547.
161. J. Duff and V. Furness, *J. Chem. Soc.*, **1951**, 1512.
162. J. Duff and V. Furness, *J. Chem. Soc.*, **1952**, 1159.
163. J. Duff and E. Bills, *J. Chem. Soc.*, **1924**, 1305.
164. P. Galimberti, *Gazz. chim. ital.*, **77**, 375 (1947), through *Chem. Abstracts*, **42**, 4558 (1948).
165. G. Dougherty and W. Taylor, *J. Am. Chem. Soc.*, **55**, 1294 (1933).
166. G. Dougherty and W. Taylor, *J. Am. Chem. Soc.*, **55**, 4588 (1933).
167. L. Hartung, *J. prakt. Chem.*, (2), **46**, 19 (1892).
168. J. Duff, *J. Chem. Soc.*, **1945**, 276.
169. S. Angyal, P. Morris, R. Rasack and J. Waterer, *J. Chem. Soc.*, **1949**, 2704.
170. H. Snyder, S. Swaminathan and H. Sims, *J. Am. Chem. Soc.*, **74**, 5110 (1952).
171. V. Evdokimoff, *Gazz. chim. ital.*, **77**, 318 (1947), through *Chem. Abstracts*, **42**, 2586 (1948).
172. S. Lukasiewicz and E. Murray, *J. Am. Chem. Soc.*, **68**, 1389 (1946).
173. C. Rizzoli, *Boll. soc. ital. biol. sper.*, **25**, 433 (1949), through *Chem. Abstracts*, **45**, 69 (1951).
174. W. Puckner and W. Hidpert, *J. Am. Chem. Soc.*, **30**, 1471 (1908).
175. C. van Zijp, *Pharm. Weekblad*, **55**, 45 (1918), through *Chem. Abstracts*, **16**, 889 (1918).
176. P. Carles, *Pharm. chim.*, (7), **13**, 279 (1916), through *Chem. Abstracts*, **10**, 1896 (1916).
177. G. Bouilloux, *J. pharm. chim.*, **24**, 58 (1936), through *Chem. Abstracts*, **31**, 4231 (1937).
178. J. Walker, *Formaldehyde*, Reinhold Publ. Corp., New York, 1944, p. 297.
179. R. Gros, *J. pharm. chim.*, **22**, 241 (1935), through *Chem. Abstracts*, **30**, 3362 (1936).
180. E. Slowick and R. Kelley, *J. Am. Pharm. Assoc.*, **31**, 15 (1942).
181. M. Rapine, *Ann. chim. anal.*, **25**, 113 (1943).
182. C. Bordeiann, *Ann. sci. univ. Jassy*, **15**, 380 (1929), through *Chem. Abstracts*, **23**, 3189 (1929).
183. J. Walker, *Formaldehyde*, Reinhold Publ. Corp., New York, 1944, p. 302–369.
184. J. Altpeter, *Das Hexamethylenetrramin und Seine Verwendung*, Verlag von Wilhelm Knapp, Halle, 1931, p. 128–162.
185. J. Lazarus, *Urol. Cutaneous Rev.*, **41**, 239 (1937), through *Chem. Abstracts*, **31**, 3991 (1937).
186. V. Brustier and G. Subra, *Toulouse med.*, **49**, 37 (1948), through *Chem. Abstracts*, **44**, 10174 (1950).

187. C. Gastaldi, *Bull. chim. farm.*, **61**, 353 (1922), through *Chem. Abstracts*, **16**, 3070 (1922).
191. F. Pollak, Brit. 515,616 (1939), through *Chem. Abstracts*, **35**, 6019 (1941).
192. F. Pollak, U. S. 2,230,121 (1941), through *Chem. Abstracts*, **35**, 3006 (1941).
193. E. Hirst et al., *J. Chem. Soc.*, **1947**, 924.
194. A. Zinke, F. Hanus and H. Pichelmayer, *Monatsh.*, **78**, 311 (1948).
195. K. Hultzsch, *Ber.*, **82**, 16 (1949).
196. A. Zinke and S. Pucher, *Monatsh.*, **79**, 26 (1948).
197. O. Peterson, U. S. 2,373,777 (1945) to DuPont.
198. E. Wolf, U. S. 2,242,565 (1941) to Heberlein Patent Corp., through *Chem. Abstracts*, **35**, 5725 (1941).
199. O. Neuss and A. Thienne, Ger. 512,956 (1929) to August Haller.
200. J. Speaker, U. S. 2,432,347 (1947).
201. Brit. 558,872 (1944) to Promedico Prod. Ltd. & S. Neumann.
202. C. Bedford and W. Scott, *J. Ind. Eng. Chem.*, **12**, 31 (1920).
203. A. Toy and T. Beck, *J. Am. Chem. Soc.*, **72**, 3191 (1950).

CHAPTER XI

s-Triazaborane and Its Derivatives

I. Introduction

s-Triazaborane has been given a variety of common names since it was first shown to possess a six-membered ring structure. The common names borazole,[1] "inorganic benzene,"[1] tribornine triamine and triboron nitride have been used to describe the parent member of the series. The Ring Index name s-triazaborane (I) has been found best adapted to naming the parent compound and its derivatives and is

$$
\begin{array}{ccc}
\text{(I)} & \text{(II)} & \text{(III)}
\end{array}
$$

used exclusively in this volume. Derivatives are named in the conventional manner, numbering starting with a nitrogen atom. The Chemical Abstracts system* of naming in this series is based on the hypothetical compound (II) called s-triazatriborine, no chemistry of which is known with certainty. All the known compounds are derivatives of (I) which, is named as a hexahydro-s-triazatriborine. Under such a system, the nomenclature of hydrogenated derivatives of (I) such as (III) becomes unduly cumbersome. Therefore the Chemical Abstracts system has been by-passed in favor of the Ring Index system.

II. s-Triazaborane

1. History; Physical Properties; Structure

The simplest compound in this series is s-triazaborane (I) which because many of its properties are similar to those of benzene, has been

---

* The name "borazine" for the parent compound (I), has been recommended by an A.C.S. advisory committee on the nomenclature of organic boron compounds. Much of the recent literature makes use of this proposal.

called "inorganic benzene." s-Triazaborane was first described by Stock and Pohland[2] in 1926 and its structure correctly surmised. Alone (I) might be regarded as strictly an inorganic compound, but its methyl and aryl derivatives fall into the classification of organic compounds. Because of their structural similarity to the s-triazines and also because no book on Heterocyclic Chemistry to date has undertaken to include a discussion of them, the s-triazaboranes are discussed in this volume.

s-Triazaborane is a colorless, mobile, moderately stable liquid with a molecular weight of 81.6. In contrast to Stock and Pohland,[2] Schaeffer[26] and his workers found traces of a non-volatile solid from s-triazaborane during periods as short as several days even at —80°. During a period of several weeks, considerable quantities of hydrogen, together with small quantities of diborane and other volatile substances are produced. The decomposition seems limited to the liquid phase; none was observed[26] in the gas phase.

Compound (I) boils at 53°/760 mm. and melts[31] at 216.9° K. Physical properties are expressed by the following formulas in which $T = °K$:

Vapor pressure[2] (mm Hg):

$$\log p = -1457.5/T + 1.75 \log T - 0.00010435T + 3.2875$$

Density[3] (g/cc):
$$d = 1.1551 - 0.001074T$$

Viscosity (poises)[31]:
$$n = (47.3 \times 10^{-5}) \, (d)^{1/3} \, e^{665.5d/T}$$

Surface tension (dynes/cm)[31]
$$\gamma = (58.3 - 0.120T)d^{2/3}$$

The density[2] of the solid (—65°) is 1.00. The refractive index[31] at 20° is 1.3821 (sodium D line).

A further tabulation of the physical properties of s-triazaborane must be preceded by a consideration of its structure. Wiberg[1] has summarized available data on the structure of (I). A consideration of the formula $B_3N_3H_6$ indicates eleven[3] possible structural formulas involving trivalent boron and trivalent nitrogen, seven (IV–X) of which are chain type structures and four (I, XI–XIII) ring structures.

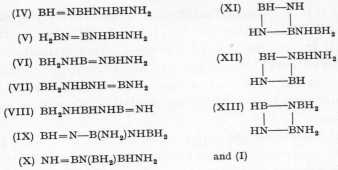

(IV) BH=NBHNHBHNH$_2$

(V) H$_2$BN=BNHBHNH$_2$

(VI) BH$_2$NHB=NBHNH$_2$

(VII) BH$_2$NHBNH=BNH$_2$

(VIII) BH$_2$NHBHNHB=NH

(IX) BH=N—B(NH$_2$)NHBH$_2$

(X) NH=BN(BH$_2$)BHNH$_2$

(XI) BH—NH
    | |
HN——BNHBH$_2$

(XII) BH—NBHNH$_2$
    | |
HN——BH

(XIII) HB——NBH$_2$
    | |
HN——BNH$_2$

and (I)

The decision that of these eleven formulas (I) is the correct one rests on a firm experimental basis. The interference rings from scattering of electrons passing through gaseous *s*-triazaborane resemble those of benzene[4] and indicate a regular hexagonal structure with alternating boron and nitrogen atoms.

The Raman spectrum of liquid *s*-triazaborane has been studied[6] and the infrared absorption of the gas measured in the region from 2.5 to 24.5 μ. The molecule was assumed to be isoelectronic with benzene and an assignment of fundamental frequencies made on this basis.[6] A comparison with the fundamental frequencies of benzene gave satisfactory correlation and from these together with structural data, the thermodynamic properties of (I) for the perfect gas at one atmosphere pressure were calculated.

There is also good chemical evidence for structure (I) for *s*-triazaborane. Hexamethyl-*s*-triazaborane has been made and is discussed later. Hydrolysis[7] of the latter compound with dilute hydrochloric acid at 100° produces, quantitatively, three equivalents each of methylboric acid and methylamine hydrochloride (1). From equation (1) it is apparent that each

$$B_3N_3(CH_3)_6 + 6\,HOH \longrightarrow 3\,BCH_3(OH)_2 + 3\,CH_3NH_2 \cdot HCl + 3\,HCl \qquad (1)$$

nitrogen atom and each boron atom must have had one and only one methyl group attached. In formulas (IV–XIII) at least one nitrogen or one boron atom would have to be methyl free. Moreover the number of isomers produced from *s*-triazaborane conforms to the six-membered ring structure. For the formula $B_3N_3H_5CH_3$ there exist two and only two isomers, one in which the methyl group is on boron and the other in which it is on nitrogen. On the other hand, from the unsymmetrical formulas (IV–XIII) either four (V, VI, VII, X, XIII) or five (IV, VIII, XI, XII) isomers may exist for a monomethyl derivative. And in experimental work[8,9,10] with di-, tri-, and tetramethyl derivatives in no case has the number of isomers obtained exceeded the number anticipated from formula (I). Structures (IV–XIII) would allow many more isomers.

s-Triazaborane might appear on cursory examination to be more analogous to cyclohexane than to benzene for its appears saturated—until one considers its electronic structure. Wiberg[1] has pointed out that the strong tendency of boron to fill its outer electron shell to the neon level results in a mesomerism between the structures (XIIA) and (XIIIA) where the electron pair from the nitrogen atom shifts to form a double bond (2). Several experimental facts support this hypothesis.

$$
\text{(XIIA)} \quad \longleftrightarrow \quad \text{(XIIIA)} \tag{2}
$$

First, the B—N bond distances[5] of 1.44 ± 0.02 Å lie between the values of 1.50 Å for a B—N single bond and 1.35 Å for a B—N double bond. Second, the experimentally determined[3] value for the parachor, 208, lies between that calculated for single bond structures (195) and a structure with three double bonds (260).

The analogy between s-triazaborane and benzene can be carried one step further by comparing the discrepancies between the observed and calculated absorption values for the vibrational deformation of the infrared[17] active C—H in benzene (calc. 783 cm^{-1}, found 671 cm^{-1}) and the B—H or N—H (calc. 756, 1278 cm^{-1}, found 622, 1098 cm^{-1}) in s-triazaborane[6]. The discrepancies are analogous and percentagewise,

(XIV)

equal. Because of its similarity to an aromatic nucleus the *s*-triazaborane ring has been written (XIV) with dotted valences to indicate the double bond character. Wiberg and Bolz have reported many of the physical properties of (I).

Critical temperature of *s*-triazaborane is 252° C,

Density at the boiling point, 0.81 g/cm^3,

Heat of vaporization, 7.0 Kcal.,

Molecular volume at the boiling point 99.7 cm^3,

Surface tension at the melting point, 31.09 dynes/cm,

Parachor 207.9,

Trouton's constant 21.4 and

Eotvos' constant 2.0.

Ramaswamy has found[10] a value of 0.67×10^{-18} for the electric moment and has also measured the compressibility at ordinary temperature[10] and the refractive index and dispersion.[11] The heat capacity of *s*-triazaborane has been calculated by Spencer.[12] The absorption spectra has been studied[13] in *n*-heptane in the 2250–1700 Å region. Four diffuse bands were found starting at 1995 Å with spacing about 900 cm^{-1}. These appear to be analogous to the 2000 Å bands of benzene but the intensity is smaller by about ten times. (I) shows no absorption bands in the region 2000 Å – 4600 Å and since bands analogous to those of benzene are expected on theoretical grounds, it is probable[14] that the analogs of the benzene 2600 Å and 1830 Å bands are the *s*-triazaborane 1995 Å and 1720 Å bands. The ultraviolet spectrum of *s*-triazaborane has been treated according to the semi-empirical method of molecular orbitals by Roothaan and Mulliken.[15] Vapor pressure data and other physical properties have been summarized by Wiberg.[3]

2. Preparation

s-Triazaborane can be directly prepared[3] by heating an equimolar mixture of ammonia and a boron hydride at 250–300° at one atmosphere pressure for one half hour.[2,3,16]

$$3\,B_2H_6 + 6\,NH_3 \xrightarrow[\substack{1\ \text{atm.} \\ 30\ \text{min.}}]{250-300°} 2 \begin{array}{c} \text{H} \\ \text{B} \\ \text{HN} \diagup \diagdown \text{NH} \\ | \quad\quad | \\ \text{HB} \diagdown \diagup \text{BH} \\ \text{N} \\ \text{H} \end{array} + 12\,H_2 \qquad (3)$$

Yields are about 50%, the remainder being condensed, polymeric material which approaches in composition the formula BNH and has

(IA)

the probable[1] structure (IA). The mechanism of formation[3] from diborane and ammonia is shown in equation (4). First dissociation to borane occurs

$$(BH_3)_2 \xrightarrow{NH_3}_{\Delta} BH_3 \cdots NH_3 \xrightarrow{-H_2} BH_2 \cdots NH_2 \xrightarrow{-H_2} BH \cdots NH \qquad (4)$$

(5)

followed by formation of an adduct with ammonia. The adducts suffers stepwise loss of two equivalents of hydrogen to a moiety, three molecules of which can condense[5] to form one of s-triazaborane in the same way that acetylene may form benzene.

There are two other methods for synthesis of s-triazaborane. One consists of treating ammonium chloride with lithium borohydride in a nitrogen atmosphere at 300° and one atmosphere (4a). Although the yields[27] are only 30–35%, no better than the older method, the use of high vacuum apparat usis avoided. The low yields are due to (1) caking, which can be minimized by using powdered Pyrex glass, and (2) the reaction between s-triazaborane and ammonium chloride, which occurs above 275° with extensive decomposition. The "diammoniate of diborane," $B_2H_6 \cdot 2NH_3$ was also probably made. The second method[26] also involves the use of lithium borohydride, in this case to reduce B-trichloro-s-triazaborane, according to equation (4b).

$$3\,LiBH_4 + 3\,NH_4Cl \xrightarrow{N_2\ 300°}_{1\ atm.} B_3N_3H_3 + 9\,H_2 + 3\,LiCl \qquad (4a)$$

$$3\,LiBH_4 + B_3N_3H_3Cl_3 \longrightarrow B_3N_3H_3 + 1\tfrac{1}{2}\,B_2H_6 + 3\,LiCl \qquad (4b)$$

If lithium aluminum hydride is used, the s-triazaborane cannot be recovered from the reaction mixture owing to the formation and presence of aluminum hydride which reacts with the product. The diborane formed as a by-product from (4b) may be collected and stored or disposed of by absorbing it in sodium trimethoxyborohydride (4c).

$$B_2H_6 + 2\,NaBH(OCH_3)_3 \longrightarrow 2\,NaBH_4 + 2\,B(OCH_3)_3 \qquad (4c)$$

3. Chemical Properties and Reactions

A. Stability

s-Triazaborane is only moderately stable[26] (see Physical Properties) even when dry in the liquid phase. At —80° a white coating appears on the vessel in the short space of several days. Slowly increasing decomposition occurs[2] as (I) is heated from 300° to 500°, mostly according to equation (6).

$$B_3N_3H_6 \longrightarrow 3(BNH) + 3\,[H] \qquad (6)$$

Heating at 500° C. for twelve hours resulted in recovery of a small quantity of undecomposed starting material.[2]

Oxygen does not affect *s*-triazaborane at room temperature ordinarily; however, a spark in the mixture caused an explosion[2] which was accompanied by a green-violet flash. Decomposition occurred according to equation (7)

$$4\,B_3N_3H_6 + 15\,O_2 \longrightarrow 6\,B_2O_3 + 6\,N_2 + 12\,H_2O \qquad (7)$$

B. Reaction with Water

s-Triazaborane is hydrolyzed[2,3,7,8,9,18] slowly by water at low temperatures and more rapidly when warm. Boric acid, ammonia and hydrogen are the products. The reaction proceeds first with formation of the complex $B_3N_3H_6 \cdot 3H_2O$ which is probably represented by (XV). Splitting then occurs (8) and is followed by hydrolysis (9, 10). It should be recognized that these steps are not intended to represent a true mechanism:

$$3\,BHOH\!\!-\!\!NH_2 + 3\,H_2O \longrightarrow 3\,BH(OH)_2\!\!-\!\!NH_2 \longrightarrow 3\,B(OH)_2\!\!-\!\!NH_2 + 3\,H_2 \qquad (9)$$

$$3\,B(OH)_2\!\!-\!\!NH_2 + 3\,H_2O \longrightarrow 3\,B(OH)_3\!\!-\!\!NH_2 \xrightarrow{3\,HCl} 3\,B(OH)_3 + 3\,NH_4Cl \qquad (10)$$

When *s*-triazaborane is treated with ice water the complex (XV) is formed and can be isolated by removing excess water in a vacuum. If (I) is warmed with three equivalents of water, at a temperature of

$$
\begin{array}{c}
\text{H} \\
\text{HN}^{\diagup\text{B}\diagdown}\text{NH} \\
| \quad\quad | \\
\text{HB}_{\diagdown\text{N}\diagup}\text{BH} \\
\text{H} \quad\text{(I)}
\end{array}
+ 3\,H_2O \longrightarrow
\begin{array}{c}
\text{OH} \\
\text{HN}^{\diagup\text{B}\diagdown}\text{NH} \\
| \quad\quad | \\
\text{HOB}_{\diagdown\text{N}\diagup}\text{BOH} \\
\text{H} \quad\text{(XVII)}
\end{array}
+ 3\,H_2 \tag{11}
$$

$100°$ the evolution of hydrogen is observed[3,18] and reaction (11) occurs to give 2,4,6-trihydroxy-*s*-triazaborane (XVI).

C. Reaction with Methanol

Methanol reacts with *s*-triazaborane (12) in the same manner as cold water does to give the solid addition compound[3,18] hexahydro-2,4,6-trimethoxy-*s*-triazaborane (XVII). Hydrogen splits out after

$$
\text{(I)} + 3\,CH_3OH \longrightarrow
\begin{array}{c}
\text{H}\diagdown\quad\diagup\text{OCH}_3 \\
\text{H}_2\text{N}^{\diagup\text{B}\diagdown}\text{NH}_2 \\
\text{H}\diagdown| \quad\quad |\diagup\text{H} \\
\text{CH}_3\text{O}^{\diagup\text{B}}{\diagdown}_\text{N}{\diagup}^\text{B}\diagdown\text{OCH}_3 \\
\text{H}
\end{array}
\quad\text{(XVII)}
$$

several hours heating at $100°$, but decomposition of the ring occurs as well, resulting in a compound[1] of probable structure $B(OCH_3)=NH$.

D. Hydrogenation

s-Triazaborane resembles benzene in many physical and chemical properties. However hydrogenation presents one of the contrasts between the two compounds. While benzene can easily be hydrogenated under the proper conditions to cyclohexane, *s*-triazaborane on the other hand *evolves* hydrogen[3] when treated with palladium catalyst and hydrogen. A polymeric dehydrogenation product is obtained corresponding to the formula $BNH_{0.8}$ which probably[3] contains some "B–N" material. The reaction has been formulated[1,3] as occurring in accordance with equation (12).

$$
B_3N_3H_6 + n(H) \longrightarrow (B_3N_3H_{6-n})_x + nH_2 \tag{12}
$$

E. Bromination

s-Triazaborane and excess bromine react[1,3] at 0° to give a hard yellow solid addition compound (XVIII) which contains two equivalents of bromine. At a temperature of 60°, (XVIII) evolves hydrogen bromide (13) and gives 2,4-dibromo-*s*-triazaborane (XIX).

$$
\text{(I)} \quad + 2\,Br_2 \xrightarrow{0°} \text{(XVIII)} \xrightarrow{60°} \text{(XIX)} \quad + 2\,HBr \ (13)
$$

F. Reaction with Hydrogen Halides

At room temperature *s*-triazaborane reacts with three equivalents of either hydrogen bromide or hydrogen chloride to produce adducts (XXII) which are hard white substances, not volatile in high vacuum at room temperature. If adduct (XXII) is heated[1,2,3] to 100° or if (I)

$$
\text{(I)} \quad + 3\,HX \xrightarrow{25°} \text{(XXI)} \xrightarrow{100°} \text{(XXII)} \quad + 3\,H_2 \ (14)
$$

is treated with only the theoretical amount of halogen halide at 100°, loss of hydrogen occurs (14) and 2,4,6-trihalo-*s*-triazaboranes result[1,2,3]

Treating (XVII)—the addition compound obtained from *s*-triazaborane with ice-cold water—with hydrogen chloride[2] gave a hard colorless glassy solid with simultaneous evolution of hydrogen (15).

$$
B_3N_3H_6 + 3\,H_2O \xrightarrow{0°} B_3N_3H_6 \cdot 3\,H_2O \xrightarrow{+\,3\,HCl} B_3N_3H_3Cl_3 \cdot 3\,H_2O + 3\,H_2 \ (15)
$$

From (15) it is seen that (XVII) hexahydro-2,4,6-trihydroxy-*s*-triazaborane behaves quite differently toward[2] hydrogen halides than does the parent compound (I).

G. Reaction with Boron Halides

s-Triazaborane reacts with boron trichloride or boron tribromide at room temperature to produce a mixture[27] of products from which

can be isolated 2-chloro-*s*-triazaborane and 2,4-dichloro-*s*-triazaborane
or 2-bromo-*s*-triazaborane and 2,4-dibromo-*s*-triazaborane, respectively
in total yields of about 35%. Starting materials, hydrogen, diborane,
and non-volatile solids are also recovered. The properties of these
compounds are discussed in Section III.1.

H. Reaction with Methyl Iodide

s-Triazaborane reacts with excess methyl iodide yielding, after
twenty-four hours heating at 60–70°, an addition compound comprising
one equivalent of (I) and three equivalents of methyl iodide.[1,2] Yields
were 30 % but the reaction (16) has been investigated only summarily.

$$B_3N_3H_6 + 3CH_3I \xrightarrow[\text{24 hrs.}]{60-70°} B_3N_3H \cdot 3CH_3I \qquad (16)$$
$$30\%$$

I. Reaction with Ethers

Dimethyl ether did not react with *s*-triazaborane in the course of
two days at room temperature[1,3], but after fourteen days at 70°, a clear
glassy substance was obtained that has not been further reported on.[1]

J. Reaction with Ammonia and Amines

Compound (I) produces a glassy non-volatile solid (XXIII) which
is soluble in liquid ammonia after treatment for several days at —20°
to —30°. No hydrogen is evolved during the course of the reaction which
appears to consist of addition of one equivalent of ammonia to *s*-triaza-
borane.[1,2,3] (XXIII) evolves hydrogen when heated.[1,2,3] After several

$$\begin{array}{c} H \cdots NH_3 \\ HN \diagdown \overset{B}{} \diagup NH \\ | \qquad | \\ HB \diagdown \underset{N}{} \diagup BH \\ H \quad (XXIII) \end{array}$$

additional days with excess ammonia at room temperature, more
ammonia is taken up and a hard white amorphous mass is produced.
This gradually darkens in color, finally becoming black.

The reaction of amines with *s*-triazaborane has not been extensively
examined. An equimolar mixture of (I) and dimethylamine evolves
one equivalent of hydrogen when heated for two hours at 130°. At the

same time a glassy mass forms which crystallizes in long colorless needles. At room temperature the latter was difficult to volatilize in high vacuum.[1] When it was heated to 120°, a "borazene," $BH_2\text{-}N(CH_3)_2$, was formed.[1,16] *s*-Triazaborane did not react with excess trimethylamine after two days at room temperature,[1,3] but after two weeks at 50–60°, a viscous, tarry, non-volatile substance resulted.

K. Reaction with Trimethylborane

If an equimolar mixture of trimethylborane and (I) is heated for one day at 100°, a 60 % yield (17) of 2,4,6-trimethyl-*s*-triazaborane (XXIV) is obtained.[9] About 5 % of the product is a mixture of 2-methyl

$$\text{(I)} + 3/n\ B(CH_3)_3 \longrightarrow \text{(XXIV)} + 3/n\ BHn(CH_3)_{3-n} \qquad (17)$$

and 2,4-dimethyl-*s*-triazaborane.[9] The remaining 35 % is converted to a hydrogen deficient product, the composition of which approaches the empirical formula BNH. If the ratio of reactants is altered in favor of *s*-triazaborane, then the amount of mono and dimethyl-*s*-triazaboranes in the product mixture increases. Raising the reaction temperature to 200–225° decreased the yield of methyl-*s*-triazaboranes and increased higher condensation product yields. In a similar manner, but in poorer yields, *s*-triazaborane reacts at the boron hydrogen with dimethyl-boramine. The products are also methyl-*s*-triazaboranes.

III. Alkyl Derivatives of *s*-Triazaborane

1. History

The alkyl derivatives of *s*-triazaborane are the best known derivatives. It is only recently that some progress[1] has been made in exploring the largely unknown chemistry of these compounds as well as on synthesis of higher alkyl homologs.[30] Considerable work has been carried out since World War II on boron chemistry, much of it under government sponsorship, so it is not unreasonable to assume that some of it will be published in the near future. Undoubtedly our store of knowledge in this specialized corner of the boron field will also profit.

The first work on methyl-s-triazaboranes was done[8] in 1936 by Schlesinger and his workers who prepared a mono-, a di- and a trimethyl derivative and later[9] isolated six more methyl-s-triazaboranes. Some dozen years later Wiberg[7,18] extended the number of known compounds in this category to include the hexamethyl derivative. The first higher alkyl derivatives were prepared by Hough, Schaeffer and their workers[30] in 1955.

The total number of possible isomers of the methyl-s-triazaboranes is nineteen compared with only twelve methylbenzene isomers, owing to the different compounds which can result from a methyl group on either a boron or a nitrogen atom. For example, there are two compounds both of which are analogs of toluene, N-methyl-s-triazaborane and B-methyl-s-triazaborane.

The methyl-s-triazaboranes are conveniently discussed collectively because of the similarity in their methods of preparation and because of their interrelationships due to isomerization during synthesis.

2. Physical Properties

The known physical properties of the methyl-s-triazaboranes and other alkyl-s-triazaboranes are listed below in Table XI-1.

In general it is safe to say that the alkyl derivatives of s-triazaborane are clear colorless liquids or (in two cases) white crystalline solids at room temperature. They are soluble in ether, benzene, carbon tetrachloride, chloroform, and other common organic solvents; somewhat soluble in methanol, ethanol, and glacial acetic acid; and insoluble in water. The liquids are mobile and have a typical "aromatic" odor. All compounds are quite stable to heat and only at temperatures above 300° do they begin to undergo decomposition.

3. Preparation

The methyl derivatives of s-triazaborane with few exceptions, are all prepared by the same fundamental method—heating diborane and/or one of its methyl derivatives with the proper equivalent of ammonia and/or methylamine at temperatures[7,8,9,18,19] which vary

TABLE XI-1. Physical properties of the Methyl-s-triazaboranes

Compound	Melting point,a °C.	Boiling point, °C.	Heat of vaporization, Kcal/mole	Trouton's constant	Vapor pressure, mm./°C.	Remarks	Ref.
(structure: ring with CH_3)	−59	87	8.2	—	20 mm./0°		1
(structure: ring with BCH_3)	liq.	84	8.0	22.2	24 mm./0°		2
(structure: ring with CH_3, BCH_3)	−48	107	9.2		7 mm./0°		1
(structure: ring with NCH_3)	liq.	108	8.4	21.9	8 mm./0°		2
(structure: ring with CH_3, NCH_3 or CH_3, NH, CH_3)	liq.	124	8.0	20.2	8 mm./0°	b	1

(*Table continued*)

TABLE XI-1 (continued)

Compound	Melting point[a], °C.	Boiling point, °C.	Heat of vaporization, Kcal./mole	Trouton's constant	Vapor pressure, mm./°C.	Remarks	Ref.
(structure: CH₃–B–NH, HN–B–BCH₃, N–H)	31.8	127	10.1	23	5 mm./20° 304 mm./100°	Rhombic crystals. Sol. ethyl ether, dioxane, benzene, acetone, carbon tetrachloride, chloroform, S. sol. alc., methyl alc., acetic acid. Insol. water	1, 3
(structure: H–B–NCH₃, H₃CN–B–NCH₃, HB–BH, N–CH₃ or CH₃–B–NH, HN–B–BCH₃, HN–NH, HB–N–CH₃)	−9	132–134	9.3	22.7	9 mm./20° 276 mm./100° 27 mm./37° 160 mm./85°	Clear, colorless, light weight liquid $N_D^{25} = 1.4404$ $d_{20} = 0.8519^c$	2, 3, 5, 6, 7
(structure: CH₃–B–NCH₃, HN–B–BCH₃, HB–N–H)	liq.	139	8.9	21.6	241 mm./100°	b	2
(structure: CH₃–B–NH, HN–B–BCH₃, N–CH₃)	liq.	158	10.4	24.2	112 mm./100°		2
(structure: CH₃–B–NCH₃, H₃CN–B–BCH₃, N–CH₃)	97.1	221[a]	11.5	—	17 mm./100°	Colorless, odorless, tasteless	4

Compound	Melting point[a],°C.	Boiling point,°C.	Heat of vaporization, Kcal./mole	Trouton's constant	Vapor pressure, mm./°C.	Remarks	Ref.
$\begin{array}{c} H \\ B \\ H_5C_2N \quad NC_2H_5 \\ HB \quad BH \\ N \\ C_2H_5 \end{array}$	−49.6	184	9.21	20.2	1.2/5.8 5.0/31.5 7.7/40.6 17.2/59.3 34.8–78.2	$N_D^{25} = 1.4344$ $d^{20} = 0.8419c$	6
$\begin{array}{c} H \\ B \\ H_7C_3N \quad NC_3H_7 \\ HB \quad BH \\ N \\ C_3H_7 \end{array}$ *normal*	glass	225	10.02	20.2	5.2/56.6 9.8/75.2 16.1/88.0 43.1/114.7 70.7/130.1	$N_D^{25} = 1.4484$ $d^{20} = 0.8347c$	6
$\begin{array}{c} H \\ B \\ H_7C_3N \quad NC_3H_7 \\ HB \quad BH \\ N \\ C_3H_7 \end{array}$ *iso*	−6.5	203	10.29	21.6	11.8/71.3 24.7/89.1 47.1/106.3 74.3/119.4 94.5/126.5	$N_D^{25} = 1.4434$ $d^{20} = 0.8476c$	6

a Indicates extrapolation.
b It is not known which structure is correct.
c For liquid density constants in the range 0–60°, see reference 6.

1. H. Schlesinger, L. Horvitz and A. Burg, *J. Am. Chem. Soc.*, 58, 409 (1936).
2. H. Schlesinger, D. Ritter and A. Burg, *J. Am. Chem. Soc.*, 60, 1296 (1938).
3. E. Wiberg, K. Hertwig and A. Bolz, *Z. anorg. Chem.*, 256, 177 (1948).
4. E. Wiberg and K. Hertwig, *Z. anorg. Chem.*, 255, 141 (1947).
5. G. Schaeffer and E. Anderson, *J. Am. Chem. Soc.*, 71, 2143 (1949).
6. W. Hough, G. Schaeffer, M. Dzuras and A. Stewart, *J. Am. Chem. Soc.*, 77, 864 (1955).
7. T. Bissot and R. Parry, *J. Am. Chem. Soc.*, 77, 3481 (1955).

from 200–450°. This method is discussed first. Diborane or the methyldiboranes would be expected to dissociate in the vapor phase at elevated
temperatures. In the presence of ammonia or methylamine the borane
fragment forms a complex with the latter. The nature of the fragment
depends on the methyldiborane used. For example, monomethyl-
diborane, $CH_3H_2BBH_3$, with ammonia would give two fragments,
H_2BNH_2 and CH_3HBNH_2; symmetrical dimethyldiborane and ammonia would give one fragment, CH_3HBNH_2; and unsymmetrical
dimethyldiborane would give two fragments H_2BNH_2 and $(CH_3)_2BNH_2$;
etc. These fragments then lose an equivalent of hydrogen and form a
trimer. The overall reaction may be represented by equation (18). By
(1) using mixtures of ammonia and/or methylamine and diborane

$$B_2H_6 + 2NH_3 \longrightarrow 2BH_3 \longrightarrow 2[BH_3 \cdot NH_3] \xrightarrow{-H_2} 2BH_2NH_2$$

$$2BH_2NH_2 \xrightarrow{-H_2} 2BHNH \longrightarrow s\text{-triazaborane} \tag{18}$$

and/or methyldiboranes, or (2) employing the complex; as for example,
$B(CH_3) \cdot NH_2CH_3$, where available, and heating at optimum temperatures, pressures and for optimum lengths of time, a number of the
methyl-s-triazaboranes may be prepared. In only a few cases is the
reaction clean enough to produce one compound to the exclusion of all
others. More often it is complicated by side reactions, difficulty in
separating closely boiling products, and the appearance of non-volatile
solids of unknown composition.[8] The equations for reactions which have
been reported, the conditions and the yields are listed in Table XI-2.
For simplification the diboranes are written as the boranes to which
they dissociate at some stage of the reaction.

   1,3,5-Trimethyl-s-triazaborane, or N-trimethylborazole, has been
prepared[28] by the action of lithium borohydride on methylamine hydrochloride according to equation (19). The reaction proceeds in two steps
at room temperature. Only a portion of the hydrogen is evolved and

$$3CH_3NH_3Cl + 3LiBH_4 \longrightarrow B_3N_3H_3(CH_3)_3 + 9H_2 + 3LiCl \tag{19}$$

the intermediate boron-nitrogen compound is non-volatile. At this
stage the solvent may be removed and the residue heated to 250°,
whereupon additional hydrogen is evolved and the N-trimethylborazole
recovered from the volatile product in 98% yield. If the reaction is

TABLE XI-2. Synthesis of Methyl-*s*-Triazaboranes

Reactants	Conditions	Major product	Yield, %	Ref.
$2\,BH_3 + BH_2CH_3 + 3\,NH_3$	200° 2–6 atm. 20–30 min.	$\underset{\underset{H}{N}}{\overset{CH_3}{\underset{HB\quad BH}{HN\quad NH}}}$ (ring) $+\ 6\,H_2$	—	1
$BH_3 + 2\,BHCH_3 + 3\,NH_3$	200° 2–6 atm. 20–30 min.	$\underset{\underset{H}{N}}{\overset{CH_3}{\underset{HB\quad BCH_3}{HN\quad NH}}}$ (ring) $+\ 6\,H_2$	—	1
$3\,BH_2CH_3 + 3\,NH_3$	200° 5 atm. 30 min.	$\underset{\underset{H}{N}}{\overset{CH_3}{\underset{H_3CB\quad BCH_3}{HN\quad NH}}}$ (ring) $+\ 6\,H_2$	40	2
$3\,BH_3 + 2\,NH_3 + NH_2CH_3$	200° 30 min.	$\underset{\underset{H}{N}}{\overset{H}{\underset{HB\quad BH}{HN\quad NCH_3}}}$ (ring) $+\ 6\,H_2$	—	3
$3\,BH_3 + NH_3 + 2\,NH_2CH_3$	200° 30 min.	$\underset{\underset{CH_3}{N}}{\overset{H}{\underset{HB\quad BH}{HN\quad NCH_3}}}$ (ring) $+\ 6\,H_2$	—	3
$3\,BH_3 + 3\,NH_2CH_3$	190° 20 atm. 2 Hrs.	$\underset{\underset{CH_3}{N}}{\overset{H}{\underset{HB\quad BCH_3}{H_3CN\quad NCH_3}}}$ (ring) $+\ 6\,H_2$	90	3,4
$3\,BCH_3 + 3\,NH_3$	330° 20 atm. 2 Hrs.	$\underset{\underset{H}{N}}{\overset{CH_3}{\underset{H_3CB\quad BCH_3}{HN\quad NH}}}$ (ring) $+\ 6\,CH_4$	—	4
$3\,BCH_3 + NH_2CH_3$	450° 20 atm. 3–4 Hrs.	$\underset{\underset{CH_3}{N}}{\overset{CH_3}{\underset{H_3CB\quad BCH_3}{H_3CN\quad NCH_3}}}$ (ring) $+\ 6\,CH_4$	—	5

1. H. Schlesinger, L. Horvitz and A. Burg, *J. Am. Chem. Soc.*, **58**, 409 (1936).
2. H. Schlesinger, N. Flodin and A. Burg, *J. Am. Chem. Soc.*, **61**, 1078 (1939).
3. H. Schlesinger, D. Ritter and A. Burg, *J. Am. Chem. Soc.*, **60**, 1296 (1938).
4. E. Wiberg, K. Hertwig and A. Bolz, *Z. anorg. Chem.*, **256**, 177 (1948).
5. E. Wiberg and K. Hertwig, *Z. anorg. Chem.*, **255**, 141 (1947).

run in dihexyl ether (b.p. 210°), the two steps may be combined and the product recovered in 70 % yield by distilling to a head temperature of 134°. This method has recently[30] been used as a general synthetic method by which the N-triethyl, N-tri-*n*-propyl and N-tri-isopropyl-borazoles were prepared in yields of 80–90%.

1,3,5-Trimethyl-*s*-triazaborane has recently been prepared[33] by de-hydrogenation of the hexahydro derivative. The latter was made in 80 % yield by heating methylamine-borane at 100°. It hydrolyzes slowly in cold water but rapidly in 20 % hydrochloric acid. The compound is a solid of density 0.9 g/cm³ which is soluble in benzene, diethyl ether and chloroform, but insoluble in carbon tetrachloride and petroleum ether.

The 2-, 2,4-, and 2,4,6-methyl derivatives of 1-methyl-*s*-triaza-borane have not been prepared by either of the above methods. Synthesis of these compounds was accomplished[9] by treating 1-methyl-*s*-triazaborane with trimethylborane (20). The yields are not good; the

(XXIV)   (XXV)   (XXVI)   (20)

mixtures are complex and difficult to separate. The method has also been used successfully to methylate *s*-triazaborane at the 2-position, but is not as useful as the procedure of heating trimethylborane with ammonia.

4. Structure

Preparation of the mono-, di- and tri-B-methyl-*s*-triazaborane and the mono-, di- and tri-N-methyl-*s*-triazaborane (these six compounds) furnishes additional proof for the ring structure of *s*-triazaborane. The analogy between *s*-triazaborane and benzene may be extended to the methyl derivatives of both. As a result of replacement of a hydrogen atom by a methyl group, the resemblance of a methyl *s*-triazaborane to its benzene analog is modified. Rector[20] compared the ultraviolet spectra of 1,3,5-trimethyl, 2,4,6-trimethyl- and 2,4,6-trichloro-*s*-triazaborane in *n*-heptane solution with the spectra of *s*-triazaborane and the carbon analogs, benzene and mesitylene; he found that, by N-substitution, the negative charge on the boron atoms is increased. This increases the double-bond character and the spectral resemblance to a benzene derivative. By boron substitution the opposite effect is produced, with an increase in the spectral resemblance to a cyclohexane derivative.

An extensive comparison of the properties of the methyl-*s*-triazaboranes with analogous methyl benzenes has been made by Wiberg[1] and an interpretation of the infrared spectra of borazole and N-trimethylborazole has been made by Price.[17]

5. Chemical Properties and Reactions

D. Reaction with Hydrogen Halides

The methyl-*s*-triazaboranes react with hydrogen chloride or hydrogen bromide at room temperature[7,18] forming primary addition compounds with three equivalents of hydrogen halide. The halogen adds to the boron atom and the hydrogen to the nitrogen atom. The reaction (21) produces white solids which are insoluble in carbon tetrachloride and not volatile in high vacuum[7] at 40–50°. In the case of

$$(21)$$

hexamethyl-*s*-triazaborane (XXIX), hexahydrohexamethyl-2,4,6-trichloro-*s*-triazaborane (XXX) is produced. The analogous products obtained from 1,3,5-trimethyl and 2,4,6-trimethyl-s-triazaborane are (XXXI) and (XXXII) respectively.[18]

If the reaction is conducted at a higher temperature (330° for hexamethyl-s-triazaborane[7]) in the presence of excess hydrogen halide, complete ring cleavage results and the products[7] are methyldichloroborine and methylamine hydrochloride (22). On the other hand, when

$$(XXIX) + 9\,HCl \xrightarrow{330°} 3\,B(CH_3)Cl_2 + 3\,CH_3NH_2 \cdot HCl \qquad (22)$$

the reaction is conducted at high temperature (100° for s-triazaborane; 450° for the hexamethyl derivative; probably intermediate temperatures for other methyl-s-triazaborane) in the absence of an excess of hydrogen halide [over the 3:1 ratio required stoiciometrically] or if the primary addition compounds (XXX, XXXI, and XXXII) are heated to these temperatures, hydrogen and/or methane is evolved[1,18] and 2,4,6-trihalo-s-triazaboranes are formed. Methyl groups on boron are eliminated as methane; those on nitrogen remain in the final product. The reaction may be illustrated (23, 24) by the two extreme cases,

$$(I) + 3\,HCl \xrightarrow{100°}$$

$$\begin{array}{c} Cl \\ HN \diagup B \diagdown NH \\ | \qquad | \\ ClB \diagdown N \diagup BCl \\ H \end{array} + 3\,H_2 \qquad (23)$$

(XXXIV)

$$(XXIX) + 3\,HCl \xrightarrow{450°}$$

$$\begin{array}{c} Cl \\ H_3CN \diagup B \diagdown NCH_3 \\ | \qquad | \\ ClB \diagdown N \diagup BCl \\ CH_3 \end{array} + 3\,CH_4 \qquad (24)$$

(XXXV)

s-triazaborane with no methyl groups and hexamethyl-s-triazaborane in which each boron and each nitrogen bears a methyl group.

It is probably not a simple molecular displacement. Wiberg has suggested[1,7] that it proceeds by first forming an addition compound which splits into three equal fragments at 150°. These eliminate the elements of methane and recombine forming 2,4,6-trichloro-1,3,5-trimethyl-s-triazaborane (XXXV), reaction (25).

$$
\begin{array}{ccc}
\underset{\text{(XXIX)}}{\text{(ring structure with B--CH}_3\text{, N--CH}_3\text{)}} + 3\,HCl & \xrightarrow{20°} & \underset{}{\text{(ring, Cl, NH}_2\text{, CH}_3\text{, H}_2\text{)}} \xrightarrow{150°} \text{(H}_3\text{CNH, ClBCH}_3\text{ structure)}
\end{array}
$$

$$
\downarrow{\substack{-\,3\,CH_4 \\ 450°}}
$$

$$
\text{(XXXV ring structure)} \quad \longleftarrow \quad \text{(CH}_3\text{N, ClB, BCl structure)} \tag{25}
$$

B. Reaction with Water

The reactions of 1,3,5-trimethyl, 2,4,6-trimethyl, and hexamethyl-*s*-triazaborane with water have been studied. The primary reaction parallels the one with hydrogen halides. Three equivalents of water react (26, 27, 28) to form addition compounds which can be isolated at

$$
\text{(XXXVI)} + 3\,H_2O \xrightarrow{0-20°} \text{(XXXVII)} \tag{26}
$$

$$
\text{(XXXVIII)} + 3\,H_2O \xrightarrow{0-20°} \text{(XXXIX)} \tag{27}
$$

$$
\text{(XXIX)} + 3\,H_2O \xrightarrow{20°} \text{(XL)} \tag{28}
$$

or below room temperature[7,18]. In all cases, the hydroxyl group becomes attached at the boron atoms.

With excess water, at 150° slow hydrolysis[2,7,8,9,18] to boric acid and ammonia derivatives occurs according to the following equation:

$$(BHNCH_3)_3 + 6\,H_2O \longrightarrow 3\,B(OH)_3 + 3\,CH_3NH_2 + 3\,H_2$$
$$(BCH_3NH)_3 + 6\,H_2O \longrightarrow 3\,B(CH_3)\,(OH)_2 + 3\,NH_3$$
$$(BCH_3NCH_3)_3 + 6\,H_2O \longrightarrow 3\,B(CH_3)\,(OH)_2 + 3\,CH_3NH_2$$

It is apparent that hydrogen is evolved in the case of 1,3,5-trimethyl-*s*-triazaborane (XXXVIII). Indeed if an excess of water above the 3:1 ratio required for formation of the addition compound (XXXIX) is avoided and the reaction (29) is carried out at 100°, 1,3,5-trimethyl-2,4,6-trihydroxy-*s*-triazaborane can be isolated.[1,7,18]

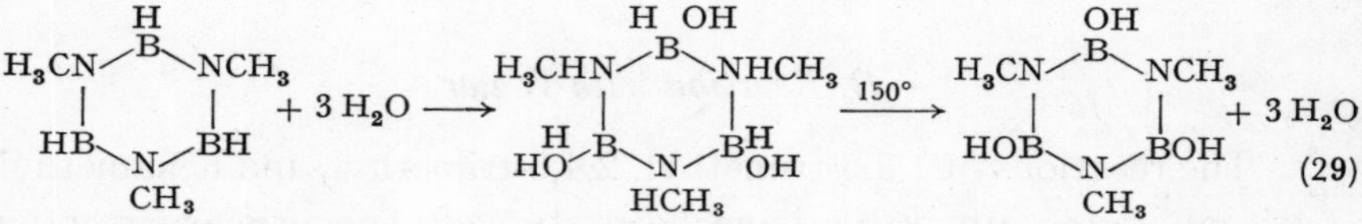

(XXXVIII) (XXXIX) (XLI) (29)

The same type (XLI) product is *not* obtained when 2,4,6-trimethyl-(XXVI) or hexamethyl-*s*-triazaborane (XXIX) is treated with three equivalents of water under the same conditions. Instead trimethyl boroxol (XLII) is obtained together with ammonia and methylamine, respectively (30, 31). The reaction, in the cases of all three methyl-*s*-

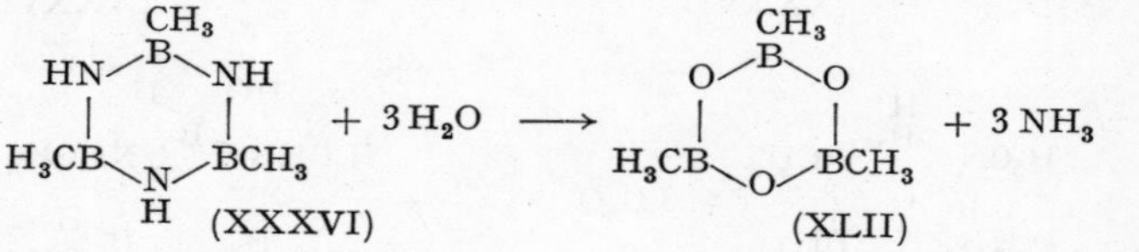

(XXXVI) (XLII) (30)

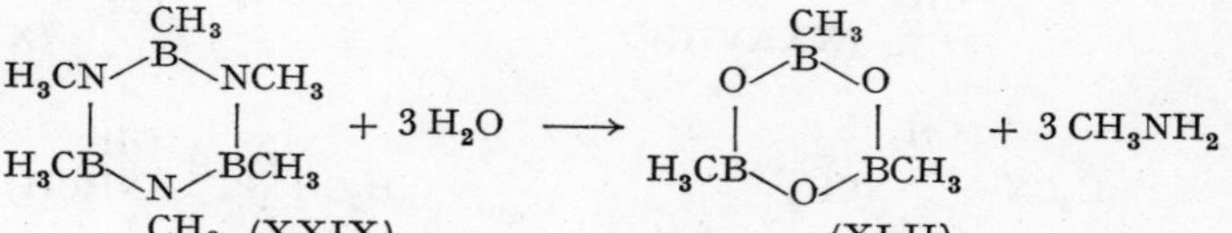

(XXIX) (XLII) (31)

triazaboranes under consideration, may proceed in the manner suggested by Wiberg for the reaction with hydrogen halides. The addition compound with three equivalents of water undergoes cleavage into three equivalent moieties; these each lose an equivalent of hydrogen, but only if there is *boron* hydrogen available. Recondensation yields the 2,4,6-trihydroxy compound (32).

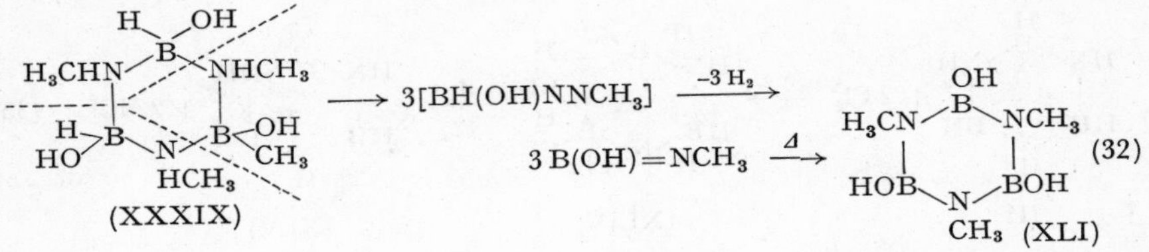

$$3[BH(OH)NNCH_3] \xrightarrow{-3\,H_2} 3\,B(OH)=NCH_3 \xrightarrow{\Delta} \tag{32}$$

(XXXIX)

(XLI)

In the absence of boron hydrogen, the reaction takes the course indicated in equation (33).

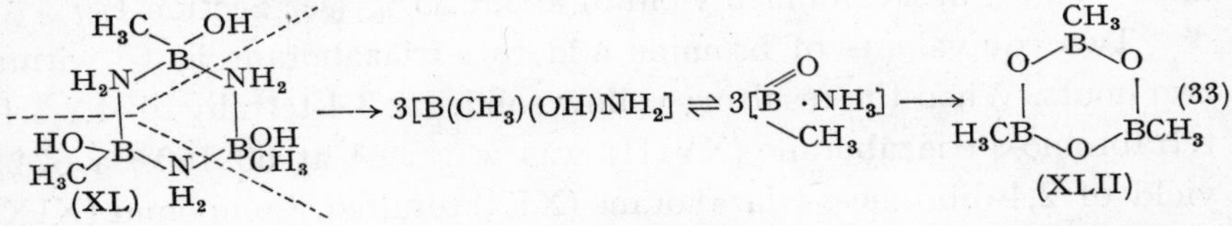

$$\longrightarrow 3[B(CH_3)(OH)NH_2] \rightleftharpoons 3[\overset{O}{\underset{CH_3}{B}}\cdot NH_3] \longrightarrow \tag{33}$$

(XL)

(XLII)

Wiberg has discussed the end transformation above in detail.[1]

C. *Reaction with Alcohols*

The reaction of 1,3,5-trimethyl-*s*-triazaborane with ethanol at room temperature or below gives[18] an addition compound (XLIII) which is analogous to that obtained with water or with hydrogen halides under similar conditions (34).

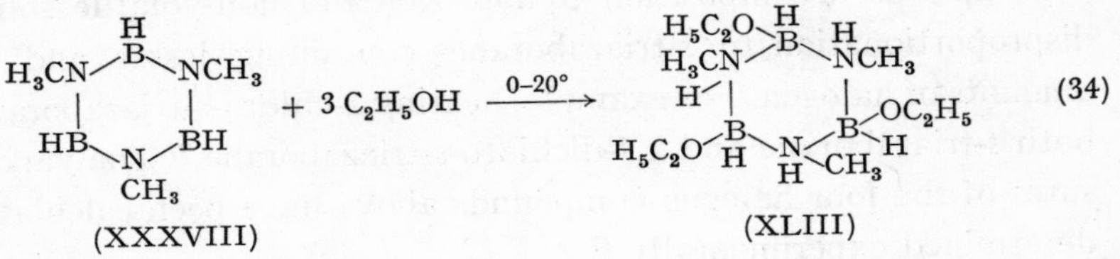

$$+\ 3\ C_2H_5OH \xrightarrow{0-20°} \tag{34}$$

(XXXVIII)

(XLIII)

IV. Halogen Derivatives of *s*-Triazaborane

1. Halogen Derivatives of *s*-Triazaborane and Hexahydro-*s*-triazaborane only

The action of chlorine[3] on *s*-triazaborane produces 1,2,3,4-tetrahydro-1,2,3,4-tetrachloro-*s*-triazaborane, a solid adduct which upon warming evolves hydrogen chloride and is converted to 2,4-dichloro-*s*-triazaborane (XLV). Because of the similarity of XLV to its bromine analog (below), the reaction is believed to take the course postulated in equation (35). (XLV) is a white crystalline compound which melts[27]

$$\text{(I)} \qquad\qquad\qquad \text{(XLIV)} \qquad\qquad\qquad \text{(XLV)}$$

at 33–33.5°. It can also be obtained as a result of the action of boron trichloride on s-triazaborane, together with 2-chloro-s-triazaborane, m.p. —34.6°, in a combined yield of about 35% (see Section I. 7).

Two equivalents of bromine add to s-triazaborane at 0° within two hours. When the resulting yellow solid, 1,2,3,4-tetrahydro-1,2,3,4-tetrabromo-s-triazaborane (XVIII) was warmed[3] at 60–100°, a 67% yield of 2,4-dibromo-s-triazaborane (XIX) resulted. Compound (XIX) is a colorless, crystalline sublimable solid which melts[27] at 49.5–50°. It can also be obtained along with 2-bromo-s-triazaborane (m.p. —34.8°, combined yield 35%) from the mixture obtained as a result of the action of boron tribromide on s-triazaborane.[27] The 2-halo and 2,4-dihalo-s-triazaboranes discussed above are moderately stable compounds which are hydrolyzed by moist air and water to steam volatile products. They are attacked by grease. At higher temperatures they undergo simultaneous decomposition to hydrogen and non-volatile solids and disproportionation to s-triazaboranes containing lesser and greater amounts of halogen. For example, heating 2-chloro-s-triazaborane gave both s-triazaborane and 2,4-dichloro-s-triazaborane.[27] The vapor pressures of the four halogen compounds above have been calculated and determined experimentally.[27]

2,4,6-Trichloro-s-triazaborane[2] (XLVI) and 2,4,6-tribromo-s-triazaborane have both been made.[2,3,26,29] They are white crystalline-compounds, soluble in common organic solvents.[1] 2,4,6-Trichloro-s-triazaborane (XLVI) was obtained in the form of orthorhombic crystals[29] melting at 83.9–84.5°, specific gravity 1.5. It sublimes readily, has a heat of sublimation[32] of 17 Kcal./mole and has a heat of vaporization of 12.3 Kcal/mole. Equations 35A and 35B express the vapor pressure-temperature relationships in the solid range 40.7–83.7°

and the liquid range 86.6–113.3°, respectively. (XLVI) is soluble in benzene, chloroform, ethers, carbon disulfide, and cyclohexane, but

$$\log P_{mm.} = -3.743/T + 11.73 \tag{35A}$$

$$\log P_{mm.} = -2.497/T + 8.25 \tag{35B}$$

reacts with solvents such as pyridine, alcohols, acetone, and water. Aqueous hydrolysis ruptures the ring giving boric acid and ammonium chloride. When 2,4,6-trichloro-*s*-triazaborane is heated above 100°, decomposition takes place with the evolution of hydrogen chloride and formation of non-volatile solids. It is best synthesized (90 % yield[26]) by passing boron trichloride into a suspension of ammonium chloride in chlorobenzene (35C). (XLVI) can be purified by vacuum sublimation

$$3\,BCl_3 + 3\,NH_4Cl \xrightarrow[C_6H_5Cl]{} B_3N_3H_3Cl_3 + 9\,HCl \tag{35C}$$
$$\text{(XLVI), 90\%}$$

at 50–60°. 2,4,6-Tribromo-*s*-triazaborane is prepared by an analogous synthesis using ammonium bromide in bromobenzene and heating the reaction mixture for 8–12 hours at 120–130°. 2,4,6-Tribromo-*s*-triaza-borane can be purified by vacuum sublimation at 60–70°. It melts at 126–128° although some decomposition takes place as low as 90°. At 220°, 75 % decomposes[26] in five hours probably giving boron nitride and hydrogen bromide.[3] Both 2,4,6-trichloro- and 2,4,6-tribromo-*s*-triazaborane may be prepared from *s*-triazaborane by treatment with three equivalents of hydrogen halide at 100° (36). Both compounds add

$$\text{(I)} \qquad + 3\,HX \xrightarrow{100°} \qquad \text{(XLVI)} \qquad + 3\,H_2 \tag{36}$$

water readily at room temperature giving[2,3] 2,4,6-trihydroxy-*s*-triaza-borane (XVI) which is very easily hydrolyzed further to boric acid and ammonia (37).

$$\text{(XLVI)} \qquad + 3\,H_2O \longrightarrow \qquad \text{(XVI)} \qquad + 3\,HCl \tag{37}$$

Compounds which are intermediates in the preparation of the above two halogen compounds are also known. Hexahydro-2,4,6-tri-bromo- and hexahydro-2,4,6-trichloro-s-triazaborane (XXI) are hard white substances which are not volatile in high vacuum at room temperature. They can be isolated when the reaction of (I) with hydrogen halide is conducted at 0° with no excess hydrogen halide (38). On heating to 100°, hydrogen is lost and the 2,4,6-trihalo-s-triaza-boranes result.

$$(I) + 3\,HX \xrightarrow{\ 0°\ } \begin{array}{c} \text{H X}\\ \text{H}_2\text{N}-\overset{|}{\underset{|}{\text{B}}}-\text{NH}_2 \\ \overset{\text{H}}{\underset{\text{X}}{\text{B}}}-\underset{\text{H}_2}{\text{N}}-\overset{\text{H}}{\underset{\text{X}}{\text{B}}} \end{array} \quad \text{(XXI)} \tag{38}$$

2. Halogen Derivatives of Methyl-s-triazaboranes

2,4,6-Trichloro-1,3,5-trimethyl-s-triazaborane (XXXV) is a white substance, easily sublimable in high vacuum. It melts with decomposition at 285° and is soluble in benzene and many other organic solvents.[21] Compound (XXXV) is slightly soluble in ether and is decomposed by water or low molecular weight alcohols.

It may be prepared by either of two methods:

(1) Heating an equimolar mixture of boron trichloride and methyl-amine[21] (39) or

(2) Heating hexamethyl-s-triazaborane to 450° with three equivalents of hydrogen chloride[1,7] (40).

$$3\,BCl_3 + 3\,CH_3NH_2 \xrightarrow[\text{1 hr.}]{250°} \begin{array}{c} \text{Cl} \\ \text{H}_3\text{CN}-\overset{|}{\underset{|}{\text{B}}}-\text{NCH}_3 \\ \text{ClB}-\underset{\text{CH}_3}{\text{N}}-\text{BCl} \end{array} + 6\,HCl \quad \text{(XXXV)} \tag{39}$$

$$\begin{array}{c} \text{CH}_3 \\ \text{H}_3\text{CN}-\overset{|}{\underset{|}{\text{B}}}-\text{NCH}_3 \\ \text{H}_3\text{CB}-\underset{\text{CH}_3}{\text{N}}-\text{BCH}_3 \end{array} + 3\,HCl \xrightarrow{\ 450°\ } \text{(XXXV)} + 3\,CH_4 \tag{40}$$

Compound (XXXV) is stable[7] at temperatures of 500°, but reacts with water at room temperature[1] to give the corresponding 2,4,6-tri-hydroxy derivative.

In addition to the compounds discussed above, all of which possess fairly well established structures, a hard glassy colorless compound of uncertain structure is formed when the adduct of *s*-triazaborane and three equivalents of water is treated[2] with hydrogen chloride (44).

$$B_3N_3H_3 \cdot 3\,H_2O + 3\,HCl \longrightarrow B_3N_3H_3Cl_3 \cdot 3\,H_2O + 3\,H_2 \qquad (41)$$

It is different from 2,4,6-trichlorotriazaborane (formed from dry *s*-triazaborane and hydrogen chloride).

3. Halogen Derivatives of Aryl Substituted *s*-Triazaboranes

Three 2,4,6-trichloro-1,3,5-triaryl-*s*-triazaboranes are known although no aryl derivatives without halogen have been made. Apparently monomers such as $C_6H_5N{=}BCH_3$ do not trimerize.[1]

A. 2,4,6-Trichloro-1,3,5-triphenyl-s-triazaborane

2,4,6-Trichloro-1,3,5-triphenyl-*s*-triazaborane (XLVII) is a crystalline solid, m.p. 265–270°, which is soluble in benzene and easily sublimed in vacuum.[1,16,22,23] It is prepared (42) by heating the boron trichloride-aniline complex at 260° for an hour.[22,23] The major reaction product is the monomer $C_6H_5N{=}BCl$.

$$3\,BCl_3 + 3\,C_6H_5NH_2 \longrightarrow
\begin{array}{c}
Cl \\
C_6H_5N{\overset{\displaystyle B}{\diagup}}{\diagdown}NC_6H_5 \\
| \qquad\qquad | \\
ClB{\diagdown}{\underset{\displaystyle N}{}}{\diagup}BCl \\
C_6H_5 \quad (XLVIII)
\end{array}
\qquad (42)$$

B. 2,4,6-Trichloro-1,3,5-tri-p-tolyl-s-triazaborane

The *p*-tolyl derivative is a crystalline solid[23] which gradually changes to a powder melting at 308–309°. The solid usually contains some benzene of crystallization. It is slowly decomposed in air and gives off hydrogen chloride as a result of the presence of moisture in air. Under dry benzene, it remains stable. The compound is insoluble in cold dry benzene, carbon tetrachloride, ethyl acetate and ether. It is prepared by heating the 1:1 adduct of boron trichloride and *p*-toluidine in benzene under reflux. Water causes decomposition to boric acid and *p*-toluidine hydrochloride. The decomposition is slow in cold water; rapid in hot water.

C. 2,4,6-Trichloro-1,3,5-tri-p-anisyl-s-triazaborane

This compound forms cubic crystals containing benzene of crystallization and melting at 229–235° after purification by washing with benzene and petroleum ether.[24]

It is also prepared by heating the boron trichloride adduct of *p*-anisidine, suspended in benzene, at reflux for 18 hours.

With hot water 2,4,6-trichloro-1,3,5-tri-*p*-anisyl-s-triazaborane is quickly hydrolyzed to boric acid and *p*-anisidine hydrochloride. But cold water hydrolyzes the chloro groups to give a compound melting at 112–120°, apparently impure 2,4,6-trihydroxy-1,3,5-tri-*p*-anisyl-s-triazaborane.[24]

V. Hydroxy-s-triazaboranes

A compound can be isolated from the reaction mixture of s-triazaborane and water at 0° which probably[3] has the structure hexahydro-2,4,6-trihydroxy-s-triazaborane.

The compounds 2,4,6-trihydroxy-s-triazaborane and 1,3,5-trimethyl-2,4,6-trihydroxy-s-triazaborane have been mentioned[1,3,7] but their properties have not been described in the literature. They are formed by the action of three equivalents of water on s-triazaborane and 1,3,5-trimethyl-s-triazaborane, respectively, at 100°. With excess water or more rapidly with aqueous acids, the ring structures are broken down giving boric acid and ammonia and methylamine.

VI. Methoxy-s-triazaboranes

Hexahydro-2,4,6-trimethoxy-s-triazaborane (XLVIII) and hexahydro-2,4,6-trimethoxy-1,3,5-trimethyl-s-triazaborane are non-volatile white solids prepared[1,18,25] by treating s-triazaborane (43) and 1,3,5-

$$(43)$$

trimethyl-*s*-triazaborane, respectively, with methanol at room temperature. Heating the derivative (XLVIII) at 100° causes the ring to break down with the evolution of hydrogen[1] (44).

$$(\text{XLVIII}) \xrightarrow{100°} 3\,H_2 + \left[\begin{array}{c} \text{OCH}_3 \\ \text{B} \\ \text{HN} \diagdown \diagup \text{NH} \\ | \qquad\qquad | \\ \text{CH}_3\text{OB} \diagdown \diagup \text{BOCH}_3 \\ \text{N} \\ \text{H} \end{array} \right] \longrightarrow 3\,\text{CH}_3\text{OB}{=}\text{NH} \quad (44)$$

VII. Other *s*-Triazaborane Derivatives

The adduct of *s*-triazaborane and three equivalents of methyl iodide has been prepared in 30% yield but has not been characterized further.[1,3] An adduct of *s*-triazaborane and one equivalent of ammonia has been made but also not characterized. It was prepared from liquid ammonia in which it is soluble.[1,2,3]

References

1. E. Wiberg, *Naturwissenschaften*, **35**, 182, 212 (1948).
2. A. Stock and E. Pohland, *Ber.*, **59**, 2215 (1926).
3. E. Wiberg and A. Bolz, *Ber.*, **73**, 209 (1940).
4. A. Stock and R. Wierl, *Z. anorg. Chem.*, **203**, 228 (1931).
5. S. Bauer, *J. Am. Chem. Soc.*, **60**, 524 (1938).
6. B. Crawford and J. Edsall, *J. Chem. Phys.*, **7**, 223 (1939).
7. E. Wiberg and K. Hertwig, *Z. anorg. Chem.*, **255**, 141 (1947).
8. H. Schlesinger, L. Horvitz and A. Burg, *J. Am. Chem. Soc.*, **58**, 409 (1936).
9. H. Schlesinger, D. Ritter and A. Burg, *J. Am. Chem. Soc.*, **60**, 1296 (1938).
10. K. Ramaswamy, *Proc. Indian Acad. Sci.*, Sect. A2, 364 (1935), through *Chem. Abstracts*, **30**, 1622 (1936).
11. K. Ramaswamy, *Proc. Indian Acad. Sci.*, Sect. A2, 630 (1935), through *Chem. Abstracts*, **30**, 2817 (1936).
12. H. Spencer, *J. Am. Chem. Soc.*, **67**, 1859 (1945).
13. J. Platt, H. Klevens and G. Schaeffer, *J. Chem. Phys.*, **15**, 598 (1947).
14. J. Platt and G. Schaeffer, *J. Chem. Phys.*, **16**, 116 (1948).
15. C. Roothaan and R. Mulliken, *J. Chem. Phys.*, **16**, 118 (1948).
16. E. Wiberg, and A. Bolz, unpublished data.
17. W. Price, R. Fraser, T. Robinson and H. Longuet-Higgins, *Discussions Faraday Soc.*, **1950**, 131.
18. E. Wiberg, K. Hertwig and A. Bolz, *Z. anorg. Chem.*, **256**, 177 (1948).
19. H. Schlesinger, N. Flodin and A. Burg, *J. Am. Chem. Soc.*, **61**, 1078 (1939).
20. C. Rector, G. Schaeffer and J. Platt, *J. Chem. Phys.*, **17**, 460 (1949).
21. P. B. 95688 FIAT Review of German Science 1939–1946, Inorganic Chemistry Part I, pp. 215–238, *The Boron Compounds* by Josef Goubeau.
22. R. Jones and C. Kinney, *J. Am. Chem. Soc.*, **61**, 1378 (1939).

23. C. Kinney and M. Kolbezen, *J. Am. Chem. Soc.*, **64**, 1584 (1942).
24. C. Kinney and C. Mahoney, *J. Org. Chem.*, **8**, 526 (1943).
25. E. Wiberg and K. Hertwig, *Z. anorg. Chem.*, **257**, 138 (1948).
26. R. Schaeffer et al., *J. Am. Chem. Soc.*, **76**, 3303 (1954).
27. G. Schaeffer, R. Schaeffer and H. Schlesinger, *J. Am. Chem. Soc.*, **73**, 1612 (1951).
28. G. Schaeffer and E. Anderson, *J. Am. Chem. Soc.*, **71**, 2143 (1949).
29. C. Brown, *Dissertation*, Cornell University, 1948.
30. W. Hough, G. Schaeffer, M. Dzuras, and A. Stewart, *J. Am. Chem. Soc.*, **77**, 864 (1955).
31. L. Eddy, S. Smith and R. Miller, *J. Am. Chem. Soc.*, **77**, 2105 (1955).
32. C. Brown and A. Laubengayer, *J. Am. Chem. Soc.*, **77**, 3699 (1955).
33. T. Bissot and R. Parry, *J. Am. Chem. Soc.*, **77**, 3481 (1955).

INDEX

This index lists only compounds of sufficient interest to be mentioned in the text. Many other compounds, catalogued by group, are listed in tables together with physical properties, methods of preparation, and references. These tables are listed under a general group name in this index and should be consulted for compounds not individually indexed.

C

E

F

G

H